THE SHORE FISHES OF HAWAII

THE SHORE FISHES
OF HAWAII

THESE FISHES ARE FOUND THROUGHOUT
THE PACIFIC OCEAN

by

DAVID STARR JORDAN

and

BARTON WARREN EVERMANN

CHARLES E. TUTTLE COMPANY
Rutland, Vermont & Tokyo, Japan

An Abridgment of the
Bulletin of the United States Fish Commission for 1903 (vol. 23),
published by the U.S. Government Printing Office in Washington,
1903. Being *Part I, The Shore Fishes, The Acquatic Resources of
the Hawaiian Islands*

Representatives
Continental Europe: Boxerbooks, Inc., *Zurich*
British Isles: Prentice-Hall International, Inc., *London*
Australasia : Book Wise (Australia) Pty. Ltd.
104-108 Sussex Street, Sydney 2000

*Published by the Charles E. Tuttle Company, Inc.
of Rutland, Vermont & Tokyo, Japan
with editorial offices at
Suido 1-chome, 2-6, Bunkyo-ku, Tokyo, Japan*

Library of Congress Catalog Card No. 73-77578

International Standard Book No. 0-8048-1106-7

*First Tuttle edition, 1973
Second printing, 1986*

Printed in Japan

TABLE OF CONTENTS

LIST OF ILLUSTRATIONS

COLOR PLATES

The following plates are placed at the end of the book.

PLATE I.

Echidna nebulosa (Ahl)

    Painting by A. H. Baldwin from a specimen 29 inches long, collected at Honolulu by Jordan and Evermann in 1901.

PLATE II.

Synodus varius (Lacépède)

    Painting by A. H. Baldwin from a specimen 10 inches long, collected at the Hawaiian Islands by Jordan and Evermann in 1901.

PLATE III.

Parexocœtus brachypterus (Solander)

    Painting by A. H. Baldwin from a specimen 7 inches long, collected at Honolulu by Jordan and Evermann in 1901.

PLATE IV.

Holotrachys lima (Cuvier & Valenciennes)

    Painting by A. H. Baldwin from a specimen 5 inches long, collected at Honolulu by Jordan and Evermann in 1901.

PLATE V.

Myripristis murdjan (Forskål)

    Painting by A. H. Baldwin from a specimen 8 inches long, collected at Hilo by Jordan and Evermann in 1901.

PLATE VI.

Myripristis chryseres Jordan & Evermann

    Painting by A. H. Baldwin from the type, No. 50629, U.S.N.M., a specimen 9 inches long, collected at Hilo by Jordan and Evermann in 1901.

PLATE VII.

Flammeo scythrops Jordan & Evermann

    Painting by A. H. Baldwin from the type, No. 5063 , U.S.N.M., a specimen 9.25 inches long, collected at Hilo by Jordan and Evermann in 1901.

PLATE VIII.

Holocentrus spinifer (Forskål)

    Painting by A. H. Baldwin from a specimen 15 inches long, collected at Honolulu by Jordan and Evermann in 1901. **Holocentrus leo** Cuvier & Valenciennes on the plate.

PLATE IX.

Holocentrus xantherythrus Jordan & Evermann

    Painting by A. H. Baldwin from the type, No. 50635, U.S.N.M., a specimen 6 inches long, collected at Honolulu by Jordan and Evermann in 1901.

PLATE X.

Holocentrus diadema (Lacépède)

    Painting by Kako Morita from a specimen 6.1 inches long, collected at Honolulu by Jordan and Evermann in 1901.

PLATE XXXIX.

Hemipteronotus baldwini Jordan & Evermann

Painting by A. H. Baldwin from the type, No. 50644 U.S.N.M., a specimen 8.5 inches long, collected at Honolulu by Jordan and Evermann in 1901.

PLATE XL.

Novaculichthys woodi Jenkins

Painting by A. H. Baldwin from a specimen 6.2 inches long, collected at Hilo by Jordan and Evermann in 1901.

PLATE XLI.

Novaculichthys kallosoma (Bleeker)

Painting by Kako Morita from a specimen 2.4 inches long, collected at Samoa by Jordan and Kellogg in 1902.

PLATE XLII.

Iniistius pavoninus (Cuvier & Valenciennes)

Painting by A. H. Baldwin from a specimen 13 inches long, collected at Honolulu by Jordan and Evermann in 1901.

PLATE XLIII.

Callyodon lauia (Jordan & Evermann)

Painting by A. H. Baldwin from the type, No. 50648, U.S.N.M., a specimen 14 inches long, collected at Hilo by Jordan and Evermann in 1901.

PLATE XLIV.

Pseudoscarus jordani Jenkins

Painting by Kako Morita from a specimen 15 inches long, collected at the Hawaiian Islands by Jordan and Evermann in 1901.

PLATE XLV.

Antigonia steindachneri Jordan & Evermann

Painting by A. H. Baldwin from a specimen 6.2 inches long, collected at Hilo by Jordan and Evermann in 1901.

PLATE XLVI.

Forcipiger longirostris (Broussonet)

Painting by Kako Morita from a specimen 5.6 inches long, collected at Honolulu by Jordan and Evermann in 1901.

PLATE XLVII.

Chætodon setifer (Bloch)

Painting by A. H. Baldwin from a specimen 4.75 inches long, collected at Honolulu by Jordan and Evermann in 1901.

PLATE XLVIII.

Chætodon miliaris (Quoy & Gaimard)

Painting by A. H. Baldwin from a specimen 4.2 inches long, collected at Hilo by Jordan and Evermann in 1901.

PLATE XLIX.

Chætodon quadrimaculatus Gray

Painting by A. H. Baldwin from a specimen 5 inches long, collected at Honolulu by Jordan and Evermann in 1901.

PLATE L.

Chætodon unimaculatus Bloch

Painting by A. H. Baldwin from a specimen 5.25 inches long, collected at Honolulu by Jordan and Evermann in 1901.

PLATE LI.

Chætodon fremblii Bennett

Painting by A. H. Baldwin from a specimen 6.5 inches long, collected at Hilo by Jordan and Evermann in 1901.

PLATE LII.

Chætodon trifasciatus Mungo Park

Painting by Kako Morita from a specimen 6 inches long, collected at Honolulu by Jordan and Evermann in 1901.

PLATE LIII.

Chætodon ornatissimus Solander

Painting by A. H. Baldwin from a specimen 4.5 inches long, collected at Honolulu by Jordan and Evermann in 1901.

PLATE LIV.

Chætodon lunula (Lacépède)

Painting by A. H. Baldwin from a specimen 5.5 inches long, collected at Honolulu by Jordan and Evermann in 1901.

PLATE LV.

Heniochus acuminatus (Linnæus)

Painting by A. H. Baldwin from a specimen 6.75 inches long, collected at Honolulu by Jordan and Evermann in 1901. **Heniochus macrolepidotus** (Linnæus) on the plate.

PLATE LVI.

Holacanthus bispinosus Günther

Painting by Kako Morita from a specimen collected at Samoa by Jordan and Kellogg in 1902.

PLATE LVII.

Zanclus canescens (Linnæus)

Painting by A. H. Baldwin from a specimen 4.5 inches long, collected at Honolulu by Jordan and Evermann in 1901.

PLATE LVIII.

Hepatus achilles (Shaw)

Painting by A. H. Baldwin from a specimen 8.4 inches long, collected at Honolulu by Jordan and Evermann in 1901.

PLATE LIX.

Zebrasoma flavescens (Bennett)

Painting by A. H. Baldwin from a specimen 5.3 inches long, collected at Honolulu by Jordan and Evermann in 1901.

PLATE LX.

Callicanthus lituratus (Forster)

Painting by A. H. Baldwin from a specimen 11 inches long, collected at Hilo by Jordan and Evermann in 1901. **Acanthurus unicornis** (Forskål) on the plate.

PLATE LXI.

Balistes vidua Solander

Painting by A. H. Baldwin from a specimen 8.75 inches long, collected at Hilo by Jordan and Evermann in 1901.

PLATE LXII.

Balistapus aculeatus (Linnæus)

Painting by A. H. Baldwin from a specimen 8.5 inches long, collected at Honolulu by Jordan and Evermann in 1901.

PLATE LXIII.

Balistapus rectangulus (Bloch & Schneider)

Painting by C. B. Hudson from a specimen 7.5 inches long, collected at Honolulu by Jordan and Evermann in 1901.

PLATE LXIV.

Melichthys radula (Solander)

Painting by A. H. Baldwin from a specimen 9 inches long, collected at Honolulu by Jordan and Evermann in 1901.

PLATE LXV.

Stephanolepis spilosomus (Lay & Bennett)

Painting by A. H. Baldwin from a specimen 5.4 inches long, collected at Hilo by Jordan and Evermann in 1901.

PLATE LXVI.

Tetraodon hispidus Linnæus

Painting by C. B. Hudson from a specimen 9 inches long, collected at Honolulu by Jordan and Evermann in 1901.

PLATE LXVII.

Paracirrhites forsteri (Bloch & Schneider)

Painting by C. B. Hudson from a specimeu 7 inches long, collected at Honolulu by Jordan and Evermann in 1901.

PLATE LXVIII.

Paracirrhites cinctus (Günther)

Painting by C. B. Hudson from a specimen 3.75 inches long, collected at Honolulu by Jordan and Evermann in 1901.

PLATE LXIX.

Paracirrhites arcatus (Cuvier & Valenciennes)

Painting by C. B. Hudson from a specimen 4.2 inches long, collected at Honolulu by Jordan and Evermann in 1901.

PLATE LXX.

Cirrhites marmoratus (Lacépède)

Painting by C. B. Hudson from a specimen 7 inches long, collected at Honolulu by Jordan and Evermann in 1901.

PLATE LXXI.

Scorpænopsis cacopsis Jenkins

Painting by A. H. Baldwin from a specimen 12 inches long, collected at Honolulu by Jordan and Evermann in 1901.

PLATE LXXII.

Scopæna ballieui Vaillant & Sauvage

Painting by A. H. Baldwin from a specimen 3.3 inches long, collected at Honolulu by Jordan and Evermann in 1901. **Sebastapistes ballieui** (Vaillant & Sauvage) on the plate.

PLATE LXXIII.

Dendrochirus barberi Steindachner

Painting by C. B. Hudson from the type of *D. hudsoni* Jordan & Evermann, a specimen 4 inches long, collected at Honolulu by Jordan and Evermann in 1901.

BLACK AND WHITE PLATES.
The following plates are placed at the end of the book.

Pl. 1. **Carcharias melanopterus** Quoy & Gaimard

Drawing by W. S. Atkinson from a specimen 31 inches long, collected at Honolulu by Jordan and Evermann in 1901.

2. **Carcharias phorcys** Jordan & Evermann

Drawing by W. S. Atkinson from the type, No. 50612, U.S.N.M., a specimen 27.5 inches long, collected at Honolulu by Jordan and Evermann in 1901.

3. Fig. 1. **Carcharias insularum** Snyder

Drawing by W. S. Atkinson from the type, No. 50859, U.S.N.M., a specimen 84 inches long, collected at Station 3815, off Diamond Head, Oahu Island, by the *Albatross* in 1902.

3. Fig. 2. **Carcharias nesiotes** Snyder

Drawing by W. S. Atkinson from the type, No. 50860, U.S.N.M., a specimen 60 inches long, collected at French Frigate Shoals by the *Albatross* in 1902.

4. Fig. 1. **Dasyatis hawaiensis** Jenkins

Drawing by W. S. Atkinson from the type, a specimen 6.5 inches long, collected at Honolulu by O. P. Jenkins in 1889.

4. Fig. 2. **Dasyatis sciera** Jenkins

Drawing by W. S. Atkinson from the type, a specimen 41 inches long, collected at Honolulu by O. P. Jenkins in 1889.

5. Fig. 1. **Veternio verrens** Snyder

Drawing by Sekko Shimada from the type, No. 50862, U.S.N.M., a specimen 11 inches long, collected at Honolulu by the *Albatross* in 1902.

5. Fig. 2. **Sphagebranchus flavicaudus** Snyder

Drawing by Sekko Shimada from the type, No. 50863, U.S.N.M., a specimen 13 inches long, collected at Station 3874, between Maui and Lanai islands, by the *Albatross* in 1902.

6. **Microdonophis fowleri** Jordan & Evermann

Drawing by A. H. Baldwin from the type, No. 50613, U.S.N.M., a specimen 23 inches long, collected at Honolulu by Jordan and Evermann in 1901.

7. **Brachysomophis henshawi** Jordan & Snyder

Drawing by Sekko Shimada from the type, No. 51399, U.S.N.M., a specimen 20 inches long, collected at Honolulu by E. L. Berndt in 1902.

Pl. 24. **Exonautes gilberti** Snyder

> Drawing by Sekko Shimada from the type, No. 50872, U.S.N.M., a specimen 10.2 inches long, collected between Stations 3799 and 3800 by *Albatross* in 1902.

25. **Cypsilurus atrisignis** Jenkins

> Drawing by W. S. Atkinson from the type, No. 50713, U.S.N.M., a specimen 13.5 inches long, collected at Honolulu by O. P. Jenkins in 1889.

26. **Myripristis symmerricus** Jordan & Evermann

> Drawing by C. B. Hudson from the type, No. 50632, U.S.N.M., a specimen 5.5 inches long, collected at Hilo by Jordan and Evermann in 1901.

27. **Myripristis argyromus** Jordan & Evermann

> Drawing by C. B. Hudson from the type, No. 50631, U.S.N.M., a specimen 9 inches long, collected at Honolulu by Jordan and Evermann in 1902.

28. **Holocentrus ensifer** Jordan & Evermann

> Drawing by C. B. Hudson from the type, No. 50637, U.S.N.M., a specimen 6.25 inches long, collected at Honolulu by Jordan and Evermann in 1901.

29. **Promethichthys prometheus** (Cuvier & Valenciennes)

> Drawing by A. H. Baldwin from a specimen 17 inches long, collected at Honolulu by Jordan and Evermann in 1901.

30. **Decapterus sanctæ-helenæ** (Cuvier & Valenciennes)

> Drawing by A. H. Baldwin from the type of *D. canonoides* Jenkins, No. 5 846, U.S.N.M., a specimen 9 inches long, collected at Honolulu by Dr. A. B. Wood in 1899.

31. **Carangus elacate** Jordan & Evermann

> Drawing by Kako Morita from the type, No. 50638, U.S.N.M., a specimen 27 inches long, collected at Honolulu by Jordan and Evermann in 1901.

32. **Carangus helvolus** (Forster)

> Drawing by Sekko Shimada from a specimen 15 inches long, collected at Honolulu by the *Albatross* in 1902.

33. Fig. 1. **Carangus cheilio** Snyder

> Drawing by Sekko Shimada from the type, No. 50873, U.S.N.M., a specimen 28.5 inches long, collected at Honolulu by the *Albatross* in 1902.

33. Fig. 2. **Carangoides ajax** Snyder

> Drawing by Sekko Shimada from the type, No. 50874, U.S.N.M., a specimen 39 inches long, collected at Honolulu by the *Albatross* in 1902.

34. Fig. 1. **Collybus drachme** Snyder

> Drawing by W. S. Atkinson from the type, No. 50875, U.S.N.M., a specimen 3.5 inches long, collected at Station 4176, off Niihau Island, by the *Albatross* in 1902.

34. Fig. 2. **Amia erythrinus** (Snyder)

> Drawing by W. S. Atkinson from the type, No. 50876, U.S.N.M., a specimen 1.9 inches long, collected in Puako Bay, Hawaii, by the *Albatross* in 1902.

35. **Mionorus waikiki** (Jordan & Evermann)

> Drawing by Kako Morita from the type, No. 50640, U.S.N.M., a specimen 2.2 inches long, collected at Honolulu by Jordan and Evermann in 1901.

36. **Amia snyderi** (Jordan & Evermann)

> Drawing by Kako Morita from the type, No. 50640, U.S.N.M., a specimen 5.25 inches long, collected at Honolulu by Jordan and Evermann in 1901.

37. **Ariomma lurida** Jordan & Snyder

> Drawing by W. S. Atkinson from the type, No. 51400, U.S.N.M., a specimen 7.5 inches long, collected at Honolulu by E. L. Berndt in 1902.

38. **Etelis evurus** Jordan & Evermann

> Drawing by W. S. Atkinson from the type, No. 50662, U.S.N.M., a specimen 12.5 inches long, collected at Hilo by Jordan and Evermann in 1901.

39. **Upeneus arge** Jordan & Evermann

> Drawing by C. B. Hudson from the type, No. 50667, U.S.N.M., a specimen 8.5 inches long, collected at Honolulu by Jordan and Evermann in 1901.

40. **Abudefduf sindonis** (Jordan & Evermann)

> Drawing by Kako Morita from the type, No. 50669, U.S.N.M., a specimen 3.75 inches long, collected at Honolulu by Jordan and Evermann in 1901.

41. **Thalassoma aneitense** (Günther)

> Drawing by Sekko Shimada from a specimen 6 inches long, collected at Honolulu by the *Albatross* in 1902.

TEXT FIGURES.

INTRODUCTION TO THE
NEW EDITION

This classic study of Hawaiian shore fishes was first printed in Washington in 1905 as "Part I: The Shore Fishes" of a report entitled "The Aquatic Resources of the Hawaiian Islands," *Bulletin of the United States Fish Commission for 1903*, Vol. 23. The present reprint is an abridgment into handbook form, now newly titled *The Shore Fishes of Hawaii*.

In condensing this *magnum opus* of Hawaiian ichthyology the editors have omitted only those parts of little reference value today to the fisherman, scuba divers, fish fanciers, or other readers who are likely to use the book. The deleted parts relate mainly to nineteenth-century literature, historical background, and other data of scant contemporary interest. However, the description of each fish is intact with illustration, whether text figure or plate.

The authors are Dr. David Starr Jordan, then president of Stanford University, and Dr. Barton Warren Evermann, the incumbent ichthyologist with the U.S. Fish Commission at the time the book was written. This study is a monument to their industry, to the work of their artists, and indeed to all who assisted in putting it together. The history of its preparation is most interesting. In the years 1901–2, a party of scientists and artists was sent to Hawaii by the U.S. Fish Commission to report on the aquatic life of the Hawaiian Islands. The commission's steamer *Albatross* was also assigned to the expedition, although its work was more related to the deep-sea fishes (islands as far away as Necker, to the northwest of the Hawaiian group, were visited), while the work on shore fishes was largely based on the island of Oahu.

Strange as it may now seem, the Honolulu fish market, in the years 1901 and 1902, provided the authors with their richest and most abundant study materials. Mr. E. L. Berndt, the inspector of that market, was a fish enthusiast whose practical knowledge added many new species to the Hawaiian fish list. Hawaiian fishermen, whose ancestors had known the habitats and watched the habits of local fish for a thousand years, were of indispensable help. The authors collected at such familiar spots as Waikiki, Waianae, and Waimea . . . seventy years ago, when the coasts still looked much as they did when Capt. James Cook discovered Hawaii in 1778. For such diversity and abundance of fish one now must collect widely.

The twentieth century, with its enormous multiplication of resident and visitor population, has been a disaster for the fish of Hawaii, especially around the island of Oahu. Silt from industrial or housing development, as well as the usual polluting wastes of human and industrial discharge, has caused extensive damage to reefs and sea bottom. Modern man's attitude toward the sea is in great contrast to that of the old-time Hawaiians, who regarded fish, fishing grounds, hook, line, canoe, and fisherman as sacred to the gods. Their society's protective taboos were in effect protective and conservationist. With the arrival of Western man, such respect for the environment declined until the indigenous fauna of land and sea grew scarce along Hawaii's beautiful shores. Antipollution endeavors and rejuvenation efforts are being made around Hawaii, among which, paradoxically, is the transfer of abandoned auto bodies to the sea floor to form artificial shoals. One such artificial reef at Maunalua, not far from Honolulu harbor, contains 916 car bodies. These steel caverns provide young fish with refuge from predators and at the same time furnish hard surfaces on which food algae can grow.

The rich fish fauna of Hawaii is derived, for the most part, from the seas around the Philippines and Indonesia. Over millions of years, sea currents have carried fishes into Hawaiian waters. The distinctly "Hawaiian" of these fishy immigrants are those species that have best adapted to the new environment by changing habits and certain physical characteristics. A few of the most recent arrivals have come by the agency of man, either by deliberate introduction or as uninvited passengers in the bottom weed of slow-moving ships. There are records of several new species of fish coming since World War II in the seaweed of the fouled bottom of a barge that was towed to Honolulu from Guam. This fact alone makes it clear that no book on Hawaiian fishes can ever be completely up to date. Also the variability of scientific names for fish genera and species is a matter of confusion, even to ichthyologists; so the reader of this book must keep in mind that the scientific fish names given here are those of seventy years ago. When precision of scientific names is essential to some purpose, it would be well to check it against the most recent literature.

The inclusion of artists in scientific expeditions was necessary before the days of color photography. Fish change color after being caught. Quick water-color sketches served scientists as a reference in their laboratories as well as the lithographers who printed color plates. The charm of the present work lies chiefly in its detail of description and its attractive illustrations. No other book on Hawaiian fishes can begin to compare with it on these two counts.

The illustrations are a marvel of patient drawing and of the lithographer's art. The color plates belong to an era when color illustrations could be made only by laborious manual processes, in this instance by printing from lithographic plates that were printed many times to achieve the delicate hues and tints essential to Hawaiian fish illustration. The original plates are a collector's delight in their own right and are much favored by antiquarian print sellers. Also decorators use them to hang framed on walls. For example a Honolulu waterfront restaurant has a framed set in one of its bars. This interest in the prints alone explains one of the reasons why the book is so rare—namely that many copies have been torn up for the illustrations. And since the book was originally published in a limited edition, original copies are now almost unavailable.

The individual illustrations of this book are of three kinds: line figures incorporated in the text, black-and-white plates, and color plates. The two groups of plates are placed at the end of the book, while the line text figures are located with the descriptions of the fish they serve to illustrate.

Terence Barrow, Ph.D.

DESCRIPTIVE CATALOGUE OF SHORE FISHES.

INTRODUCTION.

In the following pages we have attempted to present with sufficient completeness and detail a statement of our present knowledge of the fish-fauna of the Hawaiian Islands. Keys and descriptions are given by means of which all the species of shore fishes known from the islands may be identified. All the species of deep-water fishes are described by Dr. Charles H. Gilbert in Section II of this volume. As some families contain both shore and deep-water species, all the families are described in the present part. The keys for the identification of the species are necessarily to some extent artificial, but characters of real taxomomic significance are made use of in most instances. The keys are dichotomously arranged, that is, if the statements under a given letter do not apply to the specimen in hand, those under the multiple or double of that letter will be true.

The synonymy given includes all Hawaiian references which we have been able to find and references to all other faunal works of importance mentioning Hawaiian species. The type locality is given as a part of each original reference and is printed in heavy-faced type. All locality references not type localities are printed in ordinary type and inclosed in parentheses.

The name of the authority for the specific name, in accordance with the rule of the American Ornithologists' Union, is not preceded by a comma, but the name of an author quoting a scientific name is separated from the specific name by a comma. In sequence and arrangement of species we follow with some modifications our Fishes of North and Middle America. The common or local Hawaiian names which we have been able to identify with particular species are printed in italics and inclosed in quotation marks. For the verification of the spelling of these names we are indebted to the kindly interest and assistance of Mr. W. E. Safford, of the Bureau of Plant Industry, U. S. Department of Agriculture. But few English names of fishes have, as yet, come into use in Hawaii, and they are practically limited to species of wide distribution.

Special attention is called to the illustrations in this volume. The colored paintings, representing 73 species, were made by Mr. Albertus H. Baldwin (51), Capt. Charles Bradford Hudson (12), and Mr. Kako Morita (10). Messrs. Baldwin and Hudson painted from life, the specimen in each case having been placed alive in a specially constructed aquarium and the work completed before the colors materially changed. Those by Mr. Baldwin were done in water colors, those by Capt. Hudson in oil. The paintings by Mr. Morita are from life color sketches made by Dr. Jordan at Samoa or by Mr. Walter K. Fisher at Laysan Island in 1902. The black and white drawings were made by Messrs. Baldwin, Hudson, William Sacketon Atkinson, Robert Logan Hudson, and Sekko Shimada, and Mrs. Chloe Lesley Starks. About 50 of the text figures are from photographs of illustrations which have appeared in previous publications, chiefly in Günther's Fische der Südsee or in Steindachner's Fische aus dem Stillen Ocean.

CHARACTER OF THE HAWAIIAN FISH FAUNA.

The fish fauna of the shores of the Hawaiian Islands is frankly and entirely tropical, all the species belonging to genera characteristic of the tropical Pacific; but while the families and genera are those of the South Seas, the species are in a large degree distinct from the species of Samoa and Tahiti. This fact is evidently connected with the relative isolation of this group as compared with Polynesia, which is connected with the East Indies by an almost continuous chain of islands and atolls.

It is perhaps true that the isolation of Hawaii is due in part to the direction of the marine currents. These do not much influence free-swimming fishes like the mackerels, but they may serve to transport young fishes from one place to another. It is known that the young of shore fishes are often borne out to deep water, so that each island becomes the center of a "sphere of influence" so far as its species are concerned. Many young fishes are borne along in the Gulf Stream of our Atlantic coast and in the corresponding Kuro Shiwo of Japan. It is likely that the currents of the eastern central Pacific have a similar influence.

One of these currents, originating to the northward of the Philippines, passes eastward between Melanesia and Micronesia, thence along the north shores of Fiji, Tonga, Samoa, and Tahiti. Approaching the shores of America, it turns to the northward, touching the Revillagigedo and other offshore islands, leaving there a few Polynesian species, then returns westward via Hawaii toward the shores of Japan. This current may help to give the Polynesian Islands their identical fauna. Since it is inadequate to carry these species to Hawaii, the long separation of these latter islands has given them a fauna practically distinct, although made up entirely of tropical elements. What these elements are is shown in the following table:

Total number of species of shore fishes found in Hawaii ----------------------------------- 441
Number of species confined to Hawaii----- --- 232
Number of species common to Hawaii and Polynesia (Samoa, Tahiti, Fiji)-------------------- 142
Number of species common to Hawaii and Japan-- 53
Number of species common to Hawaii and Mexico --- 34

ANALYSIS OF THE CLASSES OF FISH-LIKE VERTEBRATES.[a]

a. *Acraniata:* Anterior end of the central nervous axis not dilated into a brain and not surrounded by a protective capsule or skull.
  b. Notochord perfect, persistent, extending throughout the body, included in a membranous sheath, as is the cord-like nervous axis above it; body elongate, lanceolate, not worm-like, nor enveloped in a tunic; walls of the body with muscular myotomes; middle line of body with rudimentary fins; no proboscis; the mouth slit-like, fringed with cirri; heart a longitudinal tubular vessel giving off branchial tubes which unite in an aorta; gill-slits inclosed externally by a fold in the integument, which incloses a chamber (atrium), which opens below; vent remote from mouth... Leptocardii, I.
aa. *Craniata:* Anterior end of nervous axis dilated into a brain, which is contained within a protective capsule, the skull; notochord not continued forward beyond the pituitary body; heart developed and divided at least into two parts.
  c. Skull well developed and with jaws; shoulder-girdle and pelvis more or less developed; nostrils not median; gills not purse-shaped; limbs, if present, developed as rayed fins, never with fingers and toes like those of the higher vertebrates; gills persistent through life .... Pisces, II.

Class I LEPTOCARDII.—The Lancelets.

Skeleton membrano-cartilaginous; notochord persistent and extending to the anterior end of the head, inclosed in a membranous sheath as is the cord-like axis above it; heart a longitudinal tubular vessel giving off branchial vessels which unite in an aorta; end of the nervous axis not dilated into a brain, and not surrounded by a protective capsule or skull; blood colorless; respiratory cavity confluent with the cavity of the abdomen; gill-slits in great number, the water being expelled through an abdominal pore in front of the vent; jaws none, the mouth a longitudinal fissure with cirri on each side; body lanceolate in form, more or less fish-like, and not enveloped in a tunic; dorsal fin present, low; anal fin usually more or less developed.

Small marine animals, highly interesting to the zoologist as exhibiting the lowest degree of development of the vertebrate type. The class includes but the single order, *Amphioxi* or *Cirrostomi.*

---

[a] In this, as well as in all other analytic keys in this work, only the Hawaiian fish-fauna is considered.

Order A. AMPHIOXI.—The Cirrostomes.

This order is equivalent to the family *Branchiostomidæ*.

Family I. BRANCHIOSTOMIDÆ.—The Lancelets.

Body elongate, lanceolate, compressed, naked, colorless; fins represented by a low fold extending along back, with usually a rudimentary fold below, which passes by the vent to the abdominal pore; mouth inferior, appearing as a longitudinal fissure, surrounded by conspicuous, rather stiff cirri; eye rudimentary; liver reduced to a blind sac of the simple intestine.

Small, translucent creatures, found embedded in sand on warm coasts throughout the world. Eight species are now recognized, referable to two or three genera, all very similar in appearance and habits. Only one genus represented in the Hawaiian fauna.

Genus 1. AMPHIOXIDES Gill

"Branchiostomids with bilateral (?) gonads, no rayed sympodium (?), low dorsal fin, expanded caudal membranes, and oral cirri aborted (?)." (Gill.)

As the species on which this genus is based really lacks oral tentacles, it should stand as a distinct genus. To say that this trait is due to its pelagic habit, as Tattersall suggests, is not to discredit its generic value.

1. **Amphioxides pelagicus** (Günther). Fig. 1.

Buccal tentacles absent;[a] gonads not fully developed, extending from the first to the twenty-sixth myocomma and forming 2 series in the middle; atrial cavity extending somewhat behind the supposed position of the atrial pore; anterior end of the notochord enveloped in a very strong sheath;

FIG. 1.—*Amphioxides pelagicus* (Günther); after Günther.

the posterior ($\frac{1}{2}$ mm.) not covered by the myocommas, which lean off abruptly, and extending right to the hind margin of the caudal fin; eye distinct; nerve-cord with minute pigment-spots arranged intracentrally with regard to the myocommas; dorsal fin-rays low, but very distinct, about five to each myocomma; dorsal fin-fringe becoming distinct about the twenty-seventh myocomma, gradually becoming somewhat higher behind, its rise more abrupt where it passes into the caudal fin, which is paddle-shaped and bilaterally symmetrical with regard to the notochord; lower half of caudal passing uninterruptedly into the ventral, in which no rays are developed, this fin seeming to be continued forward as a low fringe for some distance beyond the supposed position of the atrial pore; nearly the whole of this fringe showing a minute vertical striation, especially in its higher portions; myocommas 27, of which 15 belong to the tail; how many should be attributed to the portion between vent and atrial pore is uncertain on account of the difficulty in ascertaining the position of the latter. This pore could not be made out, and its position is supposed to be opposite to the thirty-sixth myocomma only from analogy or comparison with other species, and from a slight contraction of the muscular layer at this point.

One specimen 2 inches long was taken by the *Challenger* on July 26, 1875, in latitude 23° 3′ N.. longitude 156° 6′ W., a few degrees north of Honolulu. (Günther.) Other specimens were secured by the *Albatross* in 1902. The species is supposed to differ from other lancelets in living toward the surface in deep water instead of burying itself in the sand at small depths. There is considerable doubt as to this, however, and as to some of the characters ascribed to the species.

Class II. PISCES.—The Fishes.

The Pisces, or fishes, may be defined as cold-blooded vertebrates adapted for life in the water, breathing by means of gills which are attached to bony or cartilaginous gill-arches, the gills persistent throughout life; having the skull well developed and provided with a lower jaw; the limbs present and developed as fins, rarely wanting through atrophy; shoulder-girdle present, furcula-shaped, curved forward below, rarely obsolete or represented by cartilage; pelvic bones present; exoskeleton developed as scales, bony plates, or horny appendages, or sometimes entirely wanting; and with the median line of the body provided with one or more fins composed of cartilaginous rays connected by membrane, the fins rarely atrophied.

---

a This can not be due to the age of the individual, as they are clearly developed in specimens of *Branchiostoma belcheri* (?) of only half the size of this specimen.

Subclass SELACHII.—The Sharks and Skates.

This group includes among recent fishes, the sharks and rays, marine fishes, mostly of large size, abounding in all seas.

Order B. ASTEROSPONDYLI.

The essential character of this order is the structure of the vertebræ. The calcareous lamellæ within each vertebra radiate from the central ring. The group contains the great body of living sharks, including all of those with 5 gill-openings, 2 dorsals, and an anal fin.

Suborder GALEI.—THE TRUE SHARKS.

Asterospondylous sharks with the palato-quadrate apparatus not articulated with the skull; gill-openings always 5 and always lateral; dorsal fins 2, well developed, each without spines. This suborder contains most of the living sharks.

Family II. SCYLLIORHINIDÆ.—The Cat Sharks.

Dorsal fins 2, both rather small, without spines, the first more or less behind ventrals; anal fin present, usually before the second dorsal; caudal fin rather long, usually with a basal lobe; tail not keeled, and not bent upward. Spiracles present; no nictitating membrane; gill-openings small, the last one above the root of the pectorals. Mouth usually broad, with small teeth, several series being in junction; teeth each with a median cusp and 1 to 4 small cusps on each side; nostrils near mouth, sometimes confluent with it, sometimes provided with cirri. Mucous pores about head numerous, especially on lower side of snout. Egg cases large, quadrate, with prehensile tubes at angles.

Genus 2. CATULUS Smith.

As here understood, this genus is very close to the European genus *Scylliorhinus*, from which it is distinguished by the separate nasal valves. Gill has further divided the group into *Catulus*, having the nasal valves provided with lobes or grooves, *Halælurus* having the nasal valves simple, and *Cephaloscyllium*, which has a very broad head and the stomach inflatable. The latter group, with possibly *Halælurus*, is perhaps generically distinct. *Catulus* differs from *Pristiurus* in having the scales on the upper edge of the tail not much, if at all, enlarged and usually not differentiated from the others. The prickles on the body are usually much coarser in *Catulus* than in *Scylliorhinus* or *Pristiurus*. Species numerous, usually in rather deep water. The single species known from Hawaiian waters is described in Section II of this volume.

Family III. CARCHARIIDÆ.—The Typical Sharks; Manos.

Sharks with 2 dorsal fins, the first short and high, entirely before the ventrals, the second comparatively small, opposite the anal; no spines; gill-openings moderate, the last above the base of the pectoral; tail more or less bent upward from base of caudal fin; sides of tail not keeled; eyes with nictitating membranes; head not hammer-shaped, the snout being longitudinally produced, as usual among sharks; spiracles small or obsolete. Ovoviviparous.

A large family found in all seas. The species are often closely related and difficult of determination.

Genus 3. GALEUS Rafinesque.

First dorsal opposite the space between the pectorals and ventrals; mouth crescent-shaped with teeth alike in both jaws, oblique, notched and serrated; spiracles present, small; nictitating membrane present; no pit at base of caudal; caudal fin with a single notch. Tropical seas.

2. Galeus japonicus Müller & Henle. Fig. 2.

Spiracles small; a short labial fold on each jaw; second dorsal fin not much smaller than the first

Fig. 2.—*Galeus japonicus* Müller & Henle; after Müller and Henl

and slightly in advance of the anal; length of caudal fin rather less than distance between the 2 dorsals (Müller & Henle).

This species was not obtained by us, the only Hawaiian reference being that of Dr. Steindachner, based upon a single specimen more than 5 feet long, from Laysan. It is more likely to be the Japanese species, *Galeus japonicus*, than the Californian, *Galeus zyopterus*. Neither of these differs much from the European *Galeus galeus*.

Genus 4. GALEOCERDO Müller & Henle.

Mouth crescent-shaped; teeth alike in both jaws, large, oblique, coarsely serrated on both margins, with a deep notch on outer margin; spiracles present; caudal fin with a double notch; a pit on the tail above and below at base of caudal fin; first dorsal opposite the space between pectorals and ventrals.

Large sharks found in most warm seas. Only one species known from Hawaiian or American waters.

3. Galeocerdo tigrinus Müller & Henle.   *Tiger Shark.*

Head 7.25 in length; depth about 10; snout 3.33 in head; interorbital space 1.33; width of mouth at corners about 1.6; eye 5.66 in the interorbital space; space between nostrils 2.

Body elongate, tapering to caudal; head very much broader than deep, depressed; eyes small, lateral, nearer snout than gill-opening; snout broad, short, rounded; mouth very broad, rounded; teeth numerous, rather large, compressed, with several basal cusps, and with edges more or less serrated; a labial fold at corners of mouth; nostrils large, inferior, about midway between tip of snout and eye; interorbital space very broad, flat; spiracles very small, behind eye; gill-openings large, posteriorly above base of pectoral. Body very finely roughened. First dorsal beginning about first fourth of interspace between origin of pectoral and that of ventral; second dorsal small, a little nearer origin of first dorsal than tip of caudal; anal small, beginning behind origin of second dorsal; pectoral rather long; ventrals very much nearer anal than pectorals; caudal very long, lower lobe produced; caudal peduncle rather short.

Color brown above, whitish or pale below, upper surface with blackish markings, mostly in the form of dark crossbars.

This shark is known from the East Indies northward to Japan, whence Günther recorded a small example. Jordan and Snyder also record it from Japan, having examined the dried skin of a young male from Nagasaki. A good specimen was sent to us from Honolulu by Mr. E. L. Berndt. The species differs from *G. maculatus* of the Atlantic in having dark cross-bands instead of dark brown spots on the upper surface.

Genus 5. PRIONACE Cantor.   *Blue Sharks.*

Large sharks with the body and head slender; no spiracles; the teeth in both jaws strongly serrated in the adult, those in the upper jaw broad, those below narrower, straight, and claviform; first dorsal large, inserted midway between axils of pectorals and ventrals; second dorsal much smaller, usually not larger than anal; embryo not attached to the uterus by a placenta. Species rather few; large, slender, swift, voracious sharks of the warm seas. The groups called *Prionace*, *Hypoprion*, *Aprionodon*, and *Scoliodon* are usually placed as subgenera under *Carcharhinus* or *Carcharias*, as the group has been commonly called. Their retention as distinct genera is apparently justified on the ground of convenience.

4. Prionace glauca (Linnæus).   Fig. 3.

Snout very long; nostrils rather nearer to mouth than to extremity of snout; no labial fold except a groove at angle of mouth; teeth of upper jaw oblique, scarcely constricted near base; lower teeth slender, triangular in young examples, lanceolate, with a broad base, in old ones; pectoral fin long, falciform, extending to dorsal, which is nearer ventrals than root of pectorals. Color light bluish gray above, paler below.

FIG. 3.—*Prionace glauca* (Linnæus); after Jordan and Evermann.

A large shark of the warm seas, occasionally taken in Europe and on the coasts of Japan and California. A mounted specimen from off Misaki is in the Imperial Museum of Tokyo, and in the Imperial University is a photograph of a large specimen secured at the same place. A female, taken with a hand line at *Albatross* Station 3801, 28° 31′ N., 141° 47′ W., contained 47 embryos, each measuring 15.3 inches in length. The following measurements of the adult were taken: Tip of snout to end of caudal lobe 274 cm., to dorsal fin 110; to eye 23; to first gill-opening 55; to pectoral 65; length of gill-area 18; height of first gill-slit 5; of second and third 7.5; of fourth 7; of fifth 5; length of pectoral 62; base of pectoral 23; free edge of pectoral 56; axil to ventral 77; anterior margin of ventral 17.5; free margin of ventral 20.5; base of ventral 16.5; axil of ventral to front of anal 24; base of anal 13.5; anterior margin of anal 17; anal to caudal pit 22; base of dorsal 23; anterior margin of dorsal 30.5; free edge of dorsal 28; posterior edge of first dorsal to second dorsal 63.5; base of second dorsal 13; front margin of second dorsal 13.5; posterior end of second dorsal to caudal pit 21.5; upper lobe of caudal 58.5; spread of caudal 67; lower caudal lobe 37; girth at front of ventral 76; girth at front of pectorals 91.

Whether this species is really identical with the European *P. glauca* is uncertain.

Genus 6. CARCHARIAS Rafinesque.

Body rather robust, the head broad and depressed; mouth inferior, with the teeth in both jaws strongly serrated in the adult, less so or entire in the young, those in the upper jaw broad or narrow, those below narrow, straight, and nearly erect; no spiracles; first dorsal large, placed not far behind pectoral; pectoral falcate; second dorsal small. Embryos attached by placenta to the uterus. Species very numerous and difficult of separation. Voracious sharks of the warm seas.

5. Carcharias melanopterus Quoy & Gaimard. Plate 1.

Head about 5.85 in length; depth about 7.67; width of head 1.25 in its length; depth of head nearly 2; snout about 3 in head; interorbital space 1.5; space between tip of snout and front of mouth 2.6; width of mouth 2; eye 5 in interorbital space; internasal space 2; least depth of caudal peduncle 3; caudal 3.5 in body; pectoral 5.5.

Body elongate, rather robust, the trunk and tail compressed; head very broad and depressed; snout very broad, rounded, appearing pointed when viewed laterally; eyes small, their posterior margins about midway between tip of snout and first gill-opening; nictitating membrane well developed; mouth large, very convex, so that the anterior margin of the mandible is below front rim of orbit; teeth in upper jaw broad, compressed, sharply pointed, the edges serrate and with 4 or 5 basal cusps behind; teeth in mandible rather long, pointed, the compressed edges smooth, without any serratures; nostril with a small flap, inferior, about midway in length of snout; interorbital space very broad, more or less convex, especially in the center, behind which the top of the head rises more or less gradually to back of neck; gill-openings of moderate length, close together, the posterior above base of pectoral; peritoneum silvery.

Body very finely roughened when stroked forward; first dorsal with its length about equal to depth of body, its origin midway between that of the second dorsal and tip of snout; origin of second dorsal nearer origin of first dorsal than tip of caudal; anal similar to second dorsal, and below it, the origins of the 2 fins at the same point; caudal rather long, with a notch near its tip; length of lower lobe 2.2 in entire length of fin; pectoral large, margin of fin nearly straight or only very slightly concave; ventrals small, their origin a little nearer origin of first dorsal than that of second, or nearly midway between; back in front of first dorsal slightly keeled, and between first and second dorsals with a shallow groove; base of caudal, above and below, with pit. Another example, a female, gave the following measurements, recorded in centimeters: Total length 156; tip of snout to dorsal 52; to eye 12.8; to first gill-opening 30.5; to pectoral 36.2; length of gill-area 7.7; height of first, second, third, and fourth gill-slits 6.3; fifth 5.6; anterior margin of pectoral 28; base of pectoral 10.8; posterior margin of pectoral 27.3; axil of pectoral to ventral 36.8; anterior margin of ventral 12; free margin of ventral 10; base of ventral 10; axil of ventral to front of anal 13.3; base of anal 8.3; anterior margin of anal 10; base of anal to caudal pit 9; base of dorsal 11; anterior margin of dorsal 19.5; free edge of dorsal 15.3; distance between dorsals 38; base of second dorsal 7.6; second dorsal to caudal pit 10; upper lobe of caudal 38; spread of caudal 35.5; lower lobe of caudal 19; width of mouth 17; preoral length of snout 9.5; girth behind pectorals 63.5; girth at front of ventrals 53.

Color in life (field No. 03535), upper parts of body and head light brown, lower parts white; fins tipped with black; upper and lower borders of caudal also black. Another example, 4.5 feet long and similarly marked, was seen in the market of Honolulu.

Color in alcohol, pale brown above, the lower portions white; a brown longitudinal band along side from below front of first dorsal backward over base of ventral; upper surface of pectorals and ventrals brown like the back; upper extremity of dorsal, broadly and abruptly blotched with black; margins of caudal narrowly black, the greater part or outer half of the lower lobe black; outer portion of anal black; lower tip of pectoral blackish, the upper edge or marginal portion also blackish or dusky, and the lower tip of ventrals broadly blackish. Description from a male 31 inches long taken at Honolulu.

This shark is a common form throughout Polynesia. We have a number of examples from

Honolulu, three of which were collected in 1889 by Dr. Jenkins. The species was also found at Samoa by Jordan and Kellogg. It may be known at once by the inky black tips to its fins.

6. Carcharias phorcys Jordan & Evermann. Plate 2.

Head 4.8 in length; depth 6.5; width of head 1.75 in its length; depth of head 1.8; snout about 2.2 in head; interorbital space 2.2; space between tip of snout and front of mouth 2.5; width of mouth 2.5; eye 6 in interobital space; internasal space 1.8; least depth of caudal peduncle a little over 4.8; caudal 3.5 in body; pectoral 5.75.

Body elongate, rather robust, the tail compressed; head elongate, somewhat narrow and depressed, snout long and narrowly pointed when viewed above, the tip rounded; eyes small, their posterior margins about midway between tip of snout and first gill-opening; nictitating membrane well developed; mouth large, very convex, the anterior margin of mandible below front rim of orbit; teeth in upper jaw narrow, with broad basis, not notched, compressed, serrate, and with four or five basal cusps behind; teeth in mandible rather long, pointed, not serrate, the edges smooth; nostril without flap, inferior, and nearer eye than tip of snout; interorbital space broad and convex; upper profile of head rising gradually in a nearly straight line to back of head; gill-opening of moderate length, posterior, over base of pectoral; peritoneum white or pale; body very finely roughened when stroked forward; height of first dorsal less than depth of body, its origin a little nearer tip of snout than origin of second dorsal; origin of second dorsal nearer origin of first dorsal than tip of caudal; fin small, about over anal, so that origins of the 2 fins are opposite; caudal long, with a notch at its tip, deep, the lower lobe 2.25 in length of fin; pectoral with margin slightly concave; ventrals small, their origins a little nearer base of lower caudal lobe than origin of the pectoral; back convexly ridged, broader between the dorsals; base of caudal with a pit above and below.

Color in alcohol, pale brown, the lower parts pale or whitish with a brown streak the color of the back along side from gill-opening to over origin of ventral; tips of dorsals, edge of caudal, and tip of pectoral blackish.

This description from an example 27.5 inches long, field No. 03747, taken at Honolulu. Type, No. 50612, U. S. Nat. Mus. We have 4 other examples also from Honolulu, one a fœtus, besides 2 from the same locality collected by Dr. Jenkins in 1889. Specimens were also secured by the *Albatross* in 1902 at Honolulu and at Hanalei Bay, Kauai.

7. Carcharias insularum Snyder. Plate 3, fig. 1.

Head, measured to last gill-opening, 3.1 in length (tip of snout to caudal pit); depth at front of pectorals 6.1; at front of ventrals 6.7; snout 3 in head; interorbital width 2; pectoral 4 in length; upper lobe of caudal 2.7.

Mouth semicircular, its width equal to distance between tip of snout and posterior border of eye, distance between edge of mouth and tip of snout 1.7 times width of mouth, or a little more than distance between nostrils; upper teeth serrated from base to tips, the lower ones smooth on base, upper parts weakly serrated; teeth of upper jaw a little broader at base than they are high, the cutting edges of median ones straight; lateral teeth with edges slightly concave, concavity of outer edges deepening somewhat as they approach corners of mouth; teeth not pointing outward in either jaw, those of lower jaw much more slender than those above, the bases somewhat wider than height of teeth; cutting edges concave; 30 rows on each jaw, teeth of the 2 median rows minute or absent. Tip of pectoral fin acutely rounded; first dorsal broadly rounded; second dorsal slightly smaller than anal; caudal very large, underside of upper lobe with a deep notch; free edges of dorsals, pectorals, and ventrals concave; claspers of male 1.5 times as long as ventral fin is high.

In life, bluish slate-color, somewhat lighter below; first dorsal broadly tipped with lighter color; second dorsal, pectorals, ventrals, and caudal with slightly darker tips. In alcohol the fins and upper parts of the body are rather indistinctly spotted with a darker shade than that of body; spots of body somewhat larger than eye, the spaces between them somewhat wider than diameter of spots; spots on fins smaller and more closely crowded.

The following measurements were taken before the specimen, a male, was preserved: Total length 213 cm.; tip of snout to dorsal 71; to eye 17.8; to first gill-opening 40.5; to pectoral 48; length of gill-area 10; height of first gill-slit 7.5; of second 8.2; of third 8.8; of fourth 8.2; of fifth 5.7; length of pectoral 39; base of pectoral 14; free edge of pectoral 37; axil of pectoral to ventral 47; anterior margin of ventral 14; free margin of ventral 12; base of ventral 12.7; axil of ventral to front of anal 17.8; base of anal 9; anterior margin of anal 12.7; anal to caudal pit 8.2; base of dorsal 21; anterior margin of dorsal 32; free edge of dorsal 23.5; first to second dorsal 71; base of second dorsal 6.3; front margin of second dorsal 9; second dorsal to caudal pit 12.7; upper lobe of caudal 59.5; lower lobe of caudal 30; spread of caudal 61; girth at front of ventrals 66; girth at front of pectorals 78.5.

Seven young were obtained from a large female of this species taken at station 4111, between Molokai and Oahu, each measuring 61 cm. in length. Color bluish; pectorals, second dorsal, anal, and lower caudal lobe broadly tipped with black; ventral surface of body and paired fins, except the terminal dark areas, yellowish; tip of first dorsal yellowish. The head measured to last gill-opening 2.9 in length; depth at front of pectorals 5.5; depth of caudal peduncle 5.5 in head; snout 3; interorbital width 2.1. Curve of mouth elongate instead of circular, as in adult, its width being an eye's diameter less than distance between tip of snout and anterior border of orbit. Distance between edge of mouth and tip of snout 1.1 times width of mouth. Height of dorsal 6.25 in length of head and body; length of pectoral 3.4; upper lobe of caudal 2.7. Dorsal and pectorals broadly rounded.

This shark appears to be closely related to *Carcharias lamia* Rafinesque, of the Atlantic. Not common about the Hawaiian Islands.

8. Carcharias nesiotes Snyder.   Plate 3, fig. 2

Head, measured to last gill-opening, 3.1 in length (tip of snout to caudal pit); depth at front of pectorals 5.5; at front of ventrals 6.25; snout 3.1 in head; interorbital width 2.4; pectoral 3.7 in length; upper lobe of caudal 2.8. Mouth elliptical, not semicircular in shape, width equal to distance from tip of snout to posterior edge of orbit; width of space between tip of snout and anterior edge of mouth equal to distance between outer edges of nostrils, 3.9 in head; teeth of upper jaw strongly serrated, those near center of jaw symmetrical in shape, the width at base equal to or a little greater than height; laterally the outer edges of teeth grow concave, then notched; inner edges becoming convex, teeth pointing away from symphysis; teeth of lower jaw narrow, with wide bases, their edges smooth or very slightly serrated, symmetrical in shape on both middle and lateral parts of jaws. Pectorals pointed at tips when depressed, reaching as far back as posterior part of first dorsal, the free edge concave; first dorsal bluntly pointed; second dorsal and anal equal in size, edge of anal deeply notched; edge of upper caudal lobe notched, distance from notch to tip of lobe 4.54 in length of lobe.

Color bluish gray above, the fins growing darker toward the tips; ventral surface lighter.

The following are the measurements of a male taken at station 3902, off the northern coast of Molokai: Total length 224 cm.; tip of snout to dorsal 71; to eye 17.8; to gill-opening 44; to pectoral 54; length of gill-area 13.5; height of first gill-slit 6.5; of second 7; of third and fourth 6.5; of fifth 5.8; anterior margin of pectoral 49; base of pectoral 14; posterior margin of pectoral 42; axil of pectoral to ventral 49.5; anterior margin of ventral 12.8; free margin of ventral 12.8; base of ventrals 10.8; axil of ventral to front of anal 19; base of anal 8.3; anterior margin of anal 12; anal to caudal pit 13.4; base of first dorsal 19.7; anterior margin of first dorsal 30.5; free edge of dorsal 26; distance between dorsals 58; base of second dorsal 7; second dorsal to caudal pit 19; upper lobe of caudal 61; spread of caudal 66; lower caudal lobe 29; width of mouth 20.5; preoral length of snout 15.

Type, No. 50860, U. S. Nat. Mus., a female about 4.86 feet long, taken at French Frigate Shoals. A smaller example, also a female, from Laysan Island, does not differ from the type, except that it is darker in color, the under parts being quite dusky. Cotype, No. 12790, L. S. Jr. Univ. Mus., a female 32 inches long (No. 03741), and the heads of 2 larger examples were obtained at Honolulu.

A large and voracious shark seen everywhere about the islands. Compared with *Carcharias japonicus* of Japan, it is more robust in form, having a shorter and broader head.

Family IV. SPHYRNIDÆ.

General characteristics of the *Carchariidæ*, but the head singularly formed, kidney-shaped or "hammer"-shaped, from the extension of its sides, the nostrils being anterior and the eyes on the sides of the "hammer"; mouth crescent-shaped under the "hammer"; teeth of both jaws similar, oblique, each with a notch on the outside near the base; no spiracles; last gill-opening over the pectoral; first dorsal and pectorals large, the dorsal nearer pectorals than ventrals; second dorsal and anal small; a pit at the root of the caudal; caudal fin with a single notch toward its tip, its lower lobe developed. One genus with 5 species, inhabiting most warm seas. Large sharks, known at once by the singular form of the head, which is not quite the same in any two species.

Genus 7. SPHYRNA Rafinesque.

Characters of the genus included above. In the form of the head there is a perfect gradation among the species from the narrow hammer of *S. blochii*, with the lobes three times as long as broad and deeply grooved along the anterior edge, to the kidney-shaped head of *S. tiburo*, in which the anterior grooves are obsolete.

9. Sphyrna zygæna (Linnæus).   *Hammer-headed Shark;* "*Mano kihikihi.*"

Head truly hammer-shaped; width of head about twice its length; length of hinder margin of hammer nearly equal to its width near the eye; nostril close to eye, prolonged into a groove which runs along nearly the whole front margin of head; first dorsal large; second quite small, smaller than anal; pectoral rather large. Color gray. A large voracious shark reaching a length of 15 feet or more, found in all warm seas; occasionally on our coasts from Cape Cod and Point Concepcion, southward.

A number of examples of this species were obtained at Honolulu, and it was taken by the *Albatross*

at Station 3844, off the southern coast of Molokai. Dr. Jenkins also brought 13 examples from
Honolulu in 1889, the largest measuring 20.5 inches. The species is also common in the South Seas
and in Japan.

Family V. ALOPIIDÆ.—Thresher Sharks.

Body moderately elongate, the snout rather short; mouth crescent-shaped; teeth equal in both
jaws, moderate sized, flat, triangular, not serrated; the third tooth of the upper jaw on each side
much smaller than the others; gill-openings moderate, the last one above the root of the pectorals; no
nictitating membrane; spiracles just behind eye, minute or absent; first dorsal large, midway between
pectorals and ventrals; second dorsal and anal very small; caudal fin exceedingly long, about as long
as rest of body, a pit at its root, a notch on the upper lobe near its tip; lower lobe moderately
developed; no caudal keel; ventrals rather large; pectorals very large, falcate. A single species,
reaching a large size, inhabiting most seas, known at once by the great length of the tail.

Genus 8. ALOPIAS Rafinesque.

The characters of this genus are included with those of the family.

10. Alopias vulpes (Gmelin). Fig. 4.

Body fusiform, cylindrical, thickest before dorsal fin; back regularly arched from above pectorals
to end of snout, and gradually decreasing in size posteriorly to caudal. Head short, bluntly conical;
snout blunt; eye rather large; mouth horseshoe-shaped; teeth about $\frac{22+22}{19+19}$, third or fourth tooth on
either side of center of upper jaw smaller than others; spiracles very small or wanting; last gill-
openings above or slightly in front of pectorals.

Body more or less roughened. First dorsal high, triangular, somewhat higher than its base is

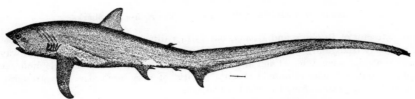

Fig. 4.—*Alopias vulpes* (Gmelin); after Jordan and Evermann.

long, slightly slender toward its summit, superior angle rounded; second dorsal similar in shape, but
much smaller; anal small, placed behind second dorsal, which it resembles; pectorals long, wide,
emarginate, with small process behind; ventrals wider than high, nearest first dorsal; caudal nearly
as long or longer than body, composed of 3 distinct lobes, one small, triangular, at under side of
tip, a second long and low, extending along upper side of tail, and a third short and broad, at lower
base of tail.

Color, slate-blue above, beneath soiled white, marked with obsolete bluish spots; pupil a longitudinal slit, edged with golden.

Length, 12 feet.

One large specimen received from the Honolulu market through Mr. Berndt.

A large shark, abounding in all warm seas, common on the east coast of Japan. It was seen by
Dr. Jordan at Misaki, Nagasaki, Tokyo, and Yokohama. No one has yet compared specimens of the
Japanese fish with those from California or the Mediterranean, and the species may prove different.

Family VI. LAMNIDÆ.—The Mackerel Sharks.

Sharks of large size, with the body stout, the mouth wide with large teeth, and the tail slender;
the caudal fin lunate, the 2 lobes being not very unequal, the upper lobe strongly bent upward;
caudal peduncle with a strong keel on each side; gill-openings wide, all in front of the pectoral, entirely
lateral, not extending under the throat; first dorsal large; pectorals large; ventrals moderate; second
dorsal and anal very small; a pit at the root of the caudal; spiracles minute or absent. Genera 3,
species 6 or more, besides numerous fossil species. In this family the dentition, as well as the muscular system, reaches its highest degree of specialization.

Genus 9. ISUROPSIS Gill.

Snout rather long and pointed; the body formed much like that of a tunny or mackerel; first dorsal large, inserted entirely behind pectorals, nearly midway between pectorals and ventrals; pectorals

large; second dorsal and anal very small; caudal peduncle slender; teeth long, lanceolate, with sharp entire cutting edges and no basal cusps.

11. Isuropsis glauca (Müller & Henle).   Fig. 5.

Snout long, pointed; teeth in 4 rows, very long, flexuous, without denticles at base; spiracles very small; first dorsal inserted well backward, midway between pectoral and ventral, scarcely longer than high, its upper angle rounded.

Color, dark blue, white below.

Coasts of Japan and southward, rather common about Nagasaki.   Many jaws and a stuffed fœtus

FIG. 5.—*Isuropsis glauca* (Müller & Henle); after Müller and Henle.

are in possession of Mr. Yahiro at Nagasaki.   A specimen 7 feet long was taken by Jordan and Snyder at Matsushima, of which the head was preserved.   Many teeth and jaws of specimens from Honolulu are in possession of Mr. E. L. Berndt, of Honolulu.

Genus 10. CARCHARODON Smith.   The Man-eater Sharks.

General character of *Isuropsis* and *Lamna*, but with a different dentition, the teeth being large, flat, erect, regularly triangular, their edges serrated; first dorsal moderate, nearly midway between pectorals and ventrals; second dorsal and anal very small; pectorals large; ventrals moderate; caudal peduncle rather stout; spiracles minute or absent.   Sharks of very large size; the strongest and most voracious of all fishes; pelagic, found in most warm seas.

12. Carcharodon carcharias (Linnæus).   "*Niuhi.*"

Body stout; depth about 5.5 in total length; mouth very large; each jaw with 5 rows of large, triangular, serrated teeth, those in lower jaw narrower, about $\frac{24}{22}$ in each row; first dorsal somewhat behind pectorals; caudal fin large and strong.   Color leaden gray; tips and edges of pectorals black. One of the largest of sharks, reaching a length of 30 feet; found in all temperate and tropical seas, and occasionally taken both in the Atlantic and Pacific.   One caught near Soquel, California, was about 30 feet long and had a young sea lion, weighing about 100 pounds, in its stomach.   (Jordan and Evermann.)

A large pair of jaws is preserved in the museum of the Imperial University at Tokyo, from a specimen taken somewhere off the east coast of Hondo, near Misaki.   This constitutes the only record of the species from Japan.   It was not seen by us in Hawaii, but we have unquestionable information of its occurrence off the coast of Puna, south of Hilo, whither it was attracted by the body of a dead horse. There are other statements of its frequent visits to Hawaii.

Order C. TECTOSPONDYLI.

Calcareous lamellæ arranged in one or more concentric series or rings about a central axis in each vertebra; spiracles present; anal fin wanting; dorsal fins 2, with or without spine.   As here understood, the order *Tectospondyli* includes the sharks of the groups called *Cyclospondyli* and *Tectospondyli* by Hasse.   The vertebræ in the rays show a similar structure, and it is probably from sharks of this group that the rays are descended.

Family VII. SQUALIDÆ.—The Dog Sharks.

Body more or less elongate; head depressed; eyes lateral, without nictitating membrane; mouth inferior, rather large, arched, a deep groove on each side; teeth compressed, variously formed; nostrils inferior, separate; spiracles rather large; gill-openings moderate, all in front of the pectoral fins;

dorsal fins 2, each armed with a spine; the first dorsal in front of the ventrals; anal fin wanting; caudal fin with the lower lobe small or obsolete; ventral fins inserted posteriorly, not much before second dorsal. Oviparous.

Genera 6 or more; species about 15. Rather small sharks, chiefly of the Atlantic. These sharks represent a comparatively primitive type, apparently not descended from any other existing *Squali*.

Genus 11. SQUALUS (Artedi) Linnæus.

Body rather slender; mouth little arched, with a long, straight, deep, oblique groove on each side; no labial fold; teeth rather small, all simple, equal in the 2 jaws, their points so much turned aside that the inner margin forms the cutting edge; spiracles rather wide, just behind the eye; fins moderately developed, the first dorsal larger than the second, much in advance of the ventral fins, which are behind the middle of the body although in advance of the second dorsal; dorsal spines strong, not grooved, tail scarcely bent upward. Small sharks abounding in the temperate seas; 4 or 5 species known.

13. Squalus mitsukurii Jordan & Snyder. " *Mano.*" Fig. 6.

We have 4 fœtal examples (No. 03752) of a species of this genus, obtained at Kailua, Hawaii, August, 1901. They were brought to us by a fisherman after having been removed from the body of the parent fish, which we did not see; this example was about 3 feet long. The species was said by the fisherman to be common in that region. The fœtuses each measured about 4.25 inches in total length, and may be described as follows:

Head 3.5 in length; depth 12; eye 3; snout 3.5. Body slender; head broad, depressed; mouth

Fig. 6.—*Squalus mitsukurii* Jordan & Snyder; from the type.

between posterior edges of eyes, its width equal to half its distance from tip of snout; snout broad, obtusely pointed; interorbital space nearly flat, its width equal to diameter of eye; origin of first dorsal fin nearer tip of snout than base of caudal fin; body entirely smooth, asperities scarcely, if at all, perceptible.

Color in alcohol, yellowish white; upper parts dusky or brownish; dorsal fins pale at base, black on distal part; caudal black, tips of lobes white.

Adult examples were taken by the *Albatross* and recorded by Professor Snyder, who is unable to separate the species from *Squalus mitsukurii* of Japan. The latter is thus described by Snyder:

Head, measured to last gill-opening, 3.9 in length (snout to caudal pit); measured to first gill-opening 4.5; width of head 2 in its length to last gill-opening; snout 2.4 in head measured to first gill-opening; interorbital space 2.4; height of first dorsal fin 2; second dorsal 3.4.

Teeth in both jaws similar, except that the lower ones are slightly larger than those above; placed in 3 closely apposed rows, pointing away from middle of jaw; outer edge with a deep notch, inner serving as cutting edge; distance between mouth and tip of snout 2 in length of head to first gill-opening; width of mouth 3.4; length of fold at corner of mouth equal to distance between nostrils; distance between nostril and tip of snout 3.9 in head; between nostril and middle of mouth equal to distance between nostril and tip of snout; distance between spiracles 2.3 in head; length of gill-area 4.5; diameter of eye 5.

Length of exposed portion of first dorsal spine equaling distance from tip of spine to tip of fin; height of spine equaling base of fin; second spine 0.75 as high as fin; distance between dorsals 3.66 times length of snout; pectoral, when depressed, reaching to a vertical through posterior edge of base of dorsal, the tip bluntly pointed; edges of pectoral and first dorsal concave, that of second dorsal emarginate; edge of ventrals straight; distance from anterior edge of anal opening to tip of depressed ventral 2.4 in head; upper caudal lobe 3.7 in its length; a low lateral keel on caudal peduncle.

Color, dark slaty blue above, lighter below.

Some of the specimens examined have the head slightly narrower than examples of the same species from Japan, while others are like them in every particular.

Genus 12. ETMOPTERUS Rafinesque.

Mouth little arched; teeth of lower jaw with the point so much turned aside that the inner margin of the tooth forms the cutting edge; upper teeth erect, each with a long pointed cusp and one or two smaller ones on each side; spiracles wide.

Of the 2 known species one occurs in Hawaiian waters. It is described in Section II of this work.

Genus 13. CENTROSCYLLIUM Müller & Henle.

Teeth equal in both jaws, very small, straight, pointed, each with 1 or 2 smaller cusps on each side at base; mouth crescent-shaped, with a straight, oblique groove at its angle; spiracles moderate; gill-openings rather narrow; dorsal fins small, each with a strong spine; the second dorsal entirely behind the ventrals. One species in the Arctic Seas and another recently discovered by the *Albatross* off Kauai. The latter is described in Section II.

Order D. BATOIDEI.—The Rays.

Gill-openings 5, slit-like and inferior; spiracles present; no anal fin; dorsal fins, if present, inserted on the tail; body typically disk-like, broad and flat, the margin of the disk being formed by the expanded pectorals; tail comparatively slender, the caudal fin small or wanting; vertebræ cyclospondylous. With the exception of the *Rajidæ*, most or all of the rays are ovoviviparous.

Family VIII. DASYATIDÆ.—The Sting Rays.

Disk usually more or less broad than long; pectoral fins uninterruptedly confluent in front, forming the tip of the snout; tail variously formed, usually whip-like, sometimes short and stout, sometimes bearing a single dorsal or caudal fin, but never with 2 dorsals; usually one or more vertical folds of skin on the tail, rarely a lateral fold; tail generally armed with a large, sharp, retrorsely serrate spine on its upper surface toward the base; 2 or 3 spines occasionally present; ventral fins not emarginate; skin smooth or variously prickly or spinous, roughest in the adult; no differentiated spines on the pectorals in the males, the sexes similar; mouth rather small; teeth small, paved, usually more or less pointed or tubercular; nostrils close together, nasal valves forming a rectangular flap, which is joined to the upper jaw by a narrow frenum; spiracles large, placed close behind the eyes; skull not elevated, the eyes and spiracles superior. Ovoviviparous. Genera about 10; species 50. Found in most warm seas, some of them in the fresh waters of the northern parts of South America. The large, jagged spine on the muscular tail is capable of inflicting a severe and even dangerous wound.

Only the genus *Dasyatis* is thus far known to be represented in Hawaiian waters.

Genus 14. DASYATIS Rafinesque.

Disk oval, flat, with rounded angles; tail very long and slender, whip-like without fin, but often with one or 2 vertical membranous folds; a strong serrated spine toward the base of the tail; skin more or less spinous or prickly, rarely smooth; teeth small, paved; a few papillæ usually present in the mouth behind the lower jaw. Species about 30. Sting rays of large size, abundant in warm seas. Many of the spinous species are nearly or quite smooth when young, becoming rough with age.

14. Dasyatis sciera Jenkins. Plate 4, fig. 2.

Snout about 4 in length to base of tail; eye a little over 3 in interorbital width, which is 1.3 in snout or twice width of mouth; internasal width 1.4 in snout.

Body very rhomboid, the width of the disk being much greater than its length, greatest width somewhat in front of center of length; head very broad, the anterior margins of the disk nearly straight, very slightly undulated; snout broad and obtuse; eye small; mouth small, only slightly undulated; posterior margins of disk very slightly rounded; teeth small, in about 26 very oblique series in the upper jaw; upper buccal flap with a broad fringe; floor of mouth with 4 median short tentacles and each side with 2 smaller ones; nostrils large, the border of the broad nasal flap with a fine fringe; interorbital space more or less flattened and concave in the middle; gill-openings of about equal length, the fourth level with the greatest width of the fish; body more or less smooth, except the upper surface of the tail, which is covered with many asperities; many pores below; tail a little less than twice length of disk and with a narrow cutaneous fold beneath, beginning under insertion of dorsal.

The above description is from the type, a specimen about 41 inches in total length (to base of tail 12.63 inches, length of tail 28 inches), collected at Honolulu by Dr. O. P. Jenkins in 1889.

Of this species we know but few examples. One is described above, and another was also taken at Honolulu by Dr. Jenkins. In the latter the tail has been severed from the body. In all essential characters it agrees with the type. This species was also recorded by Snyder.

15. Dasyatis lata (Garman).

Disk quadrangular, one-fourth wider than long; anterior margins nearly straight, forming a very blunt angle at the snout, rounded near the outer extremities, convex posteriorly; inner margins straight a portion of their length; ventrals truncate, rounded; snout produced, forming a rounded prominence in front of the margins of the disk; length from forehead less than width of head; a line joining the wider portions of disk passes nearer to the head than to the shoulders; tail more than twice as long as body, subcylindrical, without a trace of keel above, roughened with small tubercles, with an irregular series of broad-based conical tubercles on each side; a long narrow cutaneous expansion below has its origin opposite the beginning of the spine, and terminates in a keel which continues to the extremity; a pair of large, compressed, erect tubercles immediately in front of caudal spine, and a single one over the middle of the pelvic arch; these suggest a continuous series in larger specimens; 3 larger elongated tubercles with points directed backward—similar to those of *hastata*— occupy the middle of the shoulder-girdle; mouth curved, 6 (5–6 ?) papillæ at the bottom; 2 of these are in the middle in front where usually there is but one.

Color light olive, probably greenish in life, white below. Distinguished from *Dasyatis centrura* by the prominent snout, the shape of the tubercles on the middle of the back, and the narrowness of the posterior portion of the disk.

Length of body 16, length of tail 35.3, and width of pectorals 20.5 inches. Collected at the Hawaiian Islands by Andrew Garrett. (Garman.)

16. Dasyatis hawaiensis Jenkins. Plate 4, fig. 1.

Snout 4.5 to base of tail; eye about 3.67 in interorbital space; interorbital space broader than length of snout; width of mouth 2.3 in interorbital space; internasal space 2 in head.

Body more or less circular, the width of the disk a little greater than its length and its greatest width a little in advance of the center of its length; head very broad, the anterior margins of the disk very slightly undulated; snout very broad, only slightly pointed; eye small; mouth very small, very slightly undulate; teeth very small, in about 30 very oblique series in the upper jaw; upper buccal flap with a broad fringe; floor of mouth with 5 tentacles; nostrils large, the border of the broad nasal flap with a fine fringe; interorbital space broad, more or less flattened; gill-openings of about equal length, the fifth about level with the greatest width of the fish; body more or less smooth; tail without any asperities; caudal spine broad, flattened, the sides strongly serrate; pores more or less obsolete; tail about 1.67 longer than disk and with a somewhat broad cutaneous fold both above and below, the latter beginning below base of dorsal spine; pectorals rounded obtusely; ventrals very broad, the width of their bases a little less than their height or length.

Color in alcohol, dark brown above with the edges of the disk pale, or dull, and the lower surface creamy white with margins of the disk soiled or dirty brown; posterior margins of pectorals and ventrals with their edges below very narrowly white.

The specimen upon which this description is based was obtained at Honolulu by Dr. Jenkins. It has a total length of 16.5 inches (5.87 inches to base of tail; tail 10.63 inches) and is the only example of the species thus far known from the Hawaiian Islands. It is allied to *Dasyatis dipterura* Jordan & Gilbert, from San Diego Bay.

Family IX. AETOBATIDÆ.—The Eagle Rays.

Disk broad; pectoral fins not continued to end of snout, but ceasing on sides of head and reappearing in front of snout as one or 2 fleshy protuberances (cephalic fins), which are supported by fin rays; tail very long, slender, and whip-like, with a single dorsal fin near its root, behind which is usually a strong, retrorsely serrated spine; nasal valves forming a rectangular flap, with the posterior margin free, attached by a frenum to the upper jaw; skull less depressed than usual among rays, its surface raised so that the eyes and spiracles are lateral in position; teeth hexangular, large, flat, tessellated, the middle ones usually broader than the others; skin smooth; no differentiated spines on the pectorals in the males, the sexes being similar; ventrals not emarginate. Genera 3; species about 20. Large sting-rays inhabiting warm seas, feeding chiefly on mollusks, which they crush with their large grinding teeth. Ovoviviparous.

GENUS 15. STOASODON Cantor.

General form of *Aetobatis*. Muzzle entire; teeth flat, broad, forming a single series corresponding to the middle series in *Myliobatis*, there being no small lateral teeth; upper dental lamina straight, lower curved, the latter projecting beyond the upper; free border of the nasal valve deeply emarginate; skin smooth. Tropical seas.

17. Stoasodon narinari (Euphrasen). *Spotted Sting-Ray;* "*Hihimánu.*" Fig. 7.

Disk nearly or quite twice as broad as long; tail very long, about 2.5 times length of disk; snout 7 in length of disk; distance from snout to eye 10 in width of disk; width of mouth 10 in length of disk; a long furrow in middle of interorbital space, deepest in front; spiracles obliquely placed.

Color in life (No. 03387) mostly bluish gray above, edges of fins slightly darker; back covered with bluish white spots, smallest at edges of fins and largest in middle of back; belly and under part of head white.

General color of whole upper surface (taken from another example) light chocolate-brown, everywhere covered with roundish or oblong pearly or bluish spots or blotches, largest about size of eye,

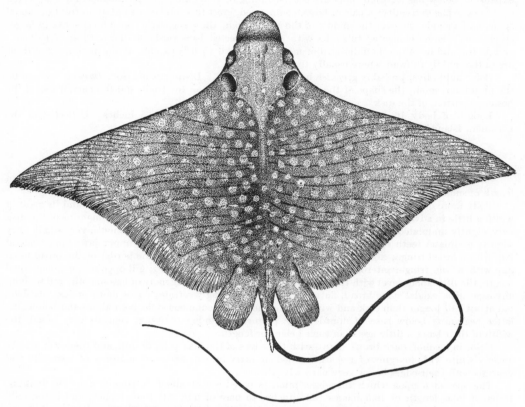

FIG. 7.—*Stoasodon narinari* (Euphrasen); after Jordan and Evermann.

smallest less than half as large; under surface milky white except margin of snout, which is dark gray; tail uniform chocolate-brown; iris yellowish gray.

This large ray, common in most tropical seas, was obtained by us at Honolulu and Hilo, and one example has been recorded by Steindachner from Laysan.

Family X. MOBULIDÆ.

Rays of enormous size, with the disk broader than long and the pectoral fins not continued on the sides of the head, the anterior or cephalic portion being separate, developed as 2 long horn-like or ear-like appendages; mouth wide, terminal or inferior; teeth very small, flat or tubercular, in many series, those of the upper jaw sometimes wanting; eyes lateral; nostrils widely separated, their valves united, forming a flap as wide as the cleft of the mouth; tail long and slender, whip-like, with a single dorsal fin at its base and with or without a serrated spine; ventral fins not emarginate; skin more or less rough; males without differentiated spines on the pectorals, the sexes similar.   Ovoviviparous. Genera 2, species about 7.   Largest of all rays and among the largest of all fishes; found in the tropical seas.

Genus 16. MOBULA[a] Rafinesque.

Head free from pectoral fin, truncated in front, with the cephalic fin on each side developed as a straight horn-like appendage pointing forward; nostrils widely separated; mouth inferior, wide; teeth in both jaws very small, flat or tubercular, in many series; tail very slender, with a dorsal fin between the ventrals; the serrated spine present or absent.   Species about 5; in the tropical seas, reaching an enormous size and therefore not well known.

---

[a] The name *Aodon*, accepted for this genus by Jordan & Evermann, was originally based on a shark of the Red Sea. *Aodon massua*, said to have microscopic serrated teeth and very large pectoral fins. It may belong to the *Scylliorhinidæ*,

The family name *Mantidæ* must give way to *Mobulidæ*, inasmuch as the same name is used for the group of insects typified by the genus *Mantis*.

18. Mobula japonica (Müller & Henle). "*Híhimánu.*"

On August 16, 1901, some fragments of 2 large sea-devils were found in the Honolulu market. The individuals had been cut up and many of the pieces sold. The left cephalic fin of one was secured (No. 03556). Its length from tip to eye is 1 foot, and the eye is 1.25 inches in diameter; distance from eye to nasal opening 7 inches. From other pieces seen it appears that the color on the dorsal surface was a light gray; ventral surface whitish; skin very rough; mouth evidently inferior.

These fragments are not sufficient for definite identification. They resemble *Mobula japonica* (Müller & Henle), a species known from Japan, a fœtus of which was obtained by Dr. Jordan at Misaki. *M. tenkee* (Russell) has been recorded from the East Indies, Coromandel coast, etc.; and *M. kuhlii* (Müller & Henle) from the Indian Ocean. Our species is probably identical with *M. japonica*, but of this we can not be sure. It is called "Híhimánu" by the local fishermen, a name which they apply also to *Stoasodon narinari*.

Subclass HOLOCEPHALI.—The Chimæras.

Skeleton cartilaginous. Gill-cavity with 4 clefts within, but having only one external opening, which is covered by a fold of skin. No spiracles; mouth inferior; jaws with teeth, confluent into bony plates; upper jaw, palate, and hyomandibular coalescent with the skull; intestine with a spiral valve; pectoral fins normally developed, placed low; ventral fins abdominal, with claspers in the male; derivative radii sessile on the sides of the basal bones of the limbs; skin scaleless, its muciferous system well developed. This group contains a single order, Chimæroidei.

Order E. CHIMÆROIDEI.—The Chimæroids.

Characters of the order included above. The group contains one existing family, Chimæridæ.

Family XI. CHIMÆRIDÆ.—The Chimæras.

Body elongate, rather robust anteriorly, tapering posteriorly. Head compressed; mouth small, inferior, the upper lip deeply notched; nostrils confluent with the mouth, separated by a narrow isthmus; jaws with the teeth confluent into 4 bony laminæ above and 2 below; no spiracles; pectoral fins free, placed low; ventral fins abdominal, many-rayed, provided in the male with claspers; dorsal fin usually divided, anteriorly with a very strong spine which is grooved behind; caudal fin low, fold-like; skin naked, rarely somewhat prickly; lateral line present, usually with numerous branches anteriorly; 3 free gills and 2 half gills, 1 on each side; isthmus moderate; gillrakers small. Oviparous, the egg cases long, elliptical, with silky filaments. Genera 4; species about 7. Fishes of singular appearance, found chiefly in the seas of the cold regions. Numerous extinct genera are also referred to this family.

Genus 17. CHIMÆRA Linnæus. Elephant Fishes.

Head somewhat compressed, the snout bluntish, protruding, fleshy, not armed at tip with an appendage; eyes very large, lateral; teeth rather strong; lips thickish, the lower with a frenum; lateral line simple on the body, but forking anteriorly, forming several series of mucous tubes on the head; male with a club-shaped cartilaginous hook on the head above the snout; this hook is curved forward and downward, and is armed at its tip with decurved spines; its tip fitting into a depression in front of the eyes; females without this appendage; gill-opening small; pectorals moderate; ventrals rather large, with large bifid claspers in the male; male also with rough appendages at the base of ventrals, protruding from a sheath of skin; first dorsal triangular, preceded by a strong spine, which is grooved behind and serrated on its edges; second dorsal and caudal fins low, often more or less notched; tail extending in the line of the axis of the body, more or less produced in a filament at tip. Skin smooth. Fishes of singular appearance; mostly of the northern seas; not valued for food. The single Hawaiian species is fully described in Section II of this work.

Subclass TELEOSTOMI.—The True Fishes.

Skeleton usually bony, sometimes cartilaginous; skull with sutures; membrane bones (opercle, preopercle, etc.) present; gill-openings a single slit on each side; gills with their outer edges free, their bases attached to bony arches, normally 4 pairs of these, the fifth pair being typically modified into tooth-bearing lower pharyngeals; median and paired fins developed, the latter with distinct rays; ova small;

no claspers; heart developed, divided into an auricle, ventricle, and arterial bulb; lungs imperfectly developed or degraded to form a swim-bladder, or entirely absent.

Order F. ISOSPONDYLI.—The Isospondylous Fishes.

Soft-rayed fishes with the anterior vertebræ simple, unmodified, and without auditory ossicles; symplectic present; no interclavicles; opercular bones distinct; pharyngeal bones simple above and below, the lower not falciform; mesocoracoid arch always well developed, as in the Ostariophysi and the Ganoidei, forming a bridge from the hypercoracoid to the hypocoracoid; bones of jaws developed, the maxillary broad, always distinct from premaxillary and forming part of margin of upper jaw; no barbels; shoulder-girdle well developed and connected with the cranium by a bony post-temporal; gills 4, a slit behind the fourth; air-bladder, if present, with a pneumatic duct; dorsal and anal fins without true spines; ventral fins abdominal, sometimes wanting; scales usually cycloid, sometimes ctenoid, occasionally wanting; no developed photophores; adipose fin present or absent; a large group comprising most of the marine soft-rayed fishes, excepting those found in the deep sea, these composing the degenerate group called Iniomi. Some of the forms, as Elopidæ, Albulidæ, etc., show analogies with the ganoid allies of the Cycloganoidei. This indicates the descent of the Isospondyli from a ganoid stock, Amioidei, and from this order or its ancestors doubtless all the bony fishes have sprung.

Family XII. ELOPIDÆ.—The Tarpons.

Body elongate, more or less compressed, covered with silvery cycloid scales; head naked; mouth broad, terminal, the lower jaw prominent; premaxillaries not protractile, short, the maxillaries forming the lateral margins of the upper jaw; maxillary composed of about 3 pieces, extending backward beyond the eye; an elongate bony plate between the branches of the lower jaw (analogous to the gular plate in *Amia*); bands of villiform teeth in each jaw and on vomer, palatines, pterygoids, tongue, and base of skull; no large teeth; eye large, with an adipose eyelid; opercular bones thin, with expanded membranaceous borders; a scaly occipital collar; gill-membranes entirely separate, free from the isthmus; branchiostegals numerous (29 to 35); gillrakers long and slender, pseudobranchiæ present or absent; belly not keeled nor serrated, rather broad and covered with ordinary scales; lateral line present; dorsal fin inserted over or slightly behind ventrals; caudal fin forked; no adipose fin; dorsal and anal depressible into a sheath of scales; pectorals and ventrals each with a long accessory scale; parietal bones meeting along top of head; pyloric cæca numerous. Genera 3, species about 5, forming 2 well-marked subfamilies, both widely distributed in the tropical seas. The species are not much valued as food, the flesh being dry and bony.

Genus 18. ELOPS Linnæus. The Tenpounders.

Body elongate, covered with thin, small, silvery scales; dorsal fin slightly behind ventrals, its last rays short, the fin depressible into a sheath of scales; anal fin smaller, similarly depressible; pectorals and ventrals moderate, each with a long accessory scale; opercular bones thin, with expanded, membranaceous borders; a scaly occipital collar; lateral line straight, its tubes simple; pseudobranchiæ present, large; vertebræ 43+29=72. Large fishes of the open seas, remarkable for the development of scaly sheaths. The young are ribbon-shaped and elongate, passing through a series of changes like those seen in *Albula*.

19. Elops saurus Linnæus. Fig. 8.

Head 3.75; depth about 5; D. 25 (counting rudiments, of which there are 7); A. 16; P. 18; V. 15; vertebræ 47+19=66; scales 14–96–17, counting to middle of belly; eye nearly 5 in head, or 1 in snout or interorbital space; mouth a little over 1.75 in head; pectoral 1.75; ventral a little more than pectoral, less than 2; least depth of caudal peduncle 3 in head.

Body elongate, compressed; head compressed, elongate, pointed; snout short, pointed, more or less rounded above; eye rather large, with broad adipose eyelid covering a good portion; maxillary very long, expanded backward beyond the eye, and with several longitudinal ridges; teeth in broad patches or bands in the jaws, also along edge of maxillary, and on the vomer and palatines; tongue large rather long, free in front; nostrils close together; interorbital space flattened and with a couple of ridges; gill-openings large; gillrakers 8 + 15, long, the outer portion more or less slightly expanded or enlarged; pseudobranchiæ numerous and rather short; intestine straight, without any convolutions; peritoneum silvery; scales small, of even size; basis of dorsal and anal with broad scaly sheaths; pectoral with scaly flap more than half length of head; ventral flap scaly, more than half length of fin; lateral line continuous, superior at first and then running midway along side of caudal peduncle; origin of dorsal nearer base of caudal than tip of snout, slightly behind base of ventrals, the anterior rays elevated; origin of anal a little behind tip of dorsal, the anterior rays longest; caudal deeply forked, the lobes pointed; pectoral rather short, reaching scarcely halfway to origin of ventrals; ventrals a little shorter than pectorals, reaching more than halfway to anal; caudal peduncle rather long, compressed.

This is one of the greatest of game fishes, in the estimation of anglers who have had the good fortune to fish for it on the coast of Florida, and will doubtless prove one of the most interesting of Hawaiian fishes to sportsmen who visit those islands.

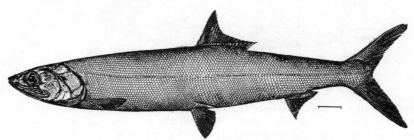

FIG. 8.—*Elops saurus* Linnæus; after Jordan and Evermann.

This description is from a specimen (No. 04982), 11 inches long, from Honolulu. We have examined many examples, some of them taken by Dr. Jenkins at Honolulu in 1889, and others dredged in the same locality in November, 1896, by the *Albatross*. Jordan and Snyder obtained it in the same locality in 1900.

Family XIII. ALBULIDÆ.—The Bonefishes or Ladyfishes.

Body rather elongate, little compressed, covered with rather small, brilliantly silvery scales; head naked; snout conic, subquadrangular, shaped like the snout of a pig, and overlapping the small, inferior, horizontal mouth; maxillary rather strong, short, with a distinct supplemental bone, slipping under the membranous edge of the very broad preorbital; premaxillaries short, not protractile; lateral margin of upper jaw formed by the maxillaries; both jaws, vomer, and palatines with bands of villiform teeth; broad patches of coarse, blunt, paved teeth on the tongue behind and on the sphenoid and pterygoid bones; eye large, median in head, with a bony ridge above it, and almost covered with an annular adipose eyelid; opercle moderate, firm; preopercle with a broad, flat, membranaceous edge, which extends backward over the base of opercle; pseudobranchiæ present; gillrakers short, tubercle-like; gill-membranes entirely separate, free from the isthmus; branchiostegals about 14; a fold of skin across gill-membranes anteriorly, its posterior free edge crenate; no gular plate; lateral line present; belly not carinate, flattish, covered with ordinary scales; dorsal fin moderate, in front of ventrals, its membranes scaly; no adipose fin; anal very small; caudal widely forked; pyloric cœca numerous; parietal bones meeting along top of head; vertebræ numerous, 42+28=70. A single species known, found in all warm seas.

In this, and probably in related families, the young pass through a metamorphosis analogous to that seen in the Conger Eels; they are for a time elongate, band-shaped, with very small head and loose, transparent tissues; from this condition they become gradually shorter and more compact, shrinking from 3 or 3.5 inches in length to 2 inches. According to Dr. Gilbert, this process, like that seen in various eels, is a normal one, through which all individuals pass. In the Gulf of California, where these fishes abound, these band-shaped young are often thrown by the waves on the beach in great masses.

Genus 19. ALBULA (Gronow) Bloch & Schneider. The Bonefishes.

The characters of this genus are included above. Only one species known.

20. Albula vulpes (Linnæus). *Bonefish;* "*Oio.*" Fig. 9.

Head 3.75 in length; depth 5; D. 15; A. 8; scales 9–71–7; upper lobe of caudal the longer; a broad band of peculiar, elongate, membranaceous scales along middle line of back; accessory ventral scale large.

Brilliantly silvery; olivaceous above; back and sides with faint streaks along the rows of scales; fins plain; axils dusky. Length 18 inches to 3 feet. Tropical seas, on sandy coasts, almost universally distributed and generally abundant. A beautiful and active fish, in most places little valued as food, but in some regions, as Key West, highly appreciated. Highly esteemed as a game fish.

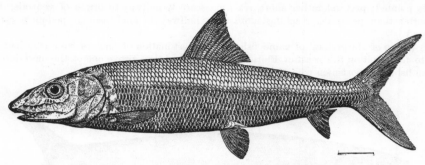

FIG. 9.—*Albula vulpes* (Linnæus); after Jordan and Evermann.

We have a number of specimens from Honolulu and Hilo, all of which have the streaks on the back and upper surface dark and well defined. We have also examined specimens taken at Honolulu by Dr. Wood, and others from the same locality by Jordan and Snyder.

Family XIV. CHANIDÆ.—The Milk-fishes.

Body oblong, compressed, covered with small, firm, adherent scales; lateral line distinct; abdomen broad and flattish; snout depressed; mouth small, anterior, the lower jaw with a small symphyseal tubercle; no teeth; premaxillary joined to upper anterior edge of maxillary; eye with an adipose eyelid; gill-membranes broadly united, free from the isthmus; branchiostegals 4; pseudobranchiæ well developed; an accessory branchial organ in a cavity behind the gill-cavity; dorsal fin opposite the ventrals; anal fin shorter than the dorsal; mucous membrane of œsophagus raised into a spiral fold; intestine with many convolutions; vertebræ about 45. Coloration silvery. Large fishes of the warmer parts of the Pacific. One genus and 3 species known.

Genus 20. CHANOS Lacépède.

Characters of the genus included above.

21. Chanos chanos (Forskål). Fig. 10.

Milkfish; "*Awa;*" "*Awa-awa;*" "*Awa kalamoku;*" "*Puawa.*"

Head 4.4 in length; depth 4; D. II, 12; A. II, 9; scales 12–86–14; vertebræ $19 + 26 = 45$; eye 3.5 in head; snout 3.5; maxillary 4.3; pectoral 1.6; ventral 1.8; caudal .3 longer than head; dorsal 1.25 in head; B. 4.

Aspect of a large cyprinoid. Body elliptical, moderately compressed; caudal peduncle slender, head pointed, rounded above; eye and side of head covered by a large, transparent, imperforate, adipose eyelid; mouth small, terminal, toothless, transverse, lower jaw included; maxillary broad, slipping under the adipose preorbital, without supplemental bone; opercle truncate behind; pseudobranchiæ very large; gillrakers fine and flexible, very close set, rather long; bones of gillrakers flexible; gill-arches all connected by membrane; lateral line well developed; scales firm, cycloid, with strongly marked longitudinal striæ; scales rather large, hard, firm, enameled, becoming bony when dry, used by the Indians for ornamental work; dorsal inserted somewhat nearer snout than base of caudal, before ventrals, its first ray falcate, its last produced in a short filament, longer than pupil; base of fin with a large scaly sheath; pectoral and ventral each with scaly axillary appendage; anal similar to dorsal, but much smaller; pectorals and ventrals rather small; caudal very long, forked to the base, its lobes subequal, straight; base of fin with small scale; ventrals somewhat falcate.

Color in life of example from Moanalua, silvery, bluish olive above; upper fins dirty whitish; lower fins soiled cream color; lower lobe of caudal with some yellowish.

Color in alcohol, greenish above, the sides brilliantly silvery, fins more or less darkened; inside of ventrals and pectorals blackish.

Length 2 to 5 feet. Pacific and Indian oceans, on sandy shores, north to the Hawaiian Islands, where it is abundant. Our specimens from Honolulu are all under a foot in length.

We have recently received from Mr. Berndt a singular-looking specimen extraordinarily short and deep. It is apparently a dwarf or hunchback example of this species. It has a much shorter and deeper head and body than the species usually possesses and the scales are narrower, but in other respects it differs but slightly from the ordinary type. Head 3.4; depth 2.5; depth of caudal peduncle 7.5; length of caudal 1.8; pectoral 4; ventral 5; eye 3 in head; interorbital width 2.33; snout 3.5; D. 12; A. 9; scales 76, 26, 21 in front of dorsal.

The awa is one of the most important food fishes of the Hawaiian Islands. It occurs about the various islands, but is most abundant around Honolulu. It is, next to the mullet (Ama ama), the most common species frequenting the artificial ponds, into which it runs with the mullet and with the tide and is restrained in the same way. It is held in esteem as a food fish, but we know nothing of

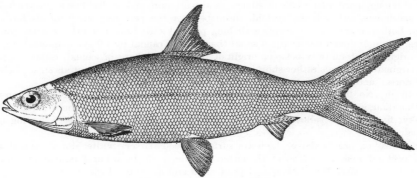

FIG. 10.—*Chanos chanos* (Forskål).

its game qualities. Like the mullet, it is known by different names at different ages. The young are called "puawa;" those of medium size "awa awa;" those of ordinary commercial size "awa;" while very large individuals are "awa kalamoku."

Family XV. CLUPEIDÆ.—The Herrings.

Body oblong or elongate, more or less compressed, covered with cycloid or pectinated scales; belly sometimes rounded, sometimes compressed, in which case it is often armed with bony serratures; head naked, usually compressed; mouth rather large, terminal, the jaws about equal; maxillaries forming the lateral margins of upper jaw, each composed of about 3 pieces; premaxillaries not protractile; teeth mostly small, often feeble or wanting, variously arranged; adipose eyelid present or absent; gill-rakers long and slender; gill-membranes not connected, free from the isthmus; no gular plate; gills 4, a slit behind the fourth; branchiostegals usually few (6 to 15); posterior lower part of opercular region often with an angular emargination, the tips of the larger branchiostegals being abruptly truncate; pseudobranchiæ present; no lateral line; dorsal fin median or somewhat posterior, rarely wanting; no adipose fin; ventrals moderate or small (rarely wanting); anal usually rather long; caudal fin forked; vertebræ 40 to 56. Genera about 30; species 150; inhabiting all seas, and usually swimming in immense schools; many species ascend fresh waters, and some remain there permanently. The northern and fresh-water species, as in many other families, differ from the tropical forms in having a larger number of vertebral segments.

Genus 21. ETRUMEUS Bleeker.

Body elongate, subcylindrical or somewhat compressed; abdomen rounded, not compressed or serrated; snout pointed; adipose eyelid covering the eye wholly without pupillary slit; mouth terminal, of moderate width, formed as in *Clupea*, but the maxillary more slender; teeth moderate, in patches on jaws, palatines, pterygoids, and tongue; gill-membranes separate, with numerous fine branchiostegals; pseudobranchiæ well developed; pyloric appendages numerous; scales cycloid, entire, and very deciduous; pectoral and ventral fins shielded; no lateral line; dorsal fin rather long, of 18 to 20 rays, placed entirely in advance of ventrals; anal fin low, of moderate length; caudal deeply forked; the scales of the breast more or less adherent, dilated and forming a membranous ventral flap which covers the closed pectoral fins, leaving only the dorsal edges and the extreme tips of the fins visible; axillary scales very large, that of pectoral extending nearly to its tip, that of ventral reaching slightly farther than tip of fin; lateral scales extending continuously on center of caudal fin almost to margin of middle rays.

22. Etrumeus micropus (Schlegel). "*Makiawa.*" Fig. 11.

Head 4.5 in length; depth 5.5; D. 20; A. 11; P. 16; V. 9; scales about 52; eye 3 in head; snout 3.5; mandible 2; interorbital space 4.3; maxillary 3; width of head 2 in its length; P. 1.5 in head; V. 2.67; least depth of caudal peduncle 3.67 in head.

Body elongate, subcylindrical, somewhat compressed; head elongate, compressed, pointed; snout long, pointed, flattened above, the sides somewhat compressed; eye large, covered by the thick adipose eyelid; mouth small, terminal, the mandible very slightly projecting when the mouth is closed; teeth in fine villiform bands on vomer and palatines, those in jaws minute; maxillary slipping under the preorbital ridge and extending posteriorily a little beyond the anterior edge of eye; nostrils together on upper side of snout, much nearer its tip than anterior edge of eye; interorbital space and top of head flattened and with ridges forming an elongated *W;* preopercle with radiating branching mucous canals giving a striated appearance; opercles more or less smooth; gill-openings large, membranes free from isthmus; gillrakers long, slender, and fine; gill-filaments longer, fine, and the pseudo-branchiæ also long; peritoneum pale or silvery; scales all more or less deciduous, mostly falling off in alcoholic specimens, rather large, cycloid, those between the pectorals and ventrals forming a thin broad flap; both pectorals and ventrals with long pointed scaly flaps but little shorter than the fins themselves; origin of dorsal nearer tip of snout than base of caudal by 1.3 eye diameters; anal fin very small, its origin about midway between origin of ventrals and base of caudal; caudal rather small, deeply emarginate; pectorals rather short, about 2.5 in space to ventrals; ventrals small, behind tip of depressed dorsal, and 2 in space to origin of anal; caudal peduncle compressed.

Color in life (No. 03222), steel-olive above, side slightly yellowish, belly silvery; centers of scales above with a diamond-shaped darker olive blotch, there forming lines along the rows of scales; tip of snout dusky; fins pale, not yellowish; base of pectoral a little dusky; some dusky shading on caudal; ventrals pale.

Color in alcohol, brown above, the lower surface of body silvery white; dorsal, caudal, and basal portion of pectoral dusky, portions of the latter, together with the other fins, pale or whitish; each scale on back with a dark brownish spot; tips of snout and mandible dusky brown.

This description from an example from Honolulu, about 9.25 inches long. Our numerous speci-

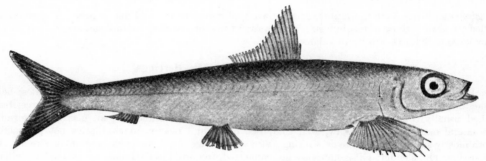

Fig. 11.—*Etrumeus micropus* (Schlegel); after Schlegel.

mens, all from Honolulu, range in length from 3.75 to 9.25 inches. Upon comparing them with Japanese examples, we are unable to detect any specific differences. We have also examined specimens dredged by the *Albatross* off Honolulu in November, 1896, others taken by Dr. Jenkins at Honolulu, 1889, and still others by Doctor Wood.

Family XVI. ENGRAULIDÆ.—The Anchovies.

Body elongate, more or less compressed, covered with thin cycloid scales; head compressed; mouth extremely large, more or less oblique, usually overlapped by a pointed, compressed, pig-like snout; gape very wide, the maxillary very long and slender, formed of about 3 pieces, extending backward far behind the eye, in some species behind the head; premaxillaries not protractile, very small, firmly joined to the maxillaries; teeth usually small, sometimes obsolete, usually fine and even, in a single row in each jaw; canines sometimes present; eye large, well forward, without adipose eyelid; pre-orbital narrow; opercles thin and membranaceous; gillrakers long and slender; branchiostegals slender, 7 to 14 in number; gill-membranes separate or joined, free from isthmus; pseudobranchiæ present; no lateral line; belly rounded or weakly serrate; fins various, the dorsal usually short and median; no adipose fin; caudal forked. Small carnivorous shore fishes, usually swimming in large schools on sandy shores; abundant in all warm seas, occasionally entering rivers. This group is often regarded as a subfamily under the *Clupeidæ*, from which it differs in no character of high importance.

A large family of about 80 species, only one of which is thus far known from the Hawaiian Islands.

Genus 22. ANCHOVIA Jordan & Evermann.

Body oblong, compressed, covered with rather large, thin, deciduous scales; belly rounded or weakly compressed; snout conical, compressed, projecting beyond the very large mouth; maxillary narrow, little movable, usually formed of 3 pieces, extending backward far behind the eye, to the base of mandible or beyond, not beyond gill-opening; premaxillaries very small; teeth small, sub-equal, present at all ages, usually on the jaws, vomer, palatines, and pterygoids; anal fin moderate free from caudal (its rays 12 to 40); no pectoral filaments; dorsal inserted about midway of body, posterior to ventrals; pectorals and ventrals each with a large axillary scale; adipose eyelid obsolete; vertebræ about 40 (40–42) in species examined; flesh rather pale and dry, more or less translucent; bones firm; pseudobranchiæ present; branchiostegals 9 to 14; gillrakers long and slender; gill-membranes separate, free from the narrow isthmus. Species about 50; small, carnivorous shore fishes, swimming in large schools on sandy shores of all warm seas, occasionally entering rivers. Most of them are marked by a broad, distinct, silvery band.

23. Anchovia purpurea (Fowler). *"Nehu."* Fig. 12.

Head 2.67 in length; depth 5.67; D. 13; A. 17; P. 13; V. 7; eye 3.5 in head; snout 4.67; maxillary 1.25; pectoral 1.88; ventral 2.75.

Body elongate, compressed; head elongate, laterally compressed and pointed; snout short, rounded at tip; eyes lateral, anterior to center of head, greater than snout; mouth large, the long maxillary produced backward beyond the posterior margin of eye but falling some distance short of gill-opening, the pig-like snout projecting well beyond the tip of mandible; teeth in the jaws small, fine, extending all along the lower edge of the maxillary; nostrils close together, about midway in snout; interorbital space a little convex; gill-openings large, the isthmus long and narrow, forming a narrow keel in front; gillrakers about 18 + 28, very long, slender, pointed, the longest nearly equal to

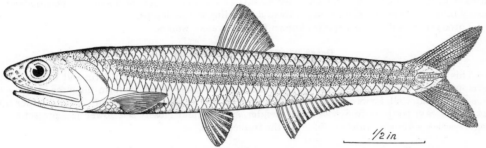

FIG. 12.—*Anchovia purpurea* (Fowler).

eye; gill-filaments rather shorter than the gillrakers; pseudobranchiæ moderately large; intestine short and straight; peritoneum black; scales large, cycloid, deciduous, falling off in preserved examples; pectorals with scaly flaps; origin of dorsal a little nearer tip of snout than base of caudal, and a little behind origin of ventral; origin of anal behind base of last dorsal ray, the first rays of fin encroaching but little upon tip of depressed dorsal; base of anal 1.67 in head; caudal deeply emarginate; pectoral short, about equal to snout and eye; ventrals a little in advance of dorsal and reaching a little more than half way to anal; caudal peduncle rather long, compressed, its least depth a little over 3 in head.

In alcoholic specimens there is a broad silvery longitudinal band from head to base of caudal, rather broader posteriorly; head silvery; dorsal and caudal marked with fine narrow wavy series of pale brownish dots forming cross-bars. This description from an example 2.5 inches long, taken in the market at Honolulu.

We have large series of this species from Honolulu and Hilo, at each of which places it is very abundant. Dr. Jenkins obtained a number of examples at Honolulu in 1889. It was also dredged by the *Albatross* in that vicinity in 1896, and a number of examples were obtained at Kailua, December 31, 1899, by Mr. Richard C. McGregor. The types are 2 specimens (Nos. 23329 and 23330, Mus. Phila. Acad.) each about 2.4 inches long, collected by Dr. Wm. H. Jones.

This species is well marked and has a broader silvery lateral band than either *Anchovia commersoniana* or *Anchovia ischana*. While the anal rays agree with the latter, the fin of *commersoniana* is still longer. The insertion of the anal fin also is more in advance in both *ischana* and *commersoniana*.

Suborder INIOMI.—The Lantern Fishes.

Soft-rayed fishes with the anterior vertebræ simple, unmodified, and without auditory ossicles; symplectic present; no interclavicles; opercular apparatus sometimes incomplete; pharyngeal bones unmodified; gill-openings ample; mesocoracoid arch wanting or atrophied; bones of jaws variously developed, the maxillary sometimes cognate with the premaxillary; shoulder-girdle with its post-temporal not normally connected with the skull, but touching it at or near the nape; gills 4, a slit behind the fourth; air-bladder, if present, with a duct; dorsal and anal fins without true spines; ventral fins, if present, abdominal; scales mostly cycloid, often wanting; adipose fin present or absent; skeleton mostly very weakly ossified; photophores present in most species.

Marine fishes, mostly inhabiting the oceanic abysses, closely allied to the typical *Isospondyli*, but lacking the mesocoracoid and having the connection of the shoulder-girdle with the cranium imperfect. In the character of the mesocoracoid, most of these fishes agree with the eels and with the *Haplomi* and the spiny-rayed fishes. These latter have the post-temporal differently attached. This suborder is a provisional one, and its members may be reunited with the *Isospondyli* or otherwise

.distributed when the osteology of the different families is known.   Boulenger relegates those which, like *Synodus*, lack the mesocoracoid to the Haplomi.   These lack also the orbitosphenoid, characters of the Isospondyli and the Berycoidei.

Of the 18 families of this order as here defined, only 5 have representatives in the Hawaiian fauna

Family XVII. SYNODONTIDÆ.—The Lizard-fishes.

Body oblong or elongate, little compressed, covered with cycloid scales, rarely naked; mouth very wide, entire margin of upper jaw formed by the long, slender premaxillaries, the latter mostly rudimentary or obsolete, never widened at tip; teeth mostly cardiform on both jaws, tongue, and palatines; canines rarely present; large teeth usually depressible; no barbels; opercular bones usually thin, but complete; gill-membranes separate, free from isthmus; branchiostegals usually numerous; pseudobranchiæ present; gillrakers tubercular or obsolete; no orbitosphenoid or mesocoracoid; lateral line present; adipose fin present, rarely obsolete; dorsal fin short, of soft rays only; pectorals and ventrals present; anal fin moderate or long; caudal forked; skeleton rather well ossified; air-bladder small or wanting; intestinal canal short; sides sometimes with phosphorescent spots or photophores; eggs inclosed in the sacs of ovary and extruded through an oviduct.   Genera about 10, species about 40, mostly inhabiting shore waters, some of them descending to the depths.

Three genera and about 4 species known from Hawaiian waters.

Genus 23. TRACHINOCEPHALUS Gill.

This genus is closely related to *Synodus*, from which it differs chiefly in form and in the relative development of the fins.   Body stout; head short, blunt, compressed, its form much as in the genus *Trachinus;* vent well forward, very slightly nearer base of caudal than base of ventrals, under tip of last dorsal ray; teeth as in *Synodus*, but slender, smaller, and closely set; lower jaw projecting.   A single species is known, widely diffused in the tropical seas.

24. Trachinocephalus myops (Forster).   *"Kawelea;" "Welea."*   Fig. 13.

Head 3.5 in length; depth 5; D. 13; A. 16; P. 12; V. 8; scales 4–55–5; width of head only a very little less than twice its length; depth of head 1.6 in its length; snout 1.5 in eye; eye 3 in maxillary; maxillary 1.85 in head; interorbital space 1 in snout, 1.5 in eye; pectoral 2.25 in head; ventral 1; base of anal 3.67 in body; length of depressed dorsal 3.75.

Body elongate, compressed, deepest forward or about the neck, gradually tapering backward with a long tail; head large, elongate, deep, compressed laterally, the upper profile very blunt, gibbous in front; the lower profile a rather long shallow convex curve from tip of snout to below pectoral; snout very short, blunt, obtuse; eye small, its posterior rim nearly midway in space between tip of snout and end of maxillary, the latter considered in the vertical until level with tip of snout; mouth cleft very large and oblique, the maxillary long, with its posterior portion gradually constricted until it is much narrower than at middle of its length; mandible very large, the rami broad and powerful; lips broad, thin; teeth in jaws sharp, more or less unequal, in double series; in upper jaw the outer series more or less concealed by the broad lips; in the lower jaw those in inner series the larger; no vomerine teeth; those on palatines in a single series; tongue a triangular ridge, free in front, with a triangular patch of depressible teeth above, and with a single median series extending backward over the basibranchials; nostrils close together on the sides of snout, the anterior with a ciliated flap; interorbital space deeply concave, each of the supraorbital ridges raised in front; top of head more or less rugose,

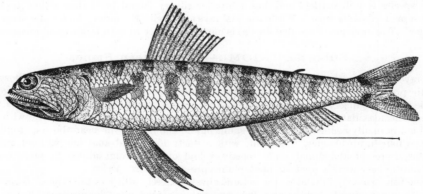

Fig. 13.— *Trachinocephalus myops* (Forster); after Jordan and Evermann.

also the posterior lower border of orbit; gill-openings large, the membranes free from isthmus; no gillrakers, the inner surface of the branchial arches covered with minute asperities; gill-filaments short; no pseudobranchiæ; peritoneum silvery; scales large, cycloid, 6 rows on cheek, a number along edge of preopercle and on opercle; occiput scaly, rest of head bare; scales between ventrals forming a broad scaly flap; scale at axil of pectoral somewhat pointed; ventrals with a scaly flap 2.5 in length of fin; lateral line slightly decurved at first and then straight along side to base of caudal; origin of dorsal nearer tip of snout than origin of adipose fin by an eye diameter; length of last dorsal ray half the length of first developed ray and when depressed the tip of first developed ray reaching 0.75 length of depressed fin; adipose dorsal nearer tip of last depressed dorsal than base of caudal; origin of anal midway between axil of pectoral and base of caudal, and behind base of last dorsal ray; caudal deeply forked; pectoral small, tip not reaching origin of dorsal; ventrals very long, reaching origin of anal, inserted a little before tips of pectorals.

Color in life (No. 03233), pale grayish, silvery below; side of back with 3 wavy stripes of dull yellow, each edged with darker olive, the uppermost most wavy, joining its fellow across the back in about 12 irregular crossbars of dirty yellow, edged with darker, the interspaces pearly-bluish; below the lowest yellow streak are 2 very faint similar streaks lost in the white color of the side; head with streaks continued from the sides but fainter; top of head mottled sand-color; an oblique jet-black spot on the scapular region; dorsal with 2 faint cross-streaks of light yellow and 2 of pearly-blue, besides 2 or 3 dark dots; caudal faint yellowish; lower fins whitish; the ventrals creamy.

This description from a large example (No. 03599), 8.75 inches long, taken at Hilo. Many specimens were obtained from Hilo and Honolulu. We can not separate *T. limbatus* from *T. trachinus* of Japan or *T. myops* of the Atlantic. Probably all constitute a single species.

Genus 24. SYNODUS (Gronow) Bloch & Schneider.

First superior pharyngeal cartilaginous; second without teeth; third and fourth separate, with teeth; lower pharyngeals separate; body elongate, subterete; head depressed; snout triangular, rather pointed; interorbital region transversely concave; mouth very wide; premaxillaries not protractile, very long and strong, more than half length of head; maxillaries closely connected with premaxillaries, very small or obsolete; premaxillaries with 1 or 2 series of large, compressed, knife-shaped teeth, the inner and larger depressible; palatine teeth similar, smaller, in a single broad band; lower jaw with a band of rather large teeth, the inner and larger ones depressible; a patch of strong, depressible teeth on tongue in front, a long row along the hyoid bone; jaws nearly equal in front; eye rather large, anterior; supraorbital forming a projection above the eye; pseudobranchiæ well developed; gillrakers very small, spine-like; gill-membranes slightly connected; top of head naked; cheeks and opercles scaled like body; body covered with rather small, adherent, cycloid scales; lateral line present; no luminous spots; dorsal fin short, rather anterior; pectorals moderate, inserted high; ventrals anterior, not far behind pectorals, large, the inner rays longer than the outer; anal short; caudal narrow, forked; vent posterior, much nearer base of caudal than base of ventrals; branchiostegals 12 to 16; stomach with a long, blind sac and many pyloric cœca; skeleton rather firm. Species numerous. Voracious fishes of moderate size, inhabiting sandy bottoms at no great depth, in most warm seas.

Two species known from the Hawaiian Islands, the one here described and a deep-water form (*Synodus kaianus*), described in Section II.

25. Synodus varius (Lacépède). "*Uláe.*" Plate II and Fig 14.

Head 3.5 in length; depth 6; D. 13; A. 8; P. 13; V. 8; scales 5–65–11; width of head 1.67 in its length; depth of head 1.8 in its length; snout 4.75 in head; maxillary 1.6; interorbital space 7; eye 1.5 in snout, 4.25 in maxillary; interorbital space 1.75 in snout; pectoral 2; ventral 1; base of anal 3; length of depressed dorsal 1.17.

Body elongate, rounded, the back and ventral surface depressed; head large, elongate, broadly depressed, pointed, with the eyes impinging upon upper profile, and the lower profile from tip of mandible shallowly convex; snout rather long, depressed, sharply pointed; eye well anterior, though the posterior rim is not midway in space between tip of snout and end of maxillary, the latter considered in the vertical until level with tip of snout; mouth-cleft very large, oblique, the maxillary long, with its greatest width a little anterior to the middle of its length; mandible very large and powerful; jaws about equal in the closed mouth; symphysis pointed; lips thin and broad; teeth in jaws sharp, depressible, directed forward, in 2 irregular series, those forming the outer series in upper jaw more or less concealed by the broad lip, so that only the tips of these larger ones are seen when the mouth is closed; teeth on vomer and palatines depressible, sharp; in a narrow band on each side of the latter; tongue and basi-branchials with a band of depressible teeth, forming a triangular patch of large ones on the former; tongue rather sharply pointed, a little free in front; nostrils on the sides of snout, each pair close together, nearer front margin of eye than tip of snout, the anterior pair with an elevated fleshy rim which ends in a fleshy point; interorbital space concave, a bony ridge rather prominent in front of each eye; top of head all more or less roughened, also the space behind eye; gill-opening large, the narrow membrane free from isthmus; gillrakers developed as small sharp asperities on the inner surface of branchial arches; gill-filaments short; pseudobranchiæ small; peritoneum silvery;

scales large, cycloid, 6 rows on cheek; a series of enlarged scales along the margin of preopercle; occiput and sides of head scaly, the rest bare; scales between ventrals forming a broad flap; no scaly flap at base of pectoral; a small short scaly flap at base of ventral; lateral line nearly straight to base of caudal; origin of dorsal midway between tip of snout and origin of adipose dorsal; last dorsal ray a trifle over half length of longest ray of fin, tip of latter reaching a little over two-thirds length of fin when depressed; origin of adipose dorsal about midway between tip of last dorsal ray and base of caudal; anal small, its origin well in front of that of adipose fin and about midway between tip of ventral and base of caudal; caudal deeply emarginate, the lobes pointed; pectoral small, not reaching origin of dorsal; origin of ventrals about midway in length of pectoral.

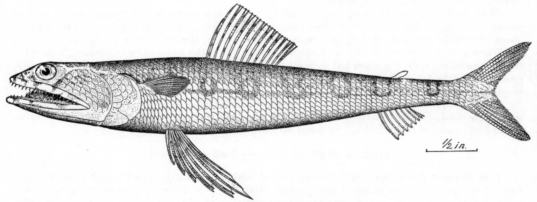

FIG. 14.—*Synodus varius* (Lacépède).

Color when fresh (field No. 03430) ground white; a series of light reddish-brown quadrate spots along side, the markings over the back darker reddish brown; an indistinct bluish longitudinal band showing through just above the lateral row of quadrate spots along the side; a reddish spot on the upper angle of gill-opening; dorsal crossed by light-brown lines transverse to the fin rays; pectoral also crossed by narrow light-brown lines; ventral with 6 orange-colored crossbars.

We have two other examples, the first of which (No. 03236) was light gray when fresh, with dark markings all olive, washed with brownish red; belly white; upper fins pale, with narrow crossbands of white dots; lower fins white. The other specimen (No. 03010) when fresh had the back flesh color, with about 6 reddish-brown lines made up of dark borders to the scales; side with a narrow pale-yellow line, below this a fainter one; lower side and belly white; dorsal fin pale, with small white specks; other fins all pale; iris green.

Another example (No. 03011) in life was pale grayish on back and sides, crossed by 5 or 6 broad greenish-red bars or saddles, red at lower ends; belly white; head marbled with brown, orange, and white; lower jaw white, with some pale brown; fins all pale; iris orange and yellow.

In life another example (No. 03235) was rose red, with dark-brown streaks and marks; lower parts silvery, with bars of salmon-color; side of head with salmon-colored bars below, especially distinct on lower jaw and breast; dorsal and caudal with bars of fine white specks.

Color in spirits, pale brown, darker above, the edge of each scale dark brown, crossed by 5 broad cross-bands, between which are as many similar cross-bands of lighter shade; 3 broad cross-bands across the mandible.

This description from an example (No. 03817), 10.2 inches long, taken at Hilo. Our numerous specimens range in length from 2 to 10 inches. An unusually large specimen recently received from Mr. Berndt, at Honolulu, measures 13.75 inches.

We have many specimens from Hilo and Honolulu.

In some cases the dark mottlings are of the deepest scarlet, others brick red, while those found on sandy shores are olive-green. The species is found in 2 colors, red and green, on the coasts of Japan, as in Hawaii.

Genus 25. SAURIDA Cuvier & Valenciennes.

Body subcylindrical, rather elongate; tail tapering; head oblong, depressed; snout rather short, pointed; eye moderate; mouth cleft very wide; intermaxillary very long, styliform, tapering; maxillary thin, long, closely adherent to intermaxillary; teeth cardiform, those in the inner series being the longest, slender, depressible both downward and inward, and present in the jaws, on tongue, and on palatine bones, the latter forming a double band on each side, the inner band being much shorter than the outer; gill-opening very wide, gill-membranes not attached to isthmus; branchiostegals numerous; dorsal fin nearly in the middle of length of body, with 13 or fewer rays; adipose fin small; anal short; caudal forked; pectoral short or of moderate length; ventral 9-rayed, the inner rays not much longer than the outer ones, and inserted before the dorsal, not far from the pectorals. Species few, in the tropical seas of the East Indies, China, Australia, and the Western Pacific.

26. Saurida gracilis (Quoy & Gaimard). "*Uláe.*"

Head 4.5 in length; depth 6.5; D. 11; A. 10; P. 19; V. 9; scales 4-52-5; width of head 1.5 in its length; depth of head 1.67 in its length; snout 4.5 in head; maxillary 1.5; interorbital space 4.5; eye 1.25 in snout, 4 in maxillary; interorbital space 1 in snout; pectoral 1.3; base of anal 2.5; length of depressed dorsal only slightly less than the length of head.

Body elongate, rounded, the back and ventral surfaces depressed; head small, elongated, broadly depressed, pointed, the eyes impinging slightly upon the upper profile, the lower profile from tip of mandible slightly convex; snout rather long, depressed, flattened, very broad at front of eye, where it is about 0.4 broader than long; eye well anterior, about midway in the space between tip of snout and end of maxillary, the latter considered in the vertical until level with tip of snout; mouth cleft large, oblique, becoming narrow toward its posterior extremity; mandible large, powerful, the jaws equal when mouth is closed; teeth in jaws unequal, those forming an inner series the larger, the lips very narrow, so that most all the teeth are visible when mouth is closed; palatines with 2 bands of teeth, most of them depressible, some of those in front enlarged, the inner band short; tongue very small, rounded, without any teeth, free in front; a median series of fine teeth along the basibranchials; nostrils small, close together on sides of snout, nearer tip of latter than anterior margin of eye, anterior pair with a small fleshy flap; interorbital space broad, somewhat concave but flattened in the middle; a depressed bony ridge rather prominent above each eye in front; top of head roughened on each side of occiput; gill-openings large, the narrow membrane free from the narrow compressed isthmus; gill-rakers as minute asperities; gill-filaments rather short; pseudobranchiæ moderately large; peritoneum pale; scales large, cycloid, about 4 rows on cheek; opercles and occiput scaly, rest of head bare; origin of dorsal midway between tip of snout and posterior margin of adipose fin; last dorsal ray about three-sevenths length of longest ray of fin, tip of latter reaching as far posteriorly as tip of the former when fin is depressed; origin of adipose dorsal midway between tip of depressed dorsal and base of caudal; origin of anal nearer base of caudal than tip of ventral, the greater part of its base anterior to adipose dorsal; caudal deeply emarginate, the lobes pointed; pectoral small, falling from origin of dorsal; ventrals large, inserted below last third of pectoral and reaching about three-sevenths of the space to origin of anal.

Color in alcohol, dull or muddy brown above, marked with about 6 or more deep-brown saddles or broad cross-bands, the spaces between with deep-brown blotches; similar blotches also along the side; dorsal, caudal, and pectoral dull brownish, with blackish brown crossbars, the last 3 broad and very distinct; lower surface of body dull silvery white, with a very dull yellowish green tint; ventrals very light yellowish green. This description from an example 8.5 inches long, from Hilo.

We have a number of examples from Hilo and Honolulu, many of the small ones deeply colored. This species common on sandy shores at moderate depths.

Family XVIII.—AULOPIDÆ.

Allied to the *Synodontidæ*, but with the maxillary separate, well developed and dilated behind; hypocoracoids extended downward as in many spiny-rayed fishes; gillrakers mostly long and slender, needle-shaped; eyes normal, large or small; no luminous spots; jaws without fang-like teeth; dorsal fin moderate, nearly median in position; body elongate; pectorals present, normal in form and position; adipose fin normally present; pseudobranchiæ present. This family, as here understood, includes some half-dozen species, fishes of moderate depths, chiefly of the Atlantic. Only one species known from the Hawaiian Islands.

Genus 26. CHLOROPHTHALMUS Bonaparte.

Head elongate; body subterete, covered with moderate-sized, adherent, pectinate or ctenoid scales, which are arranged in straight, parallel, oblique lines; mouth rather large; maxillary well developed, dilated behind, reaching to beyond front of orbit; lower jaw projecting; teeth very small, sharp on jaws, vomer, and palatines, usually minute teeth on tongue; eye very large; dorsal short, inserted before middle of length of body; adipose fin small; anal short; caudal forked; pectorals and ventrals well developed, the ventrals inserted under dorsal and not far behind pectorals, none of the rays forming exserted filaments; gill-openings wide; branchiostegals 10; pseudobranchiæ well developed; gill-rakers needle-shaped, rather numerous; color silvery, with darker markings. Deep seas.

Of 4 known species only one, *C. proridens*, occurs in Hawaiian waters. (See Section II.)

Family XIX. BATHYPTEROIDÆ.

Characters of the family included below in those of its single genus.

Genus 27. BATHYPTEROIS Günther.

Shape of body like that of *Aulopus*. Head of moderate size, depressed in front, with the snout projecting, the large mandible very prominent beyond upper jaw. Cleft of mouth wide; maxillary much developed, very movable, much dilated behind. Teeth in narrow villiform bands in the jaws; on each side of the broad vomer a small patch of similar teeth; none on palatines or tongue; eye very small; scales cycloid, adherent, of moderate size; rays of pectoral much elongate, some of the upper being separate from the rest and forming a distinct division; ventrals abdominal, 8-rayed, with the outer rays prolonged; dorsal fin inserted at middle of body or absent; anal short; caudal forked; gill-openings very wide; gill-laminæ well developed, separate from each other; gillrakers long; pseudo-branchiæ none. Deep-sea fishes.

Family XX. MYCTOPHIDÆ.—The Lantern Fishes.

Body oblong or moderately elongate, more or less compressed, covered with scales which are usually cycloid, but sometimes ctenoid; mouth wide; entire margin of upper jaw formed by the long and slender premaxillaries, closely adherent to which are the slender maxillaries; teeth various, mostly villiform, in bands in the jaws, also on the pterygoids, palatines, and tongue, and on the vomer in adults; no barbels; gill-membranes separate, free; branchiostegals 8 to 10; pseudobranchiæ well developed; gillrakers long and slender; lateral line usually present; scales prominent and often enlarged; cheeks and opercles scaly; adipose fin present; dorsal fin short, median, of soft rays; pectorals and ventrals present; anal fin moderate; caudal forked; air-bladder small; intestinal canal short; luminous spots or photophores more or less regularly placed along sides of body; larger luminous glands often present on head or on caudal peduncle.

Species about 100. Small fishes, very widely distributed in the open sea. They live away from the shores, ordinarily at a considerable depth, coming to the surface at night or in stormy weather, descending by day.

Genus 28. DIAPHUS Eigenmann & Eigenmann.

This genus is closely related to *Æthoprora*, its chief character being the division of all or nearly all of the photophores by a horizontal cross-septum of black pigment, giving them the form of the Greek letter Φ, *theta*. This septum is readily injured or destroyed in badly preserved specimens, and perhaps all species called *Æthoprora* have it. Of the 5 known species 3 have been taken in Hawaiian waters, and are described in Section II.

Genus 29. NANNOBRACHIUM Günther.

This genus is closely allied to *Lampanyctus*, from which it differs chiefly in the small pectorals. Caudal peduncle with luminous blotches above and below; photophores small, arranged as in *Lampanyctus;* scales of lateral line enlarged in all species, so far as known; last ray of dorsal more or less behind front of anal. Several species, only one Hawaiian (*Nannobrachium nigrum*) described in Section II.

Genus 30. RHINOSCOPELUS Lütken.

Body oblong, slender, compressed, with slender and elongate caudal peduncle covered with smooth, stiff scales, those in the lateral line much larger than the others; head compressed; cleft of mouth very wide; jaws about equal; snout projecting beyond tip of lower jaw; premaxillary long and slender; maxillary well developed, reaching nearly or quite to angle of preopercle, without considerable posterior dilation; teeth in villiform bands in the jaws, on the palatines, pterygoids, and tongue; eye moderate, its diameter less than one-third length of head; gillrakers very long and slender; dorsal fin premedian; pectoral large; adipose dorsal small; anal fin larger than dorsal; pectoral narrow, elongate; precaudals 2; supraanals about 18, in 2 groups, the break being over middle of the long anal fin and at end of first third of the series, approximately; anterolaterals 1 or 2; mediolaterals 2 or 3. Species few, mostly of the Atlantic.

27. Rhinoscopelus oceanicus Jordan & Evermann. Fig. 15.

Head 3.5 in length; depth 4.1; eye 2.5 in head; snout very short, about 6; interorbital 3.5; D. about 12; A. about 18; scales 2–35–3.

Body strongly compressed, particularly posteriorly, where it tapers into the long, slender caudal peduncle; head exceeding depth of body; mouth large, somewhat oblique, the jaws equal, the maxillary reaching beyond the orbit, its posterior end club-shaped; eye large; anterior profile rather evenly convex from tip of snout to nape; teeth difficult to make out, but a single row of minute ones can be seen on the edge of each jaw, the exterior granular or short; the villiform stripe, if it exists, being invisible even with the aid of a good lens; teeth on vomer and edges of palatines more distinct than those on jaws, forming a broader line as if there were 2 or more rows; no granular patches visible on disk of palatine bone; an elevated acute mesial line separating one nasal prominence from the other; interorbital space convex, rounded; preopercle nearly vertical, sloping slightly backward from above downward; scales large, undulated and very irregularly and sparingly toothed or crenate, and having about 3 basal furrows; scales of lateral line conspicuous and more persistent; 7 photophores along base of anal, 5 along lower edge of caudal peduncle, 2 at base of caudal, 1 on middle of side above last anal photophore, 4 on each side of belly between ventrals and origin of anal fin, 5 between base of ventral and gill-opening, 1 on side above base of ventral, a row of 3 upward and backward from front of anal, 1 above and 1 below base of pectoral, and 1 on lower anterior portion of opercle; origin of dorsal somewhat behind base of ventrals, the posterior rays, together with those of anal, divided to the base; no spine at base of caudal.

Color in alcohol, uniform brownish, the scales, especially on middle of side, metallic steel blue; top of head brownish; side of head bluish; photophores black with silvery center; fins dusky whitish.

During the Agassiz South Pacific expedition of the *Albatross* in 1899–1900, 2 examples of this species were taken in the surface tow net at 8 p. m., September 8, 1899, at latitude 10° 57′ N., longitude 137° 35′ W., southeast of the Hawaiian Islands. These are apparently distinct from *R. coruscans*, the type of which came from between St. Helena and Ascension islands, and other specimens from

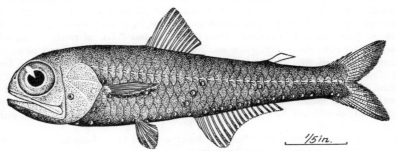

FIG. 15.—*Rhinoscopelus oceanicus* Jordan & Evermann; from the type.

between Australia and New Zealand. They are near *R. andreæ* Lütken, from which they seem to differ in the blunter snout, the more slender tail, and in having the postero-lateral photophore somewhat before the adipose fin.

Type, No. 50622, U. S. N. M. (field No. 05805), 1.3 inches long, collected by the *Albatross* at 8 p. m., September 8, 1899, at the surface at 137° 35′ W., 10° 57′ N.; cotype, No. 2736, U. S. F. C., same size, collected at same time and place.

Genus 31. CENTROBRANCHUS Fowler.

This genus is close to *Rhinoscopelus*, from which it seems to differ in the character of the gillrakers, which are short sparse clusters of asperities on the first arch. Two species known, both from Hawaiian waters. (See Section II.)

28. Centrobranchus chœrocephalus Fowler.

This species, fully described in Section II of this work, was based by Mr. Fowler on 4 specimens in the Museum of the Philadelphia Academy, which were originally identified by Mr. Fowler with *Rhinoscopelus coruscans* (Richardson), and later thought by us to be identical with the specimen which we described as *R. oceanicus*. Upon a reexamination of his specimens Mr. Fowler finds them to represent a distinct genus as indicated above.

Genus 32. MYCTOPHUM Rafinesque.

Body oblong, compressed, covered with cycloid scales, those in the lateral line not much enlarged; caudal peduncle rather slender; head short, compressed, with limb of preopercle nearly vertical; mouth large; jaws about equal; premaxillaries long and slender; maxillaries well developed; snout more or less blunt and declivous; teeth in villiform bands on jaws, palatines, pterygoids, and tongue; eye large, gillrakers long and slender; air-bladder small; dorsal fin entirely in front of anal, overlapping it little or not at all; ventrals 8-rayed, under or but slightly in front of first dorsal rays; pectorals well developed; soft dorsal slender; precaudal photophores 2; supraanals in 2 groups, with 1 or 2 postero-laterals above the interval between them. Species rather numerous, widely distributed, 4 known from Hawaiian waters, and described in Section II.

Genus 33. DASYSCOPELUS Günther.

Dorsal and anal fins touching the same vertical, but not overlapping; scales hard, persistent, ctenoid, those of lateral line much enlarged; anal terminating below adipose dorsal; body elevated, somewhat compressed; caudal peduncle rather slender; luminous scales on the back of caudal peduncle; arrangement of photophores much as in *Myctophum*. Species few, remarkable for the firm, rough scales. Two species known from the Hawaiian Islands (*D. spinosus* and *D. pristilepis*) described in Section II.

Genus 34. NEOSCOPELUS Johnson.

Body oblong, compressed; mouth-cleft not extending beyond eye, the upper borders formed entirely of the premaxillary; the maxillary dilated below and furnished with a small supplementary piece; scombinate bands of teeth in both jaws, on palatine bones, and on vomer. also scombinate patches of teeth on the entopterygoids; body covered with large, caducous scales; first dorsal placed over the abdominal ventral fins; pectoral fins long, their inferior rays not thicker than the rest. (Goode & Bean.)

29. Neoscopelus alcocki Jordan & Starks.

Head 3 in length; depth 4; D 13; A. 12; scales 4–33–4; eye 5 in head; snout 3.5; maxillary 2.

Body rather robust, subfusiform; head rather pointed in profile, broad and somewhat depressed above; mouth large, oblique, maxillary extending to below posterior margin of orbit, not dilated behind, posterior border truncate; teeth small, in villiform bands; eye moderate, cheek broad, not oblique in position; scales large, entire, firm, roughened on the surface, nearly all fallen in specimen examined; lateral line well developed; luminous spots large, in about 6 rows on breast, about 14 in a lengthwise series from isthmus to ventrals, then a median and 2 lateral rows, to opposite front of anal, 10 spots in outer row, the posterior one smaller; an oblong circle of 10 small photophores about the vent; a row of 15 small photophores, continuous with inner lateral row before vent, from opposite vent to base of caudal, most of the median members of this series double; there is also an inner series of minute white dots along base of anal rays; a median row of small photophores behind anal below caudal peduncle. Dorsal rather large, inserted before ventral, its longest rays about half head; longest anal ray 2.4 in head; caudal well forked; pectoral long, 1.1 in head; ventral long, 1.75; gillrakers long and slender, 3+12 in number.

Color, pale or brownish above, belly black; a dusky shade at base of caudal and pectoral; inside of mouth black; luminous spots pale, with a dark ring.

This species is very close to *Neoscopelus macrolepidotus* of the Atlantic. The sole important difference apparently lies in the arrangement of the photophores on the posterior part of body. In the figures (Nos. 108 and 109) given by Goode & Bean (Oceanic Ichthyology), the arrangement is quite unlike that seen in the Japanese fish; the two lateral rows of spots found on the abdomen are represented as continuous to the base of caudal.. In the Japanese fish the outer row is not continued behind the front of anal. The inner lateral series is continued, the spots becoming smaller. There is a ring of little spots about the vent, and a series of little dots along base of anal.

The species abundant about Hawaii, called *Neoscopelus macrolepidotus* by Gilbert & Cramer, seems to be the same as the Japanese fish.

Family XXI. MAUROLICIDÆ.

Body moderately elongate, compressed, scaleless; barbels none; margin of upper jaw formed by the maxillary and premaxillary, both of which are provided with teeth; opercular apparatus incomplete; gill-opening very wide, the outer branchial arch extending forward to behind the symphysis of lower jaw; pseudobranchiæ present; air-bladder none; adipose fin rudimentary; series of luminous photophores present along the lower side of head, tail, and body; a single dorsal fin without spines. (Goode & Bean.) Genera 4 or 5, with some 8 or 10 species. Deep-sea fishes, represented in the Hawaiian Islands by a single known species.

Genus 35. ARGYRIPNUS Gilbert & Cramer.

Body much compressed, oblong or elongate, passing gradually into the slender tail, covered with very thin, flexible, cycloid, deciduous scales; head longer than deep, without spines, its bones thin and flexible; maxillary sickle-shaped, with spatulate supplemental bone; eye large; dorsal fin on middle of back, without anterior spinous dilatation; a large (double) luminous organ on preopercle and series of equidistant organs on branchiostegals, isthmus, breast, abdomen, and lower part of side; a continuous series from above base of ventral fin to about end of anterior third of base of anal fin; a closely set series of 5 spots above middle of anal fin, and another series of 15 beginning above hinder end of anal and extending to anterior rudimentary rays of caudal. The single species of this genus (*Argyripnus ephippiatus*) is fully described in Section II.

Genus 36. ARGYROPELECUS Cocco.

Body much elevated and compressed, passing abruptly into the short tail; no scales, the skin covered with silvery pigment; series of luminous spots along the lower side of head, body, and tail;

head large, compressed and elevated, the bones thin but ossified; cleft of mouth wide, vertical, the lower jaw prominent; margin of upper jaw formed by the maxillary and premaxillary, both of which have a sharp edge beset with minute teeth; lower jaw and palatine bones with a series of small curved teeth; eyes large, very close together, lateral but directed upward; angle of preopercle with a spine usually directed downward; pectorals well developed; ventrals very small; humeral arch and pubic bones prolonged into flat-pointed processes, which project in the median line of the belly; a series of imbricated scales from the humeral bone to the pubic spine, forming a ventral serrature; dorsal fin short, median, preceded by a serrated, osseous ridge, consisting of several neural spines prolonged beyond the muscles; adipose fin rudimentary; anal fin short; caudal forked; gill-opening very wide, the outer branchial arch extending forward to behind the symphysis of the lower jaw and beset with very long gillrakers; branchiostegals 9, the arch near lower jaw and parallel with it; pseudobranchiæ and air-bladder present; 4 pyloric cœca. Small pelagic fishes found in most seas, coming to the surface at night, descending into deep water by day.

The single Hawaiian species of this genus is fully described in Section II.

Family XXII. CHAULIODONTIDÆ.

Body more or less elongate, covered with thin caducous scales, or sometimes naked; photophores present; mouth large, the teeth irregular in size; maxillary entering margin; no pseudobranchiæ; interopercle rudimentary; gill-openings wide; dorsal and anal moderate or large. Deep-sea fishes of rather small size but voracious habits. Some 7 genera and about 20 species known.

Genus 37. CYCLOTHONE Goode & Bean.

Body elongated, somewhat compressed, apparently devoid of scales; lower parts with inconspicuous series of luminous spots, with the latter arranged approximately as in *Gonostoma*, but usually much less conspicuous; head conical, compressed; cleft of mouth very wide, oblique, extending behind the eye; lower jaw strongly projecting; maxillary long and slender, sickle-shaped, somewhat dilated posteriorly, but covering only an inconsiderable portion of the cheek; upper jaw with a single series of needle-like teeth, some of which are enlarged; lower jaw with similar teeth, and in some species with a few canines in front; teeth on vomer sometimes in patches, sometimes reduced to a single pair of fangs; palatine and pterygoid teeth present or absent; eye moderate, not conspicuous; gill-opening very wide, the membranes free from isthmus; gillrakers numerous, long and slender; pseudobranchiæ none; no air-bladder; dorsal and anal moderate, opposite, the latter much the longer; adipose fin sometimes present. The 3 Hawaiian species of this genus are fully described in Section II.

Family XXIII. ASTRONESTHIDÆ.

Stomatoid fishes, with adipose dorsal present, and with scaleless body; dorsal fin inserted behind vent, but in front of anal. A single genus with few species; fishes of the deep sea.

Genus 38. ASTRONESTHES Richardson.

Body rather elongate, compressed, scaleless; head compressed; snout of moderate length; mouth wide; lower jaw prominent; teeth pointed, unequal; upper jaw with 4 long, curved canines, front of lower with 2; maxillary teeth fine, subequal; palatines with a single series of small pointed teeth, similar to those on tongue; eye moderate, not longer than snout; throat with a long fleshy barbel; dorsal fin rather long, inserted entirely in front of anal behind ventrals; adipose fin present; caudal forked; paired fins long; gillrakers minute; no pseudobranchiæ; no air-bladder; sides and belly with very many small luminous spots; a small luminous patch below eye. Small fishes of the deep sea, remarkable for their strong teeth, the lower jaw much stronger than in *Malacosteus*. The single Hawaiian species is fully described in Section II.

Family XXIV. STOMIATIDÆ.

Body elongate, tapering, naked or covered with very thin and deciduous scales; head oblong; snout short and rounded; eyes large and far forward; opercular apparatus imperfectly developed; mouth enormous, with deep lateral cleft; lateral margin of upper jaw formed by maxillary and provided with teeth along the edges; teeth usually strong, unequal, some of them often fang-like or barbed; gill-membranes not joined, free from the isthmus; branchiostegals numerous (12 to 17); a long barbel at throat; no pseudobranchiæ; dorsal fin short, median or posterior, without spines; anal free, far behind and small; caudal distinct; pectorals low down on the scapular arch and narrow; ventrals inserted far backward; stomach cœcal, and pyloric appendages absent; sides with phosphorescent spots; skeleton feebly ossified; eggs extruded through oviducts. Deep-sea fishes of extremely voracious habits.

The single Hawaiian genus and species of this family are fully described in Section II.

Family XXV. PARALEPIDIDÆ.

Body elongate, somewhat compressed, formed much as in a barracuda, covered with cycloid scales of moderate or rather large size; head long, usually scaly on the sides; mouth very large; lower jaw projecting; premaxillary not protractile, very long and slender, forming the entire margin of upper jaw; maxillary long and slender, closely adherent to premaxillary; teeth rather strong, pointed, in single series on the jaws and palatines; some of them on lower jaw and palatines sometimes very long and fang-like, and most of them freely depressible; opercular bones thin; pseudobranchiæ present; gill-membranes separate, free from the isthmus; branchiostegals about 7; gillrakers short, sharp, spine-like; eye large; lateral line present, its scales usually enlarged; dorsal fin short and small, behind the middle of the body, nearly or quite over the ventrals; adipose fin present; anal fin low, rather long; caudal fin short, narrow, forked; pectorals rather small, placed low; pyloric cœca none; no air-bladder; phosphorescent spots few or none.   Voracious fishes of the open seas or the deep seas.

The single Hawaiian genus and species of this family are fully described in Section II.

Family XXVI. STERNOPTYCHIDÆ.

Fishes " with compressed, ventradiform body, carinated contour, deeply and obliquely cleft and subvertical mouth, whose upper margin is constituted by the supramaxillaries as well as the intermaxillaries; branchiostegal arch near and parallel with lower jaw, scapular with an inferior projection, and with one or more of the neural spines abnormally developed, and projecting above the back in advance of the dorsal fin."   (Gill.)

Genera 2, species about 10; deep-sea fishes, rising toward the surface at night or in stormy weather.

Genus 39. POLYIPNUS Günther.

This genus differs from *Sternoptyx* in having the body covered with large, very thin, and deciduous scales, and in lacking the anterior spinous dilatation of the dorsal fin.   Three species known.

Only one species of this genus known from the Hawaiian Islands.   (See Section II.)

Genus 40. STERNOPTYX Hermann.

Body much elevated and compressed, passing abruptly into a short and compressed tail, the angle made by the hind margin of the trunk and the lower edge of the tail being filled up by a broad fold of the integument, of peculiar transparent appearance, resembling thin cartilage; this fold bears the anal fin and is supported by interhæmal rays; head short, compressed, deep, with extremely short snout and a wide, subvertical mouth; eyes large, lateral; margin of upper jaw formed by maxillary and intermaxillary, the latter being very short, and each of these bones having a sharp edge which is armed with a series of very small teeth, somewhat unequal in size; lower jaw with a similar dentition; vomer and palatines toothless; bones of the head firm, some of them terminating in short spines, namely the angle of the preopercle, the postero-inferior angle of the mandible, and the symphysis of the humeral bones; gill-opening very wide, the gill-membrane being attached to the isthmus; gills 4, the branchial arches long, not angularly bent, the branchial slits being closed by a membrane in their upper portion; a few of the gillrakers are prolonged, needle-shaped and widely set, the others being quite rudimentary; pseudobranchiæ present; greater portion of body scaleless, covered with a silvery pigment; a luminous organ occupies the inner side of the opercle close to its lower end, another is placed at the anterior end of the ceratohyal, and finally a very large glandular mass is lodged on the upper edge of the anterior end of the clavicle; a series of luminous spots runs along the lower edge of the abdomen and is separated from the series of the other side by a cartilaginous fold occupying the median line of the abdomen; another series runs on each side of the isthmus, a row of 3 above and behind the root of the ventrals, and another row of 3 above the vent; the luminous organs on the lower part of tail consist anteriorly of a row of 4, of which the first is prolonged toward the back as a narrow band, terminating about the middle of the depth of the body in a globular black spot with a white center; posteriorly in front of the caudal rays there is another row of 4 small spots; the dorsal fin occupies the middle of the back and consists of a triangular bony lamella, very thin in front, but strengthened along its hind margin, and followed by several rays; adipose fin absent, or represented by a very low membranous fringe of the dorsal margin of the tail; the anal fin is incompletely developed, extending from the vent to the root of the caudal fin, its rays being rudimentary, widely set, and scarcely free; caudal fin broad and forked; pectorals well developed, close to the lower profile; ventrals small, the pelvic bone with a bifid spine in front pointing forward.   (Günther.)

The single Hawaiian species (*Sternoptyx diaphana*) is described in Section II.

Order G. APODES.—The Eels.

Teleost fishes, with the premaxillaries atrophied or lost, the maxillaries lateral, and the body anguilliform and destitute of ventral fins; the most striking feature is the absence of premaxillaries, taken in connection with the elongate form and the little development of the scapular arch, which is not attached to the cranium. Other characters. not confined to the *Apodes*, are the following: The absence of the symplectic bone; the reduction of the opercular apparatus and of the palato-pterygoid arch; the absence of ventral fins; the absence of the mesocoracoid or præcoracoid arch; the reduction or total absence of the scales; there are no spines in the fins; the gill-openings are comparatively small; there are no pseudobranchiæ; the vertebræ are in large number and none of them specially modified; the tail is isocercal—that is, with the caudal vertebræ remaining in a straight line to its extremity, as in the embryos of most fishes, and in the *Anacanthini*.

We begin our discussion of the eels with the forms which seem nearest to the primitive stock from which the members of the group have descended. It is evident that among the eels the forms of simplest structure, *Sphagebranchus*, etc., are not in any sense primitive forms, but the results of a long-continued and progressive degeneration, so far as the fins and mouth parts are concerned. The *Apodes* are probably descended from soft-rayed fishes, and their divergence from typical forms is in most respects a retrogression.

Family XXVII. SYNAPHOBRANCHIDÆ.

This group consists of deep-sea eels, differing from the *Anguillidæ* in having the gill-opening externally confluent into a single slit. The following diagnosis is given by Dr. Gill:

"Enchelycephalous Apodals with conic, pointed head, moderate opercular apparatus, lateral maxillines, cardiform teeth, distinct tongue, inferior branchial apertures discharging by a common aperture, continuous vertical fins, pectorals well developed, scaly skin, and nearly perfect branchial skeleton."

Body eel-shaped, covered with linear, imbedded scales placed at right angles, as in *Anguilla*. Lateral line present; head long and pointed, the snout produced; mouth very long, the eye being over the middle of its cleft; jaws about equal; teeth small, sharp, in a broad band in each jaw, becoming a single series anteriorly; those of inner series in upper jaw and of outer series in mandible somewhat enlarged; vomerine teeth in a narrow band anteriorly; gill-openings inferior, horizontal, close together, convergent forward, somewhat confluent at the surface, but separated by a considerable isthmus within; branchiostegals peculiarly formed, in moderate number (about 15), attached to the sides of the compressed ceratohyal and epihyal, slender, abbreviated, and moderately bowed, not being curved up above the opercle; tongue long, free only at the sides; nostrils large, the anterior with a short tube, the posterior before the lower part of the eye; pectoral well developed; dorsal low, beginning behind vent; anal longer than dorsal, rather high, its rays slender, branched, not embedded in the skin; vertical fins confluent around the tail; vent near the anterior fourth of body; muscular and osseous systems well developed; stomach very distensible. Deep-sea fishes.

Genus 41. SYNAPHOBRANCHUS Johnson.

Dorsal beginning behind vent. This genus contains 2 or 3 species, deep-sea fishes from the Atlantic and Pacific.

The single Hawaiian species of this genus is fully described in Section II.

Family XXVIII. LEPTOCEPHALIDÆ.—The Conger Eels.

This family includes those eels which are scaleless and have the tongue largely free in front; the body moderately elongate; the end of the tail surrounded by a fin; the posterior nostril remote from the upper lip and near front of eye; and the pectoral fins well developed; lower jaw more or less included; teeth on sides forming a cutting edge; lateral line well developed. All the species are plainly colored, grayish or dusky above, silvery below. Species found in most warm seas, usually at moderate depth. Most of them undergo a metamorphosis, the young being loosely organized and transparent, band-shaped, and with very small head. The body grows smaller with age owing to the compacting of the tissues. The two genera found in the Hawaiian Islands are not well separated and should perhaps be considered as one.

Genus 42. PROMYLLANTOR Alcock.

Body stout, with the muscular and osseous systems well developed, and the tail about as long as the trunk; eye rather small, cleft of mouth narrow, not extending behind middle of eye; villiform teeth, in broad bands in jaws, and in a broad, confluent patch on palate; nostrils lateral; tongue free; gill-openings widely separate; 4 gills with wide clefts; no scales; muciferous cavities of head well developed; the dorsal begins some distance behind the occiput; pectoral and vertical fins well developed, the latter confluent. Allied to *Congermuræna*. (Alcock). This genus differs from *Leptocephalus* in the dentition and in the posterior position of the nostrils. Deep-sea fishes of the Arabian seas and about the Hawaiian Islands.

The single Hawaiian species (*P. alcocki*) is fully described in Section II.

Genus 43. LEPTOCEPHALUS Scopoli. The Conger Eels.

Body formed as in *Anguilla;* the skin scaleless; head depressed above, anteriorly pointed; lateral line present; mouth wide, its cleft extending at least to below middle of eye; teeth in outer series in each jaw equal and close-set, forming a cutting edge; no canines; band of vomerine teeth short; tongue anteriorly free; vertical fins well developed, confluent around tail; pectoral fins well developed; dorsal beginning close behind pectorals; gill-openings rather large, low; eyes well developed; posterior nostril near eye; anterior near tip of snout, with a short tube; lower jaw not projecting; skeleton differing in numerous respects from that of *Anguilla;* vertebræ about 56 + 100. In most warm seas. This genus contains the well known and widely distributed conger eel and 3 or 4 closely related species. The earliest generic name used for members of the group is *Leptocephalus*, based on a curious, elongate, transparent, band-like creature with minute head and very small mouth, found in the waters of Europe, and known as *Leptocephalus morrissi*. This has been shown by Gill, Günther and Facciola to be the young and larval form of *Leptocephalus conger*. A number of genera and species of the sup-posed family of *Leptocephalidæ* have been described, but there is no doubt that all of them are larvæ, some of eels, as *Conger, Congermuræna, Oxystomus,* and *Nettastoma*, others of isospondylous fishes, as *Albula, Elops, Alepocephalus, Stomias,* etc. (Günther, Cat., VIII, 136.) It is thought by Dr. Günther that the leptocephalid forms are probably "individuals arrested in the development at a very early period of their life, yet continuing to grow to a certain size, without corresponding develop-ment of their internal organs, and perishing without having attained the characters of the perfect animal." The recent observations of Dr. Gilbert on the larvæ of *Albula, Elops,* and *Conger*, however, seem to point to the conclusion that these curious forms are normal young, and that the individuals grow smaller in size for a time with increased age, owing to the increasing compactness of the tissues.

Inasmuch as the name *Leptocephalus* has been associated for more than a century with larval forms it is a decided inconvenience to accord to it precedence as a generic name over *Conger*. The strict law of priority, however, demands its retention, and the tendency among systematic zoologists is to recognize as few exceptions as may be to this rule. The unfamiliar names *Oxyurus* and *Helmictis* are both earlier than *Conger*.

30. Leptocephalus marginatus (Valenciennes). "*Puhi úha.*"

Head 2 in trunk; head and trunk about 1.67 in tail; eye 2 in snout, 1.67 in interorbital space; snout about 3.75 in head; interorbital space a little over 5; mouth about 2.3; pectoral 2.67.

Body more or less rounded, the tail posteriorly tapering and compressed; head rather long, depressed, and pointed; snout pointed, depressed above, and projecting beyond the mandible; eye small, anterior; mouth rather large, extending posteriorly slightly beyond eye; lips thick, fleshy, and broad; teeth blunt, rather short, more or less cylindrical, a patch on vomer and front of mouth above, a small patch on each side of the symphysis of mandible, those along the jaws forming a cutting edge; tongue large, thick, and free in front; anterior nostrils in short tubes near tip of snout, the posterior situated very near upper front margin of eye; interorbital space elevated convexly and flattened in the middle; sides of head rather swollen; gill-openings rather large; peritoneum silvery; skin perfectly smooth; head with a number of mucous pores; lateral line well developed and continuous, the pores about 120; origin of dorsal beginning over the first third of pectoral, its height greater than that of anal; margin of caudal rounded, its length about equal to snout and half of eye; pectoral more or less rounded, the rays just above the middle the longest. In life the young has traces of obscure crossbars.

Color in alcohol, dark lucid brown above and on the vertical fins, which are margined with black; lower surface of body pale or whitish, more or less soiled with pale brown; a dark blackish brown streak from lower margin of eye above and behind the corner of mouth; pectorals brown, their lower margins whitish, the upper portions of their extremities with a black blotch, which is always distinct.

The above description is based on a specimen 39 inches long (No. 03759) from Hilo. Three other specimens (Nos. 03758, 03359, and 03760), 30, 24, and 30 inches long, respectively, are in the collec-tions from Hilo, and 2 specimens (Nos. 03713 and 03727), 24 and 38 inches long, respectively, were obtained at Kailua. Young individuals have traces of obscure cross-bands. An example from Hilo showed the pectoral in life with a large blotch, edged with white. In the collection made by Dr. Jenkins are 4 specimens, 19 to 25 inches long. We have one larva, probably of this or some species of *Leptocephalus*, obtained at Hilo. It is about 2 inches long, and can not be certainly identified.

The species is rather abundant about lava rocks, and is common at Samoa. The native Hawaiian name, *puhi uha*, signifies slippery eel.

Genus 44. CONGRELLUS Ogilby.

Dorsal fin inserted more anteriorly than in *Leptocephalus*, over the gill-opening or anterior part of pectoral; head with muciferous cavities, more or less conspicuous; mouth rather small; teeth all pointed; body more robust than in *Leptocephalus*, the tail not much, if any, longer than rest of body, its tip white in Japanese species; dorsal and anal edged with black. The genus is not very different from *Leptocephalus*, the species *megastomus* being almost exactly intermediate.

31. Congrellus .bowersi Jenkins. Fig. 16.

Head 1.6 in trunk; head and trunk a little shorter than tail; width of head 2.5 in its length; snout 4.5 in head; eye 4.25; interorbital space 6; pectoral 3.4; pores about 147 in lateral line.

Body rather short, compressed, the tail tapering posteriorly; head elongate, rounded, conically pointed in front; snout a trifle less than eye, rounded, elongate, with its tip bluntly pointed; eyes very large, high in front of head; mouth large, the snout protruding slightly beyond tip of mandible, corner of mouth nearly under middle of eye; lips rather thick, fleshy lobes on either side of each jaw; teeth all fine and rather numerous in jaws and on vomer; anterior nostrils in short tubes at tip of snout, the posterior on sides of snout nearer front of eye than tip of snout; interorbital space flattened and with a median ridge; head without swollen appearance; gill-openings about two-thirds eye; peritoneum silvery, with small gray dots; skin smooth; head with a number of mucous pores, a large one just behind the anterior nostril; origin of dorsal at about the last sixth of the space between

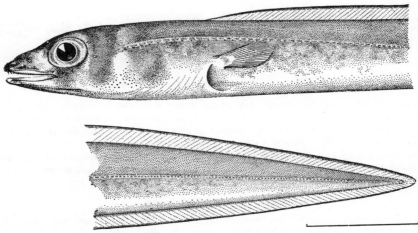

Fig. 16.—*Congrellus bowersi* Jenkins; from the type.

posterior margin of eye and origin of pectoral; caudal small, or the marginal fin around the end of tail very narrow; pectoral rather short and rounded.

Color in alcohol, brown, slightly darker above and somewhat clouded on head, where 2 dark brown crossbars are formed; fins all pale brown; edges of dorsal, caudal, and anal narrowly edged with black, especially distinct posteriorly. Color in life (No. 03419), body translucent, colorless; snout dusky; a dusky band through eye and over head; a dusky transverse band across nape and half way down on side; a dusky saddle in front of dorsal; a narrow dark margin on dorsal and anal.

This description is based primarily upon a specimen (No. 04923) 14.5 inches long, obtained at Hilo. One other specimen (No. 04922) 11 inches long was taken at Hilo; four examples (Nos. 03419, 04919, 04920, and 04921), each about 11 inches long, at Honolulu. The collection obtained by Dr. Jenkins at Honolulu contains eight examples, ranging in length from 8 to 11 inches.

32. Congrellus æquoreus (Gilbert & Cramer). Fig. 17.

Head 6.5 to 6.8; depth 15 to 18; head and trunk much shorter than tail, about 1.6 in latter; pectoral rays 14 or 15.

Body slender, compressed; head as deep as wide, tapering forward to a flat snout; snout 3.5 to 3.8 in head, slightly more than twice as long as eye, and projecting two-thirds the diameter of eye beyond tip of lower jaw; eyes somewhat elliptical, their upper margins near dorsal profile; angle of mouth reaching middle of orbit; lips thin; maxillary teeth close-set in a broad villiform band, the outer teeth longer than the inner, the vomerine teeth much larger, forming a broad transverse patch in advance of maxillary teeth, with a very few small teeth on the shaft; mandibular teeth in a narrow cardiform band anteriorly, diminishing much in size toward angle of mouth; anterior nostril a broad short tube situated on the antero-lateral part of snout, a little nearer mouth than dorsal profile; posterior nostril a large, elliptical opening in front of upper third of eye, less than its own diameter from eye; interorbital space about equal to long diameter of eye; gill-openings far apart, their width a little greater than diameter of eye, the distance between them about 5 in head; gills 4, no rakers; tongue free; peritoneum silvery, speckled, or brownish; intestine black; pores of snout arranged as follows: A small pair under tip of snout just in front of anterior teeth, a large one in front of, a second above, and a third immediately behind the anterior nostril, 4 others along the side of upper jaw, and one behind angle of mouth; a row of about 10 pores on each ramus of mandible, beginning at tip of lower jaw and extending beyond its posterior angle; lateral line above middle of body anteriorly; dorsal fin beginning slightly behind base of pectoral, its distance from occiput equaling distance of latter from center of eye; pectoral small, pointed and equal to snout.

Color in alcohol, brown, head and back dusky; a large, dark, opercular spot, another small one above each eye, and a dark streak on snout in front of eye; side of tail with coarse black specks, much

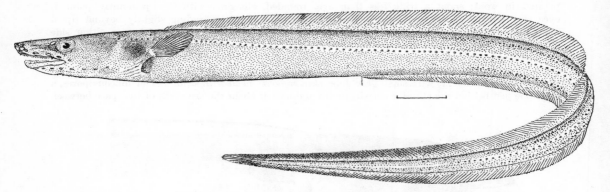

FIG. 17.—*Congrellus æquoreus* (Gilbert & Cramer); from the type.

more numerous in one of the specimens than in the other, and mainly collected into 2 lengthwise lines running parallel with the bases of the dorsal and anal; the other specimen is almost plain; marginal portions of dorsal and anal fins dusky, becoming black posteriorly, and the basal portions light; inside of mouth a little dusky (Gilbert & Cramer).

This species is known from two specimens, 16.25 and 18.5 inches long, respectively, dredged by the *Albatross*, December 6, 1891, between Molokai and Lanai in 375 fathoms, and several others dredged by the *Albatross* in 1902.

Genus 45. VETERNIO Snyder.

Body without scales; lateral line present; tail much longer than head and trunk; head long, snout pointed; lower jaw much shorter than upper. No teeth; vomer, maxillaries, and mandible with broad, smooth, hard areas; tongue free; nostrils not tubular, the anterior ones near tip of snout, with narrow rims; posterior ones oblong, near the eyes; gill-openings separate, with broad, lunate slits; fins well developed, dorsal inserted above base of pectorals. Color uniform.

The absence of teeth serves to distinguish *Veternio* from closely related genera.

33. Veternio verrens Snyder.   Plate 5, fig. 1.

Head, from tip of snout to upper edge of gill-opening, 0.64 of trunk; depth 0.42 of head; eye 0.13; snout 0.26; length of pectoral 0.36.

Head very long and pointed, upper profile sloping gently from tip of snout to occiput; interorbital space flat, its width 0.16 of head; snout slender, projecting beyond lower jaw a distance equal to 0.5 of diameter of eye; cleft of mouth somewhat oblique, extending beyond eye a distance equal to 0.3 of pupil; no teeth, the vomer, maxillaries, and mandible with broad, flat, smooth surfaces; tongue free, tip rounded; lips thin, simple; anterior nostrils at end of snout, with low rims and posterior flaps; posterior nostrils close to upper anterior part of eye, without rims, rounded oval in shape; a pair of large mucous tubes at tip of snout, a tube immediately behind anterior nostril and one on each side of snout just above the latter; gill-openings lunate, their width about 0.15 of length of head; lateral line somewhat above middle of body anteriorly, gradually extending downward and reaching middle of body a short distance beyond the vent. Pectoral inserted just below middle of body, obtusely pointed, upper rays longest, lower border convex; dorsal inserted above middle of base of pectoral, height of fin at a point above tip of pectoral equal to vertical diameter of eye, at a point twice the length of head behind the vent, the length of rays equals length of snout; 65 rays between its insertion and a vertical through the anal opening; anal inserted immediately behind vent, its height equal to 0.5 the length of snout. Color plain, fins edged with black.

Color in spirits brown, darker above than below; pectorals brownish, growing black toward tips; dorsal brownish, shading into black along edge; anal bordered with black, the band about half as wide as pupil and sharply defined.

A single mutilated specimen (type, No. 50862, U. S. Nat. Mus.) from the Honolulu market measures 10.63 inches from snout to vent. The tail was severed 12.6 inches behind the vent.

Family XXIX. NETTASTOMIDÆ.

Eels without pectoral fins, with the tongue not free, the posterior nostrils remote from the lip, the gill-openings small, separate, and subinferior, the vent remote from the head, the tail ending in a slender tip or filamant, the dorsal and anal fins moderately developed, and the jaws produced, slender, and straight, the upper the longer, and both, as also the vomer, armed with bands of sharp, close-set, recurved, subequal teeth. This family contains a few species of deep-sea eels, closely allied to the *Murænesocidæ* in technical characters, but more resembling the *Nemichthyidæ* in appearance, form of the head, and in dentition. Deep-sea fishes with fragile bodies and thin skin charged with black pigment. A single Hawaiian genus and species, described in Section II.

Family XXX. NEMICHTHYIDÆ.—The Snipe Eels.

Body excessively slender, not strongly compressed, deepest near the middle, tapering backward to the tail, which usually ends in a long and slender filament, and forward to a very long and slender neck, which is abruptly enlarged at the occipital region; no scales; lateral line represented by one or more rows of pores; head resembling that of *Tylosurus;* the head proper, small, short, and rather broad, with flat top and vertical sides; nostrils large, close together in front of the eye, without tube or flap; jaws excessively prolonged, almost needle-like, the upper the longer and somewhat recurved; teeth in both jaws small, very numerous, close-set, retrorse; gill-openings rather large, running downward and forward, separated by a narrow isthmus or partly confluent; pectorals well developed; anal fin higher than dorsal, beginning near the vent, becoming obsolete on the caudal filament; dorsal beginning close behind occiput, its anterior rays soft, succeeded by a long series of very low, simple, spine-like rays, which are slightly connected by membrane, their height rather less than the length of the interspaces; on the tail these spines again give place to soft rays; the soft rays of the fins are connected by thin membranes instead of being imbedded in thick skin, as in eels generally. Color translucent, the lower parts dark, the back pale; stomach not distensible; muscular and osseus systems well developed; abdominal cavity extending far behind the vent. The species are little known and their anatomy has not been studied; they are certainly eels, and their nearest relation seems to be with the *Nettastomidæ.*

Genus 46. SERRIVOMER Gill & Ryder.

Nemichthyids with the head behind eyes of an elongated parallelogramic form, with moderately attenuated jaws; branchiostegal membranes confluent at posterior margin, but with the branchial aperture limited by an isthmus except at the margin, and with lancet-shaped vomerine teeth in a crowded (sometimes doubled) row. A single Hawaiian species. (See Section II.)

Family XXXI. OPHICHTHYIDÆ.—The Snake Eels.

This family includes those scaleless enchelycephalous eels with end of the tail projecting beyond dorsal and anal fins; without rudiment of a caudal fin; with anterior nostrils placed in upper lip, opening downward; gill-openings not confluent; tongue more or less fully adnate to floor of mouth. The species are, for the most part, moderate or small in size, and they are very abundant in the tropical seas, especially about coral reefs. The eggs are numerous, of moderate size, similar to those of ordinary fishes. Genera about 12; species nearly 100. Many of the species are singularly colored, the bands or spots heightening the analogy between them and the serpents.

Only 8 species of this large family are thus far known from the Hawaiian Islands.

Genus 47. SPHAGEBRANCHUS Bloch.

This genus contains several little-known species of small eels, remarkable for showing no trace of fins in the adult stage. The snout projects beyond the small mouth, giving a shark-like profile, and the small teeth are mostly uniserial. The gill-slits are inferior and converging. The name *Sphagebranchus* was based on a species which evidently belongs to the genus. It has therefore clear priority over *Ichthyapus* and *Apterichthys.*

This genus is the most simple in structure among the *Ophichthyidæ,* as *Ophichthus* is probably the most specialized. The loss of fins is doubtless due to degeneration, but *Sphagebranchus* seems nearer the primitive type than *Brachysomophis* or *Ophichthus.*

34. Sphagebranchus flavicaudus Snyder. Plate 5, fig. 2.

Head, measured to upper edge of gill-opening, 18 in length, 9.5 in trunk including head, 8.3 in tail; depth 3.9 in head; snout 5.5. Snout long, slender, and sharp, projecting beyond upper jaw, tip of latter reaching beyond eye a distance equal to diameter of pupil; eye midway between tip of snout and angle of mouth, its diameter contained 3 times in length of snout; anterior nostril with a short tube on ventral side of snout a little nearer its tip than to border of eye; posterior nostril without tube, placed below anterior margin of eye; upper lip with a fold extending from nostril to angle of mouth; teeth of jaws in a single series; a group of 4 canines at end of upper jaw, all being beyond end of lower jaw when it is closed; a few sharp teeth on anterior part of vomer; gill-openings inferior, converging, the distance between them about equal to diameter of eye; width of gill-opening 7.9 in head; no fins; tail pointed.

Color in alcohol, pale olive, the tail nearly white.

The description is from the type, No. 50863, U. S. Nat. Mus., 14.45 inches long. Two examples from off the northeast coast of Hawaii. One from station 4055, depth 50 to 60 fathoms (cotype, 7509, L. S. Jr. Univ. Mus.), measures 9.6 inches. The head 17 in length, 10 in head and trunk. In life it was pinkish anteriorly, the posterior third tinged with lemon-yellow. The other specimen, from station 4061, depth 24 to 83 fathoms, measures 8.66 inches; head 15.4 in length, 8.3 in head and trunk. In life the color was light orange, fading to lemon-yellow posteriorly; an indistinct, light, median, dorsal stripe extending from occiput to tip of tail; ventral surface slightly tinged with purple, the tint extending about twice the length of head beyond anal opening; side of head with 2 white spots, the anterior one just behind eyes, the posterior one indistinctly connected over the occiput with its fellow on opposite side.

Genus 48. LEIURANUS Bleeker.

Body cylindrical; mouth small, below the sharp, projecting snout; teeth pointed, of moderate size, uniserial in jaws; no teeth on vomer; eye small; pectoral small; dorsal and anal low, the former beginning nearly above gill-opening.

Small eels, having the bright colors of *Chlevastes*, but in technical respects nearer *Ophichthus*, distinguished by the absence of vomerine teeth.

35. Leiuranus semicinctus (Lay & Bennett).

Head 6.25 in trunk; tail a little longer than trunk without head; eye about 2 in snout, 1.67 in interorbital space; snout about 6 in head; interorbital space 7.3; mouth from tip of snout 3.5; pectoral about 7.

Body more or less rounded and rather slender, the tail tapering posteriorly to a conical horny point; head pointed, rather thick and swollen; snout short, depressed, flattened, and shark-like in appearance, with the edges more or less thin; eyes small, and placed wholly before the corners of mouth; teeth in jaws in a single series, pointed, and hooked backward; no vomerine teeth; tongue adnate to floor of mouth, small; mandible small, its tip, when mouth is closed, very much nearer anterior margin of eye than tip of snout; anterior nostrils in small tubes, inferior, on lower surface of snout and opening downward; posterior nostrils large, in the lips, and opening downward; interorbital space very slightly convex, nearly flat; skin smooth; the head about the branchial region more or less wrinkled; head with a few mucous pores, those in the lateral series from head about 147; origin of dorsal about over middle of pectoral; dorsal and anal low; pectoral small and short.

Color in alcohol, whitish, with 24 deep brown broad cross-blotches, the first 2 on top of head much narrower than the others, those on trunk becoming narrower, most of them anteriorly not meeting below, and those on tail meeting more or less perfectly below; tips of snout and tail white.

This species was not obtained by us in Hawaii, but it has been recorded from those islands by Lay and Bennett, by Fowler, and by Snyder. The above description is based upon a specimen (No. 6642, Stanford University Museum) 17.5 inches long, obtained by Jordan and Snyder at Yaeyama, Ishigaka Islands, in the southern Riu Kiu Archipelago. It was also found by Jordan and Kellogg at Samoa.

Genus 49. MICRODONOPHIS Kaup.

Body more or less rounded; head and trunk much longer than tail, which is more or less rounded and pointed; head rounded; snout pointed and projecting; teeth large and somewhat canine-like, in one row on vomer; nostrils anterior, each in a small tube, the posterior pair opening in the lips downward; pores of lateral line continuous; dorsal beginning over gill-opening or origin of pectoral; pectoral short. Coloration variegated with rather large dark spots, those on the head small, absent in *M. macgregori*. Only two species known from Hawaii.

36. Microdonophis fowleri Jordan & Evermann. Plate 6.

Head about 4.8 in trunk, measured from gill-opening to vent; tail shorter than head and trunk by the length of the former; eye nearly 1.6 in snout or 1.5 in interorbital space; snout 6 in head; interorbital space about 6.75; mouth 2.75; pectoral a little over 4.25 in head.

Body elongate, cylindrical, the tail tapering gradually to a conical horny point; head cylindrical and pointed; snout moderately long and pointed, slightly flattened above, projecting over and beyond the mandible; eye elongate, small, anterior and superior, about midway in length of mouth; mouth rather large; lips somewhat fringed; teeth large and canine-like in front of jaws, and on vomer in a single row; tongue small, adnate to floor of mouth; anterior nostrils in short tubes near tip of snout, the posterior with broad flaps on the lips and opening downward; interorbital space concave, each supraocular ridge slightly elevated; peritoneum silvery; skin perfectly smooth; head with mucous pores, a series of which encircle the head above and about midway in its length; lateral line well developed, the pores about 140; origin of dorsal slightly in advance of gill-opening or base of pectoral; pectoral small, the rays just above the middle the longest, the fin rounded; dorsal fin long and low, its height about equal to length of snout; anal similar to dorsal, its height a trifle less.

General color, when fresh, white, rendered somewhat shaded on upper portions by very minute points (seen only with a good lens) of gray; back and upper surface with numerous round brown spots and about 17 indistinct transverse dark brown cross-bands which do not extend over the dorsal; interspaces between spots on head yellow; pectoral bright lemon-yellow; end of tail for about 1 inch from point bright yellow; spots on margin of dorsal brown, with yellow borders; a band of yellow from under one eye backward, upward, across top of head, and down under the other eye; a transverse series of pores with black margins encircles head above and about midway in its length, a similar series over head along margin of mouth, then up, back of eye, over head; pores of lateral line without black margins.

Three specimens of this species are now known, the type (No. 50613, U. S. Nat. Mus.), a specimen 23 inches long, obtained by us in the Honolulu market, another example obtained by the *Albatross* in the Honolulu market, and a third specimen recently received from Mr. E. L. Berndt.

37. Microdonophis macgregori Jenkins. Fig. 18.

Head 4.8 in trunk; head and trunk 1.75 in tail; eye 2 in snout, a little over one in interorbital space; snout 5.2 in head; mouth from tip of snout 3; pectoral 3.5.

Body more or less rounded, rather slender, the tail tapering posteriorly to a conical horny point; head elongate, pointed, somewhat compressed; snout small, well produced beyond mandible, pointed, and conical; eye small, much nearer corner of mouth than tip of snout or midway between tip of mandible and corner of mouth; mandible broad; lip of upper jaw with a fringe of short fleshy barbels; teeth sharp, pointed, in a single series on vomer and in jaws; nostrils anteriorly in conspicuous fleshy tubes on lower surface of snout in front; interorbital space a little more than the eye and convex; gill-openings low, the space between rather broad; skin smooth; head with many mucous pores; lateral line well developed; origin of dorsal midway in length of head; dorsal and anal low; pectoral rather small.

Color in alcohol, brownish olive; lower surface light yellowish washed with silvery; upper surface of body dark, being covered with minute blackish dots.

This species is probably the type of a new genus, *Jenkinsiella*, characterized by the fringe of short

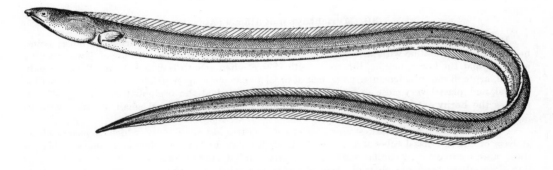

FIG. 18.—*Microdonophis macgregori* Jenkins; from the type.

fleshy barbels on upper lip. The only known specimen is an example 10.5 inches long obtained by Mr. Richard C. McGregor, February 1, 1900, at Lahaina, Maui; type, No. 50721, U. S. Nat. Mus.

Genus 50. BRACHYSOMOPHIS Kaup.

This genus differs from *Mystriophis* chiefly in the presence of a conspicuous fringe of papillæ on the lips. The vomerine teeth are canine. Species chiefly East Indian; one recently described from the Hawaiian Islands.

38. Brachysomophis henshawi Jordan & Snyder. Plate 7.

Head measured to gill-opening, 7.5 in total length, 3.8 in length to vent; depth 2.5 in head; eye 1.5 in snout; snout 10 in head.

Body cylindrical, the head greatly depressed, swollen laterally in the region of the occiput, narrowing anteriorly to the pointed snout; a conspicuous transverse depression in the postorbital region; interorbital space concave, its width equal to length of snout; a slight supraorbital crest ending in a prominent wart-like protuberance behind eye; nostrils with minute tubes, the anterior located midway between tip of snout and eye, the posterior on lip between eye and anterior nostril; mouth large, length of cleft 2.9 in head; lower jaw projecting beyond the upper; outer edge of lips with a row of rather course papillæ; teeth of upper jaw in 2 rows, the outer ones small and close-set, the inner ones larger; vomer with a single row of 5 or 6 widely spaced canines, the anterior of which is about equal in length to diameter of eye, the others growing successively smaller; tip of jaw with 3 minute teeth separated from the lateral rows by a wide space; lower jaw with a single row of widely spaced fang-like teeth; teeth all sharply pointed, many of those in each jaw depressible; no tongue; gill-openings below middle of body, their length equal to width of space between them, or to distance between tip of snout and posterior border of eye; one-fourth of base of pectoral above gill-opening; length of pectoral equal to distance between tip of snout and center of pupil; dorsal inserted behind gill-opening a distance contained 2 times in space between gill-opening and pupil; height of fin a short distance behind its origin about equal to diameter of pupil, slighly higher in region above vent; origin of anal just behind vent; height of fin equal to that of dorsal; both dorsal and anal become low on posterior part of tail; the membranes growing thick, passing into slight ridges and finally disappearing near tip of tail.

A row of large mucous tubes passing over head in the depression behind eye; 6 conspicuous tubes on top of head, 4 being on the interorbital region, 2 on the snout; 4 tubes on upper lip; anterior ends of lateral lines connected by a curved row of tubes passing over occiput; about 125 tubes in lateral line, the posterior ones very small.

Color gray, with a yellowish tint; a few brownish-black spots about as large as pupil thinly scattered above the lateral line, the mucous pores on anterior part of body edged with blackish; dorsal brownish black, with a broad marginal band of white, posterior part of fin without dark color; anal immaculate.

One specimen 20 inches long, type, No. 51399, U. S. Nat. Mus., Honolulu. Collector, Mr. E. L. Berndt. Named for Henry W. Henshaw, the well-known naturalist, now resident at Hilo, Hawaii, to whom we are indebted for several rare specimens.

The large Japanese eel described by Schlegel as *Ophisurus porphyreus* has the lips fringed and should be referred to *Brachysomophis* instead of *Mystriophis*. It may stand as *Brachysomophis porphyreus*.

Genus 51. MYRICHTHYS Girard.

Teeth mostly blunt and molar; pectoral fins small; dorsal beginning on the head before gill-opening; otherwise essentially as in *Ophichthus*. Coloration variegated. Species numerous, found in most tropical seas, one known from the Hawaiian Islands, another from Johnston Island.

39. Myrichthys magnificus (Abbott).

Body cylindrical, tapering very gradually to tail, which terminates in a conico-acute horny point; head small, facial outline with an oblique curvature; snout rather obtuse, with upper jaw extending much beyond the lower, making the nasal teeth visible when mouth is closed; teeth all very small, conical, acute, 6 standing irregularly on disk of nasal bone; teeth upon palate, vomer, and mandible biserial, and placed very close to each other; dorsal inserted at the occiput, terminating before it reaches the horny extremity of tail; anal coterminal with dorsal; pectoral small, circular, with 20 rays.

Color in alcohol, pink, darkest upon back; color nearly lost upon belly, which is nearly white; at base of anterior nasal tubes 2 very small dark chocolate-brown semicircular spots, and behind these, anterior to orbits, 2 similar markings, but larger and deeper in color; commencing at the insertion of dorsal are 2 series of spots of chocolate-color, separated only by that fin, and, if viewed from above, having the appearance of transverse bands, though they are not directly opposite in every case; upon the sides is a single series of spots of the tints of the dorsal markings, two-thirds the width of side, measuring from base of dorsal to center of belly; upon the belly are 3 rows of small circular spots which are very irregular as to position.

This description, modified from Dr. C. C. Abbott, is based upon 2 specimens, the larger having a total length of 19 inches (8 inches from snout to anus, or 1.5 to gill-opening), collected in the Hawaiian Islands by Dr. J. K. Townsend in 1835. The species was not obtained by us.

40. Myrichthys stypurus (Smith & Swain). Fig. 19.

Head 5.3 in trunk; head and trunk together slightly longer than tail, exceeding the latter by length of snout; snout blunt, 5.5 in head; eye 2.5 in snout, 3 in interorbital space; gape of mouth moderate, extending beyond eye, 3.5 in head; anterior nasal tubes turned downward, conspicuous; posterior nostrils large; teeth in lower jaw less blunt than in *M. xysturus* Jordan & Gilbert, in 2 series in front, becoming 3 posteriorly; 2 rows (the outer row being larger) of bluntish, conical teeth on each side of upper jaw, preceded by a patch of 8 on extremity of nasal bone; smaller teeth on vomer in a band of 2 series; dorsal and anal fins rather high, the highest part of dorsal exceeding length of snout; dorsal beginning at nape, at a distance from snout equal to half of length of head; pectoral short, 1.5 in its base, 1.75 in snout, its free margin lunate; gill-opening oblique, its width equaling base of pectoral and 1.75 in isthmus; end of tail rather blunt and little compressed.

Ground color, in spirits, light olivaceous; round brown spots in 4 series on side, extending on dorsal but becoming fainter on fin; second series on lateral line, the spots of third mostly smaller; spots of different series sometimes alternating regularly, sometimes without definite order; diameter of most of spots in upper 2 series exceeding snout; a fourth series of much smaller spots (not half the

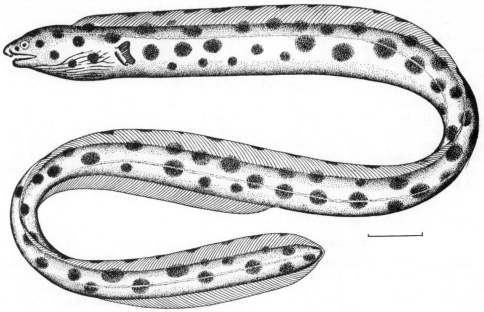

Fig. 19.—*Myrichthys stypurus* (Smith & Swain); from the type.

diameter of largest ones) along side of belly, almost disappearing on tail; small, irregular, more or less confluent spots on upper half of dorsal, the fin narrowly margined with whitish; anal plain, light olivaceous; pectoral with 1 or 2 small, obscure, brown spots.

One fine specimen (No. 26817, U. S. Nat. Mus.), 24.25 inches in length, was taken at Johnston Island, about 700 miles southwest of the Hawaiian Islands, in the spring of 1880, by the captain of a vessel belonging to the North Pacific Guano Company.

Genus 52. CALLECHELYS Kaup.

Short oval head; straight depressed snout, and very depressed mandible; fore nostril tube dependent, the hinder one situated under the eye and furnished with a small flap; no pectorals; highly developed dorsal; less expanded anal; only a solitary nasal tooth, which is large, elongated, blunt, and inclined backward; 8 teeth implanted in the elliptical palatine bone, short, slender, and curved; about 10 vomerines, of which the 6 anterior ones are stouter, and are arranged in two rows; 24 teeth stand on the entire border of the mandible. (Kaup.) This genus contains one American, three East Indian, and one Hawaiian species, which agree in the elongate, compressed body, absence of pectoral fins, and the anterior insertion of the dorsal. In other respects *Callechelys* is close to *Ophichthus*.

41. Callechelys luteus Snyder. Plate 8, fig. 1.

Head, measured to upper edge of gill-opening, 16.6 in length, 10.5 in head and trunk, 6.7 in tail; snout 7.1 in head; cleft of mouth 3.4. Body extremely long and slender, tapering gradually from head to tail; depth at gill-opening 2.7 in head; width of body 1.4 in depth; gill-pouches greatly expanded, making head deeper and broader than body; snout sharp, projecting two-thirds of its length beyond lower jaw; eye midway between tip of snout and angle of mouth; tongue small, free on sides and at tip; teeth on jaws and vomer projecting backward, movable though not depressible; 3 large canines just posterior to nostril tubes, the median one being anterior to tip of lower jaw; 2 short rows of teeth on vomer, a single row on maxillaries and on lower jaw; anterior nostril with a tube equal in length to diameter of eye, inferior in position, halfway between tip of snout and end of closed lower jaw; posterior nostrils on lip, below the eye, provided with an anterior, valve-like flap; gill-openings slit-like, inferior, distance between lower edges of openings equal to half the length of snout; width of gill-opening equal to distance from tip of snout to posterior border of eye. Dorsal inserted on occiput above angle of mouth; height at a point above gill-slit equal to distance between tip of snout and posterior border of eye, above anal opening equal to width of gill-slit; fin not reaching tip of tail; membrane thin, the rays being distinctly visible; anal inserted immediately behind vent, its height equal to half the width of gill-opening; tip of tail sharp, there being no caudal fin; pectorals absent.

Color in alcohol, white, rather finely blotched with brownish black, the spots not so numerous on ventral surface as elsewhere; fins colored like body. In life, the upper parts, including dorsal fin, are white, mottled with black and lemon-yellow; under parts white, rather sparsely mottled with black, except on throat, where the spots are numerous.

One example, 22.3 inches long, caught while swimming about the ship at night, attracted by the lights.

Type, No. 50864, U. S. Nat. Mus., southern coast of Molokai.

Family XXXII. MORINGUIDÆ.

Body cylindrical, more or less slender, the tail much shorter than rest of body, usually bluntish, with a fin at the top. Posterior nostrils in front of the small eye; mouth small; teeth small, uniserial; gill-openings rather narrow, inferior; heart placed far behind the gills; pectorals small or wanting; dorsal fin low, mostly confined to the tail. Small eels of the tropical seas, often very slender or worm-like, and noted for the extreme shortness of the tail. The genera are closely related and 2 of them, *Moringua* (=*Raitaboura*=*Stilbiscus*) and *Aphthalmichthys*, are found in the West Indies as well as in the East.

Genus 53. MORINGUA Gray.

Characters included with those of the family.

42. Moringua hawaiiensis Snyder.   Plate 8, fig. 2.

Head, measured to gill-opening, 15.4 in length; tail 3.3; depth 4.16 in head. Body cylindrical and extremely elongate, the tail tapering to a sharp point; snout pointed, its length 6.7 in head; lower jaw projecting beyond upper a distance equal to diameter of pupil; cleft of mouth extending beyond eye a distance equal to pupil; teeth on jaws and vomer sharp, long, and fang-like anteriorly; tongue adnate to floor of mouth; eye very small, the diameter equal to about 5 in snout; gill-opening a vertical slit, equal to 1.7 in length of snout; lateral line slightly arched above branchial chamber, discontinued about a head's length from tip of tail; number of pores 113. Pectorals present, minute, the rays easily distinguishable; the base equal to half the gill-opening, length a little less than diameter of pupil; dorsal and anal fins scarcely developed, indicated by slight ridges commencing about a head's length behind anal opening, growing larger and more distinct in region where lateral line ceases; caudal fin distinct, pointed, its length equal to width of interorbital space.

Color in alcohol pale brown, no spots or bars.

One specimen, 12.6 inches long, from Honolulu reef. Type, No. 50865, U. S. Nat. Mus.

Closely related to *M. javanicus* of the East Indies, but differing from that species as described in having pectoral fins with distinct rays, longer head, and longer tail.

Family XXXIII. MURÆNIDÆ.—The Morays.

The *Murænidæ* represent the most degenerate type of eels so far as the skeleton is concerned, and they are doubtless the farthest removed from the more typical fishes from which the eels have descended. The essential characters of the family are thus stated by Dr. Gill:

"Colocephalous Apodals with conic head, fully developed opercular apparatus, long and wide ethmoid, posterior maxillines, pauciserial teeth, roundish, lateral branchial apertures, diversiform vertical fins, pectoral fins (typically) suppressed, scaleless skin, restricted interbranchial slits and very imperfect branchial skeleton, with the fourth branchial arch modified, strengthened, and supporting pharyngeal jaws."

The morays may be readily distinguished from other eels by their small round gill-openings and by the absence of pectorals. The body and fins are covered by a thick, leathery skin, the occipital region is elevated through the development of the strong muscles which move the lower jaw, and the jaws are usually narrow and armed with knife-like or else molar teeth. These eels inhabit tropical and subtropical waters, being especially abundant in crevices about coral reefs. Many of the species reach a large size and all are voracious and pugnacious. The coloration is usually strongly marked, the color-cells being highly specialized. We exclude from the *Murænidæ* the genus *Myroconger*, from St. Helena, which has pectoral fins and is probably the type of a distant family. The remaining species are referable to 10 or 12 genera, most of which are found in America. About 120 species are known. The *Murænidæ* without fins are the simplest in structure, but their characters are those of degradation, and they are farther from the primitive stock than such genera as *Muræna* or *Enchelycore*.

Genus 54. MURÆNA Linnæus.

This genus, as now restricted, contains some 10 species, found in tropical seas, distinguished from *Gymnothorax* and from the rest of the family by the presence of 2 pairs of nasal barbels. The name

Muræna, originally applied to all eels, should be restricted to the group typified by *Muræna helena*. It was first limited by Thunberg & Ahl, in 1789, to the eels without pectoral fins, those with such fins being set off as *Ophichthus*. The nominal species of the following key are doubtless color variations of a single species.

43. Muræna kailuæ Jordan & Evermann.   Plate 9 and Figs. 20 and 21.

"Puhi oa;" "Puhi kauila."

Head 7 in total length; depth 11.5; eye 14 in head; snout 6; interorbital 12; gape 2.75.

Body short, stout, and moderately compressed; distance from tip of snout to vent less than that from vent to tip of tail by a distance equal to two-thirds length of head; head very small and pointed; snout long, quadrate, the jaws equal, the lower curved so that the mouth does not completely close; lips thin, the teeth showing; each side of upper jaw with a single series of unequal, sharpish canine-like teeth, inside of which is a single depressible fang-like tooth near middle of side; front of median line with 2 long, sharp, fang-like, depressible teeth; shaft of vomer with a single series of short, movable teeth; each side of lower jaw with a single series of unequal, sharp canines, those in front largest; eye small, midway between angle of mouth and tip of snout; anterior nostrils each in a pointed filament whose length is about half that of eye, situated at tip of snout just above lip; posterior nostrils each

Fig. 20.—*Muræna kailuæ* Jordan & Evermann.   Type of *M. lampra* Jenkins.

with a long filament, equal to snout in length, and situated just above anterior edge of eye; inter orbital space very narrow and flat; gill-opening small, nearly circular; dorsal fin very low anteriorly, increasing much in height on tail; anal low.

Ground color in life, dark brown, with fine yellow and blackish spots and reticulating lines, the yellow predominating on anterior part of body; end of tail dark purplish brown; edge of dorsal and anal dull dark red, with short pale bands bordered with darker and with small pale spots interspersed; ground color of cheek and throat yellow, with pale spots bordered with black; jaw orange red, with pale black-edged bars; tips of jaws bright coral red; tips of nostril filaments bright red.

Color in alcohol, body with a ground color of light grayish brown, marked with fine whitish lines or specks, and profusely covered with numerous small, round, white spots, each ocellated with black; among these are scattered larger black spots and blotches; white spots smallest on back and largest on belly, where some are as large as eye; a broad, dark brown bar over nape, extending on side to level of eye; top of head and snout with fine white spots; side of snout with a well-defined vertical white bar about midway between eye and tip; a short white line downward to mouth from front of eye, and a similar longer one downward and backward from posterior lower angle of eye; lower jaw crossed by 3 V-shaped white bars opening forward and bordered by darker; tip of jaw with 2 oblique white bars separated by a narrow brown line; last V-shaped white bar extending across angle of mouth and forming a large white area at base of upper jaw, behind which the angle of the mouth is dark brown; inside of mouth mottled brown and white; nasal filaments mottled with brown and white; throat light brown, with large white spots, some of which unite to form oblong spots or lines; gill-opening not surrounded by dark; anal fin dark brown, crossed by about 28 short white bars; posterior portion of tail crossed by about 12 distinct but somewhat irregular vertical white bars, which extend upon dorsal and anal fins; tip of tail brownish black, with 1 or 2 whitish specks.

We have examined the following specimens of this form: The type, from Kailua, Hawaii; a specimen sent from Laysan Island by Mr. Max Schlemmer; one from Honolulu, sent by Mr. E. L. Berndt; one collected by the *Albatross* at Honolulu, and another at station 3881, in Napili Harbor, Maui.

This species is subject to great variations, especially in color. The form described by Jenkins as *Muræna lampra* has been described as follows:

Head 3.25 in trunk; head and trunk 2.25 in tail; eye 1.67 in snout; interorbital space 1.5 in eye; snout about 5.3 in head; mouth about 2.2.

Body rather short, deep, compressed, the tail tapering posteriorly; head elongate, deep, compressed; snout long, conical, pointed, tip rounded, not produced; eyes lateral, much nearer corners of

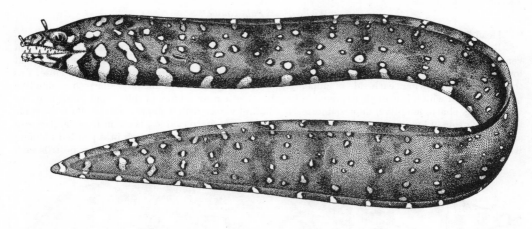

FIG. 21.—*Muræna kailuæ* Jordan & Evermann. Type of *M. kauila* Jenkins.

mouth than tip of snout; jaws rather large, equal, mouth not completely closing, so that some of the teeth are always more or less visible; teeth in jaws varying, some of them more or less fang-like, in 2 series in upper jaw posteriorly, the inner enlarged and depressible; vomer with 2 large depressible fangs in front, followed by a median series of small teeth; nostrils all in tubes, the posterior pair about as long as eye; interorbital space very narrow; gill-openings small, about midway in depth of body; head with a number of pores; origin of dorsal about over last third of space between corner of mouth and gill-opening, the fin rather high, decreasing posteriorly; anal similar to dorsal; caudal small and confluent with dorsal and anal.

Color in life, very bright, the groundwork of light brown, with conspicuous white spots intermingled with black and brown spots; 3 longitudinal rows of white spots on body, one row on outer margin of dorsal and a row of large white spots or blotches across the ventral surface, largest between head and anal fin; black as well as brown spots small, irregularly placed, but generally following the line of rows of white spots; very brilliant red on snout and jaws; no dark margin to gill-opening.

The above description is based upon the type (No. 50680, U. S. Nat. Mus.), a specimen 7.75 inches long, collected in 1889 by Dr. Jenkins from the coral reef in front of Honolulu. Another example (No. 03709), 19 inches long, was obtained for us at Kailua, Hawaii, by Mr. Goldsborough.

The form called *Muræna kauila* by Jenkins is described as follows:

Head 7.3; depth 16; tail a little longer than head and trunk; snout 4 in head; eye 1.5 in snout; interorbital 2.25; mouth 2 in head.

Body elongate, compressed; tail tapering posteriorly; head elongate, pointed, sides swollen a little above behind eyes; snout long, slightly convex in profile; mouth large; jaw arched, not completely closing, upper slightly the longer; teeth uniserial in jaws, compressed, with long canines with intervening smaller teeth; 2 large depressible canines on vomer; 3 or 4 large depressible canines below eye, forming an inner series on each side of upper jaw; lips thin, not concealing teeth when mouth is closed; eye about midway in length of mouth; nostrils in long tubes, the posterior larger, equal to eye; interorbital space flattened; gill-opening small, 0.75 in eye; roof of mouth with a single median series of small teeth beginning below front margin of eye and running back well beyond its posterior margin; dorsal beginning nearly midway between corner of mouth and gill-opening; caudal small, rounded.

Color in life, light brown, with 2 longitudinal rows of dark brown spots about the diameter of snout gradually fading into one row on the posterior portion of the tail; many clear white spots as large, or larger than pupil, over head, body, fins, and tail, many of the spots forming more or less distinct vertical rows over fins and dorsal portions, some confluent on throat and belly, each one surrounded by a dark-brown margin; about 30 white spots crossing the ventral line; nasal tubes bright red; bright red bars on snout and lower jaw, and bright red undulations posterior to angle of mouth.

Color in alcohol, brown, with the white and dark brown spots distinct; white spots edged with dark brown; bright red undulations posterior to angle of mouth fading out.

A single specimen, the type, No. 50684, U. S. Nat. Mus. (original No. 304), 13 inches long, taken by Dr. Jenkins from the coral rocks on the reef at Honolulu in 1889.   The *Albatross* also obtained an example at station 3881, Napili Harbor, Maui, in 1902.

Genus 55. ENCHELYNASSA Kaup.

Fore nostril funnel-shaped and capable of being shut up by a valvular elongation of its hinder border.   Hinder nostril nearly-as big as the eye, with a raised border.   Rictus of the jaws open in the middle.   Nasal bone reaching as far back as the middle of eye, armed with 27 teeth on its circumference, a pairless one in the middle and 5 longer ones, between the second and third of which stand 3 or 4 small ones, between the third and fourth 4 small ones, and between the fourth and fifth 1 small one.   Palatines 16, whereof the second, onward to the sixth, are supported before and behind by small teeth; on the inner row there are 9 longer acicular teeth.   On the mesial line 3.   On the vomerine no more than 2 small conical toothlets visible.   Mandibulars, 22 smaller ones in the outer, and 6 to 8 longer in the inner row, approximated to the symphysis.   The eyes are situated above the middle of the jaws.   There are 4 pores on the upper jaw and mandible difficult to find in the porous skin.   (Kaup.)

This genus is distinguished from *Gymnothorax* by the enlarged and dilated posterior nostril, which suggests the nostril of a horse.   The teeth are very numerous, some of them being long and sharp, as in the Japanese genus *Æmaria*.   These are morays of huge size, found in the Pacific, perhaps all belonging to one species; but if so, the variation in the number of teeth is considerable.

44. Enchelynassa bleekeri Kaup.   Plate 10.

Head, measured to gill-opening, 7.1 in the length; depth 9; snout 5.5 in head; eye 3 in snout; interorbital space 1.5; cleft of mouth 1.75 in head; origin of dorsal on a vertical passing midway between angle of mouth and gill-opening; height of fin about equal to length of snout, the membrane very thick and fleshy; anal arising immediately behind vent, its height equal to one-half the length of snout; both dorsal and anal continuous with the very short caudal; tail slightly longer than head and body; anterior nostril located at a point one-third the distance between tip of snout and border of eye, the edge with a low, thickened rim and a posterior flap edged with tentacles; posterior nostril situated on dorsal side of snout midway between anterior nostril and eye, the opening oval, surrounded by a broad, thin membrane; teeth lanceolate-canines, the lateral notches not evident on some of the smaller ones; those of upper jaw in 2 rows, the inner ones larger, their length about equal to two-thirds the diameter of eye; a row of 4 or 5 long teeth on vomer, followed by a short row of small teeth; anterior vomerine teeth and those of inner series of jaw depressible; teeth of lower jaw in 2 series, the inner row having 4 or 5 large, depressible ones; width of gill-opening equal to or slightly more than half the length of snout.

Color in alcohol, brownish, with a few small, darker spots scattered over the body.

A very large example, 52 inches long, apparently identical with the scantily described *Enchelynassa bleekeri* of Kaup, was obtained at Honolulu.   Another, equally large, was taken at Samoa in 1902.

45. Enchelynassa vinolentus (Jordan & Evermann).   Plate 11.[a]

Head 2.67 in trunk; head and trunk a little shorter than tail; eye 2 in snout, 1.5 in interorbital space; snout 6.5 in head; mouth about 2.

Body compressed, rather deep; head compressed, pointed, more or less swollen on top; snout long, pointed, bent over at tip; eye small, much nearer tip of snout than corner of mouth; mandible long, projecting beyond tip of snout and bent up, the mouth not closing so that only the tips of the jaws meet; lips rather thin, not concealing the teeth; teeth biserial, of more or less irregular size, those in inner series much larger and also depressible like the few large vomerine fangs; anterior nostrils in rather large tubes, situated 0.67 of an eye diameter from tip of snout, and the posterior nostrils at some little distance above and anterior to front margin of eye, with their rims somewhat expanded and flattened down; interorbital space convex; gill-opening about 0.75 of an eye diameter; body more or less smooth and with thick, tough skin; head with a number of pores; origin of dorsal well before gill-opening, or about last third or fourth of space between corner of mouth and the latter; marginal fin around end of tail rather narrow.

Color in alcohol, deep purplish brown, marked all over with very small indistinct darker spots so that it appears almost uniform.

The collections contain a single specimen, type, No. 50615, U. S. Nat. Mus. (original No. 03726), 29 inches long, obtained by Messrs. Goldsborough and Sindo at Kailua, Hawaii.   The species may be identical with *Enchelynassa bleekeri* Kaup, but its larger teeth, distinct nasal flap, and higher dorsal and anal fins seem to indicate its distinctness.

---

[a]Plate labeled *Gymnothorax vinolentus*.

Genus 56. GYMNOTHORAX Bloch & Schneider.   The Morays.   "*Puhi.*"

This genus, as here understood, comprises the great bulk of the *Murænidæ*, including nearly all the species with sharp teeth, the body normally formed, only the anterior nostrils tubular, and the dorsal fin beginning on the head.   *Priodonophis*, with serrated teeth, has been recognized as a distinct genus by Bleeker, but the character in question disappears by degrees and seems not to be suitable for generic distinction.   The morays of this genus are everywhere abundant in the tropical seas, where some of them reach a great size.   They are the most active and voracious of the eels, often showing much pugnacity.   Most of them live in shallow water about rocks or reefs.

46. Gymnothorax eurostus (Abbott).

Head large, depressed; the facial outline very slightly oblique; eye large, circular, slightly behind extremity of snout, and 1.5 diameters distant; jaws of equal length, rather slender, the lower with a slight upward curve at its extremity making the large mandibular teeth partially visible when mouth is closed; nasal teeth 10, biserial, the inner row twice as large as the outer, conical, acute, and with a decided inward inclination; palatine teeth, 28 in the outer row, 9 in the inner, the former short, very much compressed, acute and with an inward inclination; the inner series widely set, of various lengths, and more than twice as large as those of outer row, a gape in the series beginning posteriorly opposite posterior margin of orbit and ceasing opposite anterior edge of orbit; vomerine teeth 12, 9 of which are in a direct line, the remaining 3 concurrent with the central 3 of the series; lower jaw armed with a complement of 24 compressed, acute teeth having a decidedly inward inclination, the posterior 12 of these closely set in an unbroken series, and the anterior 12 arranged in pairs, except at the extremity of the jaw where they form 2 square patches of 4 teeth; fold of skin enveloping dorsal fin very thick, and arising behind occiput nearly perpendicularly; fin of uniform height for two-thirds its length, thence slowly decreasing to its termination.

Color in alcohol, head and body uniform reddish brown, nearly black upon the under surface of tail; body everywhere minutely spotted and reticulated with pale yellowish.   (Abbott.)

This species is known only from Abbott's type (No. 984, Ac. Nat. Sci. Phila.), a specimen collected in 1835 by Dr. J. K. Townsend in the Hawaiian Islands, measuring 13.5 inches in length, and 1.5 inches from tip of snout to gill-opening, or 6 inches to anus.

47. Gymnothorax laysanus (Steindachner).   Plate 12 and Fig. 22.

Head 2.3 in trunk; tail longer than head by the length of the latter without eye and snout; eye 1.67 in snout, 1.5 in interorbital space; snout 6 in head; interorbital space 7; mouth 2 and an eye diameter in head.

Body rather deep and compressed; tail tapering at its extremity to a rather sharp point; head pointed and compressed; snout pointed, the tip rounded; eye rather small, much nearer corner of mouth than tip of snout; mouth horizontal and jaws equal; teeth in jaws biserial, the inner series the larger and depressible; vomerine teeth pointed and in a single series; each jaw with some enlarged canines in front, which are depressible; anterior nostril in small tube at tip of snout; posterior nostril

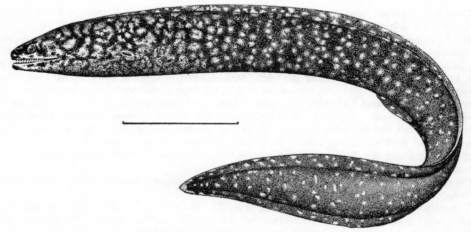

FIG. 22.—*Gymnothorax laysanus* (Steindachner).

over front of eye above; gill-openings smaller than eye; body more or less smooth; head with few pores; origin of dorsal a little nearer corner of mouth than gill-opening; fin around end of tail more or less pointed.

Color in alcohol, dark brown above; belly and lower surface pale; everywhere reticulated, speckled or mottled with darker, or blackish brown on upper portions. The above description is from a specimen (No. 04913) 10 inches long, from Honolulu. The species shows considerable variation in color and other characters with age.

Color in life (No. 03357), brown, profusely covered with rather large roundish black spots, interspersed among which are more numerous and much smaller white specks, these more or less uniformly distributed over the body and fins; edges of dorsal and anal fins darker; tip of caudal narrowly edged with white.

The young may be described as follows, from a specimen 4.5 inches long (No. 04916), taken on the reef at Honolulu, August 15, 1901.

Head 2 in trunk; head and trunk about 1.3 in tail; eye about 1.5 in snout, 1 in interorbital space; snout 5 in head; mouth 2 and a little less than an eye diameter in head.

Body elongate and compressed; head moderately compressed laterally, pointed; neck swollen and a little thicker than body; snout short, bluntly rounded, rather deep; eye small, anterior, about midway between tip of snout and corner of mouth; mouth large, jaws nearly equal, or snout only very slightly protruding and when closed the lips entirely concealing the teeth; teeth in 2 rows along edges of upper jaw extending posteriorly to eye at least; teeth in mandible in a single series, very unequal and anteriorly from the symphysis about 4 enlarged canines forming a short inner series; vomer with 2 large fangs, the posterior the larger; anterior nostril in a short fleshy tube; interorbital space rather flat; gill-openings small; body smooth, a few longitudinal wrinkles about branchial region of head; head with a number of pores, especially along upper jaw; origin of dorsal well anterior to gill-opening; dorsal and anal each rather high; caudal ending in a rounded point.

Color in alcohol, dark brown, variegated with 4 rows of longitudinal whitish spots, the third or series next to lowest not continued to end of tail; a number of similar whitish spots on the vertical fins, head, and belly; many blackish blotches of similar size between the white spots on body; edge of caudal very narrowly white.

Of this species, which is abundant in the Hawaiian Islands, we have a more or less complete series of specimens, from the young *parvibranchialis* to the adult *laysanus*. Our collection contains a total of more than 30 specimens, ranging in length from 4.5 to 13.5 inches, and representing the following localities: Honolulu; Waikiki Reef, Honolulu; Cocoanut Island, Hilo; and Hilo.

48. Gymnothorax meleagris (Shaw).

Head 2.3 in trunk; tail exceeding head and trunk by length of mouth; eye 2.67 in snout or 2 in interorbital space; snout 5.5 in head; interorbital space 7.25; mouth 2.25.

Body rather deep and compressed; tail tapering posteriorly; head compressed, pointed; snout rather long and pointed, the tip obtusely rounded; eye small, about midway between tip of snout and corner of mouth; mouth rather large; jaws about equal, closing, the thick tough lips concealing the teeth; teeth strong and sharp, those in anterior part of jaws enlarged and canine-like, the vomerine in a single series; nostrils in small tubes at tip of snout, the posterior pair above and anterior to eye; interorbital space convex; gill-opening large, eye about 1.4 in its length; skin smooth and thick; a few pores on head; origin of dorsal about midway between corner of mouth and gill-opening; caudal small and roundly pointed.

Color in alcohol, dark brown, variegated all over by very numerous small round whitish spots with borders darker brown than the body color, those on fins very small; tip of tail narrowly edged with white.

This description is based upon a specimen (No. 03391) 32 inches long, from Honolulu. Another small example (No. 03716), from the same locality, is dark brown with a slightly purplish tint; the general color between the white spots is more or less mottled with darker. In life the color (No. 03391) is olive-brown, mottled with darker, scarcely paler below or darker on fins; body covered everywhere with punctated spots of yellowish and yellowish white, each of them darker edged; tip of tail white; no margin on fins; angle of mouth uncolored; gill-opening dusky; vent dusky.

This species is apparently not common in the Hawaiian Islands. It was not found by Doctor Jenkins, and only 2 examples were secured by us.

49. Gymnothorax gracilicauda Jenkins. Fig. 23.

Head 2.75 in trunk; head and trunk 1.3 in tail; eye 1.5 in snout, one in interorbital space; snout 5.5 in head; interorbital space about 9; mouth 2.5.

Body compressed, rather deep; tail long and tapering to narrow tip; head elongate, compressed, little swollen above, blunt in front; snout rather long, compressed, convex above, tip blunt; eye moderate, a little nearer corner of mouth than tip of snout; mouth rather large, horizontal, jaws equal, not completely closing; teeth large, powerful, biserial in upper jaw, uniserial in mandible; inner series in upper jaw larger than those of outer series, 4 in number; vomer with 2 large depressible fangs in front, otherwise edentulous; anterior nostrils in short tubes near tip of snout, posterior pair without tubes, just above eyes; interorbital space narrow, convex; gill-openings small; skin rather thin; origin of dorsal a little nearer gill-opening than corner of mouth; caudal very small and roundly pointed.

Color in alcohol, pale brown, more or less uniform, marked with irregularly formed light brown spots arranged in about 40 or more ill-defined transverse bars; these bands not extending on belly or

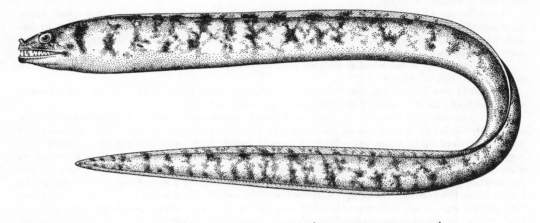

FIG. 23.—*Gymnothorax gracilicauda* Jenkins; from the type.

ventral surface of trunk, or even upon anal fin, though they are all somewhat distinct on the dorsal fin; corner of mouth brown. This may be the young of *G. steindachneri*.

This description from an example 8.25 inches long, taken at Honolulu in 1889, by Dr. Jenkins. The species is known to us only from the Hawaiian Islands and from 2 examples, the type described above and another obtained by the *Albatross* off Molokai.

50. Gymnothorax ercodes Jenkins.   Fig. 24.

Head 6.6 in total length, or 3 in distance from tip of snout to vent; depth 12; snout 6.6; eye 1.3; gape 2.6; tip of snout to vent 1.35 in tail; interorbital width slightly greater than eye, or nearly equal to snout.

Body moderately elongate and much compressed; tail more compressed and pointed; mouth

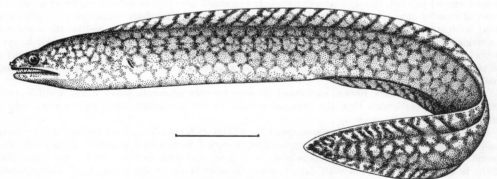

FIG. 24.—*Gymnothorax ercodes* Jenkins; from the type.

rather large, gape reaching beyond eye a distance equal to length of snout; lower jaw scarcely the shorter, not much curved; teeth all pointed, in 2 series anteriorly and 3 series posteriorly in upper jaw, lower jaw with teeth in 2 series anteriorly, laterally and posteriorly in a single series; 2 large sharp-pointed depressible teeth on anterior part of vomer, followed by a series of about 6 smaller teeth on the shaft; anterior nostril in a short tube whose length is one-fourth diameter of eye, situated near tip of snout just above lip; posterior nostril without tube, situated above margin of eye just in front of vertical through middle of eye; gill-slit moderate, its length 1.5 in eye; origin of dorsal slightly in front of gill-opening, height of fin 3.5 in head; anal similar, but lower.

Color in alcohol, body and fins light brown on a whitish background, the brown arranged in a somewhat regular network, giving the appearance of rows of indistinct whitish spots surrounded by polygonal brownish interspaces, which are most distinct on tail; no white border to the fins or tip of tail, and no dark area around gill-opening

The only specimen known is the type, No. 50843, U. S. Nat. Mus. (original number 2354), a specimen 8.5 inches long, obtained by the *Albatross* at Honolulu in 1891.

51. Gymnothorax leucostictus Jenkins. Fig. 25.

Head 2.3 in trunk; head and trunk less than length of tail by a space a trifle greater than length of latter; eye about 2 in snout, 1 in interorbital space; snout 5.5 in head; mouth 2.3.

Body deep, compressed; tail tapering gradually posteriorly where it is greatly compressed; head compressed, sides above slightly swollen; snout elongate though rather short, blunt, rounded, not projecting beyond mandible; jaws even; eye small, covered with the skin of head, a little nearer corner of mouth than tip of snout; mouth horizontal, the rather thin lips more or less concealing teeth; teeth

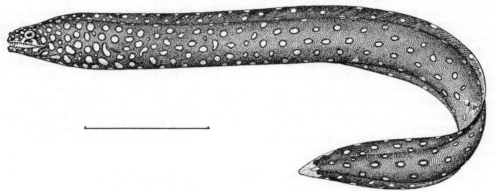

FIG. 25.—*Gymnothorax leucostictus* Jenkins; from the type.

rather large, sharp, in several series, or in a broad patch on each side of upper jaw, uniserial in mandible; large canines in front of both jaws, vomer with a single median series of small ones; anterior nostrils in short fleshy tubes near tip of snout; interorbital space narrow and convexly elevated; gill-openings small, a little below middle of its depth and about equal to eye; pores of body small; origin of dorsal a little before corner of mouth, fin rather high, and together with anal, which is more or less similar, confluent with small caudal.

Color in life, dark brown; head, body, fins, and tail covered with numerous distinct white spots, larger than eye on the trunk, smaller elsewhere; tip of tail white; margin or gill-opening brownish-black. The two specimens examined, taken by Dr. Jenkins at Honolulu, are each about 6.5 inches long, and do not differ in coloration.

The species is distinguished from *G. meleagris* by the more anterior insertion of the dorsal, and the larger and fewer white spots, which are larger on the trunk than elsewhere.

52. Gymnothorax waialuæ Snyder. Plate 13, fig. 1.

Head, measured to gill-opening, 8 in length; depth 2 in head; tail 1.9 in length; snout 5 in head; cleft of mouth 2.5 in head. Body compressed, the width in middle of trunk equal to half the depth; interorbital space slightly convex; jaws equal; cleft of mouth extending beyond eye a distance equal to longitudinal diameter of eye; width of suborbital space equal to vertical diameter of eye; gill-opening an oblique slit equal to vertical diameter of eye; teeth in jaws mostly long, sharp, and depressible, the 2 in anterior median part of upper jaw longest, those below eye in 2 series, the outer ones short and close set; 3 short, sharp teeth on vomer; anterior nostril tubes near tip of snout, their height equal to diameter of eye; posterior nostrils without rims, located above and a little anterior to eyes; dorsal inserted on head anterior to gill-opening; fin highest posteriorly, its height behind middle of tail equal to longitudinal diameter of eye; anal inserted immediately behind the vent, about half as high as dorsal; caudal slightly longer than height of dorsal.

Color in alcohol, white tinged with yellow, with 20 black bands, nearly all encircling the body and extending on fins; tip of snout white, tip of tail black; the first black band covering snout, except the tip between the nostrils, extends backward beyond eye, and sends a line downward to corner of mouth, where it meets a round, black blotch; chin and throat white; sides of lower jaw black; a white space between eye and corner of mouth; the second band passes over occiput, not complete below; third band incomplete, passing over back between gill-openings, a dusky prolongation passing downward behind gill-opening; other bands complete, anterior ones broader above than below, posterior ones of about equal width throughout; a narrow, dusky stripe extends forward along lower surface from vent to a point a little anterior to gill-openings.

This species closely resembles *G. petelli*, the young of which it may prove to be. The species differ in color and in dentition. The light spaces on the body of *G. petelli* are reddish brown; on the anal fin they are white, on the dorsal reddish brown bordered with white near edge of fin; caudal usually tipped with white; snout reddish brown; teeth in a single series, those of the jaws not depressible, except 2 or 3 on anterior median portion of upper jaw.

A single specimen, 4.2 inches long, from a small tide pool in the reef at Waialua Bay, Oahu.

53. Gymnothorax mucifer Snyder.   Plate 14, fig. 1.

Head, measured to gill-opening, 3.3 in length; depth 2.25 in head; snout 5; cleft of mouth 2.3. Snout rather slender and pointed, jaws equal, closing completely; teeth in one series, slender, lance-like with slight constrictions near base, their edges smooth; 3 depressible median canines in upper jaw, the longest (posterior) one equal in length to diameter of eye; a row of small, sharp teeth on the vomer; eye midway between tip of snout and angle of mouth; width of space between eyes 2 in snout; gill-opening a narrow slit equal to diameter of eye, located on a level with upper lip; nostril tubes 2 in eye; posterior nostrils with scarcely perceptible rims, located above and just anterior to eye; origin of dorsal anterior to gill-opening a distance equal to space between tip of snout and posterior border of eye; height of fin above gill-opening equal to diameter of eye, about 1.33 times as high near middle of tail, the membrane not very fleshy; anal inserted immediately behind vent, appearing for much of the length like a thickened fold of the skin.

Color in alcohol, rich dark brown with flakes of white, which are gathered in clouds and more or less definite vertical bars; the flakes scattered rather evenly on head, scarcely perceptible on lower jaw and snout; throat and belly lighter than other parts, the white and brown being about equal; dorsal growing darker toward the edge, where it is nearly black, with white flakes like those of the body arranged in oblique bars; anal edged with white; corner of mouth dark; no spot at gill-opening.

The species is represented by a single example, type, No. 50868, U. S. Nat. Mus., from the Honolulu market. It measures 13.5 inches from tip of snout to vent. The tail, which has been injured, measures 14.75 inches in length.

54. Gymnothorax berndti Snyder.   Plate 15, fig. 2.

Head, measured to gill-opening, 6.7 in length, 3.8 in tail; depth 1.8 in head; snout 5; cleft of mouth 2. Profile, a gently sloping straight line between tip of snout and posterior part of interorbital space, whence it abruptly curves upward over the greatly swollen occipital region; snout slender and pointed; lower jaw projecting slightly beyond upper; mouth closing completely; teeth in a single series in each jaw, large, smooth-edged, close set, firmly embedded, the anterior ones somewhat longer than the others; median canines absent; 5 small teeth on the vomer; nostril tubes equal in height to diameter of pupil; posterior nostrils without rims, located above and just posterior to border of eye; orbit round; width of space between eyes equal to half the distance between tip of snout and center of pupil; gill-opening located on a level with eye, the slit equal in width to diameter of eye; origin of dorsal on a vertical midway between gill-opening and corner of mouth, fin membrane thick and fleshy; height of fin near middle of tail equal to half the length of snout; anal inserted immediately behind vent, appearing as a ridge of skin, the highest part about 1.7 in eye; length of caudal equal to vertical diameter of eye.

Color gray, with fine brown reticulations over which is a coarse network of brown bands.

Color in alcohol, white, tinged with brown, more clear along the upper lip, on lower jaw, and on belly; finely clouded and reticulated with brown, except on jaws and anal fin, all overlaid with a brown-colored, coarse network of rather broad bands, the meshes becoming finer on head and broken up into elongate, crooked spots on jaws; gill-opening brown; dorsal with oblique bars which connect with reticulations of body; anal blackish brown, with a broad, white border.

This description is of the type, No. 50867, U. S. Nat. Mus., an example 37 inches long, obtained in the Honolulu market through the kindness of Mr. E. Louis Berndt. Two other specimens of about the same size were likewise obtained. One has the fine reticulations less distinct than those of the type and the bands of the coarse ones a little narrower, about equal to width of pupil. The snout measures 4.2 in head; jaws equal. The other, a female, 31 inches long (cotype, No. 12791, L. S. Jr. Univ. Mus.), when compared with the type, has a more slender head, the occipital region being less swollen. The color is similar, except that the bands of the large reticulations are narrower and the dorsal is conspicuously, though narrowly, edged with white. There are 2 large, depressible fangs in the anterior median portion of the upper jaw.

G. berndti may be distinguished from all other Hawaiian eels by the broad brown reticulations on the body. Named for Mr. E. Louis Berndt, the efficient inspector of fisheries at Honolulu.

55. Gymnothorax undulatus (Lacépède).   " Puhi laumili."   Plate 16.

Head 2 in trunk; head and trunk a little shorter than tail; eye 2.3 in snout, 1.5 in interorbital space; snout 5.67 in head; mouth 2 and an eye diameter in head.

Body compressed; tail tapering gradually, greatly compressed posteriorly; head compressed and swollen; snout elongate, the tip bluntly pointed and not projecting beyond mandible; jaws even; eye rather small, superior and nearer tip of snout than corner of mouth; mouth horizontal, closing, the thick lips completely concealing teeth; teeth large, uniserial, many of them more or less canine-like, those along the sides directed backward; vomerine teeth in a single series, large, fang-like depressible; anterior nostrils in short fleshy tubes, the posterior pair directly above eyes in front, interorbital space convex, the forehead rising rather abruptly behind; gill-openings a little shorter than eye; skin very rough, with many fine wrinkles; branchial region of head with many rather deep longitudinal folds or wrinkles; dorsal beginning much nearer corner of mouth than gill-opening; caudal roundly pointed.

Color in alcohol, deep purple, brown or blackish, speckled, spotted and reticulated with whitish; often very variable.

Here described from an example (No. 04802) 35 inches long, from Honolulu. This is one of the most abundant eels occurring among the Hawaiian Islands and is also very numerous at Samoa. Our collection contains more than 40 specimens, all from Honolulu except one dredged by the *Albatross* at station 3824, off the southern coast of Molokai, in 222 to 498 fathoms. The specimens range in length from 10 to 36 inches, the majority of them exceeding 20 inches.

This species is very savage and voracious. In the stomach of one example (No. 04813, from Honolulu) a *Teuthis* 7.88 inches long was found, though the eel measured only 30 inches in total length. Another eel about 22 inches in length had swallowed a large goatfish which, though more or less macerated, was as long, if not much longer, than the *Teuthis* mentioned.

56. Gymnothorax flavimarginatus (Rüppell). Plate 17.

Head 2.8 in trunk; head and trunk shorter than tail; eye 2.25 in snout, about 2 in interorbital space; snout 5.75 in head.

Body compressed, tail tapering to a point; head compressed, bluntly rounded in front; snout rather elongate, pointed, rounded above, tip blunt; eye small, a little nearer tip of snout than corner of mouth; mouth closing, jaws about even; teeth covered with thick skin of lips; teeth in jaws in a single series, some of them canine-like anteriorly, those on vomer large, fang-like, and depressible; anterior nostrils in short tubes at tip of snout, posterior pair above and over eyes; interorbital space convex; gill-opening a little longer than eye; skin smooth, and a number of pores on head; no lateral line; origin of dorsal about midway between posterior margin of eye and gill-opening; caudal small, forming a rounded point.

Color in alcohol, dark brown; head in front and fins dusky or blackish; body everywhere mottled and blotched with deep brown; gill-openings blackish; posterior edges of dorsal, anal, and tip of caudal very narrowly margined with whitish; belly and throat pale.

Color in life (No. 03548), very dark brown, nearly black; light interspaces smoky-yellow; outer margin of vertical fins lemon-yellow, below which the color is bright green, gradually losing itself in dark brown. Color in life of another example (No. 03375), 3 feet long, body and fins mottled yellowish and brown, brown forming irregular granular spots of various sizes, but all less than pupil; fins a little darker, no pale edges; gill-opening and angle of mouth black; throat streaks brownish and spots on jaws smaller.

This description is based upon the type of *G. thalassopterus*, No. 50619, U. S. Nat. Mus., a specimen 23 inches long, from Honolulu, which seems to be identical with this species.

Our collection contains 17 fine examples of this species, all from Honolulu, and ranging in length from 8 to 36 inches. A specimen was obtained in 1889 by Doctor Jenkins and others were secured by the *Albatross* in 1902. One small example was obtained by us at Cocoanut Island, at Hilo, also several young from the reef at Waikiki. Others have been recently received from Mr. Berndt, at Honolulu.

57. Gymnothorax goldsboroughi Jordan & Evermann. Fig. 26.

Head nearly 3 in trunk (exclusive of head and tail), or 9 in total length; head and trunk about 1.5 in tail; eye 1.75 in snout, 1.2 in interorbital space; snout 5 in head; interorbital space 7.5; mouth 2.

Body rather compressed, the tail gradually tapering narrowly behind; head compressed, swollen above; snout pointed, the tip blunt and the sides compressed; eye rather small, a trifle nearer tip of snout than corner of mouth; mouth large, snout slightly projecting beyond mandible; lips rather fleshy and concealing the teeth when the mouth is closed; teeth in a single series in jaws, anteriorly large and canine-like, and the vomer with a single large, depressible fang; anterior nostrils at tip of snout in small tubes; posterior nostrils directly above eye in front; interorbital space more or less flattened like top of snout; gill-opening about equal to eye; skin smooth; head with a number of mucous pores; origin of dorsal a little nearer corner of mouth than gill-opening; caudal small.

Color in alcohol, brown, covered all over body except anal fin with round or roundish white spots, those on anterior part of body small, very small and numerous on head, becoming larger on trunk, and finally increasing very much in size on tail where they are scattered and rather far apart; reticulations around the light spots blackish brown upon posterior part of dorsal fin, same color as base of anal; margins of anal and dorsal fins whitish; gill-opening and anus bordered with blackish brown. General color of body in life, brown, rather pale olivaceous anteriorly, and covered all over with small white spots which are close-set and small on head where the dark color forms a network; spots sparse and irregular on posterior parts, and also much larger; vent and gill-opening dusky; dorsal colored like the body, with a broad white edge, growing broader behind; anal dark brown, unspotted, and with a broad pale border.

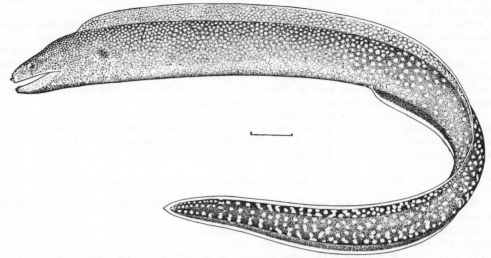

FIG. 26.—*Gymnothorax goldsboroughi* Jordan & Evermann; from the type.

This species is known from the type, a specimen 21 inches long, obtained by us at Honolulu, and another example from Honolulu recorded by Mr. Snyder.

58. Gymnothorax petelli (Bleeker).   Fig. 27.

Head 2.88 in trunk; tail a little longer than head and trunk; eye 2 in snout, 1.3 in interorbital space; snout 5.25 in head; interorbital space 8.5; mouth from tip of mandible 2.25.

Body rather deep and compressed; head compressed, branchial region and top of head swollen; snout rather short and pointed; eye small, a little nearer angle of mouth than tip of snout; mouth large, the mandible projecting well beyond snout, the jaws closing; lips rather thick and fleshy, concealing the teeth; teeth compressed, sharply pointed, in a single series in jaws, some of those in anterior part of jaws canine-like; vomerine teeth developed as 2 or 3 large depressible fangs on anterior part of roof of mouth; anterior nostrils in small tubes at tip of snout, posterior nostrils above anterior margins of eyes; interorbital space convexly flattened; gill-opening rather large, about equal to eye; skin smooth, tough, with some longitudinal wrinkles upon lower surface of head; a number of pores on head; lateral line complete; origin of dorsal midway between corner of mouth and gill-opening; caudal small, roundly pointed.

Color in life, dull reddish brown, marked above and on side with a number of slightly darker fine lines; about 22 vertical crossbars of deep rich brown as broad as space between them, and even still broader on posterior portion of tail; belly and lower surface of head light, though the broad dark vertical bands on sides meet, being narrowly constricted in the center, the edges at these places white; wrinkles on throat with dark lines; edge of dorsal fin blackish and white alternately, the dark bands forming a black margin on each side of which is a white spot, between which and the succeeding white spot is a blackish blotch, though only upon the edges of fin; anal similar, but with the white

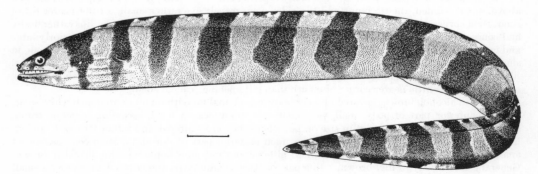

FIG. 27.—*Gymnothorax petelli* (Bleeker).   Type of *G. leucacme* Jenkins.

tracts predominating and without any of the general body color.   When fresh the specimen showed a bright chrome-yellow area from near end of snout backward between eyes, over top of head, to and encroaching on first brown band. Smaller examples do not show this yellow.

The above description is based upon a specimen (No. 03513) 28 inches long, from Honolulu, from which locality we have several other examples. The specimens vary some in respect to the bands meeting on the belly, in many cases only the posterior ones being joined. Two examples obtained at Honolulu in 1889 by Dr. Jenkins have the white tracts on the edge of the anal very distinct.

Specimens were also obtained by the *Albatross* at Honolulu in 1902. The 7 specimens which we have examined, all from Honolulu, range in length from 20 to 30 inches. The species is common at Samoa.

59. Gymnothorax steindachneri Jordan & Evermann. Fig. 28.

Head 7.3 in length; depth 9.5; eye 9.5 in head; snout 5; interorbital 7.2; gape 2; distance from tip of snout to vent less than distance from vent to tip of tail by more than half length of head.

Body moderately long and slender, much compressed; head small; snout small and pointed, the anterior dorsal profile concave above the eyes; the nape and sides of head much swollen; gape long, extending far behind eye; lower jaw shorter than the upper, curved so that the mouth does not quite completely close; lips moderately thick, entirely covering the teeth in the closed mouth; eye small, about midway between tip of snout and angle of mouth; teeth on sides of upper jaw in a single series, rather close-set, short, compressed, triangular canines, those in front scarcely enlarged; vomer with a single row of bluntly rounded teeth; each side of lower jaw with a single series of rather strong, backwardly directed canines, the anterior ones somewhat enlarged, those on tip of jaw movable; anterior nostril in a long tube, its length about half diameter of eye, situated near tip of snout just above lip; posterior nostril without tube, just above anterior edge of eye; pores on sides of jaws inconspicuous. Origin of dorsal fin about midway between gill-opening and angle of mouth, its height about equal to length of snout; anal similar to soft dorsal, but much lower; tail moderately slender and pointed; a series of inconspicuous pores along middle of side; gill-opening a long oval slit exceeding diameter of orbit.

Color in alcohol, pale brown or whitish, sprinkled with ragged or dendritic brown spots formed more or less into irregular vertical blotches or crossbands; margins of fins narrowly creamy white or yellowish, that of the anal much wider; corner of mouth and space about gill-opening deep blackish-brown; about 5 longitudinal blackish-brown grooves on lower side of head; under side of lower jaw with 2 blackish longitudinal lines which meet at an acute angle under chin; throat and belly creamy white, with few scattered brownish markings; sides and top of head whitish, with small, sparingly scattered, irregular brownish spots most numerous around and between the eyes.

This species is related to *G. kidako* (Schlegel), from which it differs much in coloration, being much paler and less reticulated, the angle of the mouth with more black, the gill-opening surrounded

FIG. 28.—*Gymnothorax steindachneri* Jordan & Evermann; after Steindachner.

by a broad black area (nearly or quite absent in *kidako*), and the white border to the dorsal fin much more distinct.

The specimens from Laysan, which Dr. Steindachner identified with *Muræna flavimarginata* Rüppell, and of which he gives a good figure, evidently belong to this species. As suspected by Dr. Steindachner, the species is quite different from *G. flavimarginatus*, of which we have examined several specimens from Pedang, on the west coast of Sumatra, from Samoa, and from Hawaii

This description is based upon a specimen (No. 03775) 2 feet long, from Honolulu. (Type, No. 50616, U. S. Nat. Mus.) The species is known from the 2 specimens which Dr. Steindachner had from Laysan, 8 obtained by Jenkins in 1889 at Honolulu, 1 by the *Albatross* at Honolulu in 1891, 3 secured by us at Honolulu in 1901, at least 1 recorded by Mr. Snyder from Honolulu in 1902, and others recently sent us from Honolulu by Mr. Berndt.

60. Gymnothorax hilonis Jordan & Evermann. Plate 18.

Head 8.2 in length; depth 16; eye 7 in head; snout 6; interorbital 6; gape 2.4; distance from tip of snout to vent 1.2 in distance from vent to tip of tail.

Body rather short, moderately compressed, the tail more compressed and bluntly pointed; head short, the nape swollen; interorbital space broad; a distinct median groove from near tip of snout to origin of dorsal; angle of mouth posterior to eye a distance equal to eye's diameter; lower jaw but slightly curved, shorter than the upper; front of upper jaw with 3 short, bluntly pointed, movable teeth; side of upper jaw with a single series of short, pointed canines directed backward; shaft of vomer with short, blunt teeth; lower jaw on each side with a single series of rather long, pointed canines, longest in front and curved backward; anterior nostril in a long tube, about 2 in eye, near tip of snout just above lip; posterior nostril small, round, without tube, situated just above anterior part of eye; gill-opening small, its direction obliquely forward toward nape; a series of 4 pores on each side of upper jaw; similar pores on lower jaw. Origin of dorsal fin on nape midway between gill-opening and middle of eye; dorsal fin well developed, its greatest height somewhat exceeding length of snout; anal similar to dorsal, but lower.

Color in alcohol, rich velvety black above, paler below where it is marbled and reticulated with narrow white lines; series of pores on side of upper jaw and those on tip of lower, white; cheek with a few irregular white spots; gill-opening whitish; side of body anteriorly with some small white specks and irregular whitish markings; lower jaw with larger, oblong, white cross-lines; dorsal fin rich brownish black, the edge posteriorly with a narrow, irregular, white border, sometimes interrupted by black; anal brown, with a narrow white edge from which extend narrow intrusions of white, some reaching base of fin; end of tail with a few small white spots, the tip narrowly white.

The only known example of this species is the type, No. 50618, U. S. Nat. Mus. (field No. 04902), a specimen 9.5 inches long, obtained at Hilo, Hawaii.

61. Gymnothorax nuttingi Snyder.   Plate 15, fig. 1.

Head, measured from tip of snout to gill-opening, 6.9 in length, 3.6 in head and trunk, 3.3 in tail; depth 2 in head; cleft of mouth 2.2; snout 5.2. Snout rounded, jaws equal, closing completely; lips very thick; teeth in a single series, firmly embedded, close-set, largest below middle of snout, growing gradually smaller posteriorly, basal halves with finely serrated edges; no median fangs; vomer with very short, blunt teeth; eye on a vertical passing midway between tip of snout and corner of mouth; distance between eyes 1.35 in snout; anterior nostril tube 2 in eye; posterior nostril located above and just anterior to margin of eye, its opening with a low rim; gill-opening a narrow slit equal to vertical diameter of eye, situated on a level with pupil; origin of dorsal on a vertical anterior to gill-opening a distance equal to length of snout, the membrane fleshy, though not greatly thickened; height in region of vent equal to length of snout; anal inserted immediately behind vent, its height near middle of tail equal to diameter of orbit; tail not slender and pointed, but rather stubby, the dorsal, caudal, and anal forming a bluntly rounded terminal fin.

Color in spirits brown, covered with white spots, those on head minute and close together, scarcely discernible on snout and end of lower jaw; spots on the body larger and more elongate, growing round on tail, where their diameter is about equal to half that of pupil; gill-opening and corner of mouth brown; dorsal spotted like tail, the spots on edge of fin elongate, narrow, and close together, coalescing posteriorly to form a white border; anal spotted, with a white border.

The species is represented by a single individual 31 inches long, obtained in the Honolulu market.

Of the spotted Hawaiian eels this species can only be confused with *Gymnothorax goldsboroughi*, which may be distinguished at a glance by its slender, pointed tail, the larger, circular spots, and dark throat-patch, which are its most striking characters.

62. Gymnothorax pictus (Ahl): "*Puhi kapa'a*." Plate 19.

Head 2.75 in trunk; head and trunk about equal to tail; eye a little over 2 in snout, 1.3 in interorbital space; mouth 3; snout 5.5 in head; interorbital space 9.5.

Body rather thick, roundly compressed; tail tapering rather thickly posteriorly; head compressed, somewhat swollen above, pointed in front; snout rather long and pointed, tip somewhat blunt; eye small, about midway between tip of snout and corner of mouth; mouth large, horizontal, closing, teeth concealed by the thick lips, snout projecting slightly beyond mandible; teeth powerful, in a single series in jaws, directed backward; teeth on vomer rounded; anterior nostrils in short tubes; posterior nostrils above eye in front; interorbital space convex; skin tough, thick, a number of pores on head; no lateral line; origin of dorsal in last fifth of space between corner of mouth and gill-opening; dorsal rather high; caudal short and rounded.

Color in life (No. 03394), light olive dusted with black, the spots forming marblings posteriorly; no black on gill-opening; no dark or light edge on dorsal fin; a slight pale margin on anal; belly pale; no black at angle of mouth.

Color in alcohol, deep brown above, everywhere clouded and mottled with darker, also marked with very fine pale broken reticulations, and sides with rather large blotches of deep brown; lower surface of body soiled whitish; gill-openings pale.

This description is based chiefly upon an example (No. 03724), 28 inches long, from Kailua, Hawaii. Our collection contains 8 fine specimens (Nos. 03710, 03711, 03717, 03720, 03721, 03722, 03724, and 03725) from the same place, and one (No. 03394) from Honolulu. Other specimens were obtained by the *Albatross* in 1902 at Honolulu and Puako Bay, Hawaii.

Length 2 to 4 feet; our specimens range from 22 to 40 inches. This species is subject to considerable variation, the form with coarser and darker markings being the *M. sidera* of Richardson.

63. Gymnothorax xanthostomus Snyder. Plate 14, fig. 2.

Head, measured to gill-opening 8 in length, 4.5 in tail; depth 1.46 in head; snout 5; cleft of mouth 1.6. Snout acutely rounded, lower jaw projecting slightly; profile from tip of snout to interorbital area convex and gently rising, that of occipital region rising abruptly, nuchal muscles well developed; diameter of eye 2.5 in snout; width of space between eyes 1.3 in snout; mouth closing completely, the cleft extending about one-third its length beyond posterior margin of orbit; teeth of jaws in a single series, close set and firmly imbedded; those at symphysis small; lateral ones large anteriorly, growing gradually smaller posteriorly, the basal two-thirds of their edges denticulate; a median, depressible canine near tip of upper jaw; vomer without teeth; anterior nostril tube equal in length to diameter of pupil; posterior nostril with a minute rim; gill-opening oval, the diameter equal to 1.5 times that of eye, the lower margin on a level with mouth. Origin of dorsal on a vertical passing midway between corner of mouth and anterior edge of gill-opening, membrane fleshy; height of fin near vent, 1.33 in snout; anal inserted immediately behind the vent, where it is but a low ridge of skin, much higher and less fleshy posteriorly, height near its middle portion equal to half the length of snout; caudal slightly longer than diameter of eye.

Color in life, yellowish olive on anterior third, becoming a rich brown posteriorly; head and body covered with conspicuous, light, ocellated spots, the light part of which is clearly defined, the dark part more intense next the white, growing diffuse without; spots on head very small, 0.1 to 0.2 diameter of eye, placed from 1 to 3 times their width from each other, their centers tinged with yellow; behind the gill-opening the spots grow rapidly larger for a short distance, then very gradually increase in size to the tail, where they are nearly as large as the eye and 1 to 2 or 3 times their diameter apart; posteriorly and on the fins the spots are pure white or cream colored; opercles with a brownish black margin; mouth, within and at corners, bright lemon-yellow.

The color in alcohol differs but little from that of the living example.

Described from the type, No. 50869, U. S. Nat. Mus., 35.83 inches long, obtained in the Honolulu market. Two other examples were obtained from the same place; one agreeing closely with the type, except that the lower jaw projects beyond the upper a distance equal to the diameter of the eye. The belly is without spots. The other (cotype, No. 12792, L. S. Jr. Univ. Mus.) has the body very thick and robust, nuchal region greatly enlarged; head 7.46 in length, 4.35 in tail; depth 1.67 in head.

This species may be known from all other Hawaiian eels by the yellow mouth and the very large, dark-bordered, white spots in few rows.

Genus 57. EURYMYCTERA Kaup.

The tube of the anterior nostril stretches considerably beyond the lips, and its tip is dilated above and below; posterior nostril surrounded by a funnel-formed border, and situated before the eye.

This genus differs from *Gymnothorax* in the slender, acuminate snout.

64. Eurymyctera acutirostris (Abbott)

Head much compressed, the facial outline moderately oblique; eye large, circular, equal to 0.2 of length of side of head, measuring from angle of jaws; jaws greatly attenuated, very slender, the lower somewhat the smaller and with a gentle upward curve at its extremity; teeth uniserial, compressed, very acute, the palatines, vomerines, and mandibulars all inwardly directed; the palatine teeth 13, of a uniform size, the series commencing below center of orbit and terminating shortly anteriorly to angle of jaws; 12 compressed acute teeth upon vomer in a direct line, the anterior tooth much the largest; mandible with 26 teeth upon each side, the anterior 4 of each side being nearly 3 times the others in size, more widely set, the posterior pair with a single, compressed, very small tooth between them; nasal teeth 14, widely set and from 3 to 5 minute teeth between each pair; 3 teeth placed upon mesial line, the second one very slender and the longest tooth in mouth; the third twice as great in circumference, and but little shorter than the second tooth; orbits one diameter distant, and the distance from upper edge of orbit to facial outline equal to distance between lower margin of orbit and free edge of upper lip; gill-opening rather small and oblique; pores upon snout and lateral line not visible; fold of skin enveloping dorsal fin unusually thin and arising within a short distance of occiput, with a slope of about forty-five degrees; gill-opening situated as far posteriorly to commencement of dorsal as that is posterior to angle of jaws; dorsal fin equal in width to 0.88 width of body, with no perceptible decrease until it approaches posterior eighth of body, when it decreases rapidly and at its termination is only equal to one-seventh of width of fin upon back.

Ground color in alcohol, dark hair-brown, nearly black upon occiput and cheek, and along base of dorsal fin; head, body, and both fins irregularly reticulated with narrow bands of white, varying in width and becoming yellow on posterior fifth of dorsal fin, and upon that portion of body, but in a less degree; 3 broken lines of black extending along body from angle of jaws to gill-opening; iris chrome yellow.

This species is known only from Abbott's type (No. 998, Mus. Phila. Acad.) collected in the Hawaiian Islands in 1835 by Dr. J. K. Townsend.

Genus 58. ECHIDNA Forster.

The name *Echidna* was suggested for these eels long before its application by Cuvier to a genus of Australian monotremes (properly called *Tachyglossus*), and includes some 12 or 15 species, most of them belonging to the western Pacific. They represent the highest degree of specialization among the morays, as *Uropterygius* represents the extreme degradation. The genus is well marked, distinguished from the other morays by the blunt teeth. It is represented in Hawaiian waters by 7 nominal species.

65. Echidna zebra (Shaw). Plate 20.

Head 5.2 in trunk; tail a little over 2 in head and trunk; eye 1.8 in snout, 2 in interorbital space; snout 7.3 in head; mouth, from tip of snout, 2.75.

Body rather deep and compressed; head deep, compressed, and swollen; eye small, anterior, midway between tip of snout and corner of mouth; mouth large, somewhat undulate; snout projecting well beyond tip of mandible; lips thick and fleshy; teeth all broad, smooth, and molar-like; anterior nostrils in fleshy tubes, the posterior pair with their rims slightly elevated, each situated above anterior margin of eye; interorbital space elevated, convex, and as the upper profile of head is concave above the eyes the forehead rises somewhat abruptly behind; gill-openings small; skin smooth, very tough and thick; no lateral line; pectoral fins obsolete; dorsal beginning behind gill-opening; tail deep, strongly compressed posteriorly; caudal with its margin bluntly rounded. The vertical fins in our specimens are rather low, almost obsolete, and not nearly so well defined as shown in Bleeker's plate.

Color in alcohol, deep or dark brown, encircled more or less completely over the body by numerous narrow white cross-bars with blackish margins, which fade away into the brown bands between; all of the bands or rings are not complete, though they are very seldom forked or broken up into small bars.

Color in life (No. 03543) dark reddish-brown, the dark stripes along or bordering each white band or ring darker brown than the general body color. Another specimen (No. 02994) rich, purplish brown throughout, crossed by about 69 pale yellowish rings, each about one-twelfth of an inch in width, or less than half the eye. Most of these rings are complete or nearly so, some fragmentary, others broken up into spots, soon fading into whitish, and bounded by darker than the general color.

The above description is based chiefly upon No. 03543, a specimen 31 inches long, obtained at Honolulu. The collection contains also a specimen (No. 02994) 26 inches long from the same place, and one (No. 03712) from Kailua. Hawaii. Another was obtained by the *Albatross* at Honolulu in 1902. This species was not obtained by Dr. Jenkins, and does not appear to be abundant among the Hawaiian Islands, but it is very abundant at Samoa.

66. Echidna psalion Jenkins. Fig. 29.

Head 7.25 in body, or 3.4 in distance from tip of snout to vent; depth 13; snout 5.5; eye slightly less than snout and slightly nearer tip of snout than angle of mouth; gape 2.5 in head; tip of snout to vent 1.2 in tail; interorbital about equal to eye.

Body moderately elongate, compressed posteriorly; tail slender, pointed; gill-opening very small, inconspicuous; anterior nostril tubular, about 2 in eye, near tip of snout, well above the lip; posterior nostril without tube, oval, above eye just anterior to its middle; a series of pores along upper lip and

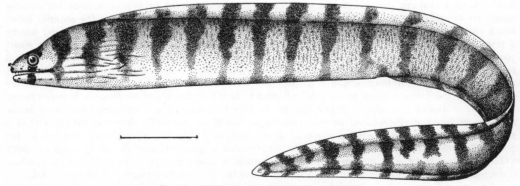

FIG. 29.—*Echidna psalion* Jenkins; from the type.

a series on each side of lower jaw; upper jaw with a single series of blunt, conic teeth in front, those on sides smaller and in a single series; roof of mouth with 2 series of large molars; vomer in front with a single series of about 3 strong, bluntly conical, depressible teeth; lower jaw with 2 series of blunt, conic teeth, the inner the larger; origin of dorsal in front of gill-opening a distance equal to one-fourth the head.

Color in alcohol, a series of 27 narrow brown bands alternating with wider light bands, the narrowest bands mostly somewhat narrower than eye, the broader ones mostly twice eye; a series of narrow parallel brown longitudinal lines on side of head in front of gill-opening; the anterior brown band running through eye, the second around head posterior to gape; angle of mouth brown.

Only one specimen, type, No. 50685, U. S. Nat. Mus. (original No. 2355), 13 inches long, obtained by the *Albatross* in 1896 at Honolulu.

67. Echidna obscura Jenkins. Fig. 30.

Head 8.3 in total length; depth 17; eye 9.5 in head; snout 5.75; interorbital 5.75; gape 2.8; distance from tip of snout to vent slightly less than from vent to tip of tail.

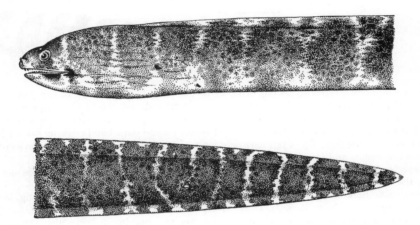

FIG. 30.—*Echidna obscura* Jenkins; from the type.

Body moderately elongate, rather deep and somewhat compressed; head narrow, somewhat swollen above; mouth large, the gape extending more than an eye's diameter beyond eye; lower jaw shorter than upper and somewhat curved; eye about midway between tip of snout and angle of mouth; interorbital equals snout; origin of dorsal in front of gill-opening a distance equal to length of mouth; dorsal fin somewhat higher than anal, its height greater than length of snout; tail compressed and moderately slender; a few short conical teeth in anterior parts of each jaw; 2 series of conical teeth in each side of upper jaw; roof of mouth paved with molars, in 2 rows anteriorly, in 4 posteriorly; molars in 2 series in each side of lower jaw; gill-opening small, narrow, length less than diameter of eye; anterior nostril tubular, near tip of snout, considerably above margin of mouth; posterior nostril round and inconspicuous, near middle of upper margin of eye.

Color in alcohol, dark brownish with about 23 dark cross-bands mostly as broad as depth of body, indistinct on middle part of body, but quite distinct anteriorly and on tail; alternating with them are white ones which are narrower than eye and which extend on anal and dorsal fins; the edges of the bands jagged, the white bands widening toward the belly; extreme tip of tail brown (in the cotypes the tip is narrowly edged with white); side of lower jaw brown, angle of mouth black with white spot in front on lower jaw; gill-opening without dark border. The 2 cotypes show some differences in color. In the larger example (No. 2351), 16.5 inches long, the body is more uniformly dark brown and the light cross-bands are very indistinct except on tail; in the other cotype (No. 2353), 9.5 inches in length, the white cross-bands are very distinct, all completely encircling the body except 3 or 4 anterior to vent.

The species was not taken by us. Three specimens were obtained by Dr. Jenkins in 1889, the type, No. 50686, U. S. Nat. Mus. (field No. 2352), a specimen 12.5 inches long, collected at Honolulu; cotypes, No. 7725, L. S. Jr. Univ. Mus. (field No. 2351), a specimen 16.5 inches long; and No. 2754, U. S. Fish Commission (field No. 2353), a specimen 9.5 inches long, both from Honolulu.

68. Echidna zonata Fowler. Fig. 31.

Head 7.2 in total length, or 3.75 in distance from tip of snout to vent; vent about midway between tip of snout and tip of tail; depth about 2.2 in head; eye 10 in head, 1.6 in snout, or 1 in interorbital space; length of mouth 2.7 in head.

Body moderately elongate, compressed; tail strongly compressed and pointed; head swollen; mouth moderate, gape reaching beyond eye a distance equal to length of snout; lower jaw shorter than upper, curved so that the mouth does not close completely; teeth bluntly conic, in a single series in front in upper jaw, in 2 series laterally; teeth on vomer bluntly conic, in a single series of 3 teeth, depressible anteriorly, in a double series of molar teeth posteriorly, about 7 teeth in each series; lower jaw with a double series of bluntly conic teeth on each side, and a median series of similar teeth.

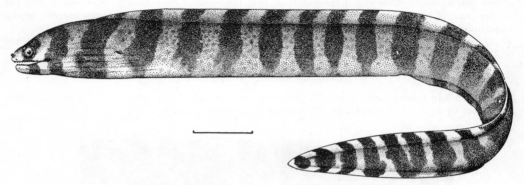

Fig. 31.—*Echidna zonata* Fowler.   Type of *E. vincta* Jenkins.

Color in life, body crossed by 25 (by error 24 in drawing) broad reddish-brown nonreticulating bands, the width of those at middle of body exceeding snout and eye; the bands completely encircling the body, and separated by somewhat narrower light bands; tip of snout yellowish white; the first dark band through eye broadening on interorbital space; second dark band crossing side of head and very broad on nuchal region; tip of tail narrowly white.   In some of the cotypes, the dark cross-bands tend to break up below and form reticulations.

This species is not rare about Honolulu among the coral rocks.   It apparently does not reach a large size, the examples in hand ranging from 15 inches down to 6 inches in length.

Echidna vincta Jenkins (type, No. 50687, U. S. Nat. Mus., a specimen 13.5 inches long, obtained at Honolulu.   Cotypes, No. 7492, L. S. Jr. Univ. Mus., 15 inches long; No. 2753, U. S. F. C.; No. 2753, Field Museum), appears to be identical with this species.   Specimens were also obtained by the *Albatross* at Honolulu in 1902.

69. Echidna zonophæa Jordan & Evermann.   Plate 21.

Head 3 in trunk, or 6.5 in total; tail longer than head and trunk by a little more than the snout; eye 2 in snout, 1.5 in interorbital space; snout 6; interorbital space 7.75; mouth 2.8.

Body compressed, the tail tapering rather narrowly posteriorly; head deep and compressed, pointed in front; snout rather long and pointed, the tip obtusely rounded and projecting considerably beyond the mandible; eye rather small, midway between tip of mandible and corner of mouth; mandible arched below so that only the anterior teeth touch the front of the jaw above, though the thick fleshy lips conceal them all; teeth molar, those in front of jaws pointed; anterior nostrils in short tubes, the posterior pair above the eye with a slightly elevated margin; interorbital space convex; top of head more or less swollen or convex in profile; gill-opening 1.67 in eye; skin smooth; head with a few pores; origin of dorsal beginning at last fourth of space between corner of mouth and gill-opening; caudal small.

Color in alcohol, grayish white, the body and tail crossed by about 25 broad rich-brown bands, extending upon the dorsal and anal fins; dark bands anteriorly broadest above and not meeting across belly, their width about equal to the distance from tip of snout to middle of eye; first brown band through eye, second across nape, the fourth across gill-opening; gray bands of ground color anteriorly broad and widening much upon belly; posteriorly the gray bands are narrower and better defined, especially on the fins, their width scarcely greater than half that of the brown bands; tip of tail very narrowly white; body anteriorly, especially within the gray bands, profusely covered with numerous small, roundish, black specks, less numerous and more scattered posteriorly; no black spots on head; angle of mouth black, with a small white blotch immediately in front on lower jaw, continued across under jaw as a broad whitish band; side of head with about 4 or 5 narrow blackish lines between mouth and gill-opening; region of gill-opening marbled with dark brown and whitish, the opening dark.   One example (No. 03545) had much yellow on the head and between the brown zones.   This species is known from the type and 3 cotypes, all obtained by us at Honolulu.

70. Echidna leihala Jenkins.   Fig. 32.

Head 7 in total length; depth 2.1 in head; tip of snout to angle of mouth 2.5 in head; eye 10 in head; interorbital 8.5; gill-opening a very small narrow slit, 3 in eye, with no distinguishing color marking; origin of dorsal well in advance of gill-opening, 3 in head; jaws curving away from each other, closing only at tip; a few sharp fixed teeth in anterior portions of jaws, the remaining all blunt; teeth in anterior portion of upper jaw sharp, in a single series; in the posterior portion a double series of blunt teeth, between which the roof of the mouth is crowded with blunt teeth, becoming as many as 6 series posteriorly; teeth in lower jaw in 2 series anteriorly, becoming blunt posteriorly and apparently in 3 series; anterior nostril tubular, near tip of snout above margin of lip; posterior nostril smooth, near the middle of the upper margin of the eye.

Color in life, uniform yellowish brown, not lighter on the belly, being distributed over the whole body in fine granular markings; no transverse bands appearing in life, but evidence of bands, especially toward tip of tail, appears some hours after death. (The figure shows alcoholic specimen.) Snout white, angles of mouth brown; iris yellow; no other conspicuous markings. (Jenkins.)

Dr. Jenkins obtained 3 specimens in 1889, as follows: The type, 17 inches in length, No. 50844, U. S. Nat. Mus. (field No. 283), Honolulu; and cotypes, No. 7783, L. S. Jr. Univ. Mus. (field No.

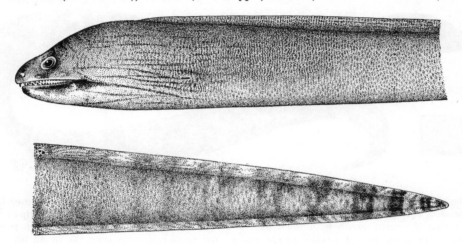

FIG. 32.—*Echidna leihala* Jenkins; from the type.

2368), 15.5 inches long; and No. 2752, U. S. Fish Commission (field No. 2369), 12 inches long, all from the reef in front of Honolulu.

It is possible that this species and *zonata*, *zonophæa*, *obscura*, and *psalion* are all color variations of one for which the earliest name is *Echidna tritor*.

71. Echidna nebulosa (Ahl). *"Puhi kápa."* Plate I.

Head 3.25 in trunk; tail shorter than head and trunk by a little more than snout and eye; eye 2.5 in snout and a little over 2 in interorbital space; snout 5.5; interorbital space 6.5; mouth 2.2.

Body compressed; tail tapering gradually; head large, thick, compressed, swollen above, so that the upper profile is convex from eyes; snout deep, compressed, rounded, the extremity blunt; eye small, high, nearer tip of snout than corner of mouth; mouth horizontal; jaws nearly equal; teeth in anterior part of jaws conical, those posterior molar-like; anterior nostrils in small tubes, posterior pair above the eyes anteriorly; interorbital space convex; gill-opening a little larger than eye; skin smooth and tough, with some pores on head; origin of dorsal about midway between posterior edge of eye and gill-opening; tip of tail rounded.

Color, in alcohol, whitish, finely spotted and speckled with blackish brown, crossed by about 27 cross-bands formed of deep blackish-brown reticulations, each divided so as to form 2 lateral series; spots on lower surface of body more or less solid, and the ground color with fewer small spots between; tip of snout and caudal white. This description from a specimen (No. 03774) 29 inches long, taken at Honolulu.

The *puhi kápa* is "a kind of eel that makes havoc among all kinds of fish. Hence Kamehameha (King of Hawaii) was called 'Puhi kápa' because 'victorious over all.'"

In life the irregular dark areas are dark brown, with chrome-yellow spots, the bars between these dark areas gray and brown; anterior tubular nostril orange; iris orange. An example from Hilo, gray with black spots and bands almost meeting on the belly, and quite meeting on the tail; spots of deep yellow in the black spots, those of belly edged with yellow; anterior nostril orange; snout and chin livid brownish; vent deep yellow, border of fins grayish white, like tip of tail.

The natives say that this eel goes ashore in the grass, wriggling quickly to the water again when disturbed. They also claim that it is savage and will bite.

We have a number of specimens from Honolulu, Hilo, and Kailua. Dr. Jenkins obtained one from Honolulu, in 1889, which we have examined, and the *Albatross* obtained one at Honolulu in 1902. The species is very common at Samoa.

Genus 59. UROPTERYGIUS Rüppell.

This genus contains most of those morays with fins altogether wanting, or developed only at the tip of tail; teeth small, pointed, subequal, the mouth of moderate size, and only the anterior nostrils provided with a tube.   The typical species have the tail about as long as the rest of the body.

72. Uropterygius marmoratus (Lacépède).   Fig. 33.

Head 2.25 in trunk; tail longer than head and trunk by a little less than half of head; eye 2.3 in snout, 2 in interorbital space; snout 5.67 in head; interorbital space 7.5; mouth 2.5.

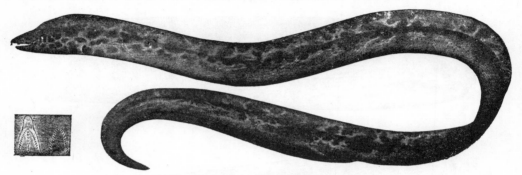

FIG. 33.—*Uropterygius marmoratus* (Lacépède); after Bleeker.

Body compressed; tail tapering gradually behind to a rather thick point; head rather large, compressed, obtusely pointed; snout long, pointed, the tip blunt; eye small, a little nearer tip of snout than corner of mouth; mouth with thick lips concealing the teeth; teeth large and sharp pointed, biserial in the jaws, the outer series much smaller and more numerous than the inner, which are depressible; vomerine teeth in a single median series; anterior nostrils in short tube, the posterior pair with elevated rims; interorbital space elevated; no fins, except an obsolete-rayed development around end of tail.

Color in alcohol, dark blackish brown above, paler beneath, marked all over with indistinct blackish reticulations; chin pale brown, somewhat soiled.

One adult (No. 03730) 11 inches long was obtained by Mr. Goldsborough at Kailua, Hawaii, and about a score of young individuals 1.3 to 4.72 inches long were dredged or taken in the tangles by the *Albatross* off the south coast of Molokai and between Maui and Lanai in 21 to 46 fathoms.   In life the young are dark brown, the throat and lower jaw much lighter, almost white in some specimens, there being no dark markings as in the adult.   The mucous pores on the head are white.

73. Uropterygius leucurus Snyder.   Plate 13, fig. 2.

Head, measured to gill-opening, 8.3 in length; tail 1.9; depth 2.6 in head; snout 5; cleft of mouth 2.9; lower jaw shorter than upper, tip extending to base of nostril tubes; teeth of jaws in 2 series, outer ones small and close set, inner ones fang-like and widely spaced; a median, depressible fang in upper jaw; a single row of sharp teeth on vomer; anterior nostrils with tubes equal in length to diameter of eye; posterior nostrils without rims, located above eyes; eye located above middle of cleft of mouth; gill-opening a horizontal slit equal to diameter of eye.   The dorsal fin becomes evident at a point about half the length of head from tip of tail, being represented anteriorly by a mere fold of the skin which extends to occiput; caudal pointed; a mere trace of an anal which joins the caudal.

Color brown, finely spotted above with white; ventrally the spots become elongate and unite, also increasing in size until on the belly the color is white with fine reticulations of brown; upper parts with figures formed by the union of elongate spots; end of snout, upper lip, lower jaw, and throat white; fin around end of tail white.

This species resembles the young of *U. marmoratus.* It differs in color, that form being neither spotted nor otherwise figured with white.   The jaws of *U. marmoratus* are equal, and no dorsal fin is evident on the tail.

One specimen, 4.3 inches long, was taken in 28 fathoms of water, station 3874, between Maui and Lanai.   Type, No. 50871, U. S. Nat. Mus.

Genus 60. SCUTICARIA Jordan & Snyder.

This genus differs from *Uropterygius* in having the posterior nostrils in tubes.

74. Scuticaria tigrina (Lesson). Plate 22.

Head 6.4 in trunk; tail a little over 2 in head and trunk; eye 2.8 in snout, 2.5 in interorbital space; snout a little over 7 in head; mouth a little over 3.

Body very elongate, round; tail compressed, tapering a little posteriorly to a very blunt and rounded tip; head round, blunt in front; snout round and blunt; eye very small, nearer tip of snout than corner of mouth; mouth nearly horizontal, jaws even; lips thick and tough; teeth all sharp-pointed, 2 series in upper jaw of which the inner are the larger; mandible with a short double series in front, those on vomer in a single series; anterior nostrils in short tubes nearer tip of snout, and posterior also in short tubes above anterior margins of eyes; interorbital space elevated and convex; gill-opening equal to eye; skin thick and tough, with a few mucous pores on head; no fins.

Color in alcohol, pale reddish brown, marked everywhere with numerous blotches of blackish brown edged with a paler brown than the general body-color; between the large dark blotches many small spots similarly edged; snout and mandible mottled with dark brown.

Here described from a specimen (No. 04815) 42 inches long, taken at Honolulu. We have also a specimen (No. 04831) 40 inches long, from the same place, and 3 others (Nos. 03706, 03718, and 03719), 48, 35, and 35 inches long, respectively, from Kailua, Hawaii.

Order H LYOPOMI.

This group, which contains the single family of *Halosauridæ*, is thus defined by Gill:

Scapular arch constituted by proscapular, postero-temporal and post-temporal, the post-temporal discrete from side of cranium and impinging on supraoccipital; hypercoracoid and hypocoracoid lamellar; a foramen in upper margin of hypocoracoid; mesocoracoid absent; actinosts normal; cranium with the condyle confined to basioccipital; opercular apparatus characteristic, the preopercle entirely detached from the suspensorium (rudimentary and connected only with the lower jaw); operculum normally connected, subopercle enlarged and partly usurping the usual position of the preopercle, in company with the suborbital chain which is extended backward to the opercular margin; bones of jaws, palatines, and pterygoid complete and normal; anterior vertebræ separate; ventrals abnormal.

Family XXXIV. HALOSAURIDÆ.

Body elongate, compressed anteriorly, tapering into a very long and slender tail, which becomes compressed and narrowed into a sort of filament; abdomen rounded; scales rather small, cycloid, deciduous; sides of head scaly; lateral line present, running along the side of the belly, its scales in the known species enlarged, each in a pouch of black skin with a luminous organ at its base; no barbels; head subconical, depressed anteriorly, the flattened snout projecting beyond the mouth; mouth inferior, horizontal, of moderate size, its anterior margin formed by the premaxillaries, its lateral margin by the maxillaries, which are of moderate width; teeth small, in villiform bands, on the jaws, the rudimentary palatines and pterygoids, none on vomer and tongue; eye rather large; facial bones with large muciferous cavities; opercular apparatus peculiar, the preopercle entirely detached from suspensorium, rudimentary and connected only with lower jaw; opercle normally connected; subopercle enlarged and partly usurping the usual position of the preopercle, in company with the suborbital chain, which is extended backward to the opercular margin; bones of head unarmed; gills 4, a slit behind the fourth; pseudobranchiæ none; gillrakers short; gill-membranes separate from the isthmus; branchiostegals numerous (about 14); dorsal fin short, rather high, inserted behind ventrals and before vent; no adipose fin; no caudal fin; anal fin extremely long, extending from vent to tip of tail (its rays about 200 in number); ventrals moderate, not very far back; pectorals rather long, narrow, inserted high; no axillary scales; shoulder-girdle weak, its uppermost bone (supraclavicle or post-temporal) touching the cranium at the nuchal region, but not connected with it laterally; air-bladder large, simple; stomach cœcal; pyloric cœca in moderate number; intestines short; ovaries not closed; vertebræ very many, 60+x. Fishes of the deep sea.

Genus 61. ALDROVANDIA Goode & Bean.

Ventrals normal; no second dorsal fin; vertex scaleless; scales of lateral line enlarged, provided with photophores; head with pointed snout and prominent lateral ridges; anal moderate, high, its height one-third to one-fourth that of dorsal. The 3 Hawaiian species of this genus are fully described in Section II.

Order I. HEMIBRANCHII.—The Hemibranchs.

Interclavicles developed; gills pectinate; post-temporal simple, not furcate; supraclavicle quite small; superior pharyngeal bones reduced in number, the bones of the gill-arches also reduced except in *Gasterosteidæ;* inferior pharyngeals present, not united; ventral fins abdominal or subabdominal, joined to the intraclavicle or else detached from it through partial atrophy of the shoulder-girdle;

mouth bounded above by premaxillaries only; shoulder-girdle simple in structure; basis of cranium simple and without tube; 4 anterior vertebræ more or less elongate; snout usually more or less produced, the small mouth at its end. A small group, well distinguished from the *Percesoces* and other *Teleocephali*, from ancestors of which it is probably descended, differing in the presence of the interclavicles and in the reduction of the shoulder-girdle and other structures. Its relations to the *Lophobranchii* are close, the characters of the latter being largely extremes of the same modifications.

Family XXXV. AULOSTOMIDÆ.—The Trumpet-Fishes.

Body compressed, elongate, covered with small ctenoid scales; lateral line continuous; head long; mouth small, at the end of a long, compressed tube; lower jaw prominent, with a barbel at the symphysis; premaxillary feeble, not protractile; maxillary broad, triangular, with a supplemental bone; teeth minute, in bands, on lower jaw and vomer; branchiostegals 4; gills 4, a slit behind the fourth; pseudobranchiæ well developed; gillrakers obsolete; gill-membranes separate, free from the isthmus; air-bladder large; spinous dorsal present, of 8–12 very slender free spines; soft dorsal and anal rather long, similiar, posterior, with 23 to 28 rays each; caudal small, rhombic, the middle rays longest, but not produced into a filament; ventrals abdominal, of 6 rays, all articulated; pectorals broad, rounded, the space in front of them scaly; first 4 vertebræ elongated; 2 pyloric cœca. A single genus, with 2 species, found in tropical seas.

Genus 62. AULOSTOMUS Lacépède.

Characters of the genus included above.

75. Aulostomus valentini (Bleeker). "*Nunu.*" Fig. 34.

Head 3; depth 3.75 in snout; snout 1.5; eye 8 in snout; maxillary 4 in snout; mandible 2.65 in snout; D. xi–27; A. 26; scales about 19–250–20.

Body elongate, compressed, covered with small ctenoid scales; lateral line continuous, slightly arched over base of pectoral; head long; eye moderate, posterior; mouth small, oblique, at the end of a long compressed tube; lower jaw prominent, hooked and with a barbel at the symphysis; premaxillary slender; maxillary broad; minute teeth on lower jaw, vomer, and palatines; dorsal similar to anal, both posterior, dorsal directly over anal, their posterior bases arching and nearly meeting on the long slender caudal peduncle.

Color in alcohol, brown with about 14 lighter colored cross-bands, about as wide as eye, extending around the body; base of dorsal and anal black; a black spot on upper anterior half of caudal, and one usually present on lower rays; a similar spot on base of each ventral; first rays of dorsal black; fins otherwise pale yellowish; a black spot on middle of maxillary; sometimes a series of 2 to 5 or 6 small black spots on median line of belly in front of anal; sometimes other black spots on belly.

The above description chiefly from a specimen (No. 03327) 19.5 inches long, from Honolulu. Other examples somewhat smaller are darker in coloration, some of them uniform chocolate-brown

FIG. 34.—*Aulostomus valentini* (Bleeker); after Günther.

without cross-bars except on caudal peduncle and between dorsal and anal fin, where there are light bars which tend to break up into white spots. The caudal usually has the 2 black spots, though the lower one is often absent.

The color of this species seems subject to great variation. Garrett, in Fische der Südsee, figured 2 forms, one a uniform lemon-yellow and another light brown with 5 or 6 rosy-brown longitudinal stripes each less than pupil in width; a narrow line of same color on caudal peduncle with a broader crossbar at each end and one at its middle; head pale rosy with 3 deeper rosy oblique bars on snout; fins all pale rosy; middle caudal rays scarcely rosy; a black spot on maxillary, one on base of ventral and 2 on caudal fin.   In the yellow figure there is a black spot on maxillary and one on upper caudal rays, but none below nor on ventral.

This species is fairly abundant at Honolulu, where specimens were obtained by Jenkins in 1889, by the *Albatross* in 1896 and 1902, by Wood in 1898, and by us in 1901.   The *Albatross* obtained it also at Laysan, and it occurs at Johnston Island.

Family XXXVI. FISTULARIIDÆ.—The Cornet-Fishes.

Body extremely elongate, much depressed, broader than deep; scaleless but with bony plates on various parts of the body, mostly covered by the skin; head very long, the anterior bones of the skull much produced, forming a long tube, which terminates in the narrow mouth; this tube formed by the symplectic, proethmoid, metapterygoid, quadrate, palatines, vomer, and mesethmoid; both jaws, and usually the vomer and palatines also, with minute teeth; membrane uniting the bones of the tube below, very lax, so that the tube is capable of much dilation; post-temporal coossified with the cranium; branchiostegals 5 to 7; gills 4, a slit behind the fourth; gill-membranes separate, free from the isthmus; gillrakers obsolete; basibranchial elements wanting; pseudobranchiæ present; air-bladder large; spinous dorsal entirely absent; soft dorsal short, posterior, somewhat elevated; anal fin opposite and similar to soft dorsal; caudal fin forked, the middle rays produced into a long filament; pectorals small, with a broad base, preceded by a smooth area as in *Gasterosteidæ;* pectoral ossicles 3; inter-clavicles greatly lengthened; supraclavicles very small; ventral fins very small, wide apart, abdominal (through partial atrophy of the girdle, by which they lose connection with the interclavicles), far in advance of the dorsal, composed of 6 soft rays; pyloric cœca few; intestine short; vertebræ very numerous (4+44 to 49+28 to 33); the first 4 vertebræ very long.   Fishes of the tropical seas, related to the sticklebacks in structure, but with prolonged snout and different ventral fins.   A single genus, with few species.

Genus 63. FISTULARIA Linnæus.

Characters of the genus included with those of the family.

76. Fistularia petimba Lacépède.

Head 2.65 in length; depth 13 in head; eye 10 in head; snout 3.5 in body; interorbital 10; mandible 4.5 in snout; D. 14 (14 to 17); A. 14 or 15.

Interorbital space slightly concave with a strong median ridge and fainter lateral ones, diverging both anteriorly and posteriorly; a rosette of short, diverging lines upon top of snout at about one-ninth distance from eye; 2 ridges on upper surface of snout nearest together mesially, then diverging slightly, inclosing a central ridge and coming together again at tip of snout; lateral ridges finely serrate, anteriorly smooth; other ridges smooth, the lower lateral ridge serrate posteriorly, not showing from above; serrations on posterior rim of orbit above and on lateral occipital ridges; body much depressed, entirely smooth; depth one-half width; lateral line along middle of side, ascending, the lines from the 2 sides coming near together on back behind pectorals for a distance about equal to postorbital portion of head; lateral line on large specimens armed posteriorly with a series of embedded keels, which become smaller anteriorly, entirely disappearing somewhat in advance of dorsal; in small examples this keeled portion is asperate; distance of origin of dorsal fin from base of caudal about half length of snout; height of dorsal about twice eye; anal opposite dorsal and similar to it; caudal lobes smaller than dorsal; caudal filament 1.5 in snout; ventrals short, equal to eye.

Color in alcohol, brown above, lighter below; fins pale.

The above description chiefly from a specimen (No. 03584) 42 inches long, from Honolulu.   We have also from Honolulu 2 examples (Nos. 02945 and 03131) 39 and 37 inches long, respectively; 98 examples 6 to 17.5 inches long, from Hilo, and 1 specimen 19 inches long from Kailua; specimens from Japan and Samoa, and numerous specimens obtained by the *Albatross* in 1902 at Honolulu, Hilo, Necker Island, and Hanalei Bay, Kauai.   We have examined 13 examples collected in 1889 by Dr. Jenkins at Honolulu, 20 small specimens obtained by the *Albatross* November 8, 1899, in the harbor of Papeete, Tahiti, and a large example from the Philippines.   Snyder mentions finding skeletons of this fish at Necker Island, where the fish had been carried ashore by birds.

77. Fistularia serrata Cuvier.

Head 3.6 in length; D. 13 to 15; A. 14 or 15; V. 6; branchiostegals 7.

The tube into which the head is produced is exceedingly long, the part of the head situated behind the orbit being contained 6.5 times in its length; it is distinctly serrated on the outer edge, as high as broad near its base, and somewhat compressed in its anterior portion; a vertical cut across its middle would be hexagonal.   The cleft of the mouth is horizontal, extending nearly as far backward as the maxillary.   Lower jaw prominent; intermaxillary styliform, not protractile; jaws and palatines armed with a series of small teeth; vomerine teeth rudimentary, if present.

The upper surface of the tube is covered with a very thin skin; the middle is much more elevated than the lateral portions, at least on the basal half of the tube, and is formed by crenulated ridges, the outer of which arise from the anterior angle of the orbit, first convergent, and then keeping a parallel direction. The lateral edge of the tube is very distinctly serrated and provided with rather prominent spines posteriorly. The eye is elongate ovate, much longer than high, its horizontal diameter one-half of its distance from the base of the pectoral fin; it is protected by prominent angles of the frontal bones anteriorly and posteriorly; the bony ridge between the orbits is concave and narrow, its width being less than the vertical diameter of the eye; crown of head rather convex, with slight crenulated striæ; nostrils close together, one before the other, in front of the anterior angle of orbit on side of head; opercle not quite twice as long as high, and covered with a thick membrane which is prolonged beyond margin of bone and fixed to base of pectoral; gill-opening wide, but not extending upward beyond base of pectoral; 6 slender branchiostegals; shields of anterior portion of trunk are the following: 1, a narrow strip along the median line; 2, a pair of broader ones occupying the sides of the back; 3, a narrow one on each side; 4, the pubic bones on the belly.

Body depressed, nearly twice as broad as high; naked, without dermal ossifications; lateral line marked by pores and small narrow bony shields, sunk in the skin anteriorly, becoming broader on the tail, and armed with a compressed spine directed backward; spines forming a kind of serrature.

Base of pectoral fin obliquely curved; fin somewhat longer than the orbit and rounded; a small foramen posteriorly in its axil; ventral fins widely apart, their distance from the pectoral 2/7 of that from the caudal; ventrals much shorter than pectoral and composed of 6 soft rays; a series of feeble spines embedded in the skin along median line of back and of abdomen; these spines do not belong to the endoskeleton for if the skin is removed these spines follow, and are easily detached from its outer surface. (Günther.)

Color in life, upper parts dark drab; lower, white; tips of dorsal, anal, and lobes of caudal rosy with dusky shades; pectoral transparent. Fifteen specimens were taken at Honolulu. (Jenkins.)

Not obtained by us in 1901 nor by the *Albatross* in 1902.

Family XXXVII. MACRORHAMPHOSIDÆ.

Body compressed, oblong, or elevated, covered with small, rough scales; no lateral line; some bony strips on side of back, and on margin of thorax and abdomen, the former sometimes confluent into a shield; bones of skull much prolonged anteriorly, forming a long tube which bears the short jaws at the end; no teeth; gill-openings wide; branchiostegals 4; branchihyals and pharyngeals mostly present, the fourth superior branchihyal and the first and fourth superior pharyngeals only wanting; 2 dorsal fins, the first of 4 to 7 spines, the second of which is very long and strong; soft dorsal and anal moderate; ventral fins small, abdominal, of 1 spine and 5 soft rays; pectorals short; caudal fin emarginate, its middle rays not produced; air-bladder large; pseudobranchiæ present; gills 4, a slit behind the fourth; vertebræ about 24. the 4 anterior ones much lengthened; no pyloric cœca; intestinal canal short.

Genus 64. MACRORHAMPHOSUS Lacépède.

Body oblong, graduating into the caudal peduncle; back straight; dorsal spines about 7; characters otherwise included above. The single Hawaiian species of this genus is fully described in Section II.

Order J. LOPHOBRANCHII.

Gills tufted, not laminated, composed of small rounded lobes attached to the gill-arches; interclavicles well developed; scapula suspended to the cranium by a post-temporal; superior branchihyals and pharyngeals, and basal branchihyals wanting or not ossified; mouth very small, bounded above by the premaxillaries; post-temporal simple, coossified with the cranium; basis of cranium simple; pectoral fins with elevated bases; anterior vertebræ modified, the diapophyses much expanded; air-bladder simple, without air-duct; snout produced, bearing the small, toothless mouth at the end; gill-covers reduced to a large simple plate; skin with bony plates; muscular system little developed; the *Syngnathidæ* have neither spinous dorsal nor ventral fins; the *Solenostomidæ* of the Indian Ocean, constituting the suborder *Solenostomi*, have all the fins well developed.

Family XXXVIII. SOLENOSTOMIDÆ.

Body compressed; tail very short; snout long, compressed, all parts covered with thin skin, below which is the dermal skeleton with star-like ossifications; spinous dorsal short; soft dorsal and anal long, with elevated base; caudal long; ventrals close together, inserted opposite spinous dorsal, each of 7 rays; the fins free in the male, in the female adnate to the body, forming a large pouch for the reception of the eggs; branchiostegals 4, very thin; intestinal canal simple. Singular fishes of the East Indies, constituting 1 genus.

Genus 65. SOLENOSTOMUS Lacépède.

Characters of the genus included above.

78. Solenostomus cyanopterus Bleeker. Fig. 35.

Head 2.2 in length; depth 5; D. v–20; P. 27; V. 7; A. 19; C. 15; depth of snout at middle 4.5 in its length; eye 6.25 in snout; dorsal spines 2 in head; ventral equal to snout or a little more; caudal a little shorter than head; caudal peduncle shorter than base of second dorsal.

Color pink, with small black dots like ink specks scattered over head and upper part of body; eye red; fins pale, the spinous dorsal with 2 long black ocelli (said to be dark blue in life) on mem-

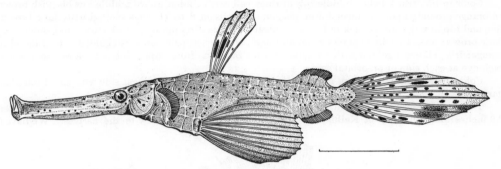

Fig. 35.—*Solenostomus cyanopterus* Bleeker.

branes of first and second spines; besides black dots, caudal with small inky spots like those on body, but more elongate, several of them drawn out into lines. The above description is taken from Jordan and Snyder's Japanese specimen. The only Hawaiian reference is that given by Bleeker. It is doubtful if the species really occurs in these islands.

Family XXXIX. SYNGNATHIDÆ.—The Pipe-Fishes.

Body elongate, usually slender, covered with bony plates which are firmly connected, forming a bony carapace; head slender, the snout long, tube-like, bearing the short toothless jaws at the end; gill-opening reduced to a small aperture behind the upper part of the opercle; tail long, prehensile or not, usually provided with a small caudal fin; male fishes with an egg-pouch usually placed on the under side of the tail, sometimes on the abdomen, commonly formed of 2 folds of skin which meet on the median line; the eggs are received into this pouch and retained until some time after hatching, when the pouch opens, permitting the young to escape; dorsal fin single, nearly median, of soft rays only; pectorals small or wanting; ventrals none; anal fin minute, usually present. Genera about 15; species 150. Small fishes, found in all warm seas, sometimes entering fresh waters.

Genus 66. HIPPOCAMPUS Rafinesque. The Sea-Horses.

Body strongly compressed, the belly gibbous, tapering abruptly to a long, quadrangular, prehensile tail; head with a distinct curved neck, placed nearly at a right angle with the direction of the body, surmounted by a compressed occipital crest, on the top of which is an angular, star-shaped coronet; top and sides of the head with spines; physiognomy remarkably horse-like, like that of a conventional "knight" at chess; body and tail covered with bony plates, forming rings, those on the body each with 6 spines or tubercles, those of the tail with 4; pectoral fins present, short and broad; anal minute, usually present; dorsal fin moderate, opposite the vent; egg-pouch in male a sac at base of the tail, terminating near the vent. Species numerous, in all warm seas. These fishes attach themselves by their tails to seaweed and other floating substances, and are often carried to great distances by currents.

79. Hippocampus hilonis Jordan & Evermann. Plate 23.

Eye about 4 in snout; snout 2 in head; D. 16, on 3 rings; rings 12 + 35. Tail a little longer than head and trunk; trunk rather deep, compressed, its width 2 in depth; eye small, equal to interorbital width, which is concave, broader posteriorly; gill-opening high, rather large; spines on head and body very blunt, rounded or obsolete, though forming knobs of more or less equal size along tail; coronet with rounded knobs, before which is a short keel or trenchant ridge; base of dorsal about 1.35 in snout.

Color in alcohol, dark or blackish brown, more or less uniform.

This species is known to us only from the example described above. It is closely related to the Japanese *Hippocampus aterrimus* Jordan & Snyder, but on comparison with the type of that species, was found to differ in the presence of the keel on the top of the head and in other minor characters. It is also close to *H. ringens.*

80. Hippocampus fisheri Jordan & Evermann.   Fig. 36.

Eye 2.8 in snout; snout 2 in head; D. 18, on 4 rings; A. 4; P. 15; rings 12+34.

Tail longer than head and trunk; trunk rather deep, compressed; its width 1.7 in depth; eye small, equal to interorbital width; interorbital space concave; gill-opening small, high; spines on head and body rather high, sharp; 2 rings on trunk between each pair of larger spines; tail with 3 rings between each pair of larger spines; coronet well developed, with 5 spines; spines over eye blunt; base of dorsal about equal to snout; anal small, long; pectoral broad, rays rather long.

Color in life, trunk below middle row of rings yellowish golden, above middle row blackish brown on orange ground; knobs orange; lower portion of knobs on 8 to 11 rings spotted with dark brown; side and top of tail same as back of trunk; ventral side pale dirty orange; head, crown and snout dirty dark brown; an orange band across snout and one before eyes; pale brownish golden over gills; chin orange; iris yellowish golden with 8 reddish streaks radiating from pupil; fins pale; a red spot before each eye at each side of preorbital spine.

Color in alcohol, pale brown, upper surface with dark brown marblings; side with small roundish dark spots.

The above description is from the type, No. 50625, U. S. Nat. Mus. (field No. 03835), a specimen 2.6 inches long, obtained at Kailua, Hawaii, where the species was new to the natives.   We have 5

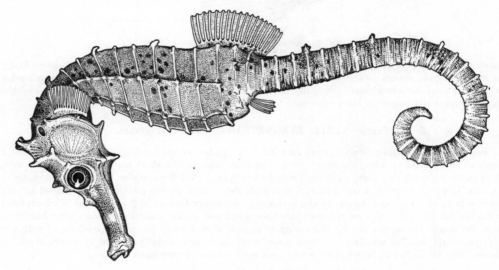

FIG. 36.—*Hippocampus fisheri* Jordan & Evermann; from the type.

other examples, each about 3 inches long, taken from the stomach of a dolphin (*Coryphæna* sp.) which was captured at Hilo, July 18, 1901.

When fresh, No. 03507, a male, was pink or pale cardinal along and near the keels; plates on back and above middle row of knobs on side mottled blackish on pale red ground; plates below middle row of knobs and on belly porcelain white; egg-pouch uniform pale cardinal-red, paler than rest of body; tail same pink or pale cardinal, mottled with blackish blotches; top of head and crown blackish on pale red; cheek, jaw, and snout pink.   Some examples had ventral side of tail and portion behind fourth prominent spine of tail uniform pale cardinal-red.

Genus 67. DORYRHAMPHUS Kaup.

This genus differs from *Siphostoma* chiefly in the position of the egg-pouch of the male, which is under the abdomen instead of the tail.   The angles of the body are strongly ridged.   Tail shorter than body.   Tropical seas.

81. Doryrhamphus pleurotænia (Günther).   Fig. 37.

D. 25; osseous rings 18+14; edge of each ring terminating in a slightly prominent spine; lateral line continuous, passing into the lower caudal edge; snout with denticulated ridges; operculum with a slightly oblique raised line, below which are several other radiating keels; snout shorter than remaining portion of head; interorbital space concave, the supraorbital ridge being raised but scarcely

serrated; vent behind middle of dorsal fin, equidistant from root of pectoral and snout; distance of snout from vent 1.16 inches; distance of vent from end of caudal 0.75 inch. Color light grayish, with a brownish-black band from snout along the middle of body and caudal fin. Off Honolulu, 18 fathoms. (Günther.) A specimen was obtained by the *Albatross* at Honolulu in 1902.

FIG. 37.—*Doryrhamphus pleurotænia* (Günther); after Günther.

Our single specimen of this species was lost. The color note taken in the field is as follows: Color in life (No. 03553) with a reddish-brown lateral band from tip of snout through eye to base of caudal, other parts of body olivaceous brown; white band on top of snout from tip to forehead; 2 red spots on each side of snout a short distance behind the angles of mouth; pectoral, dorsal, and anal transparent; caudal brilliantly colored, dusky orange with brown, margin lemon-yellow.

Genus 68. ICHTHYOCAMPUS Kaup.

Head short, with a shorter, compressed, sharp-ridged snout; orbits slightly projecting; operculum round, swollen, higher than broad, and grained like the head; tail almost as thick as the body and suddenly pointed at the setting on of the very rudimentary caudal fin; anus situated under the beginning of the dorsal fin; the edges of the concave back coalesce with those of the tail into one line which runs without interruption to the caudal fin; egg-pouch of male under the tail. A single species of this genus is known from the Hawaiian Islands. (See Section II.)

Order K. SYNENTOGNATHI.—The Synentognathous Fishes.

Lower pharyngeal bones fully united; second and third superior pharyngeals variously enlarged, not articulated to the cranium, sending processes forward, the fourth small or fused with the third; vertebræ numerous (45 to 70), the abdominal ones much more numerous than the caudal; ventral fins abdominal, without spine, the rays more than 5; scapula suspended to cranium by a posttemporal bone, which is slender and furcate; articular bone of lower jaw with a small supplemental bone perhaps corresponding to the coronoid bone; parietal bones much produced, well separated by the supraoccipital; supraclavicle not distinct; no interclavicles; no mesocoracoid; maxillary very close to premaxillary and sometimes firmly joined to it, the suture always distinct; basis of cranium double in front, but without muscular tube; no adipose fin; fins without spines; lateral line concurrent with the belly, peculiar in structure; air-bladder usually large, without pneumatic duct; intestinal tract simple, without pyloric cœca. This order is allied to the *Haplomi* on the one hand and to the *Percesoces* on the other, and like these groups, it marks the transition from the soft-rayed to the spiny-rayed fishes. In their anatomical characters the *Synentognathi* most resemble the latter, but there are never spines in the fins, and the lower pharyngeals are united. The group is divisible into 4 closely related families, which have usually been regarded as subfamilies of one family, *Exocœtidæ* or *Scomberesocidæ*.

Family XL. BELONIDÆ.—The Needle-fishes.

Body elongate, very slender, compressed or not, covered with small, thin scales; lateral line very low, running as a fold along side of belly; both jaws produced in a beak, the lower jaw the longer, very much the longer in the young, which resemble *Hemiramphus;* maxillaries grown fast to premaxillaries; each jaw with a band of small, sharp teeth, besides a series of longer, wide-set, sharp, conical teeth; no finlets; dorsal fin opposite anal, both fins rather long; air-bladder present; lower pharyngeals united to form a long, slender, narrow plate, with flat surface covered with small, pointed teeth; upper pharyngeals distinct, the third pair little enlarged, each with some 15 moderate, unequal, pointed teeth (*Tylosurus marinus*), fourth pair well developed, with similar teeth, but without anterior processes; vertebræ numerous, with zygapophyses; ovary single. Voracious, carniverous fishes, bearing a superficial resemblance to the gar-pikes; found in all warm seas, sometimes entering rivers. Genera 4; species about 50, the majority of them American. Their habits are ordinarily much like those of the pike, but when startled they swim along the surface with extraordinary rapidity, often leaping above the water for short distances. When thus leaping the large species of the Tropics are sources of danger to incautious fishermen, sometimes piercing the naked abdomens of the savages. Most of them are good food-fishes, but the green color of the bones of the larger species often causes them to be avoided for no good reason.

Genus 69. BELONE Cuvier.

This genus differs from *Tylosurus* in the possession of gillrakers, and is confined to the Old World and the islands of the Pacific.

82. Belone platyura Bennett. Fig. 38.

Head (tip of mandible slightly damaged) about 1.88 in trunk; depth in trunk a little over 16; D. 13; A. 19; P. 12; V. 6; scales about 177 or more to base of caudal; greatest width of head equal to its depth; upper jaw a little over 1.5 in head; eye 2 in postocular part of head, 1.25 in interorbital space; pectoral about 4.3 in space between tip of snout and opercle; ventral 6.5.

Body elongate, depressed on the back and upper surface and also below, the sides rounded; head long, broadened and flattened above, somewhat constrained below; eye rather large and a trifle longer than deep; jaws very long and slender, the upper much shorter than the lower, and the groove of maxillary extending well beyond anterior margin of eye; teeth in mandible not extending beyond tip of upper jaw, and with a median asperous ridge; no vomerine teeth; tongue small, bluntly pointed, a rather thin fleshy flap a little free in front; nasal cavity large and close to upper surface of eye; interorbital space broad and flattened; gill-openings large, the isthmus very narrow, long, and slender; gillrakers rather large, in moderate number; no pseudobranchiæ; peritoneum gray, or marked with numerous dark dots.

Scales moderately large and narrowly imbricated, those on middle of back enlarged; no fin flaps; scales on cheeks, opercles and a number of small ones on top of head; lateral line running low or along the ventral part of the body, and posteriorly below keel on side of caudal peduncle; origin of dorsal a little nearer that of ventral than base of caudal and well behind anal; anterior dorsal rays longest, the posterior or last rays also elongated, longer than middle ones but not as long as the anterior; anal with anterior rays longest; caudal deeply emarginate, the rays strong, the lower lobe the longer, and the entire length of the fin a little more than that of pectoral; pectoral with rays all more or less firm and strengthened, the uppermost enlarged; ventrals rather short and placed a little nearer base of pectoral than base of caudal; caudal peduncle very broad and depressed, its greatest width twice its least depth, and with a sharp keel along each side.

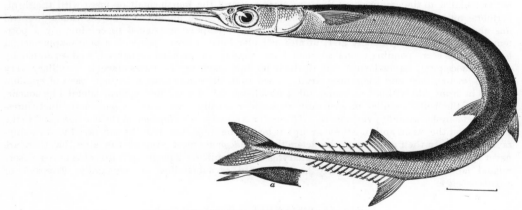

Fig. 38.—*Belone platyura* Bennett.

Color in alcohol, deep blue-black above, sharply defined along the sides from the silvery white of the lower surface; pectoral, ventrals, and anal all more or less grayish. In the young there is a black lateral band and the dorsal is high.

This description is from an example (No. 04992) 14 inches long, taken at Kailua. We have a number of examples taken at Honolulu and Kailua. Several were obtained by Dr. Jenkins at Honolulu in 1889, and others by the *Albatross* in 1902. The species also occurs in Samoa.

Genus 70. TYLOSURUS Cocco.

Body elongate, very slender, not much compressed; both jaws prolonged into a beak, the lower jaw somewhat the longer, much the longer in young fishes, the very young resembling *Hemiramphus;* each jaw armed with a band of small, sharp teeth, beside which is a series of longer, wide-set, sharp, conical, unequal teeth; no teeth on vomer or palatines; scales small, thin; lateral line running along side of belly, becoming median on the tail, no finlets, dorsal fin more or less elevated anteriorly; caudal fin short, unequally lunated or forked; pectorals moderate; ventrals small, the latter inserted behind the middle of body; gillrakers obsolete; bones usually more or less green; size comparatively large.

Species numerous. Voracious fishes, chiefly American, one species crossing to Europe; some of them entering rivers.

Only one species is known to occur in the Hawaiian Islands.

83. Tylosurus giganteus (Schlegel). "*Áhaáha;*" "*Auau.*" Fig. 39.

Head a little over 2 in trunk; depth 9.5 in trunk; D. 24; A. 22; P. 14; V. 6; scales about 370 or more to base of caudal; depth of head a little more than its greatest width; eye about 2.13 in post-ocular part of head, 1.3 in interorbital space; pectoral about 3.5 in space between tip of snout and opercle; ventral 3.85.

Body elongate, more or less rounded, the sides a little compressed; head long, flattened above, the sides compressed, somewhat constricted below; eye moderate, a little longer than deep; jaws long, strong, and rather powerful, the lower a trifle the longer; groove of maxillary extending posteriorly for nearly half the eye diameter; teeth developed as large canines in both jaws, and with villiform bands along the edges; also a median roughened ridge on the mandible; no vomerine teeth; tongue small, blunt, little free in front, and fleshy; nasal cavity large, close to upper margin of eye and with a thick fleshy flap over the nostril; interorbital space broad, slightly convex; top of head with bony striæ; gill-openings large, the isthmus very narrow, long and thin; no gillrakers; no pseudobranchiæ; peritoneum gray; scales very small, narrowly imbricated, very much smaller on back than elsewhere; no fin flaps; cheek scaled, a few scales on top of head, but opercles bare; lateral line running inferiorly along side and up on side of caudal peduncle; origin of dorsal nearer that of ventral than base of caudal by about length of pectoral, the origin of anal only slightly in advance; anterior dorsal rays elongate, those forming posterior half of fin rather long, but shorter than the former; anterior anal rays forming a rather long lobe; caudal rays strong, deeply emarginate, lower lobe the longer, length of fin about 2.3 in entire length of head; pectoral rather small, upper ray enlarged; ventrals inserted nearer base of pectoral than base of caudal by a space equal to that between middle of eye and posterior margin of opercle; least width of caudal peduncle only a trifle more than its least depth, the keel along side more or less obsolete.

FIG. 39.—*Tylosurus giganteus* (Schlegel); after Bleeker.

Color in alcohol more or less silvery white below, the upper surface greenish brown; fins tinted with yellowish about their bases.

This description taken from an example (No. 05006) 18 inches long obtained at Honolulu. We have others taken at Honolulu, one by Dr. Jenkins in 1889. In an example from Hilo the color markings are better preserved. It has a dark or blackish lateral band from over pectoral to near base of caudal, the dorsal, caudal, and pectoral are more or less blackish, and the margin of the preopercle is broadly marked with blackish brown.

This fish reaches a rather large size, one of our numerous examples being 40 inches long. It is a food-fish of considerable importance, living in the open sea.

Genus 71. ATHLENNES Jordan & Fordice.

This genus is close to *Tylosurus*, differing chiefly in the greatly compressed, almost ribbon-shaped body. The single species is American and Pacific.

84. Athlennes hians (Cuvier & Valenciennes). "*Áhaáha.*" Fig. 40.

Head (tip of beak broken) 2.6 in trunk; depth 9 in trunk; D. 25; A. 26; P. 12; V. 6; scales about 520 in a lateral series to base of caudal; depth of head about twice its width; eye about 2 in postocular part of head, 1 and a trifle over in interorbital space; pectoral 3.3 in head; ventral a little over 4.

Body very elongate, narrowly compressed, the sides flattened; head flattened on top, the sides strongly compressed and the under surface narrowly constricted; eye rather large, much longer than deep; jaws long, the upper strongly arched upward at the base, so that the mouth can not be closed, the mandible very broad and deep at the base; groove of maxillary extending to below middle of eye at least; many large canines in each jaw, and the floor of the mandible with a median asperous ridge; no vomerine teeth; tongue well developed, rather small, and free in front; nasal cavity large, near upper margin of eye, and with a thick fleshy flap over the nostril; interorbital space broad, flattened;

top of head with a few bony striæ; gill-opening large, the isthmus a thin frenum; no gillrakers; no pseudobranchiæ.

Scales very minute and narrowly imbricated; top of head and a large patch on cheeks scaled, otherwise naked; no fin flaps; lateral line running along the ventral surface of body, also along the lower side of caudal peduncle to base of caudal; origin of dorsal a little nearer base of ventral than, that of caudal, and the anterior rays very long and forming a falcate lobe; anal similar to dorsal, the anterior rays long and forming a long falcate lobe, the origin of the fin only a trifle in advance of that of the dorsal; caudal small, the rays rigid, strong, the edge emarginate, and the lower lobe the longer; pectoral with the uppermost ray enlarged; ventrals inserted a trifle nearer anterior margin of nasal cavity than base of caudal; caudal peduncle compressed, its least width two-thirds its least depth, and no keel along sides.

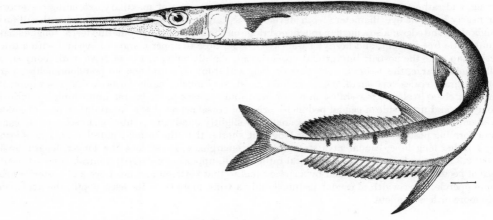

Fig. 40.—*Athlennes hians* (Cuvier & Valenciennes).

Color in alcohol, brown above, the lower portions, including the sides, silvery white, and the fins all more or less brownish; 3 large blackish blotches sometimes present on back below dorsal.

This description taken from an example (No. 03561) 30 inches long obtained at Honolulu in 1889 by Dr. Jenkins. We have also 2 others collected by him at Honolulu and 5 large examples collected by ourselves from the same locality. The species is recorded by Steindachner from Acapulco. Our specimens range in length from 29 to 40 inches.

This fish was common in the Honolulu market, where it is regarded as a good food-fish. We have thus far failed to find any difference between the Pacific species and the common *Athlennes hians* of the West Indies.

Family XLI. HEMIRAMPHIDÆ.—The Balaos.

Body elongate, more or less compressed, covered with large cycloid scales; upper jaw short, lower jaw variable, sometimes much produced, the toothed portion at base fitting against the toothed premaxillaries; teeth equal, mostly small and tricuspid; maxillaries ankylosed to premaxillaries; gillrakers long; caudal fin rounded or forked; if forked, the lower lobe the longer; anal fin modified in the viviparous species (*Zenarchopterus*), unmodified in the others and usually similar to the dorsal; no finlets; air-bladder large, sometimes cellular; third upper pharyngeal on each side much enlarged, solidly united with its fellow to form an oval plate, with slightly convex surface and covered with blunt tricuspid teeth; this is about as large as the united lower pharyngeals and fits into the concavity of the latter; fourth upper pharyngeal wanting or grown fast to the third; lower pharyngeal large, thick, triangular, with concave surface; vertebræ about 50. Probably not separable from the *Exocœtidæ*.

Herbivorous fishes of the warm seas; mostly shore species, a few pelagic. They feed chiefly on green algæ, and, like the related forms, swim at the surface, occasionally leaping into the air. Size rather small, about a foot in length. Genera about 7; species about 75.

Genus 72. HYPORHAMPHUS Gill. The Halfbeaks.

Body elongate, moderately compressed, the sides of body not vertical, but more or less convex, the dorsal outline parallel with that of the belly. Upper jaw short; lower jaw prolonged into a slender beak, bordered with membrane, this beak shorter in the young; premaxillaries forming a triangular plate, the teeth of which fit against the toothed portion of the mandible; maxillaries joined to premaxillaries; teeth feeble, mostly tricuspid; gillrakers rather long; head covered with large shield like scales; scales deciduous; caudal fin more or less forked, the lower lobe the longer; no finlets; dorsal and anal similar, opposite each other, not modified in the males; last ray of dorsal usually short; ventrals small, inserted well forward, nearly midway between opercle and base of caudal. Air-bladder large, simple, not cellular. Young with the lower jaw short. Sides in our species with a distinct silvery band, as in *Atherina*. Oviparous. Species numerous in all warm seas, going in large schools, but usually remaining near shore, feeding chiefly on green algæ. Size comparatively small.

One species known from Hawaiian waters.

85. Hyporhamphus pacificus (Steindachner). Fig. 41.

Head (from tip of snout) 4.6 in trunk; depth 9.5 in trunk; D. 15; A. 18; P. 12; V. 6; scales about 64 in a lateral series; width of head about 1.5 in its depth; snout 2.67 in head; eye 4.25, 1.5 in postocular part of head, about 1.67 in snout, and 1 in interorbital space; pectoral 1.5 in head; ventral 2.67.

Body moderately elongate, compressed, the back rounded rather broadly; head flattened above, the sides compressed, and the lower surface narrowly constricted; snout a trifle over 4 in space between front margin of eye and tip of beak; eye moderate, a trifle longer than deep; mouth a little less than eye; teeth in small villiform bands in jaws; no teeth on roof of mouth; tongue more or less rounded, rather thick and little free around edges; nasal cavity level with the upper part of eye in front and with a small fleshy flap over nostril; interorbital space flattened, and posteriorly the top of the head slightly convex; gill-opening with a long, thin, narrow and sharp-edged isthmus; gillrakers numerous, thin, sharp-pointed; no pseudobranchiæ; scales rather large, very deciduous, and the sides of the head more or less scaly; no scaly fin flaps; lateral line running low along the side to base of caudal; origin of dorsal nearer that of ventral than base of caudal by a space equal to postocular part of head, and about opposite that of anal; anterior dorsal rays the longest; anal more or less similar to dorsal; caudal well forked, the lower lobe the longer, and the length of the fin a little less than head measured to tip of snout; ventrals small, inserted a little posterior to middle of space between base of pectoral and that of caudal by a space about equal to width of head; caudal peduncle compressed, its least width 2 in its least depth.

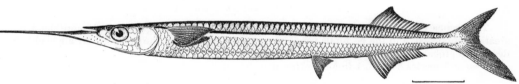

FIG. 41.—*Hyporhamphus pacificus* (Steindachner).

Color in alcohol, dull brown above, and as the scales have all more or less fallen, the edges of the pockets are narrowly blackish; side with a slaty and a silvery lateral band, both together running to caudal; lower surface of body silvery; all the fins more or less tinged with gray; beak blackish.

This description from an example (No. 03562) 10 inches long, taken at Kailua, from which place the collection contains 69 examples, ranging in length from 3 to 10 inches. The usual length seems to be 8 to 10 inches. The species was not seen at Honolulu. Two specimens in the Museum of the Philadelphia Academy (Nos. 7507 and 23338), both young, collected "near the Sandwich Islands" by Dr. Wm. H. Jones, doubtless belong to this species.

Genus 73. HEMIRAMPHUS Cuvier.

Body more robust than in *Hyporhamphus* and different in form, the sides being compressed and nearly vertical and parallel; head and jaws as in *Hyporhamphus*. Dorsal longer than anal fin and inserted farther forward, its last ray more or less produced in American species; ventral fins small and inserted well backward, much nearer base of caudal than gill-opening; air-bladder cellular, with many partitions (in *H. browni*). Species probably numerous, but most of them have not been examined as to the characters which separate the genus from *Hyporhamphus*.

Only one species known from the Hawaiian Islands.

86. Hemiramphus depauperatus Lay & Bennett. "Mē'emē'e;" "Iheihe." Fig. 42.

Head (from tip of snout) 4.3 in trunk; depth about 6.1 in trunk; D. 14; A. 13; P. 11; V. 6; scales about 60 in a lateral series to base of caudal; width of head about 1.5 in its depth; snout 3 in head; eye 4 in head, 1.4 in snout, 1.6 in postocular portion of head, about one in interorbital space; pectoral less than head by about 0.5 eye diameter; ventral 2 in head.

Body moderately elongate, rather thick, the sides compressed and flattened; head compressed, more or less flattened and rounded above, the lower surface not constricted narrowly; snout about 4.6 in space between front margin of eye and tip of beak; eye moderately large, longer than deep; mouth about 1.75 in eye; teeth in small villiform bands in the jaws; no teeth on roof of mouth; tongue more or less rounded, thick, and a little free around the edges; nasal cavity moderately large above and in front of eye, and with a thick flap over nostril; interorbital space flattened, the top of the head convex posteriorly; gill-opening large, with a long, thin, narrow sharp-edged isthmus; gillrakers rather long, thin, pointed, and numerous; no pseudobranchiæ; peritoneum dark brown; scales rather large, very deciduous and narrowly imbricated, especially along the sides; no scaly flaps at bases of pectorals or ventrals; a number of small scales on the basal portions of the anterior dorsal rays.   Lateral line running low along the side to base of caudal; origin of dorsal well before that of anal and about the last fourth of the space between front margin of eye and base of caudal; dorsal with anterior rays longest; anal similar to dorsal, its base 1.5 in that of the latter; caudal forked, the lower lobe much longer and stronger than the upper; pectoral long, the upper ray enlarged and longest; ventrals rather short, the rays all strong, flattened, and the inner ones much the longer, the margin of the fin concave, ending in sharp points; caudal peduncle compressed, its least width 2 in its least depth.

Color in alcohol, more or less deep silvery, dull bluish black on the back, and as the scales have all

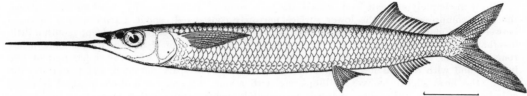

FIG. 42.—*Hemiramphus depauperatus* Lay & Bennett.

more or less fallen, the edges of the pockets are blackish; sides and lower portions silvery white; fins all more or less gray, the dorsal and caudal deeper; top of the head and beak blackish.

This description is from a specimen 14 inches long (No. 03564).   We have many specimens, varying in length from 13.5 to 15.5 inches.   All were taken at Honolulu, some in 1889 by Dr. Jenkins, who considers the species identical with *H. brasiliensis*.   It may be distinguished from the latter, however, by its longer pectoral fin.

Genus 74. EULEPTORHAMPHUS Gill.

This genus consists of pelagic species related to *Hemiramphus*, the body much more slender and greatly compressed, and the pectorals very long, approaching those of the flying-fishes; air-bladder not described, probably cellular.

Two or 3 species known, 1 from the Hawaiian Islands.

87. Euleptorhamphus longirostris (Cuvier).   "*Iheíhe.*"   Fig. 43.

Head (from tip of snout) 6 in trunk; depth 10.75 in trunk; D. 24; A. 23; P. 9; V. 6; scales about 105, according to the pockets; width of head about 1.25 in its depth; snout about 3.17 in head; eye about 3.17 in head, 1.17 in postocular part of head, a little greater than width of interorbital space; pectoral 1.6 in head to end of broken beak; ventral 3 in head (from tip of snout).

Body very long, greatly compressed, the sides flattened, and the middle of the back with a subcarinate ridge; head compressed, flattened on top and the lower surface narrowly constricted; snout about 8 in beak (broken at tip), to front margin of eye; eye rounded, as deep as long; mouth 2 in eye; teeth in small villiform bands in the jaws and on the vomer; tongue rather thick, flattened, fleshy;

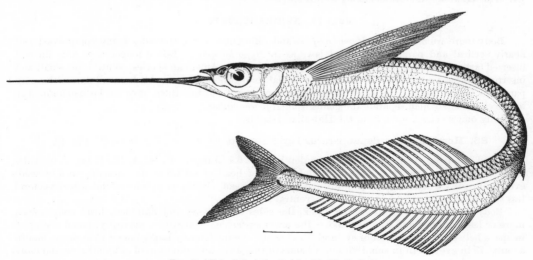

FIG. 43.—*Euleptorhamphus longirostris* (Cuvier).

and a little free in front and around the edges; nasal cavity somewhat small, above the eye in front, and with a well developed fleshy flap; interorbital space broad and flattened and the top of the head posteriorly convex; gill-opening large, the isthmus a rather long thin narrow frenum; gillrakers short, moderately numerous, rather weak, and pointed; no pseudobranchiæ; scales rather small, very deciduous, the head naked; no scaly fin flaps; lateral line running low along the side; origin of the dorsal about the last third in the space between the front of the nasal cavity and the base of the caudal and well in advance of the anal; dorsal rays long; caudal deeply forked, the lower lobe much the longer; anal long, the rays also long; pectoral very long, and reaching for more than two-thirds the distance to ventrals, the rays all strong and the upper enlarged; ventral very small, only a little posterior to the center of the space between the bases of pectoral and caudal; caudal peduncle with its least width 2 in its least depth.

Color in life (No. 02993) pale bluish silvery above; scales on back with darker edges; lower side and belly silvery; top of head dark bluish, side silvery; bill bluish black; fins pale bluish, anal white; upper lobe of caudal with a diffuse curved black band parallel with the edge.

Color in alcohol, more or less silvery, dull brown above, and as the scales have all more or less fallen, the edges of the pockets are narrowly blackish; side with a slaty silvery lateral band to caudal; all the fins more or less dull olivaceous gray, the anal and ventrals whitish; beak blackish.

This description from an example (No. 03193) 17 inches long, taken at Honolulu, where we obtained many others. We have also examined a number of examples collected by Dr. O. P. Jenkins at Honolulu in 1889. Our specimens range in length from 16 to 18 inches.

Family XLII. EXOCŒTIDÆ.—Flying-fishes.

Body oblong or elongate, covered with cycloid scales, which are rather deciduous; lateral line running very low, along the side of the belly; head more or less scaly with vertical sides; mouth moderate, terminal, the jaws not prolonged into a beak; premaxillaries not protractile, hinged at base mesially; margin of the upper jaw chiefly formed by the premaxillaries, the short maxillaries entering the lateral margin; maxillary free from the premaxillary, its edge slipping under the front of the preorbital; dentition various, the teeth small and weak; dorsal fin without spines, inserted on the posterior part of the body, opposite the anal and more or less similar to it; ventrals abdominal, of several soft rays, inserted posteriorly; pectoral fin inserted high, used as an organ of flight; shoulder-girdle and pectoral muscles very strong; caudal fin forked, the lower lobe the longer; no finlets; vent close in front of anal; nostrils large, double, near the eye; lower pharyngeals enlarged and fully united, forming a large, transversely concave plate, covered with large, close-set, blunt, tricuspid teeth; third upper pharyngeal greatly enlarged, not united with its fellow, both covered with large, blunt, tricuspid teeth; fourth superior pharyngeal wanting in the adult (probably co-ossified with the third)—these characters verified on *Exocœtus californicus*—vertebræ without zygapophyses; gill-membranes not united, free from the isthmus; pseudobranchiæ hidden, glandular; gillrakers various; gills 4, a slit behind the fourth; air-bladder very large, not cellular so far as known, and extending far backward among the hæmopophyses of the caudal vertebræ; vertebræ about 50; intestinal canal simple, without cœca. Carnivorous or herbivorous fishes. Genera 6 or 8; species about 65; abounding in all warm seas, mostly pelagic, swimming near the surface, and skipping or sailing through the air, sometimes for considerable distances.

Genus 75. EVOLANTIA Snodgrass & Heller.

This genus differs from other genera of flying-fishes chiefly in the short pectoral, which does not reach the ventrals; no teeth on roof of mouth; ventrals small, midway between pectorals and base of caudal.

88. Evolantia microptera (Cuvier & Valenciennes). "*Malolo*." Fig. 44.

Head 4.25 in length; depth 6; D. 13; A. 15; P. 12; V. 6; scales to base of caudal about 45; about 10 scales in a transverse series to middle of belly; width of head less than its depth and about 2 in its length; snout 4 in head, eye 3.5, 1.5 in postocular part of head, 1 in interorbital space; ventral 2.3 in head; base of dorsal 1.3; pectoral 2.75 in body.

Body elongate, compressed; head elongate, pointed in front, the upper profile more or less convex; snout rather short, pointed, and rounded; eye anterior, well behind center of length of head, and the bony rim behind slightly keeled outward; mouth small, superior, the mandible projecting well beyond the snout; teeth in jaws minute, none on roof of mouth; tongue rounded, and free around the edges; nasal cavity moderately small, above eye in front, and with a thick, fleshy flap; interorbital space broad, very slightly concave; gillrakers slender, pointed, rather numerous, and much shorter than the long gill-filaments; peritoneum brown; scales cycloid; lateral line running along the lower part of side; origin of dorsal apparently nearer tip of caudal (damaged) than base of pectoral, and well in advance of the anal; dorsal high, the median ridge elevated; anal high, the anterior rays elevated; caudal deeply forked, the lower lobe the longer; pectoral moderately long, not reaching the origin of ventrals; ventrals small, about midway between origin of pectoral and base of caudal, and not reaching anus; caudal peduncle moderately deep and compressed.

Color in alcohol, brown above, whitish beneath, washed with silvery; along the side a broad, leaden silvery longitudinal band; pectoral gray-brown, edged with whitish; dorsal and caudal dark, the anal and ventrals whitish.

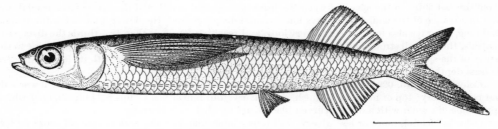

Fig. 44.—*Evolantia microptera* (Cuvier & Valenciennes).

This description from an example 7.5 inches long, obtained at Honolulu in 1889 by Dr. Jenkins. We have a number of others 6 to 7 inches in length from the same place.

This species does not appear to reach a greater length than about 8 inches.

Genus 76. PAREXOCŒTUS Bleeker.

Body moderately elongate, elliptical in cross-section; snout short; lower jaw not produced; roof of mouth (vomer, palatines, and pterygoids) fully provided with teeth; pectoral fins moderate, not reaching beyond middle of dorsal; ventrals long, inserted behind middle of body; anal fin about as long as dorsal; dorsal high. Small flying-fishes of the tropical coasts widely distributed.

89. Parexocœtus rostratus (Günther).

Head a little more than 4 in length; depth 5.5; D. 9; A. 10; scales in lateral line 40; 24 scales between occiput and dorsal fin, and 8 longitudinal series between the origins of dorsal and anal; depth of head equaling distance between extremity of snout and center of eye; eye 4.3 in head, less than width of interorbital space, which is flat.

Snout much produced, its length a little more than that of postorbital part of head; mouth cleft directed upward, subvertical; dorsal beginning scarcely in advance of anal, elevated, its anterior rays when depressed extending to caudal; anal fin low; lower caudal lobe not much shorter than the head; pectoral reaching to dorsal, its length less than one-half the total body length (without caudal); ventral extending to vent. Dorsal black, with the last ray white; pectoral black, with the upper and lower rays white; ventral and anal whitish. Length 6.5 inches. Hawaiian Islands. (Günther).

Known only from the type, which is in the British Museum.

90. Parexocœtus brachypterus (Solander). "*Malolo;*" "*Puhikiʻi.*" Plate III:

Head 4.67 in length; depth 5; D. 13; A. 14; P. 12; V. 6; scales 42 to base of caudal; 8 scales in a transverse series to middle of belly; greatest width of head 1.3 in its depth; snout 4 in head; eye 3, about 1.25 in postocular part of head, 1 in interorbital space; ventral 1.2; depressed dorsal 2.75 in body; pectoral 1.88.

Body elongate, spindle-shaped and laterally compressed; head elongate, compressed, pointed; snout short, blunt; eye moderately large, impinging upon the upper profile; maxillary small, reaching to the anterior margin of the eye; teeth small, villose, the mandible projecting and pointed; nasal cavity small, and with a small fleshy flap over nostril; interorbital space broad and flattened; gillrakers fine, slender, and rather numerous; peritoneum pale or grayish, with rather dark dots or spots; scales large, cycloid; lateral line running low along the lower part of side and also lower portion of caudal peduncle to base of caudal fin; dorsal very long, the median rays the longest, the edge of the fin rounded and when depressed reaching angle in emargination of caudal fin; origin of dorsal a little in advance of that of anal, or about midway between base of pectoral and tip of upper caudal lobe; anal rather low, the rays not prolonged; caudal deeply forked, the lower lobe much longer than the upper; pectoral very long, reaching the first third of base of dorsal; ventrals long, reaching below second and third anal rays.

Color when fresh (No. 03418) with the upper portion of body dark ultramarine blue, the lower surface silvery white; dorsal blue, except a large blackish blotch on the upper marginal portion; posterior half of caudal blue; pectoral transparent with a rosy tinge; margin of ventral red, or the color on the first, second, third, and fourth rays rosy above.

This description from an example (No. 03418) 6.5 inches long from Honolulu.

Our collections from Honolulu contain 29 examples of this species (7 of them numbered 02953 to 02958, and 03418), and 2 specimens obtained at Hilo. Dr. Jenkins obtained 8 specimens at Honolulu in 1889; 2 of these are numbered 150 and 211; 2 other examples (No. 6010) were obtained by Dr. Wood. Specimens were obtained by the *Albatross* at station 3829 off the southern coast of Molokai.

These numerous specimens are almost uniformly 7 inches in total length, which seems to be about the maximum size of this species.

This flying fish is apparently the most abundant species among the Hawaiian Islands Early in June numerous schools were seen near and in the harbor of Honolulu, and it continued a common fish in the Honolulu market during the summer.

Genus 77. EXOCŒTUS Linnæus.

This genus is characterized mainly by the short ventrals which are anteriorly placed and terminate in advance of the anal fin, not being used as organs of flight; pectoral fins very long; no teeth on palate. Open seas.

91. Exocœtus volitans Linnæus. *"Malolo."* Fig. 45.

Head 4.25 in length; depth 4.88; D. 12; A. 12; P. 15; V. 6; scales about 42 to base of caudal, 10 scales in a transverse series; head a little deeper than wide; snout 4.5 in head; eye 3.67, 1.67 in post-ocular part of head, 1.3 in interorbital space; ventral 1.75 in head; base of dorsal 1.2; base of anal 1.2.

Body elongate, the sides compressed and flattened; head subconic, blunt; snout very obtuse, short, rounded; eye anterior, the posterior margin about the middle of the head; mouth very oblique, superior, the maxillary not reaching the eye, the mandible projecting and the jaws forming a thin, horny, cutting edge; small teeth on vomer; tongue flattened, moderately broad, rounded and free; nasal cavity moderate, above the eye in front, and with a small thick flap; interorbital space broad, only very slightly convex; gillrakers slender, rather numerous and not quite half the eye; peritoneum pale; scales large, cycloid, head scaled; lateral line running low and stopping short behind anal fin; origin of dorsal nearer base of pectoral than tip of upper caudal lobe, and a trifle behind origin of anal; anterior dorsal rays elevated and the fin similar to anal; caudal deeply forked, the lower lobe much the longer; pectoral very long, the second ray divided, the second and third the longer, and extending to base of caudal; origin of ventral almost midway between tip of snout and middle of base of anal; caudal peduncle rather deep and compressed.

Color above, brown, the lower surface whitish, washed with silvery; pectorals dark brown with pale edges; dorsal and caudal more or less grayish; ventrals and anal whitish.

Here described from an example 6 inches long, taken at latitude 28° 03' 42" N., longitude 143° 10' 05" W., by the *Albatross*, December 21, 1891. We also have another example, a little larger, with the same data, and Dr. Jenkins obtained a small one at Honolulu, in 1889. None was seen by us in 1901.

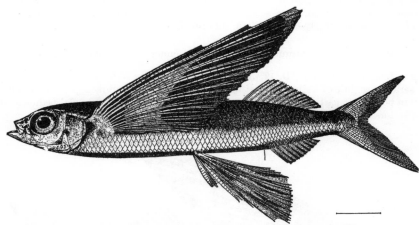

FIG. 45.—*Exocœtus volitans* Linnæus; after Jordan and Evermann.

An example came aboard the *Albatross* at night at about 24° N. and 151° W., and another at station 3808, near Oahu, during the investigations of 1902.

Genus 78. EXONAUTES Jordan & Evermann.

Exonautes differs from *Cypsilurus* in the longer anal, which is as long as the dorsal and with about as many rays.

92. Exonautes gilberti Snyder. Plate 24.

Head, to end of opercular flap, 4.6 in length; depth 7; width of body at base of pectorals 7; depth of caudal peduncle 3.6 in head; eye 3; snout 3.6; interorbital space 2.6; D. 10; A. 10; scales in lateral series beginning above base of pectoral 48; between occiput and base of dorsal 32; between lateral line and dorsal 6.

As indicated by the above measurements of the body, this is one of the most slender of the flying fishes. Body quadrangular in section; back broader than belly, convex; some of the median scales of back with low keels; interorbital space concave; snout a little shorter than diameter of eye; lower jaw slightly projecting beyond upper; maxillary extending to posterior border of nostril. No teeth on tongue or roof of mouth, those on jaws scarcely perceptible; gillrakers on first arch 25, long and slender; lateral line disappearing near end of anal fin.

The pectoral fin extends to within about an eye's diameter of base of caudal; has 18 rays, first and second simple; second a third of its length longer than first, which is 3.81 times diameter of eye; third ray divided near tip of first; tip of fin formed by branches of fourth ray, those of fifth being slightly shorter; second ray of dorsal fin longest, 2 in head; base of fin equal to 2 times diameter of eye; anal inserted the width of a scale posterior to dorsal, its base shorter than that of dorsal by an amount equal to the space between 2 rays; height of first and second rays about equal to that of fourth dorsal; ventrals inserted midway between base of caudal and a point anterior to the edge of opercle, a distance equal to diameter of pupil; extending posteriorly a little beyond the base of anal, not beyond tip of last ray when depressed; upper lobe of caudal pointed, its length 3 times the width of the interorbital space; lower lobe an eye's diameter longer.

Color in alcohol, dark brown above, silvery below; pectoral without spots, dusky, the free edge with a white area as wide as pupil, proximal to which is a blackish band two-thirds as wide as the eye; upper or anterior edge of fin light, an indistinct dark area extending along the first to fourth rays; lower or posterior edge of fin along the last 4 rays white; middle rays of ventrals dusky, the fin indistinctly bordered with white; free edge of caudal bordered with white; dorsal dusky; anal white.

In life, steel-blue above, silvery below.

This species is apparently related to *Exonautes rondeletii* (Cuv. & Val.) of the Atlantic. The type (No. 50872, U. S. N. M.) is the only specimen known. It is 10.43 inches long (snout to end of lower caudal lobe). It came aboard the *Albatross* at night near 28° 30′ N. and 140° W.

Genus 79. CYPSILURUS Swainson.

Body elongate, broad above, somewhat compressed; head short, blunt, narrowed below; mouth small; jaws very short, about equal; chin without barbel; maxillaries not joined to the premaxillaries; teeth very feeble or wanting; eyes large; gillrakers moderate; scales large, deciduous; no finlets; dorsal fin short, opposite anal, which is considerably shorter than dorsal; caudal widely forked, the lower lobe the longer; pectoral fins very long, reaching past the beginning of anal, and serving as organs of flight, their great size enabling the fishes to sustain themselves in the air for some time; ventral fins large, posteriorly inserted, also used as organs of flight; air-bladder very large; no pyloric cœca. Species numerous, in all warm seas, living mostly in the open water and swimming in large schools. The species are largely cosmopolitan, differing from *Exonautes* in the much shorter anal.

93. Cypsilurus simus (Cuvier & Valenciennes). "*Malolo*." Fig. 46.

Head 4 in length; depth 4.67; D. 12; A. 8; P. 15; V. 6; scales 43 to base of caudal; 12 scales in a transverse series to middle of belly; greatest width of head about 1.2 in its depth; snout 4.67 in head; eye 3.2, 1.3 in postocular part of head, 1.4 in interorbital space; depth of caudal peduncle about 3 in head; base of dorsal 5 in body; base of anal 3 in head; ventral about 3.6 in body.

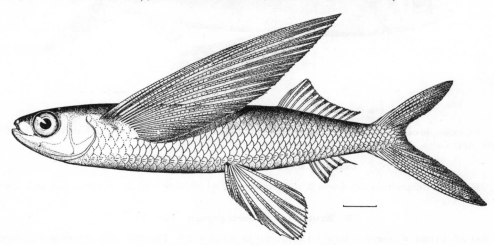

FIG. 46.—*Cypsilurus simus* (Cuvier & Valenciennes).

Body elongate, the sides compressed and flattened; head subconic, the sides constricted below; snout blunt, rounded and short; eye large, impinging upon the upper profile of the head, and also with its posterior margin a little behind the center of its length; mouth nearly terminal, small, oblique, the small maxillary reaching about below nasal cavity, the mandible included; teeth minute in jaws, none on vomer or palatines; tongue smooth, not broad, rounded and free in front; nasal cavity small, near front of eye above, and with a well developed fleshy flap; interorbital space broad, concave in the middle; about 13 gillrakers developed, the longest nearly a third the length of the eye, compressed and pointed; peritoneum pale; scales rather large, cycloid, and each with several striæ, at least on the sides; lateral line running along the lower part of the body, falling short of base of caudal by several scales, behind anal fin; origin of dorsal a little nearer base of pectoral than tip of upper caudal lobe and a little in advance of anus; anal originating below middle of dorsal, similar to dorsal with the anterior rays elevated; caudal deeply forked, the lower lobe much the longer; pectoral very long, falling a little short of base of caudal; ventrals nearer base of caudal than base of pectoral, and reaching back nearly to the posterior base of anal; caudal peduncle rather deep, much compressed.

Color in life (No. 03421) with top of head and upper parts of body reddish purple, lower parts white; membranes of pectoral covered with numerous minute black dots, upper side of rays purplish; outer edge of soft dorsal black; ventrals and anal colorless. One specimen (No. 03424) has a large black area on dorsal fin, the fin itself bright; top of head and body blue, ends silvery; belly white; caudal dusky; no spots on pectoral, upper surface bright purple; ventrals transparent. Other specimens were dark blue above, silvery below with blue reflections; pectoral purple. One (No. 03542) from Honolulu had very large black spots on pectoral.

Color in alcohol, brownish above, the lower surface whitish washed with silvery; dorsal, caudal, and pectorals brownish; ventrals and anal whitish. Color in life, dark blue above, silvery below with blue reflections; pectoral purplish, usually with many large round black spots.

This description from an example (No. 02945) 12 inches long, taken at Honolulu. Of this species we have 21 examples taken at Honolulu, and we have examined 15 examples taken at the same place by Dr. Jenkins in 1889. Specimens were obtained by the *Albatross* at Honolulu; Waimea and Hana-maula Bay, Kauai; and Napili, Molokai. The maximum length of this species is about 14 inches. This is the common flying fish seen in thousands in the sea about Honolulu.

94. Cypsilurus bahiensis (Ranzani).

Head 4.67 in length; depth 4.75; D. 14; A. 9 or 10; P. 15; V. 6; scales to base of caudal 50,–14; snout 3.5 in head; eye 4, 1.8 in postocular part of head, 1.5 in interorbital space; base of dorsal 5.5 in body; base of anal 9; length of ventral 4.

Body elongate, the sides compressed and flattened; head elongate, subconic; snout moderately elongate, flattened above, and somewhat obtuse; eye anterior, the posterior margin a little behind center of length of head, and the eyelid somewhat adipose in front above; mouth oblique, equal to eye, the maxillary reaching below nasal cavity; teeth small and sharp in the jaws, none on vomer and palatines; tongue rather small, elongate, somewhat narrow, rounded and free in front; nasal small, above and in front of eye, and with a shallow groove leading down in front of the eye, the nasal flap thick; interorbital space broad, flattened, or only slightly concave, like the top of the head in front; gillrakers in moderate number, rather short, less than the gill-filaments in length; peritoneum white; scales large, cycloid; head scaled; lateral line running along the lower part of side, stopping behind the anal a few scales before base of caudal; origin of dorsal nearer base of pectoral than tip of upper caudal lobe, before the anus, nearer origin of anal than base of ventrals, the anterior rays elongated; anal similar to dorsal, the anterior rays the longer; caudal deeply forked, the lower lobe much the longer; pectoral very long, reaching within a very short distance of the base of caudal; ventrals long, reaching well beyond first anal rays; caudal peduncle deep and compressed.

Color in alcohol, brown above, the sides and lower surface white, washed with silvery; pectorals deep brown, more or less margined with white; dorsal with a large black blotch, otherwise pale brown; caudal pale brownish; anal and ventrals whitish.

Described from a gravid female (No. 03567) 19 inches long, taken at Hilo in July. We have another example from Hilo and 8 from Honolulu, 3 of the latter taken by Dr. Jenkins in 1889 and 1 by Dr. Wood. The species is readily recognized in life when skimming over the waves by its reddish-brown pectorals. It is common in the sea about Honolulu, but less abundant than *C. simus*.

95. Cypsilurus atrisignis Jenkins. Plate 25.

Head 4.3 in length; depth 5.5; D. 15; A. 10; P. 14; lateral line about 60; scales before dorsal fin 34; scales between origin of dorsal and lateral line 9.

Body elongate, broad dorsally, narrow ventrally, broadest just in front of base of pectorals, where it is nearly as broad as the depth; top of posterior portion of head broad, narrowing toward tip of snout, somewhat concave between the eyes; interorbital space equaling distance from posterior margin of eye to margin of opercle; eye large, its center anterior to center of head; snout less than eye, some-what pointed, lower jaw slightly projecting; maxillary included and falling considerably short of anterior margin of eye; pectoral reaching tip of last dorsal ray; ventral reaching to one-third the base of anal, its origin half way between eye and base of caudal; origin of dorsal much in advance of vent, its distance from first caudal ray 1.4 times head, the longest ray, the anterior one, about 2 in head; lower lobe of caudal the longer.

Color in alcohol, dark purple above, light below; dorsal fin with black spot about 0.7 diameter of eye between the eighth and eleventh spines; caudal and ventrals colorless, unmarked; ventrals white, without spots; pectoral rays and membranes very dark purple above, the rays light below, the membranes with black spots on anterior and posterior portions.

One specimen (No. 197), 13.5 inches in length, was taken by Dr. Jenkins in 1889 at Honolulu. Type, No. 50713, U. S. N. M. Another is in the museum of Stanford University, taken by Mr. A. P. Lundin, at Kusai (Strong Island), one of the Carolines.

Order L. ACANTHOPTERI.—The Spiny–rayed Fishes

Anterior vertebræ unmodified and without ossicula auditus; no mesocoracoid and no interclavicles (so far as known); border of mouth formed by premaxillary; maxillary normally distinct from it and always present, but sometimes coossified with it; gills laminated; shoulder-girdle attached to the skull by a post-temporal, which is normally furcate and usually not coossified with the skull; hypercoracoid and hypocoracoid distinct, ossified, the former usually perforate; pharyngeals well developed, the lower rarely united, the third upper pharyngeal largest, the fourth often wanting; pectoral actinosts always present, opercular apparatus complete; gill-openings in advance of the pectorals; pectoral fins above the plane of the abdomen; ventral fins more or less anterior, normally attached by the pelvis to the shoulder-girdle, typically with 1 spine and 5 rays, these sometimes wanting, sometimes without spine or with many rays, or otherwise modified; anterior rays of dorsal and anal typically simple or spinous, but all the fin rays often articulate; air-bladder typically without duct in the adult; scales various, typically ctenoid; lateral line usually running high. To this group are referable the great body of existing marine fishes.

Suborder PERCESOCES.

Ventral fins abdominal, ɪ, 5; branchial arches well developed, the bones all present except the fourth superior branchihyal; third superior pharyngeal much enlarged; lower pharyngeals distinct; scales cycloid; pectorals elevated, about on a level with the upper posterior angle of opercle; spinous dorsal usually present.

Family XLIII. ATHERINIDÆ.—The Silversides.

Body rather elongate, somewhat compressed, covered with scales of moderate or small size, which are usually, but not always, cycloid; no lateral line; some scales often with rudimentary mucous tubes; cleft of mouth moderate; teeth small, on jaws and sometimes on vomer and palatines, rarely wanting; premaxillaries protractile or not; opercular bones without spines or serrature; gill-openings wide, the gill-membranes not connected, free from the isthmus; gills 4, a slit behind the fourth; pseudobranchiæ present; gillrakers usually long and slender; branchiostegals 5 or 6; dorsal fins 2, well separated, the first of 3 to 8 slender flexible spines, the second of soft rays; anal with a weak spine, similar to the soft dorsal, but usually larger; ventral fins small, abdominal, not far back, of 1 small spine and 5 soft rays; pectorals moderate, inserted high; air-bladder present; no pyloric cœca; vertebræ numerous, usually about 23+23=46; third and fourth superior pharyngeals coossified, with teeth. Carnivorous fishes, mostly of small size, living in great schools near the shore in temperate and tropical seas; a few species in fresh water. All the species have a silvery band along the side, this sometimes underlaid by black pigment. Genera about 15, species 60. All that are large enough highly valued as food, hence the common name of "fishes of the king," Pescados del Rey, or Pesce Re, or Peixe Rey.

Only one genus of silversides is known from the Hawaiian Islands.

Genus 80. ATHERINA (Artedi) Linnæus. The Friars.

Body oblong, compressed; mouth large, terminal, oblique; jaws about equal, their edges nearly straight; maxillary extending to front of eye; premaxillaries narrow posteriorly, strongly protractile; villiform teeth in bands on jaws, vomer, and palatines. Species numerous, mostly European.

96. Atherina insularum Jordan & Evermann. Fig. 47.

Head 4 in length; depth 4.75; eye 3 in head; snout 4; interorbital 2.8; maxillary 2.5; mandible 2.2; D. vɪ–ɪ, 11; A. 17; scales 46, 6 rows from anterior base of anal upward and forward to spinous dorsal.

Body oblong, compressed; head triangular, the sides compressed, top flat; mouth large, oblique, maxillary reaching front of pupil, lower jaw included; teeth in rather broad villiform bands on jaws, vomer, and palatines; interorbital space very broad and flat; snout broad, truncate; origin of spinous dorsal slightly posterior to vertical at vent, slightly nearer tip of snout than base of caudal; longest dorsal spine about 2.4 in head, reaching nearly to vertical at front of anal; distance between spinous and soft dorsals equal to distance from tip of snout to middle of pupil; edge of soft dorsal concave, anterior rays somewhat produced, their length 1.9 in head; last dorsal ray about one-half longer than one preceding; base of soft dorsal 1.8 in head; origin of anal considerably in advance of that of soft dorsal, the fins similar, anterior rays about 1.7 in head, base of anal 1.3 in head; caudal widely forked, the lobes equal; ventral short, barely reaching vent; pectoral short, broad, and slightly falcate, its length about 1.4 in head; scales large, thin, and deep, 19 in front of spinous dorsal, 6 rows between the dorsals and 9 on median line of caudal peduncle.

Color when fresh, clear olive-green with darker edges to scales; lateral stripe steel-blue above, fading into the silvery belly; fins uncolored.

Color in alcohol, olivaceous above, silvery on sides and below; scales of back and upper part of side with numerous small round coffee-brown specks, disposed chiefly on the edges, median line of

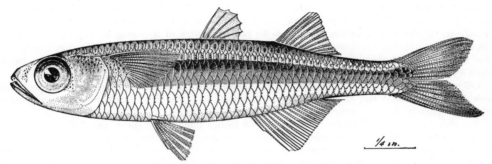

Fig. 47.—*Atherina insularum* Jordan & Evermann; from the type.

back with a darkish stripe; middle of side with a broad silvery band, plumbeous above, especially anteriorly, more silvery below; top of head and snout with numerous dark brownish or black specks; side of head silvery, opercle somewhat dusky, sides and tip of lower jaw dusky; dorsals and caudal somewhat dusky, other fins pale; pectoral without dark tip.

This small fish is common inside the reef in shallow bays everywhere in the Hawaiian Islands. Many individuals were seen off the wharf at Lahaina on Maui. Our collections of 1901 contain 20 specimens from Kailua, from 1.5 to 3.5 inches long; 43 from Hilo, 1.5 to 2.25 inches long; and 1 from Honolulu, 2.25 inches in length. Numerous specimens were obtained by the *Albatross* at Honolulu in 1902, one of which is taken as our type and three others as cotypes.

Type, No. 50819, U. S. N. M., 4.25 inches long, obtained by the *Albatross* at Honolulu. Cotypes, No. 2741, U. S. F. C., 3.9 inches long; No. 2302, Am. Mus. Nat. Hist., 3.9 inches long; and No. 4063, Field Col. Mus., 3.5 inches long, all collected at Honolulu by the *Albatross*.

Family XLIV. MUGILIDÆ.—The Mullets.

Body oblong, more or less compressed, covered with rather large cycloid scales; no lateral line, but the furrows often deepened on the middle of each scale so as to form lateral streaks; mouth small, the jaws with small teeth, or none, the teeth various in form; premaxillaries protractile; gill-openings wide, the membranes separate, free from the isthmus; branchiostegals 5 or 6, gillrakers long and slender; gills 4, a slit behind fourth; pseudobranchiæ large; 2 short dorsal fins, well separated, the anterior with 4 stiff spines, the last one of which is much shorter than the others; second dorsal longer than the first, similar to anal; anal spines 2 or 3, graduated; ventral fins abdominal, not far back, composed of 1 spine and 5 rays; caudal forked; air-bladder large, simple; intestinal canal long; peritoneum usually black; vertebræ 24. Genera 8 or 10, species about 100, inhabiting the fresh waters and coasts of warm regions, feeding on organic matter contained in mud. "In the genus *Mugil*, a considerable indigestible portion of the latter is swallowed, and in order to prevent larger bodies from passing into the stomach or substances from passing through the gill-openings, these fishes have the organs of the pharynx modified into a filtering apparatus. They take in a quantity of sand or mud, and, after having worked it for some time between the pharyngeal bones, they eject the roughest and indigestible portion of it. The upper pharyngeals have a rather irregular form; they are slightly arched, the convexity being directed toward the pharyngeal cavity, tapering anteriorly and broadening posteriorly. They are coated with a thick soft membrane, which reaches far beyond the margin of the bone, and is studded all over with minute horny cilia. Each branchial arch is provided with a series of long gillrakers, which are laterally bent downward, each series closely fitting to the sides of the adjoining arch; together they constitute a sieve admirably adapted to permit a transit for the water, retaining at the same time every solid substance in the cavity of the pharynx." (Günther.)

Genus 81. MUGIL (Artedi) Linnæus.

Body oblong, somewhat compressed, covered with large scales; head large, convex, scaled above and on sides; mouth small, subinferior, the lower jaw angulated; jaws with one or a few series of short, flexible, ciliiform teeth; no teeth on vomer or palatines; eye large, with a large adipose eyelid, which is little developed in the young; stomach muscular, like the gizzard of a fowl. Species very numerous, living on mud and running in great schools along the shores and in brackish lagoons of all warm regions.

97. Mugil cephalus Linnæus. *"Ama-ama;"* Mullet. Fig. 48.

Head 4 in length; depth 4.2; snout 4.2 in head; eye 3.9; D. iv–i, 8; A. iii, 8; scales 40,–13, transverse series counted from anus upward and backward to soft dorsal; dorsal spine 1.75 in head; soft dorsal 1.6 in head; anterior base of spinous dorsal midway between end of snout and base of caudal.

Body oblong, rather robust, slightly compressed; head subconic; lower jaw slightly included; maxillary hidden; no teeth, except a single row of very small teeth in outer fleshy part of upper jaw; jaw narrow, the distance from the symphysis to posterior edge of lip being equal to greatest width of mouth; eye anterior, moderate, the adipose lid covering entire eye except pupil; head scaly; soft dorsal and anal almost naked; soft dorsal concave; anal similar to dorsal but not so concave; caudal deeply forked, upper lobe slightly the longer; pectoral not quite reaching to spinous dorsal.

Color in life, from a 10.5-inch specimen (No. 02995) taken at Honolulu, bluish gray, white below; cheek dusky; spinous dorsal and pectoral dusky; caudal pale, finely dusted with dark specks, edges dark; anal sparsely dusted; ventrals white.

Ten specimens from Honolulu, from 1.5 to 10.5 inches long, and 3 specimens, 3.75 to 4.75 inches long, from Kailua. We have also examined a number of specimens collected by Dr. Jenkins at Honolulu in 1889 and 1 specimen 10 inches long collected by R. C. McGregor on Molokai in March, 1900.

This species of mullet, the *ama ama* of the natives, is perhaps the most abundant and important food-fish of the Hawaiian Islands. It is the species which has received most attention from the natives in the way of protection and cultivation. The mullet ponds have been an institution of importance

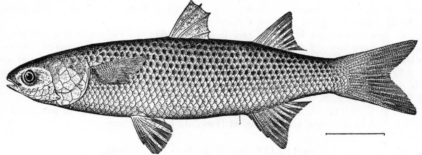

Fig. 48.—*Mugil cephalus* Linnæus; after Jordan and Evermann.

ever since the days of the earliest kings. A full discussion of this subject is given elsewhere in this report.

We are unable to find any difference between the Hawaiian *ama ama* and the striped mullets of the United States, Japan, Chile, or the Mediterranean. If different from any of these it is distinct from all and should receive a new name.

Genus 82. CHÆNOMUGIL Gill.

Cleft of mouth lateral; lower jaw narrow; dentiform cilia in very many series, broad, flat, and somewhat paved; upper lip very thick; no adipose eyelid. Small mullets of the tropical shores.

98. Chænomugil chaptalii (Eydoux & Souleyet) *"Uouóa."* Fig. 49.

Head 4 in length; depth 3.9; snout 3.75 in head; eye 3.4; D. iv–i, 9; A. iii, 10; scales 43,–13.

Body robust, more compressed posteriorly; head moderate; snout subconic, rather pointed; mouth slightly oblique, its cleft deeper than long; maxillary entirely hidden; front part of upper lip very thick; lower margin of each lip covered with rather strong papillæ or weak pectinate teeth; lower jaw included, rather narrow; no teeth evident; eye large, anterior; interorbital space convex, 2 in head; first dorsal spine 2 in head; soft dorsal and anal slightly convex; caudal forked, lower lobe the longer and heavier; ventrals truncate; pectoral falcate, 1.3 in head.

Color in alcohol, dull olivaceous above with silvery reflections gradually fading into lighter and becoming white on belly; top of head and snout brown; indications of brown on opercles; dorsal, caudal, and pectorals dusky, pectorals the darkest; other fins pale.

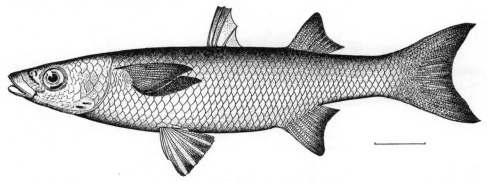

FIG. 49.—*Chænomugil chaptalii* (Eydoux & Souleyet).

Eight specimens 1 to 9.2 inches long from Honolulu; 33 from 1.2 to 6.5 inches long from Hilo, and 18 specimens from 2 to 4.5 inches long from Kailua. We have also examined several specimens taken by Doctor Jenkins at Honolulu in 1889.

Genus 83. MYXUS Günther.

Cleft of mouth extending on sides of snout, but not to orbit. Small teeth in a single series in upper jaw, and sometimes in lower and on palate. Upper lip not particularly thick; anterior margin of mandible sharp. Anal spines 3.

99. Myxus pacificus Steindachner.

Head about 4 in length; depth nearly 4; snout 4 in head; D. IV–I, 8; A. III, 8; scales 39 or 40,–13.5, about 24 scales before the dorsal; head moderately small, the greatest depth about 1.4 in length; greatest breadth between opercles about 1.6 in length of head; upper profile very slightly curved to origin of second dorsal, then falling suddenly the length of the base of this fin; eye with well developed lids; upper lip moderately small; mouth cleft a little longer than broad; preorbital with the lower and posterior edge serrate; between the jaws a band of small movable teeth, those of the outer row larger than those of inner; origin of first dorsal a trifle nearer base of caudal than tip of snout, the first dorsal moderately strong, a little more than 1.65 length of head; caudal a little longer than head, length of its middle rays about 1.6 times length of head; ventral flap shorter than half length of fin; a dark band along upper edge of pectoral. Length, 5.85 inches. Laysan. (Steindachner.) This species is known from Dr. Steindachner's description only.

Family XLV. SPHYRÆNIDÆ.—The Barracudas.

Body elongate, subterete, covered with small cycloid scales; head very long, pointed, pike-like, scaly above and on sides; mouth horizontal, large; jaws elongate, the lower considerably projecting; upper jaw nonprotractile, its border formed by the premaxillaries, behind which are the broad maxillaries; large sharp teeth of unequal size on both jaws and palatines, none on the vomer; usually a very strong, sharp canine near tip of lower jaw; opercular bones without spines or serratures; gill-openings wide, the gill-membranes not united, free from the isthmus; gillrakers very short or obsolete; branchiostegals 7; gills 4, a slit behind the fourth; pseudobranchiæ well developed; air-bladder large, bifurcate anteriorly; many pyloric cœca; lateral line well developed, straight; pectoral fins short, placed in or below line of axis of body; ventrals I, 5, abdominal, in advance of middle of body; first dorsal over ventrals, of 5 rather stout spines; second dorsal remote from first dorsal, similar to anal and opposite to it; caudal fin forked; vertebræ 24; first superior pharyngeal not present; second, third, and fourth separate, with teeth; lower pharyngeals separate. A single genus of about 20 species; carnivorous, pike-like fishes, often of large size, active and voracious, inhabiting warm seas, many of them highly valued as food.

Genus 84. SPHYRÆNA (Artedi) Bloch & Schneider.

Characters of the genus included above.

100. Sphyræna snodgrassi Jenkins. "*Káku.*" Fig. 50.

Head 3.25 in length; depth 6.5; eye 7.3 in head; snout 2.1; D. v–I, 9; A. I, 9; scales 11–85–9; longest dorsal spine 3.1 in head, ray 2.5 in head; anal 2.4; ventral 3.2; pectoral 2.9; interorbital 4.7, nearly twice vertical diameter of eye; maxillary 2.2.   Body and head regularly fusiform; lower jaw projecting

beyond upper a distance equal to two-thirds diameter of pupil, tip blunt, not terminated by fleshy appendages; eye slightly ovate, larger and anterior; interorbital space flat; maxillary reaching front of eye; suborbital scaled; about 18 rows of vertical scales from eye to edge of preopercle, 8 rows on opercle, those of opercle enlarged, rest of head naked; opercle without spines, but with 1 or 2 blunt flexible points; each side of upper jaw with 2 long,

FIG. 50.—*Sphyræna snodgrassi* Jenkins; from the type.

sharp, canine teeth in front and 5 or 6 nearly as large but broader teeth, growing gradually smaller posteriorly; lower jaw with 2 large anterior median teeth similar to anterior teeth in upper jaw and back of them a single series of about 15 smaller teeth on each jaw; second and third dorsal spines the longest; caudal forked, lobes equal; anal fin slightly behind soft dorsal, the 2 similar in form; lateral line slightly decurved on body before second dorsal, posterior part straight.

Color in life, dark olive-brown above; side silvery; about 20 very faint short blackish bars just above lateral line, their depth about 4 rows of scales, the bars rather wider than the silvery interspaces; membraneous edge of opercle jet black; first dorsal blackish, second with a jet-black central blotch, the tips white; caudal black with white tips; anal like the second dorsal, the blackish blotch fainter; pectoral dusky at base; ventrals white; young with 13 dark crossbars.

Description from a specimen 17 inches long.   We have 5 specimens 13 to 18 inches long from Honolulu, one 8.25 inches long from Hilo, 6 about 5 inches long from Waialua, and one very large example (No. 04515), 33 inches long, from Honolulu.   Specimens 4 to 6 feet in length were seen in the market at Honolulu.   This is a large voracious species of wide range, entering the open sea.

101. Sphyræna helleri Jenkins.   "*Kawal*.   Fig. 51.

Head 3.1 in length; depth 7.8; eye 6.1 in head; snout 2; maxillary 3.1; interorbital 6, slightly greater than vertical diameter of eye; D. v–1, 9; A. 1, 8; scales 14–135–15; 13 rows of scales on preopercle, 14 on opercle; longest dorsal spine 3.8 in head; ray 4.5; longest anal ray 3.8; pectoral 3.6; ventral 3.6.

Body long and slender, the head tapering, the snout long, the lower jaw projecting nearly the width of pupil beyond upper, terminating in a fleshy appendage; eye large, posterior; maxillary not reaching eye, being separated from it by a distance about equal to diameter of eye; opercle without spines; 2 sharp canine-like teeth hooked backward, the second the larger, on the front row of upper jaw, back of these on each jaw 5 or 6 similar teeth bent inward; 2 large close-set teeth like those in upper jaw, in median part of lower jaw; back of these on each side a row of 15 to 18 smaller teeth; distances between occiput and first dorsal fin, first dorsal and sec-

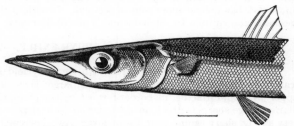

FIG. 51.—*Sphyræna helleri* Jenkins; from the type.

ond dorsal, and second dorsal and last vertebra equal, and each equal to distance from tip of snout to posterior margin of eye; insertion of ventrals below front of first dorsal fin, two-thirds of eye behind tip of pectoral; caudal deeply forked; anterior base of anal on line with that of dorsal.

Color in alcohol, brown above, with bluish silvery reflections, becoming lighter below, white on belly and lower part of side; spinous dorsal color of back; soft dorsal pale, caudal dusky; anal and ventral pale; pectoral dusky.

Six specimens from Honolulu 13 to 26 inches long, and 2 from Hilo 24 inches long.   This fish is very abundant in the mullet ponds, where it is destructive to the mullet.   It reaches but a small size, and is rarely found except near shore.

Suborder HYPOSTOMIDES.

Characters included with those of the following family:

Family XLVI. PEGASIDÆ.

Body entirely covered with bony plates, ankylosed on the trunk and movable on the tail; barbels none; the margin of the upper jaw formed by the intermaxillaries and their cutaneous prolongation, which extends downward to the extremity of the maxillaries; gill-cover formed by a large plate, homologous to the opercle, preopercle and subopercle; interopercle a long fine bone, hidden below the gill-plate; one rudimentary branchiostegal; the gill-plate united with the isthmus by a narrow membrane; gill-opening narrow in front of base of pectoral fin; gills 4, lamellated; pseudo-branchiæ and air-bladder absent; one short dorsal and anal fin, opposite to each other; ventral fins present; ovarian sacs closed.

Genus 85. PEGASUS Linnæus.

This genus contains those species of *Pegasidæ* which have the tail short and not attenuate and compressed toward the tip, and in which the pectoral rays are all slender and simple, none of them spine-like. The single Hawaiian species of this genus is fully described by Dr. Gilbert in Section II.

Suborder RHEGNOPTERI.

Actinosts of pectoral fin of 3 forms, 2 of them normal, supporting the pectoral fin, one of them longitudinal, without rays, and the fourth a plate on the coracoid, supporting 3 to 10 free and separate rays or feelers; post-temporal and shoulder-girdle normal; vertebræ $10 + 14 = 24$; 2 separate dorsal fins, the first of a few spines; pseudobranchiæ concealed; ventrals subabdominal, behind pectorals. One family, *Polynemidæ*, of uncertain origin and affinities.

Family XLVII. POLYNEMIDÆ.—The Threadfins.

Body oblong, compressed, and covered with rather large, loosely inserted, ctenoid scales; lateral line continuous, continued on the tail, usually forked, with a branch on each lobe; head entirely scaly, snout more or less conical, projecting over the mouth, which is rather large, inferior, with lateral cleft; premaxillary protractile, its basal process vertical; maxillary without supplemental bone, extending much beyond the eye, which is anterior, lateral, rather large, with a well-developed adipose eyelid; villiform teeth on jaws, palatines and sometimes on vomer; pseudobranchiæ concealed; branchiostegals 7; gill-membranes separate and free from the isthmus; gills 4, a slit behind the fourth; 2 separate dorsals, somewhat remote from each other, the first of 8 feeble but rather high spines, the first and last spines very short, the third longest; the second dorsal of soft rays only, equal to first in height, but with base somewhat longer; anal fin either similar to or much longer than soft dorsal; caudal fin rather long, widely forked; second dorsal, anal and caudal fins more or less covered with small scales; the first 3 or 4 dorsal spines winged; ventrals i, 5, abdominal, but not far removed from pectorals; pectoral fins moderate, placed low, in 2 parts, the lower and anterior portion of several fili-form articulated appendages free from each other, used as organs of touch. In the young, the dorsal, caudal, and pectoral fins are dusky, the anal and ventral fins white; all the fins grow darker with age, the pectorals usually becoming black, the opercle blackish. Bones of the skull with a well devel-oped muciferous system as in *Sciænidæ*. Basis cranii double, with muscular tube; post-temporal bifur-cate; hypercoracoid with median foramen; superior pharyngeal bones 4; pectoral actinosts divided, 2 of them normal, supporting the pectoral fin, 1 longitudinal without rays, and 1 a plate on the coracoid, supporting the pectoral filaments; stomach cœcal with many pyloric appendages; air-bladder various, sometimes wanting; vertebræ $10 + 14 = 24$. Genera 4, species about 25, inhabiting sandy shores of tropical seas, and sometimes entering rivers. Most of them are valued as food-fishes, their flesh being like that of the *Sciænidæ*. The relations of this peculiar family appear to be with the *Sciænidæ* on the one hand, and with the *Mugilidæ* on the other, but all these resemblances may be superficial.

Genus 86. POLYDACTYLUS Lacépède.

Anal fin not much longer than soft dorsal, of about 13 or 14 rays; vomer with teeth; free filaments of pectorals mostly shorter than body; teeth in villiform bands on both jaws, vomer, palatines, and pterygoids; preopercle sharply serrated on its posterior margin, its angle with a scaly flap; scales rather small, finely ctenoid; first dorsal with 7 or 8 feeble, rather high spines, the first and last short; soft dorsal and anal fins about equal; pectoral filaments 3 to 9; pyloric cœca in great number. Species numerous, in warm seas.

102. Polydactylus sexfilis (Cuvier & Valenciennes). "*Moi*," "*Moi-lii.*"

Head 3.3 in length; depth 3.5; eye 4 in head; snout 5.5; maxillary 2.2; interorbital 3.6; preorbital 2.75 in eye; D. vii–i, 13; A. iii, 11; scales 8–66–12; third dorsal spine longest, 1.4 in head; ray 1.4; longest anal 1.6; 6 pectoral filaments, longest 3.1 in body; pectoral ray 1.5 in head; ventral 2.1; caudal peduncle 2; distance from anterior base of soft dorsal to upper edge of gill-opening equal to distance from same base to base of caudal fin; this last distance equals distance from posterior base of soft dorsal to fork of caudal fin; distance between anterior bases of dorsals equaling distance from anterior base of spinous dorsal to posterior edge of eye; base of soft dorsal slightly greater than base of anal.

Body rather deep, compressed, back slightly arched, anterior profile from snout to tip of first dorsal when depressed evenly arched; head moderate, snout conic, projecting almost its entire length beyond mouth, which is large, inferior, with lateral cleft; premaxillary protractile, maxillary without supplemental bone, extending for nearly half its length beyond eye; teeth in villiform band on jaws, vomer, palatine, and posterior end of tongue; the tongue free for a distance equal to two-thirds of orbit, not quite rounded in front, its straight front edge nearly equal to orbit, the front portion rather thin, becoming thick and heavy posteriorly; eye large, anterior, lateral, with a well-developed eyelid; gill-membranes free from isthmus; gillrakers 16+13, long and slender, longest equal to diameter of pupil; preopercle serrated on its posterior margin, not serrated at angle; first dorsal falcate; second deeply forked; caudal deeply forked, upper lobe slightly the larger and longer and slightly longer than head; anal similar to soft dorsal but not so deeply forked; scales moderate, finely ctenoid on entire body and head; lateral line straight on body, slightly decurved on base of caudal, extending to tip just below angle.

Color in alcohol, yellowish white with silvery reflections, becoming lighter, almost white on belly; upper edge of spinous dorsal dark; soft dorsal tipped with dark; tips of caudal lobes dark; anal with light brown on lower half, upper part paler; ventrals pale with small plumbeous spots; pectorals dark bluish on outer third, rest dusky pale. The color in alcohol of the young examples, 2 to 4 inches long, is quite different from the larger examples. The young are brown above lateral line with 3 broad bands of darker, the first band extending over head and to spinous dorsal, second wedge-shaped, extending from anterior base of spinous dorsal to and including about half of soft dorsal, the rest of soft dorsal pale; third band extending from posterior base of soft dorsal to base of caudal; between these bars below lateral line, silvery white; posterior half of anal and ventral white; pectoral pale; spinous dorsal dark; caudal lobes dark; a light band across base of caudal.

Six specimens 9 to 11 inches long from Honolulu and 25 specimens 3 to 4.6 inches long from Hilo. We have also examined a specimen 9 inches long taken by Dr. Jenkins in 1889 and a similar specimen obtained by the *Albatross* in 1891, both from Honolulu. The species is known also from Johnston Island.

Suborder BERYCOIDEI.—The Berycoid Fishes.

Body naked or variously scaly, the scales sometimes highly specialized; dorsal fin with few or many spines, ventral fins thoracic or subabdominal, each with 1 spine and usually 7 soft rays, the number of soft rays varying from 5 to 10; in one family (*Monocentridæ*) the spine is greatly enlarged and the number of rays reduced; head with conspicuous mucous cavities; air-bladder in some species retaining its duct through life (a character verified only in *Beryx*); vertebræ in species examined 24 to 30; shoulder-girdle and pharyngeals normal; no suborbital stay, orbitosphenoid bone always present. A varied group allied to the *Percoidei* and *Scombroidei*, but characterized as a whole by the retention of the archaic characters of the persistent air-duct and the increased number of ventral rays. In the deep-sea forms the spinous dorsal is scarcely developed and the scales are usually either cycloid or wanting. In the species of tropical shores the spinous armature of fins and scales is better developed than in most of the percomorphous fishes. The group is a very old one in geologic time, the allies of *Beryx* being among the earliest spiny-rayed fishes known. All are marine fishes, inhabiting the tropical shores or the abysses of the ocean.

Family XLVIII.—BERYCIDÆ.

Body oblong or ovate, compressed, covered with ctenoid or cycloid, foliate or granular scales; head with large muciferous cavities, covered by thin skin; eye lateral, usually large; mouth wide, oblique; premaxillaries protractile; maxillary rather large, usually with a supplemental bone; suborbitals narrow, not sheathing the cheeks; bands of villiform teeth on jaws, and usually on vomer and palatines; canines sometimes present; opercular bones usually spinous; branchiostegals 7 or 8; gill-membranes separate, free from the isthmus; gills 4, a slit behind the fourth; pseudobranchiæ present; gillrakers moderate; cheeks and opercles scaly; no barbels; dorsal fin continuous, with 2 to 8 weak spines; anal with 2 to 4 spines; ventral fins thoracic, mostly i, 7, the number of rays usually greater than i, 5; caudal fin usually forked; pyloric cœca numerous. Fishes mostly of the deep seas; general color, red or black.

Genus 87. MELAMPHAES Günther.

Head large and thick, with nearly all the superficial bones modified into wide muciferous channels; cleft of mouth of moderate width, obliquely descending backward, with the jaws nearly equal in front; eye small; a narrow band of villiform teeth in each jaw; palate toothless; eight branchiostegals; pseudobranchiæ present; no barbels; opercles not armed; scales large, cycloid, rather irregularly arranged; one dorsal; ventrals with 7 rays; caudal forked; anal spines very feeble. The single Hawaiian species of this genus is fully described in Section II.

Genus 88. CAULOLEPIS Gill.

Contour laterally oval or broad pyriform, the body compressed, covered with small, pedunculated leaf-like scales; forehead abruptly declivous; eye small; a pair of very long pointed teeth in front of upper jaw, closing in front of lower; a similar pair of still longer pointed teeth in the lower, received in foveæ of the palate; on the sides of each jaw 2 long teeth, terminating in bulbous tips; a row of minute teeth on the posterior half of the supramaxillaries; palate toothless. The single Hawaiian species (*Caulolepis longidens*) of this genus is described in Section II.

Family XLIX. HOLOCENTRIDÆ.—The Squirrel-Fishes.

Body oblong or ovate, moderately compressed, covered with very strongly ctenoid or spinous scales; head with large muciferous cavities; eye lateral, very large; preorbital very narrow; mouth moderate, oblique; premaxillaries protractile; maxillary very large, with supplemental bone; bands of villiform teeth on jaws, vomer, and palatines; opercular bones and membrane bones of head generally serrated or spinescent along the edges; branchiostegals 8; gill-membranes separate, free from isthmus; gills 4, a slit behind fourth; pseudobranchiæ present; gillrakers moderate; no barbels; sides of head scaly; lateral line present; dorsal fin very long, deeply divided, with about 11 strong spines depressible in a scaly groove; anal with 4 spines, the third longest and strongest; ventrals thoracic, with 1 spine and 7 rays; caudal deeply forked, with sharp rudimentary rays or fulcra at the base; vertebræ about 27; pyloric cœca 8 to 25; air-bladder large, sometimes connected with the organ of hearing. General color red. Young with snout sharp and produced (constituting the nominal genera *Rhynchichthys*, *Rhamphoberyx*, and *Rhinoberyx*, based on peculiarities of immature examples). Genera about 7; species about 70; gaily colored inhabitants of the tropical seas, abounding about coral reefs.

Genus 89. HOLOTRACHYS Günther.

This genus is close to *Myripristis*, from which it differs in the small, very rough scales and in the projecting lower jaw, which fits in a deep notch in the upper jaw.

103. Holotrachys lima (Cuvier & Valenciennes). Plate IV.

Head 2.6 in length; depth 2.5; eye 3.5 in head (4.3 in an example 6 inches long); snout 5.5; interorbital 5.5; maxillary 1.65; D. XII, 15; longest dorsal spine 2.4 in head; A. IV, 11; longest anal spine 3.1; scales 5–42 (40 to 42)–8.

Body oblong, compressed; dorsal outline evenly arched from tip of snout to base of soft caudal; ventral outline almost straight; head subconic, compressed; mouth large, nearly horizontal; jaws equal, a knob at tip of lower fitting into a depression in upper, the bony portion of preorbital slightly overhanging lip; blunt, conic, pavement-like teeth on jaws, vomer, and palatines; tongue broad, free anteriorly, rounded and rather thin on anterior and thin portion; eye high, anterior; maxillary long, reaching beyond eye, its broadest part nearly equaling diameter of eye; gillrakers 11+8, longest half diameter of eye, finely serrate; fourth and fifth dorsal spines longest; soft dorsal rays of nearly equal length; caudal slightly forked; soft anal rounded; posterior edges of pectoral and ventral nearly equal; lateral line slightly arched anteriorly, thence obliquely downward to middle of caudal peduncle, across the middle of which it extends to base of caudal fin; edges of scales very rough, each scale with many rather long sharp spines, these longer on scales on posterior part of body.

Color in life (No. 03164) upper parts of head and body bright rock-candy red, becoming paler on side; under parts pale rosy white, edges of scales darkest, forming red lines; membranes of spinous dorsal blood-red, the spines white; soft dorsal, caudal, and anal bright red; anal spines white; pectoral and ventrals paler rosy; iris blood-red, with yellow blotches.

Color in alcohol, grayish-yellow, fins all pale.

This species is a very common market fish at Honolulu and Hilo, and was also obtained by us at Kailua, by the Albatross at Honolulu and Laysan Island, and by Doctor Jordan at Samoa, where it was found to be a common fish. Our numerous specimens range in length from 4 to 7.5 inches. *H. rosea* from the South Sea Islands is probably *H. lima*.

Genus 90. OSTICHTHYS (Langsdorf) Jordan & Evermann.

This genus is closely related to *Myripristis*, differing especially in the very rough surface of the large scales. The opercular spine is usually elongate and rough edged. *Holotrachys*, another genus with similarly rough scales, differs from *Ostichthys* in having the scales very much smaller, about 40 to 45 in the lateral line, instead of 29 as in *Ostichthys*.

104. Ostichthys pillwaxii (Steindachner). Fig. 52.

Head 2.45 in length; depth 2.5; eye 3.75 in head; snout 3.75; maxillary 1.9; interorbital 7.3; D. XII, 14, A. IV, 11; scales 4–29–6; Br. 7; gillrakers short, blunt, about 7+5.

Body oblong, compressed; dorsal outline somewhat more arched than ventral, in a long, low curve from nape to origin of soft dorsal, thence descending abruptly to caudal peduncle; ventral outline straighter; base of anal abruptly ascending to caudal peduncle; head very large and rugose, mouth very large, the maxillary reaching posterior edge of pupil; supplemental maxillary very broad; tip of maxillary (with supplemental bone) 1.25 in eye; jaws about equal, the lower fitting in a deep notch in the upper; jaws, vomer, and palatines with broad bands of villiform teeth; eye large, high up, far above axis of body; interorbital space narrow, more than 2 in eye; bones of head rough everywhere; interorbital with 4 low rough ridges; prenasals rough, ending in 3 blunt, more or less serrated points; preorbital, postocular, preopercle, subopercle, and opercle all strongly toothed, no enlarged spine at angle of preopercle; nape rugose, with ridges radiating posteriorly; bones of mandible rough; edge of each branchiostegal rough; opercle with a moderately stout spine above, its surface rugose; caudal peduncle short and slender, its length about equal to diameter of eye, its least width 2.5 in its least depth, which is 1.4 in eye; origin of spinous dorsal about equidistant between tip of snout and base of first dorsal ray, almost directly over base of pectoral; dorsal spines strong, folding well in a groove, the fourth longest, about 2.6 in head; base of soft dorsal very oblique, 3 in head, the longest ray slightly longer than base; first anal spine very short, the third longest and strongest, its length 3.25 in head, base of anal oblique like that of soft dorsal, 2.5 in head, longest anal ray equaling that of soft dorsal; caudal forked, the longest rays about 2.1 in head; ventrals short, reaching about two-fifths the distance to vent, their length about 2.25 in head; pectoral coterminous with ventrals, its length 2

FIG. 52.—*Ostichthys pillwaxii* (Steindachner); after Steindachner.

in head; scales very large, firm and very spinigerous, each scale with about 16 to 22 very sharp, short spines, each of which is continued as a ridge on the surface of the scale; lateral line following curvature of back; nape and breast with strong scales; cheeks scaled, rest of head naked; base of pectoral with smaller scales; a sheath of small triangular scales at base of soft dorsal and anal; membranes of caudal fin with small, spinescent scales.

Color in alcohol, pale yellowish with orange, silvery, brassy, and rosy reflections; back along spinous dorsal orange; nape rosy red; back and side with traces of about 3 or 4 rosy streaks; under parts white, with some rosy; branchiostegals orange at base.

The color in life was doubtless deep red or rosy.

This species differs from *Holotrachys lima* chiefly in the much larger scales and the more numerous spines on the scales; also in the larger eye and in having but 1 enlarged spine instead of 2 at the upper edge of the opercle; the mandible and maxillary are less rough.

The above description is based upon No. 05500, a specimen 12 inches long, obtained in the Honolulu market by Mr. E. Louis Berndt, through whose kindness it came into our possession. No other specimens have been seen by us.

Genus 91. MYRIPRISTIS Cuvier.

This genus is closely related to *Holocentrus*, differing externally chiefly in the absence of the large spine at the angle of the preopercle. The air-bladder is divided into 2 parts by a transverse constriction, the anterior part extending to the otocrane. The plyoric cœca are rather few (9).

Species numerous in the tropical seas; gaily colored inhabitants of reefs and rock pools.

105. Myripristis multiradiatus Günther.

Head 3 in length; depth 2.3; eye 2 in head; snout 7; maxillary 1.9; mandible 1.9; interorbital 3.9; D: x or xi–i, 16 or 17; A. iv, 15; scales 4–40 to 43–5.

Body short, deep, and compressed; dorsal outline evenly convex from tip of snout to origin of soft dorsal; ventral outline nearly equally convex, somewhat flattened under ventrals; head short, snout blunt; mouth small, the jaws equal, the maxillary reaching posterior line of pupil, triangular, the posterior side concave, the end nearly straight, the anterior edge with a few blunt teeth at the angle; mandible smooth, without knob at tip; no distinct notch in tip of upper jaw; eye moderate, somewhat greater than postocular part of head; interorbital space nearly flat, the 2 median ridges convex, close together in front, then diverging, then coming nearly together on the nape; outside of these on the nape on each side, 4 short diverging striæ; suborbital rim finely serrate on both edges; edges of opercular bones all serrate, the serræ strongest at the angles; the teeth on jaws small, in narrow villiform bands. Scales comparatively small, much deeper than long, the edges striate and finely dentate; humeral scale small; lateral line gently arched. Origin of spinous dorsal slightly posterior to base of pectoral, the spines slender, the first 1.8, the second about 1.2 in eye, the others increasing to the fourth, the last very short; interval between dorsals very short; anterior dorsal rays slightly produced, their length about 2 in head, the edge of the fin somewhat concave, the last rays about 2.5 in first; anal similar to soft dorsal, the anterior rays rather longer than those of dorsal, anal spines graduated, the first very small, the second somewhat larger, the third considerably longer and stronger, its length about 1.3 in eye; fourth anal spine still a little longer than the third but more slender; caudal fin widely forked, the lobes equal, their length about 1.2 in head; pectoral slender, its length equal to that of caudal lobes, its tip reaching beyond those of ventrals; ventrals short, the spine slender, its length equal to diameter of orbit, the longest rays about equal to snout and orbit.

Color of a nearly fresh specimen (No. 03163) 6.5 inches long, top of head and upper part of side rich rosy red; lower parts and side below lateral line pale rosy with silvery reflection; jaws rich rosy; cheeks and opercles rosy and whitish; upper half of edge of opercle rusty reddish brown, this extending to shoulder-girdle; axil of pectoral dark reddish; spinous dorsal pale rosy, anterior membrane and outer part of others orange; soft dorsal pale rosy, first ray white, outer half of next 6 or 7 rays rich rosy red; caudal rich rosy red, edges paler; anal spines white, the soft part same color as caudal; pectoral pale rosy; ventrals very pale rosy, the spine and its membrane white, the second membrane deeper rosy; iris clouded red above, pale yellow below

Another example (No. 03480) was red in life, though paler than *M. murdjan;* side coppery silvery; black opercular bar covering axil; first dorsal rosy, distal half yellowish orange; soft dorsal, anal, and caudal deep cherry red, the edge scarcely paler; pectoral and ventral pink, a little darker on first rays, also on anal rays behind last spine; iris red.

Color in alcohol, rather uniform yellowish silvery, most yellow above, most silvery below lateral line and on belly; upper edge of opercle black; cheek and opercle silvery; axil of pectoral dusky; fins all pale yellowish white; upper edge of eye dusky, the rest whitish and golden; side below lateral line with about 5 broad lighter horizontal stripes showing plainly only in certain lights.

There is some variation in the number of rays in the dorsal, there being usually 17, but sometimes 16, and more rarely 18. The scales in the lateral line vary from 40 to 43.

This species was originally described by Doctor Günther from a small example, 6 inches long, from the island of Vavau, of the Tonga or Friendly Group. It seems to be an abundant fish among the Hawaiian Islands and at Samoa. Five specimens were obtained by Dr. Jenkins at Honolulu in 1889, one by Dr. Wood in 1896, a fine series was taken by us at Honolulu and Hilo, and it was obtained by the *Albatross* at Laysan Island. Our numerous specimens range in length from 3.8 to 7.5 inches.

106. Myripristis chryseres Jordan & Evermann. "*Pauú.*" Plate VI.

Head 2.75 in length; depth 2.5; eye 2.4 in head; snout 5.5; maxillary 1.9; mandible 1.8; interorbital 5; D. x–i, 14; A. iv, 12; scales 4–34–6.

Body short, stout, and compressed; dorsal profile evenly convex from tip of snout to origin of soft dorsal; ventral outline nearly straight to origin of anal, whose base is equally oblique with that of soft dorsal; caudal peduncle short but slender and not greatly compressed, its length from base of last dorsal ray to first short spinous caudal ray 1.3 in eye, its least width about 3 in its least depth, which is 1.8 in eye; head heavy, short; mouth moderately large, the gape in closed mouth reaching vertical of middle of eye; maxillary very broad, triangular, reaching nearly to vertical of posterior line of eye, with a broad, curved supplemental border; surface of maxillary roughly striated, anterior edge near the angle strongly dentate; lower jaw strong, somewhat projecting, the tip with 2 rounded, rough prominences fitting into a distinct notch in upper jaw; teeth short, in narrow villiform bands in jaws and on palatines, a small patch on vomer, none on tongue; eye very large, orbit exceeding postocular part of head; lower edge of eye on level with axis of body; snout short, 2 in orbit; interorbital space nearly flat, strongly rugose; 2 long ridges from preorbitals to nape; outside of these a short ridge beginning above front of pupil, extending backwark, and branching upon nape; supraocular ridge spinescent posteriorly; suborbital narrow, strongly dentate below, upper edge in front somewhat roughened; opercular bones all strongly toothed; opercular spine short and obscure (stronger in most of the cotypes); dorsal spines slender, fifth longest and strongest, its length 2.5 in head; first dorsal spine somewhat posterior to base of pectoral, its length 2 in eye, spines gradually shorter from fifth;

space between dorsals very short, about equal to length of tenth spine; dorsal rays long, length of longest a little greater than orbit, last equal to pupil; first anal spine very short, second short and triangular, its length about 1.5 in pupil; third anal spine long, strong, and straight, longer than fourth, its length equal to diameter of orbit; fourth anal spine slender, its length 1.3 in orbit; anal rays longer than those of dorsal; caudal widely forked, lobes equal, their length 1.5 in head; pectoral long and narrow, its length 1.4 in head, the tip reaching past tips of ventrals; ventrals slender, pointed, nearly reaching vent and nearly as long as pectoral.

Scales smaller than in *M. murdjan*, number in lateral line 34 in type, 35 to 38 in some of the cotypes; scales strongly dentate, and striate near the edges; a strongly dentate humeral scale.

Color in life, bright scarlet, centers of the scales paler; a blackish-red bar behind and on edge of opercle, continued as red (not black) into the axil; first dorsal golden, with red basal blotches on membranes; second dorsal golden, with crimson at base, spine and first ray white; caudal golden, first ray white above and below; anal golden, the spines and first ray white; all the vertical fins narrowly edged with red; ventrals mostly pink, with golden wash on first rays; pectoral plain crimson; axil light red.

Color in alcohol, yellowish or orange white, the edges of the scales paler; some of the scales with small brownish dustings on the edges; edge of opercle black; opercle and cheek somewhat silvery: fins all pale yellowish, without dark edges. In some individuals the general color is more silvery, and in one example (No. 04860) the axil of the pectoral is somewhat dusky. In life the color is more scarlet than in *M. murdjan* and the fins yellow, not red as in the latter and all other Hawaiian species.

Myripristis chryseres is close to *M. murdjan*, from which it differs in the smaller scales, larger eye, less black in the axil, and the absence of black edges to the dorsal and anal fins as in the life colors already noted, the yellow fins being the most conspicuous character in life. It reaches a length of 9 or 10 inches and appears to be moderately abundant at Honolulu and Hilo.

Type, No. 50629, U. S. N. M. (field No. 03463), a specimen 8 inches long, obtained at Hilo, Hawaii.

Our collections contain 17 excellent specimens from Honolulu and Hilo, ranging in length from 4 to 9.5 inches.

107. Myripristis symmetricus Jordan & Evermann.   Plate 26.

Head 3.2 in length; depth 2.4; eye 2.2 in head; snout 5; interorbital 3.8; D. x–1, 15; A. iv, 14; P. i, 14; V. i, 7; scales 4–36–6.

Body elongate, deep, compressed, greatest depth about midway between origin of ventrals and anal; upper and lower profiles evenly convex; head compressed, as long as deep, its width 1.7 in its length; snout short, broad, blunt, and steep; upper profile of head straight from above nostril to occiput; eye very large, high, hardly impinging upon the upper profile of head, its diameter greater than postocular region; mouth very large, oblique; mandible slightly projecting and reaching posteriorly to below posterior rim of pupil; distal expanded extremity of maxillary 2.35 in eye; several enlarged blunt teeth on outer front edges of mandible; teeth in jaws, on vomer, and palatines very fine, in bands; tongue thick, pointed, free; suborbital rim narrow, finely serrate; lower posterior margin of maxillary smooth; lips rather thick and fleshy; nostrils close together, posterior very large, close to front rim of orbit; bones of head all finely serrate; opercle with well-developed spine; gill-opening large, filaments large; gillrakers long, fine, the longest longer than longest gill-filament; pseudobranchiæ very large; dorsal spines slender, sharp, first 2.75 in head, second 2.1, third 2, fourth 1.9, tenth 6, and last 3.6; soft dorsal with anterior rays elevated, produced into a point which projects beyond tip of posterior rays when fin is depressed, first ray 1.4 in head, third 1.35, and last 3.75; anal spines graduated to last, third enlarged, 2.5 in head, fourth 2.9; soft anal similar to soft dorsal, anterior rays produced, first 1.4, third 1.3, and last 4.6; caudal elongate, deeply forked, the lobes pointed, 1.2 in head, and reaching slightly behind tips of ventrals; ventrals sharp-pointed, 1.4 in head, spine 2.2; caudal peduncle elongate, compressed, its length 1.8 and its depth 3.2; scales large, finely ctenoid, deep on middle of side; lateral line running obliquely back, slightly curved at first, and posteriorly along upper side of caudal peduncle; 4 rudimentary, slender, sharp-pointed, graduated rays along upper and lower edges of caudal; scales narrowly imbricated along middle of side.

Color in alcohol, pale straw-color; fins paler, except the anterior dorsal and anal rays, which are grayish; margin of opercle above blackish; axil of pectoral black.

This species was found both at Honolulu and Hilo, but does not appear to be common at either place. Our 4 specimens each about 5 inches long.

108. Myripristis sealei Jenkins.   Fig. 53.

Head 3 in length; depth 2.5; eye 2.5 in head; snout 5; maxillary 1.8; interorbital 4; D. x–1, 15; A. iv, 13; P. i, 15; V. i, 7; scales 4–37–8.

Body elongate, deep, compressed, greatest depth at about tip of pectoral; upper and lower profiles about evenly convex; head compressed, rather elongate, a little longer than deep, its width 1.8 in its length; snout short, broad, blunt, convex, steep; upper profile of head nearly straight from above nostril to occiput; eye large, high, hardly impinging upon the upper profile of head, about equal to postocular part; mouth large, oblique; mandible slightly projecting, reaching below posterior rim of pupil; distal expanded extremity of maxillary 1.7 in eye; teeth sharp, minute, not enlarged on edges of jaws; teeth in jaws and on vomer and palatines in bands; tongue elongate, rounded, free; suborbital rim narrow, finely serrate; lower posterior margin of maxillary smooth; lips rather thick, fleshy; nostrils close together, posterior very large, close to front rim of orbit; bones on head all finely serrate; opercle with well-developed spine; gill-opening large, filaments large; gillrakers long, fine, longest longer than longest gill-filaments; pseudobranchiæ very large, free for distal half; dorsal spines slender, sharp, first 3.2, second 2, third 1.9, tenth 4.6, last 3.3 in head; anterior dorsal rays elongate, bluntly pointed, second ray 1.7, last 5.5; third anal spine large, 2.5 in head; soft anal similar to soft dorsal, second ray 1.7, last 6.4; caudal elongate, forked, the lobes pointed; pectoral small, pointed, 1.5; ventral 1.5, spine 2.25; scales large, finely ctenoid; lateral line slightly convex, running

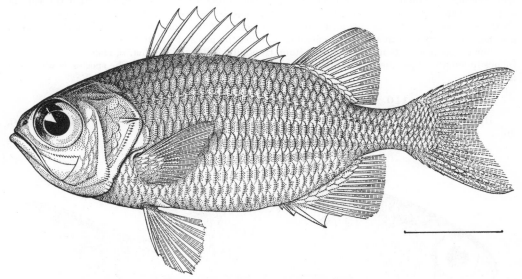

FIG. 53.—*Myripristis sealei* Jenkins; from the type.

down obliquely to base of caudal along upper side of caudal peduncle; 4 slender, sharp-pointed graduated rays above and below.

Color in alcohol, pale brown, or brownish white, fins pale or whitish; no black or brown on edges of gill-opening or in axil of pectoral.

This species is known only from the type and 11 other examples collected by Dr. Jenkins at Honolulu in 1889, ranging in length from 2.2 to 5.25 inches.

109. Myripristis murdjan (Forskål). "*U'u.*" Plate V.

Head 2.75 in length; depth 2.3; eye 2.4 in head; snout 4.7; maxillary 1.75; interorbital 4.9; D. x–i, 14; A. iv, 13; P. i, 14; V. i, 7; scales 4–28 to 30–7.

Body elongate, rather deep, compressed, its greatest depth about base of ventral; head rather large, its depth about equal to its length; snout blunt, obtuse, broad, its upper profile convex, beyond which the upper profile of the head is nearly straight from above the nostril to occiput; eye very large, high, hardly impinging upon the upper profile of head, and its diameter nearly equal to postocular part of head; mouth very large, oblique; mandible slightly projecting, and maxillary not reaching posteriorly to below posterior margin of eye; distal expanded extremity of maxillary 1.65 in eye; several enlarged and blunt teeth on the outer front edges of jaws; teeth fine, in broad bands in jaws, on vomer, and palatines; tongue rather thick, pointed, free; suborbital rim narrow, finely serrate; lower posterior margin of maxillary with blunt denticulations; lips rather thick and fleshy; nostrils very close together, the posterior very large, close to front rim of orbit; bones on head all finely serrate; opercle with well-developed spine; gill-opening large, filaments large; gillrakers long, fine, the longest longer than longest gill-filaments; pseudobranchiæ very large, longer than gill-filaments; dorsal spines rather slender, first spine 3.5 in head, second 2.8, third 2.25, tenth 6.8, and eleventh 4; anterior dorsal rays the highest, base of fin 2.3 in head; origin of soft anal behind soft dorsal, base of fin 2.5 in head, anterior rays highest; third anal spine enlarged, equal to fourth, which is slender; caudal rather small, forked; pectoral small; ventral reaching two-thirds distance to anus, 1.7 in head; ventral spine slender, 2.2 in head; caudal peduncle elongate, compressed, its length 2.3 in head and its depth 3.6; scales large, ctenoid, deep on middle of side, lateral line obliquely curved at first, then running obliquely down to base of caudal, also running obliquely along upper side of caudal peduncle; 4 rudimentary caudal rays above and below, slender, sharp pointed, and graduated.

Color in life, red, the center of each scale pale; a black bar across opercular region down to axil of pectoral; first dorsal with pink spines, membranes of basal half translucent pearly, of upper half orange-yellow; soft dorsal, anal, and caudal crimson, the first rays white in each case; pectoral red, its axil blackish blood-red.   Another example (No. 03487) was ·deep brick-red in life; the opercular blotch very plain, including axil; first dorsal orange, whitish at base; lobes of second dorsal, anal, and caudal largely black; soft anal, caudal, and ventral with first ray white; iris red.

In alcohol, pale straw-color, fins plain and paler; upper margin of opercle and axil of pectoral blackish.

Described from an example (03464) taken at Honolulu.

This species is the common *U'u* of Hawaii, a food-fish always in the markets, taken in rocky places with the hook.   The natives have a curious method of fishing for it.   A live individual of the same or a closely related species is attached to a line and dropped in the water in front of the rocks inhabited by the *U'u*, where, with fins spread, it arouses the enmity of its rivals, who at once attack it.   They are then drawn upward in a net, and one of them takes the place of the first decoy.

Our collections contain 25 specimens from Honolulu, Hilo, and Kailua, ranging from 4 to 11.25 inches in length.   Specimens were also secured by the *Albatross* at Laysan.   The species is abundant at Samoa.

110. Myripristis berndti Jordan & Evermann.   Fig. 54.

Head 2.8 in length; depth 2.4; eye 2.7 in head; snout 4.7; maxillary 1.7; interorbital 4.9; D. x–i, 16; A. iv, 14; P. i, 14; V. i, 7; scales 4–32–7.

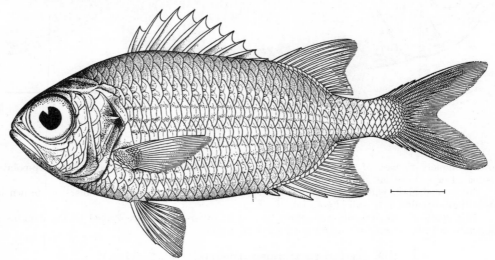

FIG. 54.—*Myripristis berndti* Jordan & Evermann; from the type.

Body elongate, deep, compressed, its greatest depth at base of ventral; head large, compressed, its depth less than its length; snout short, blunt, convex, its width about twice its length; upper profile of head straight from above nostril to occiput; eye large, high, its diameter a little less than posterior part of head and its upper rim hardly impinging upon upper profile of head; mouth very large, oblique; mandible slightly projecting, the maxillary not reaching posterior margin of eye; distal expanded extremity of maxillary 1.7 in eye; several enlarged, blunt teeth on outer front edges of jaw and sides of mandible; teeth in jaws fine, in broad bands, also on vomer and palatines; tongue thick, pointed, and free in front; suborbital rim narrow, finely serrate; lower posterior margin of maxillary with blunt denticulations; lips rather thick and fleshy; nostrils close together, posterior very large, close to front rim of orbit; bones of head all finely serrate; opercle with well-developed spine; gill-opening large, filaments rather large; gillrakers long, fine, the longest longer than longest gill-filaments; pseudobranchiæ very large, outer portions free for half their length; dorsal spines slender, first 3.4 in head, second 2.6, third 2.2, fourth 2.2, tenth 6.4, and last 3.5; anterior dorsal rays elevated, produced into a point, first 1.8, second 1.7, and last 8; first and second anal spines short, third 2.6, and fourth 2.8; soft anal similar to soft dorsal, anterior ray 1.75, third 1.8, and last 6; caudal forked, lobes pointed, 1.2; pectoral rather small, pointed, 1.4; ventral 1.6, reaching 0.65 distance to anus; caudal peduncle elongate, compressed, 2.2 in head, its depth 3.25; scales large, ctenoid, deep; lateral line slightly arched, running obliquely down on side along upper part of caudal peduncle; 4 rudimentary caudal rays above and below, slender, sharp pointed, and graduated.

Color in life (03370), deep red, with silvery luster; no stripes on side, a blood-red band across gill-opening and base of pectoral; fins deep red, without white edgings, distal half of spinous dorsal shading into orange.

Color in alcohol, pale straw-color, fins plain and paler; upper margin of opercle blackish, and axil of pectoral black; anterior margins of soft dorsal and anal whitish.

Described from one of 16 excellent specimens 7 to 9 inches long, obtained at Honolulu. It was not seen at Hilo.

111. Myripristis argyromus Jordan & Evermann.   Plate 27 and Fig. 55.

Head 3.5 in length; depth 2.75; eye 2.4 in head; snout 5; maxillary 1.8; mandible 1.6; interorbital 3.75; D. x–i, 15; A. iv, 13; scales 4–33–5.

Body rather long and compressed, dorsal and ventral outlines about equally and evenly convex

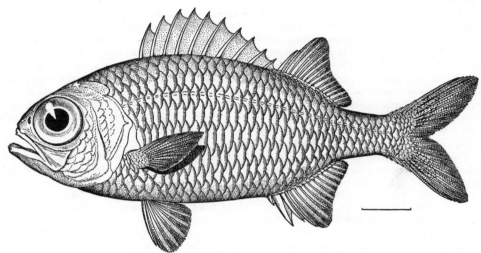

Fig. 55.—*Myripristis argyromus* Jordan & Evermann; from the type.

from snout to origin of anal and soft dorsal fins; head rather large but short; mouth moderate, maxillary reaching vertical at posterior edge of pupil, the exposed portion broad, triangular, the upper edge concave, the end rounded, and the anterior edge with short blunt teeth, strongest at angle; tip of upper jaw with a shallow notch roughened at its outer edges; jaws equal, lower fitting into the notch of upper and with 2 patches of strong blunt tooth-like tubercles at its tip; eye large, its middle above level of tip of upper jaw; interorbital space wide and slightly convex; 2 low, nearly parallel median ridges from tip of snout to nape, diverging slightly at their middle, another low ridge from above orbit backward to nape, and another backward around orbit; ridges on nape divergent; suborbital narrow, dentate on both edges; opercular bones all striate and dentate at the edges; opercle with a short, flat, triangular spine; scales large, rough, striate near the edges, which are finely toothed; a series of 4 or 5 large modified scales across nape, and a series of triangular scales along bases of dorsal and anal; about 10 scales in front of dorsal; origin of dorsal about over lower base of pectoral; dorsal spines slender, the first 3.2 in head, third and fourth longest, about equal to orbit; interval between dorsals very short; anterior dorsal rays somewhat produced, their length equal to snout and eye; edge of fin concave, last rays nearly 3, or equal to pupil; anal spines graduated, the first very small, second short but stout, third much longer and stoutest, its length 1.3 in eye, fourth still longer and more slender; anterior anal rays produced, their length about equal to that of longest dorsal rays, free edge of fin concave; caudal evenly forked, the lobes equal to length of head; pectoral long and pointed, reaching beyond tips of ventrals, about 1.3 in head; ventrals shorter, 1.6 in head, their tips equally distant between their bases and that of first anal ray.

Color in alcohol, pale yellowish-white, brightest above, more silvery on side and belly; opercular bones with fine round brownish specks; edge of opercle not black, scarcely dusky; axil dusky inside but not showing above fin; fins pale yellowish-white without any dark on edges.

Type, No. 50631, U. S. N. M. (field No. 04829), a fine specimen 9.5 inches long, obtained by us at Hilo, Hawaii.

M. argyromus is related to *M. berndti*, but is distinguished by the more slender body, the absence of black on the opercle, and the paler axil. It does not appear to be abundant and is represented in our collections by only 8 specimens, ranging in length from 6.5 to 9 inches. All but the type are from Honolulu.

Genus 92. FLAMMEO Jordan & Evermann.

This genus is distinguished by the very large mouth and projecting chin. The lower jaw is considerably more than half length of head, and the chin projects beyond upper jaw. In the species properly referable to *Holocentrus*, the lower jaw is slightly projecting or included and its length is less than one-half the head. Renewed comparison of the varied forms seems to show that *Flammeo* should be regarded as a subgenus of *Holocentrus*.

112. Flammeo sammara (Forskål). Fig. 56.

Head 2.75 in length; depth 3.25; eye 3.75 in head (3 to 3.75); snout 4.5; interorbital 4.2; maxillary 2.6; D. xi, 12, longest dorsal spine 2.2 in head, ray 2.2; A. iv, 8, longest spine 1.6 in head; pectoral ray 2; ventral ray 1.9; scales 4–38 to 44–6; opercular spines 2, about equal, rather short; preopercular spine short.

Body oblong, compressed, very spindle-shaped in large examples; dorsal outline arched from tip of snout to caudal peduncle; ventral outline less arched than dorsal, not so marked in small examples; head subconic, compressed; mouth large, nearly horizontal; lower jaw prominent, produced, its produced tip forming a straight line with anterior part of head; each jaw, vomer, and palatines with blunt, or slightly conic, close-set, rather pavement-like teeth, 1 on tongue; tongue long, narrow, rounded, the long, narrow anterior part and sides, free; maxillary extending to anterior edge of pupil in large examples, nearly to posterior edge in small ones; eye high, anterior; interorbital flat; first dorsal spine two-thirds second; the third the longest, tapering evenly from it to the last, which is one-half the first; third soft dorsal longest; caudal evenly forked; fourth anal spine three-fourths of third, the latter sheathed, its upper part almost hidden in the latter when fin is depressed.

Color in alcohol, dull silvery, with bluish reflections, darker above; each scale, with many dark punctulations, these more numerous and distinct in the posterior center of each scale, and forming longitudinal stripes along each row of scales; upper portion of membrane before third dorsal spine black, making a black blotch on fin; other fins pale.

Color in life, dull crimson brown or maroon; sides silvery, faint dark stripes and dots along rows of scales; lateral band in a distinct maroon stripe; sides of head much dotted; eye silvery with a streak of red anteriorly; spinous dorsal translucent, the base and tip opaque white, the outlines irregular, a large blood-red blotch on anterior 3 spines and membranes; soft dorsal maroon in front and at base, the rest pale golden; caudal maroon on each lobe, the middle dull orange; anal pale yellowish, membranes of first spines maroon; pectoral light red; ventrals pure white.

The above description from specimen 03374, 10.75 inches long, from Honolulu, where the species is rather common in the market.

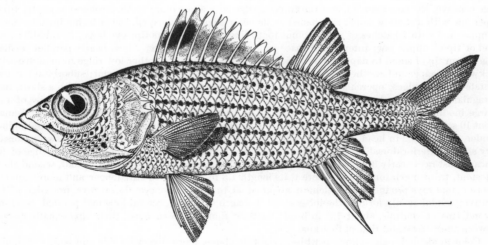

FIG. 56.—*Flammeo sammara* (Forskål).

Another example (No. 03407) had general color silvery in life, lake red on back, and with deeper streak along lateral line; eye silvery, with streak of red anteriorly; belly pale yellowish white; 2 parallel lines of dark spots on anterior 15 scales of the first 2 rows above lateral line; anterior edge of spinous dorsal white, tapering to a point posteriorly and below a transparent bar in which spines are tinged with lake-red; a series of milk-white spots at base of spinous dorsal just behind each spine, the first the highest and extending in front of jet black ocellus edged with lake-red which extends over first 3 spines; first 3 rays of soft dorsal lake-red, then tinged with yellow over fourth and fifth, and the rest of the fin more or less transparent; a pale yellow line on soft dorsal along upper edge and base of fin, the former growing narrower posteriorly, fourth anal spine and first ray lake-red, rest of fin like soft dorsal; caudal with outer rays lake-red, last outside ray above and below white, center colorless, edge pale yellow; pectoral with pale-red tinge on rays; ventral colorless.

Our collections contain 8 specimens taken by us at Honolulu in 1901, 4 secured by Dr. Jenkins at the same place in 1889, 1 by Dr. Wood in 1898, 4 by the *Albatross* at the island of Makemo in 1899, and many others obtained by Dr. Jordan at Samoa in 1902. The *Albatross* obtained specimens at Honolulu and Laysan in 1902. The species has been recorded from Guam by Mr. Seale, and it is common at Samoa.

113. Flammeo scythrops Jordan & Evermann. Plate VII and Fig. 57.

Head (measured to end of flap) 2.75 in length; depth 3; eye 3 in head; snout 4; maxillary 2.1; mandible 1.8; interorbital 5; D. xi, 13; A. iv, 9; scales 5–48–7, 5 rows on cheek; Br. 7.

Body oblong, rather slender; dorsal outline gently and rather evenly curved from tip of snout to origin of soft dorsal, more nearly straight from tip of snout to nape; ventral outline less convex; head long; snout long and pointed; maxillary broad, with a strong supplemental bone whose lower edge forms a broad angle; end of maxillary slightly concave; lower jaw long, much projecting, tip prominent; mouth large, not greatly oblique; maxillary nearly reaching vertical at posterior line of pupil; lips broad, rounded, and soft; eye large, lower edge of pupil on axis of body; interorbital space with a broad, shallow groove between low ridges, 1 on each side; space between ridge and eye with short, curved ridges; nape on each side with a group of 8 or 10 short, sharp ridges, diverging backward and

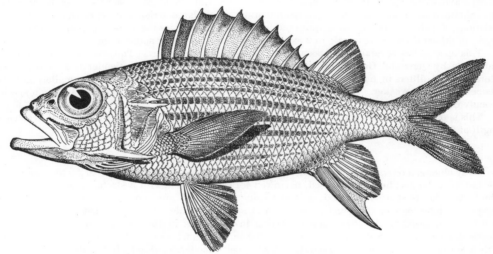

FIG. 57.—*Flammeo scythrops* Jordan & Evermann; from the type.

ending in short, sharp spines; posterior part of supraocular with a patch of short spines; suborital dentate on its lower edge; preorbital with 2 blunt prominences in front, a strong, recurved spine below, ridges and spines on its upper surface; opercular bones all strongly striate, the striæ ending in short spines; entire surface of interopercle striate; opercle with 2 strong spines, the lower the stronger, its length 1.6 in orbit; preopercle with a very strong spine at angle, its length nearly equaling diameter of orbit, its surface striate, and its base with a series of small spines; under surface of dentary somewhat roughened; surface of articular bone much rougher; jaws each with a broad band of villiform teeth, the outer series on upper jaw stronger; a narrow series on each palatine and a patch on vomer; scales moderate, the surfaces usually nearly smooth, the edges finely toothed; a series of strongly striate scales across nape, and a strong, striated plate at shoulder; lateral line well developed, little arched, with about 45 pores; bases of soft dorsal and anal each with series of modified triangular scales; caudal with small scales on base and fine scales on membranes, extending well toward tips of outer rays; origin of spinous dorsal in advance of base of pectoral or over middle of upper opercular spine; dorsal spines in a broad, deep groove, moderately strong, middle one longest, 2.3 in head, first a little shorter than snout, tenth more than half eye; dorsal rays longer than spines, longest 2.2 in head; first anal spine very short, second about 3 times as long; third anal spine very long and strong, but little curved, reaching past base of anal, its length 1.5 in head; fourth anal spine shorter and more slender, its length 2.25 in head and equaling longest anal rays; last anal ray much shorter, 1.6 in eye; pectoral long and slender, 1.2 in head, the tip nearly reaching vent; ventrals shorter, equal to snout and eye; caudal forked, the lobes equal, not strongly divergent, their length about equaling that of third anal spine; rudimentary caudal spines 5 above, 4 below, strong and sharp.

Color in life, head red above, paler on sides, nearly white below; tips of jaws rich red; side of body with about 10 or 12 narrow yellow stripes separated by red or rosy stripes of about same width, those below paler and somewhat purplish; under parts purplish or pinkish white; the stripes beginning at edge of opercle and ceasing at base of caudal peduncle, which is rich red above, becoming paler on side and below; membranes between the first and third dorsal spines rich blood-red, those between other spines white at base, each with distal portion lemon-yellow in front and red behind, last 2 or 3 membranes with little or no yellow; dorsal spines pale rosy, nearly white; soft dorsal, anal, pectoral, and ventral with rays rosy, membranes pale; ventral with a little yellow at base; anal spines somewhat dusky; caudal rich blood-red, paler distally; eye red, a narrow yellow ring around pupil. Another example (No. 03041), much faded, was bright red; stripes on side equally bright golden; fins red; edges of dorsal membranes pale; no markings evident on fins.

Color in life of another example (No. 03451), side with 10 or 11 longitudinal golden or yellow bands; spinous dorsal more or less white; membranes between first and third dorsal spines more or less deep vermillion, except the upper marginal portion behind second spine, which is white; a red blotch along margin of membranes just before each of the other dorsal spines.

Color of another specimen (No. 03490) when fresh, violet-rose with 10 stripes of bright golden on side; dorsal red, mottled with golden, the first 2 spines deep red; soft dorsal and other fins rather light red without edgings, and scarcely darker behind third anal spine; pectoral and ventrals pink; a red dash across cheek, space above and below whitish; temporal region deep red; iris red. All these colors fade in alcohol and the fish becomes a pale yellowish white, the longitudinal lines on side showing faintly as duller and brighter stripes of yellowish white; fins all whitish or yellowish white, membranes of spinous dorsal whiter.

The above description from the type, No. 50633, U.S.N.M. (field No. 03488), a specimen 9 inches long, obtained by us at Honolulu. An examination of our large series of cotypes shows but slight variations, the characters appearing quite stable. In some examples the upper opercular spine is the larger, in others the two are equal; in 2 examples we find 3 opercular spines each.

This species has several times been called *Holocentrum argenteum*. The species described under that name by Quoy and Gaimard from New Guinea resembles this in the slender body and general coloration, but differs in having the lower jaw included, eye much smaller, mouth smaller, and the preopercular spine weaker. It was intended for *Holocentrus lacteoguttatus* of the East Indies, a species wrongly called *punctatissimus* by Bleeker.

This is one of the most abundant species in the markets at Honolulu and Hilo. It reaches a length of 8 to 10 inches. Our 30 specimens range in length from 5 to 10 inches.

Genus 93. HOLOCENTRUS Scopoli. *"Alaíhi."*

Body oblong, moderately compressed, the ventral outline nearly straight, the back a little elevated, the tail very slender; head compressed, narrowed forward; opercle with a strong spine above, below which the edge is sharply serrated; a strong spine at angle of preopercle; orbital ring, preorbital, preopercle, interopercle, subopercle, occiput, and shoulder-girdle with their edges sharply serrate; mouth small, terminal, the lower jaw projecting in the adult; in the young (which constitute the supposed genera *Rhynchichthys* and *Rhinoberyx*) the snout is much produced; maxillary broad, striate, with a supplemental bone; eye excessively large; scales moderate, closely imbricated, the posterior margin strongly spinous; lateral line continuous; dorsal deeply emarginate, the spines usually 11, depressible in a groove; soft dorsal short and high; anal with 4 spines, the first and second quite small, the third very long and strong, the fourth smaller; caudal widely forked; both lobes with the rudimentary rays spinelike; ventrals large, i, 7, the spine very strong. Species numerous, remarkable for the development of sharp spines almost everywhere on the surface of the body.

114. Holocentrus diadema Lacépède. *"Alaihi kalaloa."* Plate X.

Head 3.25 in length; depth 2.75; eye 2.9 in head; snout 3.8; maxillary 3.1; interorbital 4.5; D. XI, 13; A. IV, 9; P. I. 13; V. I, 7; scales 4–47–7.

Body elongate, deep, compressed, greatest depth about midway between origin of ventral and anal; upper and lower profiles evenly convex; head compressed, longer than deep, its width half its length; snout short, broad, blunt, steep; upper profile of head slightly convex, eye very large, impinging upon upper profile, anterior, the posterior margin of pupil a little before middle of head, and its diameter a little less than postocular region; mouth small, slightly oblique; maxillary reaching a little beyond front rim of orbit, but not to pupil, small and its distal expanded extremity 1.6 in pupil; teeth in jaws, on vomer and palatines, pointed, crowded, small; tongue pointed, free; suborbital rim narrow, finely serrate; lips thick, fleshy; nostrils close together, anterior very large, close to eye; bones on head all finely serrate, the opercle with 2 well-developed spines, the upper the larger; preopercle with a strong spine reaching beyond gill-opening; gill-opening large, filaments rather long, gillrakers compressed, short, in moderate number; pseudobranchiæ large; dorsal spines sharp, pointed, first 3.5 in head, second 2.2, third 1.8, fourth 1.6, eleventh 4.2; anterior dorsal rays produced, pointed, third 1.6 in head, last 5; third anal spine enlarged 1.3, fourth 2; anal similar to soft dorsal, first ray longest,

1.5, last 4.5; caudal rather small, deeply iorked; pectoral 1.7; ventral 1.1; caudle peduncle elongate, compressed, its length 1.8, depth 3.8.

Color when fresh, side and upper parts rosy, deep or dark red in life; about 11 very distinct horizontal white lines, the upper narrower and somewhat rosy, these separating a corresponding number of rosy lines; head with 3 oblique white stripes on cheek, interspaces rosy; spinous dorsal deep blood-red, fading to blackish; a narrow white stripe near the base, ending at the fifth spine; a similar less regular stripe from ninth spine to end of fin above middle of spine, each spine tipped with white; soft dorsal light rosy, first ray deep red; caudal light rosy, upper and lower margins deep red with a very narrow white edge; anal light rosy, membrane from third spine to first soft ray deep blood red; pectoral pale rosy, without dark spot at base; ventral spine and first ray white, the second ray and membrane deep red, rest of fin light rosy; iris red.

Color in alcohol, pale silvery brown or whitish, each scale on back sprinkled with many fine dark brown dots; side with 8 narrow white longitudinal lines; inside of pectoral grayish; spinous dorsal black, except upper extremities of membranes between each 2 spines; a narrow line on lower part of fin running as far as sixth spine, and another running from seventh spine on upper part to end of fin; membrane between third anal spine and first soft ray at first whitish and then blackish; ventrals whitish.

Described from an example (No. 03162) taken at Honolulu. This is a small species, very abundant along the shores of the Hawaiian Islands; also abundant at Samoa. Our collection contains one example from Hilo and 22 from Honolulu. Dr. Jenkins records 11 specimens obtained by him at Honolulu in 1889. The *Albatross* secured specimens at Honolulu, Laysan Island, and at station 3834, on the southern coast of Molokai, in 8 fathoms. Our specimens range from 4 to 6.5 inches in length.

115. Holocentrus microstomus Günther. Fig. 58.

Head 3 in length; depth 3; eye 2.75 in head; snout 4; maxillary 2.7; interorbital 5; D. xi, 14; A. iv, 10; P. i, 14; V. i, 7; scales 4–48–8.

Body elongate, compressed, greatest depth about ventral fin, upper and lower profiles evenly convex; head compressed, longer than deep, and pointed, its width a little less than half its length; upper profile of head slightly convex; eye very large, impinging upon upper profile, the posterior margin of pupil nearly midway in length of head, and a little less than postocular reg on; mouth

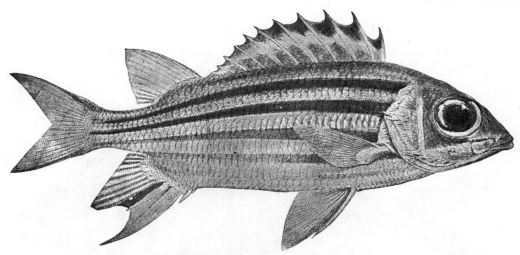

FIG. 58.—*Holocentrus microstomus* Günther; after Günther.

small, slightly oblique; maxillary reaching a little beyond anterior margin of pupil, small, its distal expanded extremity 1.25 in pupil; teeth minute, crowded; tongue pointed, free; suborbital rim very narrow, finely serrate; lips thick, fleshy; nostrils close together, anterior very large, close to eye; bones on head all finely serrate, the opercle with two well-developed spines, the upper the longer; preopercle with a strong spine reaching beyond gill-opening; gill-opening large, filaments rather long, gillrakers compressed, short, in moderate number; pseudobranchiæ large; dorsal spines sharp, pointed, first 3 in head, second 2.3, third 2, eleventh 6; anterior dorsal rays elongate, fourth 2 in head, last 5; soft anal similar to soft dorsal, last ray 5; caudal small, forked, lobes pointed; pectoral small, 1.6 in head; ventral reaching three-fourths distance to anus, fin 1.4 in head, spine 2; caudal peduncle elongate, its length 1.19, its depth 3.9.

Color in alcohol (No. 03486) pale silvery brown or whitish, side with 9 or 10 narrow white longitudinal lines; axil of pectoral brown; spinous dorsal pale, with a broad blackish band from middle of membrane between first 2 spines, edged above and below with whitish in front; fins pale or whitish.

Described from an example (No. 04263) taken at Honolulu.

We have examined 2 other specimens obtained at Honolulu by Dr. Wood and recorded by Dr. Jenkins.   They range from 5.5 to 6.2 inches in length.   The species is common at Samoa.

116. Holocentrus spinifer (Forskål).   Plate VIII.

Head 3 in length; depth 2.4; eye 4.7 in head; snout 3.4; maxillary 2.6; mandible 2; interorbital 6.4; D. xi, 16; A. iv, 11; P. i, 14; V. i, 7; scales 5–46–8.

Body rather elongate, deep, compressed, back elevated; head moderate, compressed, pointed, upper profile straight from tip of snout to occiput; snout long, pointed, its upper profile straight; lower profile of head nearly straight; eye small, high, its posterior margin about midway in length of head; mouth large, oblique, the mandible slightly projecting; maxillary broad distally, its width at that point 1.5 in eye; lips large, thick, papillose; teeth fine, in broad bands in jaws; tongue elongate, pointed, free in front; postorbital very narrow, preorbital broad with 2 strong spines, 3 small serrations in between; nasal bone with strong spine in front; bones on head all more or less serrate; margin of preopercle coarsely serrate, ending in a long strong spine below, reaching well beyond gill-opening and furnished with a thin flap; opercle with 2 strong spines, upper longer; nasal aperture very large and deep, with a small aperture in front; interorbital space flattened, rather narrow; gill-opening large, gill-rakers rather small, short, few in number; gill-filaments and pseudobranchiæ moderately long; anterior dorsal spines longest, first 2.9 in head, second 2.1, third 2, last 8.5; anterior rays longest, first ray 2.7, second 1.9, third 1.8, last 5; third anal spine very large, strong, 2 in head, third 2.35; soft anal similar to soft dorsal, first ray 1.8, third 2, last 6.5; caudal rather small, lobes broad, rounded, pointed; caudal peduncle compressed, elongate, its length 1.8, depth 3; pectoral rather small, 1.5 in head, pointed; ventral long, pointed 1.5, spine 2.3; rudimentary caudal spines 4, graduated, sharp pointed.

Color in life, bright red, each scale with central area of pearly gray with red; spinous dorsal rich vermilion, tinged with yellow; other fins yellowish red; caudal bordered posteriorly with yellow; 3 large scales behind eye and narrow area behind these dark red; axil of pectoral, and spot on under face of base of pectoral dark red.

Color in alcohol, yellowish white; spinous dorsal yellowish; other fins pale.

We have 2 specimens of this species (No. 02554, 9.75 inches long, and No. 03437, 15 inches long), both from Honolulu.   It is common at Samoa.

117. Holocentrus erythræus Günther.   Fig. 59.

Head 3 in length; depth 2.7; eye 4.5 in head; snout 4; maxillary 2.2; mandible 1.8; interorbital 5; D. xi–16; A. iv, 10; P. i, 13; V. i, 7; scales 4–48–7.

FIG. 59.—*Holocentrus erythræus* Günther; after Günther.

Body elongate, compressed, deep, greatest depth about middle of belly; head compressed, pointed, upper and lower profiles straight; snout short, pointed; eye small, high, its posterior margin well before middle of length of head, not impinging upon upper profile; mouth rather large, oblique, mandible slightly projecting; maxillary broadly expanded distally, 1.4 in eye, reaching beyond posterior margin of pupil; supplemental maxillary large, teeth minute, crowded, in bands in jaws; lips thick fleshy, papillose; suborbital ridge rather narrow, with 2 very strong short spines; 2 short nasal spines; posterior nasal cavity very large; interorbital space broad, flattened; margin of preopercle finely serrate, with a long pointed spine below; opercle with 2 spines, upper larger but not much longer; gill-opening large, filaments coarse, and pseudobranchiæ rather long; gillrakers rather short, thick, compressed, not as long as filaments, and in moderate number; dorsal spines rather low, first 4.2 in head, third 2.9, and last 4.6; anterior dorsal rays elevated, third longest, 1.5 in head, last 6; third anal spine enlarged, 1.8, fourth 2.2; soft anal similar to soft dorsal, first ray 1.7, last 5.25; caudal rather small, forked; pectoral pointed, 1.4; ventral sharp pointed, 1.4; spine slender, 2.5; caudal peduncle compressed, its length 1.8, its depth 3.2.

Color in life, very deep red, golden shades along rows of scales below, alternating with brighter shades of vivid violet; some faint dark spots on anterior part of body, in axil, and one on base of pectoral, these small, round spots larger than nostril; fins deep red without edge; a row of whitish spots on membrane of first dorsal; third anal spine white; ventral spine clear violet.

Another example (No. 03471) was brilliant red in life, with violet shades along the rows of scales; fins scarlet or crimson, nearly plain; no dark marks anywhere.

Color in alcohol, pale brown or brownish white, side with about 10 broad longitudinal bands.

This very handsome species resembles *H. tiere* Lesson=*H. pœcilopterus* Bleeker, from the South Seas, differing principally in the fewer scales and single series of pale spots on the spinous dorsal.

Described from an example (No. 04962) taken at Honolulu. We have 6 specimens 7.6 to 13.5 inches long, from Honolulu and Kailua. The species was obtained at Honolulu, also by the *Albatross*, and we have one specimen from Samoa.

118. Holocentrus punctatissimus Cuvier & Valenciennes. Fig. 60.

Head 3.25 in length; depth 3; eye 3.4 in head; snout 4; maxillary 2.7; interorbital 3.6; D. xi, 14; A. iv, 9; P. i, 14; V. i., 7; scales 4–47–7.

FIG. 60.—*Holocentrus punctatissimus* Cuvier & Valenciennes; after Günther.

Body elongate, compressed, greatest depth about tip of ventral spine, upper and lower profiles nearly evenly convex; head elongate, compressed, depth 1.25 in its length, width 2; eye rather small, well anterior, and impinging a little on upper profile; snout blunt, oblique; mouth rather small, oblique; maxillary reaching posteriorly behind front margin of pupil, its distal expanded extremity 2.6 in eye; supplemental maxillary large; lips thick, fleshy; teeth in jaws, and on vomer and palatines minute, in broad bands; tongue elongate, pointed, free in front; nostrils close together, posterior one a small cavity; lower margin of preorbital serrate; suborbital rim narrow, also finely serrate; bones of head all more or less finely serrate; margin of preopercle below with a large dagger-shaped spine reaching well beyond gill-opening; margin of opercle above with two nearly equal, rather short spines; interorbital space broad, flattened; a small, fleshy axillary flap; gill-opening large, filaments moderately long; gillrakers much shorter than filaments, compressed, few in number; pseudobranchiæ large; spinous dorsal long, spines very sharp, first 3 in head, second 2.1, third 1.8, last 7.5; anterior dorsal rays longest, second ray 1.7, last 5.5; anal with third spine longest, reaching beyond tip of anterior rays, 1.5 in head, fourth spine 2.25; soft anal similar to soft dorsal; caudal small, forked, lobes pointed; caudal peduncle elongate, compressed, its length 1.6, depth 3.7; pectoral 1.25; ventral pointed, 1.4, spine 2.

Color in life, upper part of side bright rosy red with a silvery gleam, deeper and lighter lines alternating; lower two-thirds of side with alternating lines of silvery white and very pale rosy; belly plain white; top of head and nape rich rosy, snout paler; humeral region rich rosy; body at base of soft dorsal rich rosy; side of head silvery white, an obscure rosy line across cheek from lower level of eye; spinous dorsal silvery white with a large blood-red blotch on distal part of each membrane becoming smaller posteriorly; similar but smaller and paler spots on bases of fourth to ninth membranes; spines all white, soft dorsal and pectoral very pale rosy; caudal pale rosy; anal white except first and second rays, which are pale rosy; ventral white; iris yellowish silvery. Another example (No. 03202) was rosy when fresh, with silvery below; about 9 faint white streaks along side; a deep blood-red blotch on opercle behind eye, spinous dorsal with a row of faint white spots on the membranes, these near the base of the first 2 spines, toward the tips of the others; no white shade on back of tail; no shade on anal; fins all pale, probably light red in life.

Color in alcohol, very pale brown or brownish white, more or less brassy; fins all pale. Young individuals are rather dark brown, with dark brown longitudinal bands; spots on spinous dorsal black brown; many show a pale area on middle of back like that in Günther's figure.

Described from an example (No. 02982) taken at Honolulu. A small species, and one of the most common fishes among the Hawaiian Islands. Common also at Samoa. Our collections contain no fewer than 60 specimens from Honolulu, Hilo, and Kailua, ranging in length from 2.25 to 11 inches. Specimens were obtained by the *Albatross* at Honolulu; Puako Bay, Hawaii; and Laysan Island.

119. Holocentrus xantherythrus Jordan & Evermann. *"Alaihi."* Plate IX.

Head 2.8 in length; depth 3; eye 3 in head; snout 4; maxillary 2.7; interorbital 5; D. xi–14; A. iv, 10; scales 4–47–8.

Body elongate, compressed, greatest depth about base of ventral; upper profile steep; lower profile nearly horizontal; head compressed, its depth about 1.2 in length, width 2.25; eye large, high, impinging upon upper profile in front, anterior, its diameter a little less than postocular region; snout short, pointed, its upper profile obliquely straight; jaws rather large, subequal; maxillary reaching beyond front margin of pupil or to first third of eye, its distal expanded extremity 2.7 in eye; supplemental maxillary large; lips rather thick, fleshy; teeth small, short, in rather broad bands in jaws and on vomer and palatines; tongue elongate, pointed, free in front; nostrils close together, posterior, a deep cavity in front of middle of eye; interorbital space broad, very slightly concave; preorbital with a large spine in front, its margins serrate; suborbital narrow, with finely serrate margin; preopercle with a large dagger-like spine at lower angle; opercle with 2 similar spines on upper margin, upper one much the larger; bones of head with serrate margins; gill-opening rather large, filaments and pseudobranchiæ well developed; gillrakers short, compressed, few, and much shorter than longest filaments; fleshy axillary flap small; dorsal spines sharp-pointed, first 3.2 in head, second 2.8, third 1.9, last 7; anterior dorsal rays high, second 2.4 in head, third 2.2, last 6.5; third anal spine very large, not reaching beyond soft rays, 1.7 in head, fourth 2.25; anterior anal rays longest, first 1.75 in head, second 1.9, last 6; caudal rather small, deeply forked; pectoral small, 1.6 in head; ventral sharp-pointed, 1.4, spine 2; caudal peduncle elongate, compressed, its length 2.1 in head, depth 4; scales rather large, ctenoid; lateral line nearly straight, running obliquely down along upper side of caudal peduncle.

Color in life (No. 02989), bright red, belly more or less silvery; about 10 narrow longitudinal silvery stripes, uppermost pinkish; side of head silvery with pinkish shades; a white stripe from preorbital to base of preopercular spine; spinous dorsal deep red without streaks or black marking, a white spot behind first and second spines at base, tips of third to seventh spines whitish; soft dorsal, anal, caudal, and pectoral plain pink; anal with membrane of third spine and first soft ray deep red; ventral pink, spine and first soft ray white, second ray deep red anteriorly, posteriorly whitish. One example (No. 03161) was rose-red when fresh, with about 10 very faint light rosy streaks along rows of scales, these much less distinct than in other species; cheek rosy with 1 broad oblique white band; dorsal plain red, the membranes fading to white, no light stripes on dark areas; other fins plain light red; membrane of fourth anal spine not darker; iris pink. Another example (field No. 03467) was deep crimson when fresh, with 10 narrow, sharply defined, white stripes along rows of scales; an oblique white stripe below eye from snout to base of preopercular spine; dorsal clear deep red, clouded with darker; soft dorsal, caudal, and anal light bright red; membrane between third and fourth anal spines blood red; pectoral deep red; ventrals red, spines white, their membranes blood red.

Color in alcohol, pale brown or brownish white, washed more or less with silvery or brassy white; side with 9 or 10 longitudinal white stripes; fins pale.

This species is related to *Holocentrus ensifer*, differing mainly in the presence of 2 well-developed spines on the upper margin of the opercle. It is one of the most abundant of the family in Hawaiian waters.

We have 40 specimens from Honolulu and Kailua, ranging in length from 3.75 to 6.5 inches. Examples were also obtained by the *Albatross* at Honolulu.

120. Holocentrus ensifer Jordan & Evermann. Plates XI and 28.

Head 3 in length; depth 2.7; eye 3 in head; snout 3.5; maxillary 2.25; interorbital 5; D. xi, 15; A. iv, 11; P. i, 14; V. i, 8; scales 4–47–8.

Body elongate, compressed, greatest depth at ventral fins; upper profile decidedly more convex than lower; head compressed, much longer than deep, pointed, its width a little more than half its length; eye moderate, about 1.2 in postocular part of head, and slightly impinging upon upper profile; snout pointed; mouth moderate, oblique; maxillary broad, with large supplemental bone, distally equal to half diameter of eye; lips thick, fleshy; teeth minute, in broad bands in jaws, and on vomer and palatines; tongue pointed, free in front; nostrils close together, posterior one a large cavity with several small spines projecting over; preorbital with 2 large strong spines and about 6 strong serrations on its margin; suborbital rim narrow; bones of head all more or less finely serrate, the opercle above and preopercle below each with a long, strong, dagger-like spine; interorbital space broad, very slightly concave; a fleshy axillary flap; gill-opening large, filaments moderately long, much longer than gillrakers, which are compressed and not very numerous; pseudobranchiæ large; spinous dorsal long, membrane between spines not much incised, first 2.2, second 2.1, third 2, last 4.2; anterior dorsal rays longest, fourth 1.8, last 7.5; third anal spine largest, 1.75, fourth 2.3; soft anal similar to soft dorsal, third spine not reaching beyond rays; caudal rather small, forked; pectoral 1.3; ventral 1.4, spine 2; caudal peduncle compressed, its length 2.2, depth 4; scales rather large, ctenoid; lateral line arched a little at first and running down obliquely on upper side of caudal peduncle.

Color in life, bright red; side with about 8 yellow longitudinal bands; spinous dorsal vermilion tinged with yellow; soft dorsal rosy with front margin white and behind this above, red; anal whitish with red between third spine and first ray; caudal red, margined above and along the emargination with whitish; pectoral whitish with red lines; ventral rosy with front margin white. One example (field No. 03454) in life had yellow and red longitudinal bands above and yellow and white below; spinous dorsal vermilion, other fins red with white borders. One (field No. 03472) was brilliant scarlet red with 11 golden streaks along rows of scales, upper 4 broadest, and third and fourth most distinct and oblique; a white or golden streak across cheek; fins plain scarlet without dark patches. Another, when fresh (field No. 03494), was bright red verging to scarlet; side red, with 4 golden stripes along back and 6 silver stripes below these, golden and silver, very bright; head crimson; a white band on cheek; spinous dorsal deep scarlet with crimson edge; soft dorsal light crimson with a white, then a dark crimson edge; caudal blood red, edged above and below with white, posterior part of fin abruptly pale; anal with pale spines, then blood red, then pinkish; ventral with white spine, then dark red, then pink; pectoral light red, axil deep red.

Color in alcohol, pale brown or brownish white, the longitudinal bands on sides, together with scales on cheeks and opercle, silvery; fins pale.

This species was obtained by us at Honolulu and Kailua, and appears to be common at the former place.

The 9 specimens we have examined are 6 to 9.75 inches long.

Family L. POLYMIXIIDÆ.— The Barbudos.

Body rather elongated and compressed; scales not serrated; lateral line continuous with back; head compressed and with a decurved profile; preopercle serrated; mouth with a lateral and nearly horizontal cleft; teeth villiform, on both jaws and on palate; branchiostegal apertures large, the gill-membranes separate, free from the isthmus; branchiostegals 4; dorsal moderately elongated, with several spines, increasing backward; anal opposite the posterior portion of dorsal, armed with 3 or 4 spines; pectoral with branched rays; ventral fins thoracic, each with a spine and 6 or 7 rays. Vertebræ in increased number (29). The family is distinguished by the combination of chin barbels, increased number of rays, and small number of branchiostegals. The increased number of ventral rays and the structure of the fins seem to point to bervycoid rather than percoid affinities. Mr. Starks has shown that the structure of the barbels is quite unlike that seen in the *Mullidæ*, notwithstanding the strong external resemblance.

A single genus, with 1 to 3 species, inhabiting rather deep waters in the tropical Atlantic and Pacific.

Genus 94. POLYMIXIA Lowe. Barbudo.

Characters of the genus included above. The species are fully described in Section II.

Suborder SELENICHTHYES.

This group is especially characterized by the presence of 14 to 17 rays in the ventral fins. The long dorsal is made of soft rays only, and the hypocoracoid bone is greatly dilated. It is probably allied to the group of *Scombroidei*.

One family, the *Lampridæ*.

Family LI. LAMPRIDÆ.—The Mariposas.

Body ovate, compressed and elevated, covered with minute, cycloid scales; head small, rather pointed; mouth small, terminal, without teeth in the adult, its angle with slits in the skin to permit motion of jaws, as in the tunnies; premaxillaries protractile; opercular bones entire; dorsal fin single, very long, elevated, and falcate in front, without distinct spines; anal long and low, not at all falcate; both fins depressible in a groove; ventral fins thoracic, but behind the pectorals, attached to a very long pubic bone, composed of 14 to 17 soft rays; pectoral fins large, falcate, their bases horizontal; caudal fin moderately forked, its peduncle short and slender, without keel; a pit at base of caudal, above and below, as in certain sharks; lateral line present, much arched in front; branchiostegals 6; gill-membranes free from isthmus; esophagus not armed with spinous teeth; air-bladder large, bifurcate behind; pyloric appendages very numerous; vertebræ 45; hypocoracoid very much dilated, as in *Brama*, the entire shoulder-girdle very heavy; the pubic bone much longer than in *Brama*. Fishes of large size and gorgeous coloration, inhabiting the open seas, the flesh firm and rich. A single genus with probably but one species. It resembles the tunnies in the character of the flesh, but the form is very different, and the character of the anal fin separates it widely from all mackerel-like fishes.

Genus 95. LAMPRIS Retzius. Mariposas.

Characters of the genus included above. The single species is cosmopolitan, most beautifully colored, and unsurpassed as food, the flesh rich, firm, and delicate.

121. Lampris regius (Bonnaterre).

Head 3.25 in length; depth 1.75; D. 53 to 55; A. 38 to 41; V. 14 to 17; vertebræ $23 + 22 = 45$.

Body short and very deep, sides much compressed; mouth toothless; longest dorsal ray shorter than pectorals, which are nearly as long as head; anal very low in front, a little higher behind.

Color a rich brocade of silver and lilac, rosy on belly; everywhere with round silvery spots; head, opercles, and back with ultramarine tints; jaws and fins vermilion; flesh red, of varying shades.

Skeleton strong and firm. Length 3 to 6 feet. Open waters of the Atlantic and Pacific; frequently taken off the coasts of Europe; not rare off Madeira; occasionally taken off Newfoundland, Maine, and Cuba; also at Monterey and other places in California, and in Japan. Mr. Berndt sends a photograph of a specimen of this species, weighing 176 pounds, taken off Honolulu. One of the choicest of fishes, the flesh rich, firm, and of delicate flavor.

Group SCOMBROIDEI.—The Mackerel-like Fishes.

Body variously formed, usually adapted for rapid swimming; the scales usually small and cycloid or wanting, sometimes transformed into rough or bony plates, but rarely ctenoid; lateral line various, usually undulate or with an anterior arch and a posterior straight part, at least not regularly arched; sometimes wanting; flesh in typical forms, firm, oily, and reddish in color, but in some cases pale and soft; caudal peduncle almost always slender and strong, the caudal fin, if present, more or less deeply forked, except in certain deep-sea forms and in aberrant families, the structure typically adapted for swift propulsion; dorsal fin usually long, the spinous portion generally shorter than the soft part, sometimes absent; the spines seldom very strong, sometimes not differentiated from the soft rays; anal fin always more or less similar to soft dorsal; ventrals thoracic, subjugular, or subabdominal, usually with one slender spine and 5 rays, sometimes many-rayed, sometimes rudimentary or wholly wanting; branchiostegals few, usually 7; gills 4, a slit behind the fourth; gillrakers various; gill-membranes usually separate, sometimes joined together, rarely attached to the isthmus; mouth and dentition various; skeleton firm or variously soft, the structure as in spinous-rayed fishes generally; the shoulder-girdle attached to the cranium by a distinctly forked post-temporal, which is not adnate to the cranium; no orbitosphenoid; vertebræ varying from 24 to more than 100, the high numbers found in pelagic species; intestinal canal short. This group of mackerel-like fishes is not capable of exact definition, its deviations from the ordinary type of spiny-rayed fishes being various and in various directions, so that no set of diagnostic characters will cover them. The group is not a suborder, as the term is generally understood; it is incapable of simple definition, and in its divergence some members approach to other groups more nearly than to typical or even extreme members of their own. The group is, however, a somewhat natural one, as by the common consent of ichthyologists its different types have always been kept near each other in the system of classification.

Family LII. XIPHIIDÆ.—The Swordfishes.

Fishes of great size, with the body elongate, naked, the young covered with rough granulations; upper jaw very much prolonged, forming a "sword," which is flattened horizontally and composed of the consolidated vomer, ethmoid, and premaxillaries; teeth wanting in the adult, present in the young; dorsal fin long, usually divided in the adult, continuous in the young, without differentiated spinous part, each part composed of soft rays, the posterior portion much smaller than the anterior and placed on the tail, resembling the second dorsal of a shark; fin rays enveloped in the skin; anal fin divided in the adult; caudal peduncle slender, with a strong median keel; caudal fin widely forked in the adult; ventral fins entirely wanting; no pelvic arch; gills of peculiar structure, the laminæ of each arch joined into one plate by reticulations; gills 4, a slit behind the fourth; gill-membranes separate, free from the isthmus; pseudobranchiæ present; branchiostegals 7; air-bladder present, simple, large; pyloric cœca very numerous; intestinal canal long, with many folds; vertebræ short, $14 + 12 = 26$ in number, the neural and hæmal spines normal; ribs very few. One species, an enormous fish of the open sea, rivaling the largest sharks in size and of immense strength of muscle. Very young or larval individuals differ much from the adults; the fins are high, both jaws are prolonged into a beak, and the head is armed with long spines.

Genus 96. XIPHIAS Linnæus. Swordfishes.

Teeth and ventral fins lacking; body somewhat compressed; dorsal fins 2, the anterior beginning opposite the gill-openings, falcate and elevated, its height rather less than that of the body; second dorsal very small, on the tail, opposite the small second anal. In the young, teeth are present and the 2 dorsal fins are connected, the fin being elevated as in *Istiophorus*. First anal similar to first dorsal, but smaller, less falcate, and far behind it; pectoral fins moderate, falcate; skin naked, more or less rough, especially in the young, which have rudimentary scales; sword flattened and trenchant; caudal keel single; intestines long, sinuous; air-bladder simple; pelvic arch obsolete. Fishes of great size, reaching a weight of 300 to 400 pounds, the flesh red and rich in flavor, highly valued as food.

122. Xiphias gladius Linnæus. Fig. 61. "*A'u.*"

Head about 2.25 in length; depth about 5.5; snout 3 in length; D. 40–4; A. 18–14; vertebræ 14+12; cleft of mouth extending beyond eye. Color dark metallic purplish above, dusky below; "sword" almost black above, below lighter; fins dark, with silvery sheen.

Atlantic Ocean, on both coasts; most abundant between Cuba and Cape Breton; not rare off Cape

FIG. 61.—*Xiphias gladius* Linnæus; after Cuvier.

Cod and the Newfoundland Banks; rather common in southern Europe; also found in the Pacific, occasionally taken about the Santa Barbara Islands, but not elsewhere recorded from the eastern Pacific. The object of extensive fisheries in the Atlantic. A single specimen was seen by us at Hilo. Others were seen by Mr. Snyder at Honolulu.

Family LIII. SCOMBRIDÆ.—The Mackerels.

Body elongate, fusiform, not much compressed, covered with minute cycloid scales, the scales anteriorly sometimes forming a corselet; lateral line present, its course undulate; head pointed anteriorly, subconic; mouth rather large, with lateral cleft; premaxillary not protractile; maxillary without supplemental bone; jaws with sharp teeth, large or small; vomer and palatines toothed or not; preopercle entire; opercle unarmed; in the very young the preopercle is armed with radiating spines, which are later absorbed and lost; gill-openings very wide, the membranes not united, free from the isthmus; gillrakers usually long; pseudobranchiæ present, large; gills 4, a slit behind the fourth; branchiostegals 7; dorsal fins 2, the first of rather weak spines, depressible in a groove, the second similar to the anal; the elevated anterior lobe always distinct; anal spines weak; last rays of dorsal and anal detached and separate, forming in each case a series of finlets; caudal peduncle extremely slender, keeled, the caudal lobes abruptly diverging, falcate, the fin adapted for rapid motion; ventral fins well developed, thoracic, ı, 5; vertebræ in greater number than in *Carangidæ*, the number ranging from 31 to 66; first upper pharyngeal present without teeth, third and fourth coossified, with teeth; lower pharyngeals separate; stomach sac-shaped; pyloric cœca numerous; air-bladder small, sometimes absent. Coloration metallic, often brilliant, the prevailing shade steel-blue. Genera about 12; species about 60. Fishes of the high seas, many of them cosmopolitan, and all having a wide range; most of them are valued as food-fishes, the flesh being firm and oily, but sometimes coarse.

Genus 97. SCOMBER Linnæus.   The Mackerels.   "*Opelu.*"

Body fusiform, rather elongate, somewhat compressed; caudal peduncle slender, without median keel, but with 2 small keels on each side; mouth wide, with a single row of rather small, slender teeth in each jaw and on the vomer and palatines; maxillary slipping under the broad preorbital, a fleshy lobe on each side of lower jaw near its junction with maxillary; scales very small, not forming a corselet; first dorsal of 9 to 12 feeble spines, separated from the second by an interspace greater than the base of the fin; second dorsal small, followed by 5 to 9 detached finlets; anal similar to second dorsal, with similar finlets; pectorals and ventrals small, the former placed high, on the level of the eyes; caudal fin small, widely forked; pyloric appendages exceedingly numerous; air-bladder small or wanting; vertebræ normally formed, 14+17=31; gillrakers long and slender. Species few, widely distributed, usually swimming in large schools; carnivorous and migratory; everywhere highly valued for food.

123. Scomber japonicus Houttuyn.   "*Opelu palahu;*" Chub Mackerel.   Fig. 62.

Head 3.9 in length; depth 5; eye 3.75 in head; snout 3. 1; maxillary 2.9; mandibl 2; interorbital 4.5; D. ıx–ı, 12–v; A. ı–ı, 11–v; scales 16–210–34; gillrakers 13+20, with long, slender, sparse teeth on anterior edge, the longest gillraker 1.4 in eye.

Body slender, not compressed, the dorsal outline gently elevated; caudal peduncle not compressed and not keeled; head long; snout very long and pointed, the outline from tip to nape straight; mouth large, slightly oblique, the jaws subequal; maxillary reaching near anterior edge of pupil; a single row of small teeth of uniform size in each jaw; similar teeth on vomer and palatines; no teeth on tongue; eye large, strongly adipose; preopercle broad; no blunt teeth or spines on shoulder-girdle; scales very small, covering entire body, deciduous, not forming a corselet; top of head with a large, translucent area; no groove connecting dorsals; first dorsal higher than long; origin of anal slightly behind that of soft dorsal; pectoral short, not reaching tips of ventrals, 2.3 in head; ventrals 2.6 in head.

Color in alcohol, bluish above, with about 30 wavy, darker blue streaks which reach just below lateral line, these somewhat reticulated and inclosing paler areas; middle and lower part of side paler, with small dark spots; belly pale, with small round dark spots; axil dark.

Color in life (No. 03536), upper half of head and body blue, with brilliant silvery and blue reflections; lower half white, with metallic reflections; back and upper part of side with more than 30 transverse zigzag dark bands; lower half covered with numerous inconspicuous roundish and oval

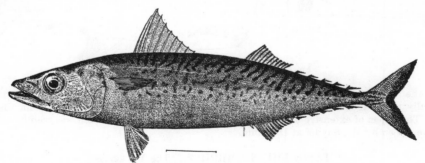

FIG. 62.—*Scomber japonicus* Houttuyn; after Jordan and Evermann.

dusky spots; spinous dorsal transparent; soft dorsal slightly dusky; anal whitish; ventrals white, with reddish base; pectoral dusky; caudal dusky, with the edge yellowish.

The above description based chiefly upon a specimen (No. 04022) 15.75 inches long, taken at Hilo. One other was obtained at Hilo. The collection contains 2 examples obtained at Honolulu August 8 and 13, and another was seen in the Honolulu market August 13.

This mackerel is not often seen among the Hawaiian Islands. The only specimens known from there are those here noted. It is apparently identical with the chub mackerel of the Atlantic and with the common Japanese *saba*.

Genus 98. AUXIS Cuvier. The Frigate Mackerels.

Body oblong, plump, mostly naked posteriorly, anteriorly covered with small scales, those of the pectoral region enlarged, forming a corselet; snout very short, conical, scarcely compressed; mouth rather small, the jaws equal; teeth very small, mostly in a single series, on the jaws only; tail very slender, depressed, with a rather large keel on each side; first dorsal short, separated from the second by a considerable interspace; second dorsal and anal small, each with 7 or 8 finlets; pectorals and ventrals small; no air-bladder; branchiostegals 7; pyloric cœca dendritical; gillrakers very long and slender, numerous; vertebræ 39 in number, peculiarly modified, essentially as in *Gymnosarda*. One species, pelagic, widely distributed.

124. Auxis thazard (Lacépède). Frigate Mackerel. Fig. 63.

Head 3.6 in length; depth 4.75; eye 5 in head; snout 4.1; interorbital 4.2; maxillary 3; D. x–12–VIII; A. 13–VII; gillrakers 30+10, serrate, longest nearly equal to eve.

Body robust, scarcely compressed, abruptly contracted at caudal peduncle; least depth of latter 1.3 in least width, strongly keeled; head long, subconic; snout pointed; jaws equal; small teeth in a single series in each jaw; tongue long, rounded, free, a thin flap on each upper side, narrowing posteriorly and giving a trough-like appearance; maxillary reaching below anterior edge of pupil, slipping under preorbital for nearly its entire length; eye moderate, high, anterior; interorbital flat; opercle very broad; fins small; dorsal spines rather stiff, longest equal to snout and eye; soft dorsal very low, its longest ray about equal to eye; caudal crescent-shaped, lobes equal; longest anal ray equaling base of fin, its origin under posterior base of soft dorsal; pectoral short, reaching slightly beyond

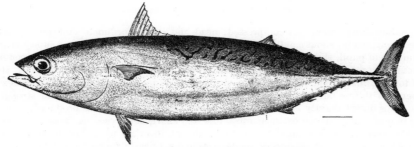

FIG. 63.—*Auxis thazard* (Lacépède); after Jordan and Evermann.

ventrals, past middle of first dorsal, longest ray 2.5 in head, its upper base on a line with upper edge of pupil; ventrals 2.6 in head, base under upper base of pectoral; scales of corselet and along anterior dorsal region comparatively large.

Color in alcohol, blackish blue above, lighter below, becoming silvery on belly; color of fins same as adjacent body color.

The above description based chiefly upon a specimen (No. 04021) 10.5 inches long, from Hilo. We have a specimen (No. 04027) 14.5 inches long, from Honolulu, and have examined one obtained by Dr. Jenkins at Honolulu. The species was found abundant at Hilo. It is taken with the trolling hook in the open sea, and is one of the best game fishes of the islands.

Genus 99. GYMNOSARDA Gill. The Little Tunnies.

This genus differs from *Thunnus* (1) in the absence of teeth on the vomer; (2) in the complete absence of scales outside of the corselet, while in *Thunnus* of the same size the skin is covered with small scales; the limits of the corselet in the tunny and albicore are obscure, so that it can not properly be said to be a distinct character in those species; and (3) in an important osteological character, namely, the peculiar development, in the form of a network or trellis, of a portion of the abdominal part of the backbone, between the vertebræ proper and the hæmapophyses; vertebræ 38. Species of smaller size than the tunnies, also pelagic and of little value as food.

125. Gymnosarda pelamis (Linnæus). "*Aku;*"[a] Ocean Bonito. Fig. 64.

Head 3.5 in length; depth 4; D. xv–12–VIII; A. II, 12–VII.

Body oblong, robust; lateral line making a decided curve immediately beneath the second dorsal; corselet strongly developed, covering the entire space between the diagonals connecting the posterior

---

[a] In ancient tradition the "*Aku*" and the "*Opelu*" (mackerel) accompanied Pili on his voyage to Hawaii. "*Aku*" helped to paddle the canoe, and "*Opelu*" calmed the winds when too strong.

extremity of the spinous dorsal and the base of the pectorals; posterior margin of preopercle about 1.5 in inferior margin; pectorals reach vertical from tenth dorsal spine.

Back bluish; belly silvery; 4 brownish stripes on each side of belly, parallel with the lower curve of body; no spots below pectorals.

Warm seas; pelagic; not very common, north to Cape Cod and Bermudas on the Atlantic coast of America; once recorded from California.

A specimen (No. 04439) 32 inches long, from Honolulu, is described as follows:

Head 3.3 in length; depth 4.4; eye 7.75 in head; snout 3.2; maxillary 2.7; mandible 2.3; gape 2.7; interorbital 3.6; D. xvi–12+8; A. ii, 12+7.

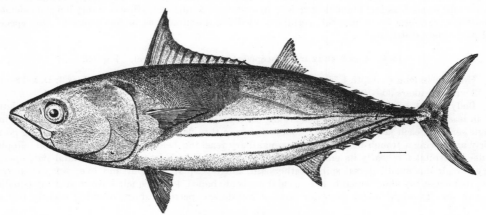

FIG. 64.—*Gymnosarda pelamis* (Linnæus).

Body rather short, stout, not compressed; head and caudal peduncle uniformly pointed; head rather large, long, conic; snout small, sharply conic; mouth moderate, the jaws subequal; maxillary reaching middle of pupil, slipping under preorbital, width at tip 1.7 in eye, lower edge convex, fitting into a concavity in mandible; teeth small in both jaws, none on vomer or palatine; short, sharp teeth on base of tongue; interorbital space broadly convex; eye rather small in anterior half of head; opercle and preopercle with fine but soft serrations; caudal peduncle short, depressed, and strongly keeled; origin of spinous dorsal slightly behind base of pectoral, the anterior spines produced, 2 in head, the fin folding in a groove; distance between dorsal fins very short, not exceeding diameter of eye; anterior dorsal ray produced, 3.1 in head; anal similar to soft dorsal, its origin under last dorsal ray, its anterior rays produced, equaling those of dorsal; caudal extremely broadly forked, the lobes small, scarcely exceeding snout and eye in length; pectoral moderately long, pointed, 1.9 in head; ventrals shorter, 2.75 in head; corselet well developed; a large naked area on side anterior to line connecting origin of soft dorsal to tip of pectoral; lateral line with an irregular arch above the pectoral, thence descending in an irregular wavy line to keel of caudal peduncle.

Color in alcohol, bluish black above, pale on sides, whitish below, lower part of side with 4 broad bluish-black lines, broadest posteriorly and separated by broad silvery bands, which are broadest anteriorly.

The above description based upon a specimen (No. 04439) 32 inches long, obtained in the market at Honolulu. We have another specimen (No. 04440), 27 inches long, from the same place, and also the head (No. 04018) of a large example seen at Hilo. In the collection made by Dr. Jenkins is a specimen (No. 798), 14 inches long, which does not agree fully with current descriptions of this species. It has 6 narrow brown lines along lower part of side instead of 4, and there is a narrow row of blunt tubercular teeth on each palatine bone.

This species is pelagic and occurs in all warm seas, being abundant about Hawaii in summer. It has been found on the Atlantic coast of America as far north as Cape Cod, and it is frequent about the Bermudas. It has been recorded from the coast of southern California.

126. Gymnosarda alletterata (Rafinesque). "*Káwakáwa;*" Little Tunny; Bonito. Fig. 65.

Head 3.6 in length; depth 3.9; eye 5.4 in head; snout 3.3; interorbital 3.75; maxillary 2.3; D. xv–12–viii; A. 13–7; gillrakers 22+9, serrate, longest nearly equal to eye.

Body robust, scarcely compressed, abruptly contracted at caudal peduncle, least depth of latter 1.3 in least width, strongly keeled; head long, subconic; snout pointed; jaws subequal, lower slightly the shorter; teeth on both jaws and palatine arch, the latter very minute; those on jaws small, sharp, conic, wide set; tongue long, rounded, free, a thin flap on each upper side narrowing posteriorly, giving a trough-like appearance; maxillary reaching center of pupil, slipping under the preorbital for nearly its entire length; eye moderate, high, anterior; interorbital rounded, wide; opercle broad; fins small; dorsal spines stiff, longest equal to snout and eye; soft dorsal very low, its longest ray not quite equal to its base; caudal crescent-shaped, lobes equal; base of anal fin equal to longest ray, its origin under posterior base of soft dorsal; pectoral short, reaching slightly beyond ventrals past middle of first dorsal, longest ray 2.4 in head, its upper base on a line with middle of pupil; ventrals 3 in head, base behind upper edge of pectoral; scales of corselet and anterior dorsal region comparatively large.

Color in alcohol, blackish blue above, lighter below, becoming silvery on belly; back with about 12 oblique, wavy, dark streaks, separated by bluish silvery interspaces; side with 10 to 13 darker bands; several black blotches size of pupil or slightly larger on side between ventrals and pectoral; fins color of body.

The above description based chiefly on a specimen (No. 04019), 10.5 inches long, from Hilo. We have one other specimen (No. 04020), 10 inches long, from Hilo, and one (No. 04025), 17.75 inches long, from Honolulu. In the larger examples the spots on the side between the ventral and pectoral are fewer—only 2 or 3 in number.

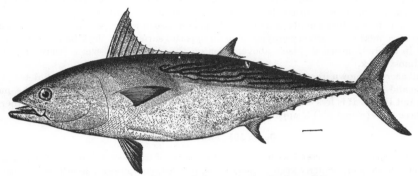

FIG. 65.—*Gymnosarda alletterata* (Rafinesque); after Jordan and Evermann.

This species is common in the markets at Honolulu and Hilo in the summer, being taken with the hook in the open sea.

Genus 100. GERMO Jordan. The Albacores.

Pectoral fins very long, saber-shaped, their length in the adult about two-fifths the length of the body. Otherwise essentially as in *Thunnus*, to which this genus is very closely related. Size large, but much less than that of the species of *Thunnus*.

127. Germo germo (Lacépède). "*Ahi;*" Albacore. Fig. 66.

Head 3.6 in length; depth 3.9; eye 5.7 in head; snout 3; interorbital 3; maxillary 2.5; mandible 2.2; gape 2.7; D. xiv–ii, 12+8; A. ii, 12+7.

Body short, stout, fusiform, scarcely compressed, dorsal and ventral profiles curving gradually,

FIG. 66.—*Germo germo* (Lacépède); after Schlegel.

body deepest at the middle; head moderate, sharply conic; snout short, pointed, the jaws subequal; maxillary reaching below middle of pupil, slipping under the thin preorbital; teeth on jaws in a single row, small and bluntly conic, villiform patch on vomer, none on palatines; eye large, in anterior half of head; opercles smooth, skin of preopercular edge finely denticulate, as is also the upper edge of opercle; caudal peduncle slender, short, depressed, least depth not exceeding half diameter of eye, the least width 1.5 in eye; origin of spinous dorsal slightly posterior to base of pectoral, the first spine 2.5 in head, the fin folding completely in a groove; soft dorsal and anal similar, rays elevated, each about 3 in head; caudal very broadly forked, each lobe about 1.3 in head; pectoral long, slender, reaching origin of anal, inserted below line of eye, the length equaling that of head; ventrals short, fitting into a depression, their length 2.7 in head; scales small, cycloid, covering entire body, somewhat larger along back; corselet distinct, scales on it large, coarsely ctenoid.

Color in life of a specimen (No. 03455), 17 inches long, from Honolulu, dark above, with steel-blue reflections; silvery below; very faint light bands, every other one a solid band separated by rows of spots curving downward and backward from pectoral region to ventral line; some very faint indications of similar narrow bands behind pectoral, vertical above, curved backward below; soft dorsal and anal and dorsal and anal finlets bright lemon-yellow; caudal dusky white with yellow border; ventrals white on under surface, black above, a small black spot on base of each; pectoral very dark-blue above, black on surface next body, silvery grayish blue on opposite surface; no dark bands or spots on body.

Color in alcohol, brownish black above, paler on the sides, bluish-white below; fins all dusky; pectoral almost black.

The albacore is known from all related species by the bright yellow color of the finlets. It reaches a large size and is occasionally taken on the hook in the open sea and brought into the markets of Honolulu and Hilo. It is less common about the Hawaiian Islands, however, than in southern Japan. The Japanese *shibi* (*germo sibi*) is apparently the same fish.

Genus 101. SARDA Cuvier.

Body rather elongate, covered with small scales, those of the pectoral region forming a corselet; caudal peduncle slender, strongly keeled; head large, pointed, compressed; mouth large; teeth in jaws rather strong, conical, slightly compressed; similar teeth on the palatines, but none on the vomer; maxillary not concealed by preorbital; gillrakers long and strong; first dorsal long and rather low, of 18 to 22 rather stout spines, which are gradually shortened behind; interval between the last spine and the second dorsal short; second dorsal small, followed by 8 or 9 finlets; anal fin similar, usually with one fewer finlets; paired fins small; pectorals placed below the level of the pupil; no air-bladder; pyloric cœca very numerous, dendritical; vertebræ normally formed, 50 to 54 in number. Fishes of rather large size, of metallic coloration. Two species known, one from the Hawaiian Islands.

128. Sarda chilensis (Cuvier & Valenciennes). California Bonito.

Head 3.75; depth 4.75; D. xviii–i, 12–viii; A. ii, 11–vi. Head pointed, conical, naked; maxillary not reaching eye; teeth strong, curved, about 40 in each jaw; pectoral placed just below the level of pupil, scarcely half as long as head; gillrakers long, strong, 16 or 17 below angle; corselet moderately developed; lateral line undulating, making a sharp curve below soft dorsal. Dark metallic blue; sides dusky; several blackish stripes running obliquely upward and backward from the pectoral region to the upper edge of the tail, these variable in number and direction. Length 2 to 3 feet; weight 16 pounds. San Francisco to Patagonia and Japan; abundant northward in summer; very similar to the Atlantic bonito, *Sarda sarda*, but with the spinous dorsal always shorter, its flesh similarly coarse, dark red, and oily.

A specimen about 2 feet long recently received from Honolulu belongs without doubt to this species. Head 3.5 in length; maxillary extending to a vertical through posterior edge of orbit; 6 dark oblique stripes on body, the uppermost and lower ones being indistinct; dorsal with 18 spines. This is the first record from Hawaii. It tends to add further probability to the supposition that *Sarda lineolata* Girard, from California, and *Sarda orientalis* (Schlegel), from Japan, are fully identical with *Sarda chilensis*, as was indicated by us in our Fishes of North and Middle America.

Genus 102. ACANTHOCYBIUM Gill. The Petos.

Body elongate, fusiform; head very long, slender, and pointed, the mandible being longer than upper jaw; jaws forming a sort of beak; cleft of mouth extending to below eye; posterior part of maxillary covered by the preorbital; both jaws armed with a close series of trenchant teeth, ovate or truncate, their edges finely serrate; villiform teeth on vomer and palatines; gills as in *Xiphias*, their laminæ forming a network; scales small, scarcely forming a corselet, those along the base of dorsal enlarged and lanceolate; keel strong; caudal spinous; dorsal very long, its spines about 25 in number. One species, a very large makerel-like fish, widely distributed; especially abundant about the Florida Straits. This remarkable genus marks a long step from *Scomberomorus* toward the type of swordfishes.

129. Acanthocybium solandri (Cuvier & Valenciennes). "Ono."

Head 4; depth 6.5; eye 5 in snout; gape more than half length of head; premaxillaries in front prolonged in a sort of beak, which is nearly half length of snout; teeth somewhat irregular, the posterior much the largest, all strong, serrated, about 50 in each jaw. Dorsal spines mostly subequal; lateral line descending abruptly under sixteenth dorsal spine, the highest, behind middle of fin, 5.66 in head; dorsal and anal lobes low; caudal lobes short, very abruptly spreading, their length about two-thirds head; pectoral 2.25 in head; corselet small.

Color steel-blue; dark above, paler below; no distinct markings; young faintly barred; fins colored like the body

This fish is not abundant, but a single specimen, 48 inches long, was seen by Doctor Jenkins in 1889, in Honolulu, and Mr. Snyder obtained it there in 1902.

The *Ono* was said by the ancient Hawaiians to be the parent of the *Opelu* (mackerel).

Family LIV. LEPIDOPIDÆ.—The Escolars.

Mackerel-like fishes with the body rather elongate, more or less compressed, covered with minute scales; lateral line various, sometimes obsolete, sometimes with a dorsal branch; head large, compressed, with very strong teeth, usually compressed, some of the anterior canine-like; lower jaw projecting; gill-openings wide, the membranes not united, free from isthmus; gills 4, a slit behind fourth; opercles in adult unarmed; in young, the preopercle with radiating spines as usual in scombroid fishes; dorsal fin long, a notch separating the weak spines from the soft part, which always forms a distinct lobe anteriorly, similar in form to the anal fin; finlets often present; caudal peduncle slender, usually not keeled, the fin moderate in size, always forked; ventrals small, often reduced to a single spine; vertebræ numerous, 32 to 53 in number; pyloric cœca rather few; air-bladder usually present. Coloration metallic, usually brilliant. Genera about 6; species about 12. Fishes of the high seas, widely distributed and descending to considerable depths; usually breeding about rocky islands; most of them used as food. The *Lepidopidæ* are closely allied to the *Scombridæ*, from which they diverge in the direction of the *Trichiuridæ*. The successive steps are indicated by the progressive elongation of the body, the progressive reduction of the ventrals and vertical fins, and on the other hand by the progressive elongation of the lower jaw and the specialization of the dentition. Dr. Lütken calls attention to the fact that the *Lepidopidæ* possess a system of dermal or subcutaneous ribs, composed of slender bony filaments, close-set, directed backward and upward, and backward and downward from the median line. This character has been verified in *Thyrsites*, *Nealotus*, and *Gempylus*.

Genus 103. RUVETTUS Cocco.

Body fusiform, moderately elongate, the skin covered with bony tubercles remote from each other and obliquely placed; mouth large, with strong teeth, some of the anterior in each jaw canine-like; lateral line obscure, little developed; abdomen keeled; tail not keeled; dorsals near together, well differentiated; dorsal and anal each with 2 finlets; ventral rays i, 5. Color black. One species. A large, deep-water fish, generally valued as food in the Tropics.

130. Ruvettus pretiosus Cocco. " *Walu.*" Fig. 67.

Head 4.15 in length; depth 5.4; eye 6.5 in head; snout 2.6; maxillary 1.9; gape 2.16; interorbital 2.25; D. xiii–ii, 15–ii; A. 16–ii; V. i, 5; P. 13; C. ix, 9+9, viii; prickles in about 85,—38 series.

Body moderately elongate, compressed, the dorsal and ventral outlines very gently elevated, body deepest under middle of pectoral fin, the outline tapering regularly to caudal; head rather large, conic; snout long and pointed; mouth large, somewhat oblique, maxillary reaching posterior line of orbit, its greatest width nearly 2 in eye, the gape reaching anterior third of pupil; lower jaw long, slightly projecting, its sides forming an acute angle; teeth strong, canine-like, a single row in each jaw and on each palatine; about 5 large, backwardly directed canines on the vomer; teeth of jaws larger on sides than at tips; eye large, entirely above axis of body, chiefly in anterior half of head; interorbital space broad and flat; anterior nostril nearly round, the opening directed forward, midway between tip of

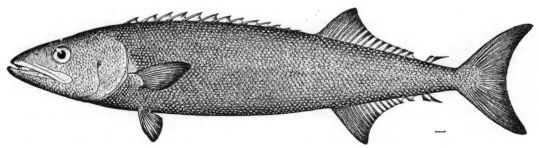

Fig. 67.—*Ruvettus pretiosus* Cocco; from our Hawaiian specimen.

snout and middle of pupil; posterior nostril a long, vertical slit, opening backward, its length 1.5 in pupil; gillrakers short, but strong, sparsely placed; opercular margin soft, the spine obscure; belly with a low, broad keel; caudal peduncle nearly round, its least depth equal to its least width or about 2 in snout; fins small, origin of spinous dorsal over edge of opercle, its distance from snout equal to half of head; spinous dorsal low, the spines slender, folding in a groove; distance between dorsals short, 1.5 in eye; origin of soft dorsal anterior to that of anal, anterior rays elevated, their length equal to snout, the last ray scarcely greater than pupil; distance between base of last dorsal ray and first ray of dorsal finlet 1.4 in eye; length of second ray of dorsal finlet 2.2 in snout; distance from base of dorsal finlet to caudal 1.6 in snout; anal similar to soft dorsal, its origin somewhat posterior, its anterior rays elevated and about equal to those of dorsal, base of fin somewhat shorter than that of soft dorsal, length of last anal ray equal to that of last dorsal ray; anal finlet with 2 rays and entirely similar to dorsal finlet; caudal large, broadly forked, a number of supporting spines along each edge, the lobes 1.6 in head; pectoral short, 2 in head; ventral shorter than pectoral, 3 in head; skin covered with small, irregular, somewhat embedded, cycloid scales, among which are rows of glossy forked prickles, arranged somewhat definitely in rows, each with 2 sharp points and 2 or 3 roots; scales of head very small, densely covering top of head, cheeks, and opercles, the head everywhere, except tip of snout, rough to the touch; body with numerous small but conspicuous pores, usually at bases of the prickles.

Color in alcohol, dark, dirty brown, the prickles showing as lighter yellowish silvery lines; fins mostly dark.

We have one large example of this species, No. 04314. It has a total length of 4 feet 6 inches, measured from tip of snout to tips of middle caudal rays, and weighs, after evisceration and having been in alcohol several months, 40 pounds. This specimen agrees with current descriptions except that the dorsal and anal spines and rays are somewhat fewer. It was sent us by Mr. E. L Berndt, inspector of the Honolulu market, and furnishes the first record of the occurrence of this species in the Pacific.

Genus 104. PROMETHICHTHYS Gill. Conejos.

Body elongate, slender, fusiform; mouth large, with 2 strong canines in front of each jaw; spinous dorsal long, contiguous to the soft, which is rather high; 2 finlets above and 2 below; pectorals comparatively low; caudal without keel; ventrals represented by a pair of minute spines; no dagger-shaped spine behind vent. Preopercle unarmed except in young. Lateral line descending in an oblique line, undulating below the front of the spinous dorsal. Scales very minute, smooth. Voracious fishes of the open seas, reaching a moderate size.

131. Promethichthys prometheus (Cuvier & Valenciennes). Plate 29.

Head 3.5 in length; depth 7.8; eye 5 in head; snout 2.6; interorbital 6.1, in eye 1.3; maxillary 2.2; D. xix–i, 19–ii; A. ii, 17–ii.

Body subfusiform, elongate, low, uniform, compressed, slender; head long, compressed; snout long, lower jaw the longer, rounded, with 2 long, sharp, canine teeth in front, slipping outside upper jaw; teeth on both jaws, vomer, palatines and tongue, the latter small and villiform as are those on the palatines, those on vomer 6, long and fang-like; rather blunt, wide-set, conic teeth in jaws; tongue thick, rather pointed, free for a short distance; maxillary reaching anterior edge of pupil; mandible reaching vertical slightly beyond posterior edge of pupil; eye large, median; interorbital concave with a deep groove, pointed posteriorly; middle dorsal spines highest, about 3.2 in head, last spine over vent; caudal forked; anal and soft dorsal similar, highest anteriorly; dorsal and anal finlets 2 each; ventrals each composed of a single spine about as long as eye, the base slightly anterior to base of pectoral; pectoral 2 in head; scales small, thin, cycloid, deciduous; lateral line straight to under fourth dorsal spine, thence abruptly downward and backward, reaching a line on middle base of pectoral at the tip of pectoral, thence straight to fork of caudal fin, running on lower side of caudal peduncle and rising slightly on posterior portion of peduncle.

Color in alcohol, uniform blackish brown; head black; fins all dark, dorsal membranes black.

The above description based upon a specimen (No. 04215) 16 inches long, obtained at Honolulu.

Three other examples were obtained at Honolulu (Nos. 04213, 14 inches; 04214, 15 inches; and 04216, 8.5 inches). We are unable to discover any differences between these and Japanese specimens with which we have compared them.

Genus 105. LEMNISOMA Lesson. Snake Mackerels.

Body very elongate, compressed and band-shaped, approaching the form of *Lepidopus;* head long, pointed anteriorly, the lower jaw projecting, the anterior teeth in upper jaw very long, canine-like; scales minute or obsolete; spinous dorsal very long, of about 30 spines; soft dorsal low, but with a distinct lobe, similar to anal, and each followed by 5 to 7 finlets; ventrals i, 5, but extremely minute; caudal fin rather small, well forked; lateral line single, arched anteriorly; vertebræ 28+25=53; air-bladder present. The young have the "*Dicrotus*" form, with large head, spinous ventrals, and spinigerous preopercle. Deep sea.

132. Lemnisoma thyrsitoides Lesson. *"Haúliuli puhi."*

Head 5.25 in length; depth 17; D. xxx–i, 13–v; A. ii–i, 11–vii; V. i, 5; vertebræ 28 + 25=53; eye 7 in head; maxillary nearly reaching front of pupil; each jaw with a series of compressed triangular, trenchant teeth; about 6 long canines in front of upper jaw, some of these with an emargination, as in *Sphyræna;* palatines with a row of small teeth, none on vomer; usually a single canine at tip of lower jaw; lateral line straight except anteriorly; dorsal spines slender; soft dorsal and anal small, with numerous finlets; pectoral pointed, rather long; ventrals minute.

Color dark metallic blue. Flesh firm. Deep seas; a rare fish, widely distributed, reaching a length of 3 feet or more.

A painting of this species made in Hilo by Andrew Garrett is preserved by Dr. Francis Wetmore, resident in Hilo. The specimen came from Puna to the south of Hilo. D. xxix–ii–vii; caudal forked; ventral very short; dorsal divided. There is also a painting in the collection of Mrs. J. B. Dillingham, in Honolulu, called "Haúliuli Puhi."

Family LV. CARANGIDÆ.—The Pampanos.

Body more or less compressed and often elevated, sometimes naked, or more usually covered with small, thin, cycloid scales; head compressed, the occipital keel prominent, usually trenchant; mouth of varying size, the dentition various, the teeth generally small; premaxillaries usually protractile; maxillary with or without a supplemental bone; preopercle usually entire in the adult, in the very young armed with 3 or more spines; lateral line complete, anteriorly arched, the posterior part straight, sometimes armed with bony plates; dorsal fins more or less separated, the spinous part rather weak, the spines usually depressible in a groove; anal fin long, similar to the soft dorsal, always preceded by 2 stiff spines, usually separate, but in the young often more or less connected with the fin or with each other; these sometimes disappear with old age, and sometimes the spinous dorsal also vanishes; often a procumbent spine before the dorsal fin; ventral fins thoracic, well developed, i, 5; caudal peduncle very slender, the fin widely forked; pectoral fins narrow; gill-openings very wide, the membranes usually not united, free from the isthmus; gills 4, a slit behind the last; gillrakers usually long; branchiostegals commonly 7; air-bladder present, often bifurcate behind; pseudobranchiæ large, present in all our genera, sometimes disappearing with age; œsophagus unarmed; pyloric cœca generally numerous; vertebræ fewer than in the *Scombridæ,* usually 10 + 14 = 24 in number; first superior pharyngeal without teeth; second, third, and fourth separate, with teeth; lower pharyngeals separate.

Coloration generally metallic and silvery or golden. Genera 29, species about 200, abounding in warm seas, often moving northward in summer, like the *Scombridæ.* They swim swiftly, often with the dorsal fin above the surface of the water. Most of the species are widely distributed, and nearly all are valued as food.

Genus 106. SCOMBEROIDES Lacépède.

Body compressed, oblong or lanceolate; caudal peduncle slender, not keeled; head short, compressed, acute; occipital keel sharp; mouth rather large, with small, sharp teeth in bands on jaws, tongue, vomer, palatines, and pterygoids; jaws about equal, the upper not protractile, except in the very young, in which it is movable as in other *Carangidæ;* maxillary very narrow. with a supplemental bone; gillrakers rather long; scales rather narrow, but more or less normally developed, embedded in the skin at different angles; lateral line unarmed; dorsal spines rather strong, 7 in number, nearly free in the adult; second dorsal very long, its posterior rays pencillated and nearly or quite disconnected, forming finlets; anal rather longer than soft dorsal, much larger than the abdomen, its last rays forming similar finlets; anal spines strong; ventral fins depressible in a groove; pectoral fins very short. Species few.

133. Scomberoides tolooparah (Rüppell). *"Lae."*

Head 4.25; depth 3.5; eye 4; snout 3.5; interorbital 3.75; maxillary 1.9; D. vii–i, 19; A. ii–i, 18.

Body fusiform, compressed; head moderate; snout rather narrow, pointed; jaws subequal, lower the longer and prominent; mouth slightly oblique, rather large; edge of upper lip on a line with upper edge of pupil; small bands of setiform teeth on vomer, palatines, and tongue, those on lower jaw slightly larger and in 2 rows, not banded anteriorly, those in upper jaw similar but smaller, in 1 row, banded anteriorly; maxillary reaching slightly past posterior edge of pupil; eye slightly above median line, anterior, not quite as long as snout; dorsal spines broad, flat, low, longest about equal to eye, tip of last spine reaching origin of soft dorsal; longest soft dorsal ray 2 in head; caudal deeply forked, lobes equal; anal similar to soft dorsal, its first ray under origin of soft dorsal, longest ray 2.4 in head; tip of ventral reaching vent, and equal to tip of pectoral, 2.2 in head; pectoral 2 in head, its anterior base slightly in advance of base of ventral; lateral line slightly arched above pectoral fin, descending to line under base of soft dorsal, thence straight to base of caudal.

Color in alcohol, bluish silvery above, white silvery below; 8 or 10 spots about size of pupil, extending on either side of lateral line to middle of soft dorsal; a dark blotch on upper anterior soft dorsal, similar spots on each dorsal ray; caudal dusky, other fins pale; no spots on anal.

The above description based chiefly on a specimen (No. 02927) 8 inches long from Honolulu.

This fish appears to be fairly common. We obtained it at Honolulu, Hilo, and Waialua. It was obtained at Honolulu also by Jenkins, Wood, and Jordan and Snyder.

Our numerous specimens are 1 to 10.25 inches long.

134. Scomberoides sancti-petri (Cuvier & Valenciennes).

Head 4.3; depth 4.3; eye 4.3; snout 3.6; interorbital 3.4; maxillary 2; D. vii–i, 20; A. ii–i, 18.

Body lanceolate, slender, and compressed; head moderate, profile slightly depressed over eyes; snout rather narrow, pointed; jaws subequal, lower being slightly the longer and prominent; mouth moderate, slightly oblique; small bands of setiform teeth on vomer, palatines, and tongue, those in lower jaw slightly larger and in 2 rows, banded anteriorly; in upper jaw similar but smaller teeth, in 1 row, banded anteriorly; maxillary reaching posterior edge of orbit; eye slightly above median line, anterior, not quite so large as snout; dorsal spines broad, flat, low, longest not quite equal to eye, tip of last spine, when depressed, reaching origin of soft dorsal; longest soft dorsal ray 2.3 in head; caudal deeply forked, lobes equal; anal similar to soft dorsal, its first ray under origin of latter, longest ray 2.65 in head; pectoral reaching tip of ventrals, 2 in head; ventrals 2.25 in head, base slightly behind upper anterior base of pectoral, tips reaching vent.

Color in alcohol, bluish silvery above, white silvery below; 3 or 4 spots slightly larger than pupil below the lateral line anteriorly, 7 or 8 similar spots above this line extending farther posteriorly; a large black blotch on anterior upper part of soft dorsal, a similar smaller spot on each following ray; anal pale; a spot the size of pupil on middle of second and third rays; ventrals pale; pectorals dark, pale at tips.

The above description based on a specimen (No. 04033), 16.25 inches long, from Honolulu.

This species does not appear to be common. It was obtained by Streets, also by Günther, Steindachner, Jordan and Snyder, and by the *Albatross*, but was not seen by Jenkins or Wood. Only one example was secured by us.

Jordan and Snyder obtained one specimen, 7.5 inches long, in 1900 at Honolulu.

Genus 107. NAUCRATES Rafinesque. The Pilot Fishes.

This genus differs from *Seriola* only in the reduction of the spinous dorsal to a few (4 or 5) low, unconnected spines. The young, called *Nauclerus* and *Xystophorus*, have the spines of the dorsals connected by membrane, and a more or less distinct strong spine at the angle of the opercle. A single pelagic species, widely distributed in the open seas.

135. Naucrates ductor (Linnæus). Pilot-fish; Romero; "Annexation-fish." Fig. 68.

Head 4 in length; depth 4; eye 5 in head; snout 3.5; D. iv–i, 26; A. ii–i, 16.

Body rather elongate, little compressed; snout rather blunt; mouth terminal, oblique, small; maxillary scarcely reaching orbit; caudal keel large, fleshy; pectoral short and broad; ventrals rather large.

Bluish, with 5 to 7 broad, dark vertical bars, extending on the fins.

Length 2 feet. A pelagic fish, found in all warm seas; occasional on our Atlantic coast from Cape Cod to the West Indies.

The earliest evidence we have of the occurrence of this fish among the Hawaiian Islands is that furnished by a painting made by Mrs. J. B. Dillingham from a specimen obtained by her in the

Fig. 68.—*Naucrates ductor* (Linnæus); after Jordan and Evermann.

Honolulu market. The painting was examined by us and is undoubtedly of this species, which is locally known as "annexation fish," having appeared at the date of the annexation of Hawaii to the jurisdiction of the United States. A specimen in good condition, collected by Dr. Julius Rosenstein, is in the museum of the California Academy of Sciences at San Francisco.

Genus 108. SERIOLA Cuvier. The Amber-Fishes.

Body oblong, moderately compressed, not elevated; occiput and breast not trenchant; head usually more or less conical, not very blunt; mouth comparatively large, with broad bands of villiform teeth on jaws, tongue, vomer and palatines; a broad, strong supplemental maxillary bone; premaxillaries protractile; scales small, lateral line scarcely arched, a keel on the caudal peduncle, not armed with bony plates; sides of head with small scales; first dorsal with about 7 low spines, connected by membrane; second dorsal very long, elevated in front; anal similar to the soft dorsal, but not nearly so long, shorter than the abdomen, preceded by 2 very small free spines, which disappear in old fishes; no finlets; ventral fins very long; pectorals short and broad; gillrakers moderate. Species of moderate or large size, often gracefully colored; most of them valued as food-fishes.

136. Seriola purpurascens Schlegel. *"Púakahála;" "Kahála."* Fig. 69.

Head 3.75 in length; depth 4; eye 6.5 in head; snout 2.9; interorbital 3; maxillary 2.4, reaching middle of pupil; mandible 2; gape 2.6; D. vi–i, 30; A. i, 19; scales about 175.

Body long and slender, the back scarcely elevated; head large, not much compressed; mouth large, jaws equal and covered with broad bands of strong, villiform teeth; vomer, palatines, roof of

FIG. 69.—*Seriola purpurascens* Schlegel; after Günther.

mouth and tongue with similar teeth; eye moderate, high up, in middle of head; interorbital space strongly convex; maxillary very broad at tip, its width equaling eye, the supplemental bone very broad; body from origin of anal fin tapering slowly to the short caudal peduncle, whose least depth is equal to eye and whose width is somewhat greater; origin of spinous dorsal over middle of pectoral; spines small and weak, longest somewhat greater than eye, the last obscure; anterior dorsal rays somewhat produced, their length 2.4 in the head and somewhat exceeding that of longest anal rays; caudal widely forked; pectoral short, its length equaling distance from tip of snout to middle of pupil, its origin somewhat anterior to base of ventrals; ventrals somewhat longer than pectoral, their length equal to snout and eye; scales very small, cycloid; lateral line well developed, nearly straight, curved slightly upward over tip of pectoral, broadly and shallowly decurved under first third.

Color in life, upper part of body, head, and tail light brown, with scales at certain angles showing bluish; lower parts lighter to whitish; a lemon-yellow band from upper articulation of maxillary through lower two-thirds of eye and along whole length of body as wide as pupil, becoming narrower and losing itself on caudal peduncle; iris edged with yellow; edge of caudal fin edged with lemon-yellow; pectoral and anal suffused with yellow; soft dorsal light brown with show of yellow on posterior portions, more marked on outer ends of rays; spinous dorsal lemon-yellow on ground of light brown; ventrals white on lower surface, somewhat dusky on upper surface. A specimen 4 inches long from Hilo had in life a golden stripe from head to tail.

Color in spirits, dull olivaceous white above, paler on sides, under parts dirty whitish; fins all dusky white.

The above description based upon a specimen (No. 03410), 31 inches long, from Honolulu market, where several other large examples were seen July 18. A smaller specimen (No. 03304), 8 inches long, may be described as follows:

Head 3.2 in length; depth 3.3; eye 5 in head; snout 3; interorbital 3.5; maxillary 2.3; D. viii–i, 31; A. ii–i, 20; gillrakers 13 + 4, serrate, longest three-fourths diameter of eye.

Body rather fusiform, compressed; head a fourth longer than deep; mouth rather large; snout rounded; jaws subequal, the lower prominent and slightly the longer; broad bands of villiform teeth on jaws, vomer, palatines, and tongue; tongue broad, rounded, thin, and free for most of its length; maxillary broad, 0.8 diameter of eye, reaching to center of pupil; eye just above median line, anterior; interorbital broad and very convex; dorsal spines short and weak, connected by membrane and folding in a groove; soft dorsal long and low, highest anteriorly, the longest ray about 2.5 in head; caudal forked, lobes moderate, equal to distance from snout to edge of preopercle; anal similar to soft dorsal, the spines very short and blunt, the longest rays equal to snout; origin of anal under first third of soft dorsal; ventral 2.1 in head; pectoral broad, falcate, short, 2.4 in head, its lower base slightly in advance of base of ventral; lateral line arched anteriorly, no caudal keel; scales small, none on opercle, snout, and top of head.

Color in life, golden olivaceous on back, golden on side below lateral line and on belly; 2 short darkish postocular lines; dorsal and anal rich orange, the dorsal with narrow bluish edge; caudal dirty yellow; pectoral pale yellow; ventrals yellow, the rays whitish; iris whitish and brown. Color in alcohol, grayish olivaceous above, becoming silvery white below; dorsal edged with dark; other fins pale.

Another example had head 3.7; depth 3.75; maxillary broad, 2.2 to front of pupil; D. i, 29; A. i, 20; color when fresh, olive with a golden stripe from head to tail. We have examined a score of examples at Honolulu, 4 to 31 inches long. This species has hitherto been known only from Japan.

137. Seriola sparna Jenkins. *"Kahala opio."* Fig. 70.

Head 3.7 in length; depth 3.7; eye 5.2 in head; snout 3.2; maxillary 2.6; interorbital 3.5; D. vi–32; A. ii, 20; scales about 220.

Body rather long, fusiform, not much compressed, the back greatly elevated, the ventral outline little convex; head rather long, conic; snout long, gently curved; mouth large, little oblique, the jaws equal; maxillary reaching front of pupil, its posterior margin oblique, its width nearly equaling vertical diameter of eye; teeth in villiform bands on jaws, vomer, and tongue; eye small, anterior, in axis of body; adipose eyelid moderately developed, especially behind; interorbital space broad, strongly convex, the nape slightly keeled; least depth of caudal peduncle less than its least width; preopercle entire; gillrakers longer than diameter of pupil, 22 on lower arm of first arch; spinous dorsal low, the rays short and weak, the second spine 6.3 in head, the first scarcely more than one-third the second, the others regularly decreasing in length, the fifth shorter than the first; soft dorsal low, the first rays scarcely elevated, their length 3.7 in head; anal similar to soft dorsal, but much shorter, its first rays

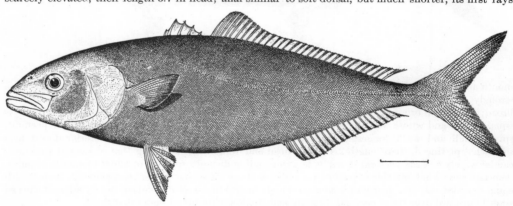

Fig. 70.—*Seriola sparna* Jenkins; from the type.

1.25 in snout; caudal deeply forked, the lobes slender, about equal, 1.3 in head; pectoral short, about 2 in head; ventrals short, 2 in head, reaching less than halfway to vent; body covered with very small scales; cheek, preopercle and upper part of opercle densely scaled, rest of head naked; breast scaled; lateral line nearly straight, slight arch above pectoral; scutes scarcely developed, perceptible only on the caudal peduncle, where they are very weak.

Color in alcohol, pale brownish or purplish above with silvery reflections, lower part of side and under parts yellowish silvery. Recently seen in the Waikiki aquarium.

The above description is based upon the type, 10.5 inches long, the only example known, obtained by Dr. Jenkins at Honolulu in 1889.

Genus 109. ELAGATIS Bennett. The Runners.

Body long and slender; second dorsal and anal long, each with one detached finlet, composed of 2 rays, behind the rest of the fin; otherwise essentially as in *Seriola*. One species, pelagic.

138. Elagatis bipinnulatus (Quoy & Gaimard).

Head 4.3 in length; depth 5.5; eye 7.3 in head; snout 2.6; D. vi–i, 25 + 2; A. i, 18 + 2; interorbital 2.9; maxillary 3.1; mandible 2.5; scales about 100.

Body oblong, pointed, the back little elevated; head moderately long and pointed; snout long, conic, the jaws subequal; maxillary broad, triangular, its greatest width 2 in its length; supplemental maxillary long and narrow, slipping under the thin preorbital; teeth in broad villiform patches on jaws, vomer, and palatines, tongue naked; eye small, somewhat anterior; interorbital space broad, convex; preopercle and opercle entire; gillrakers about all below the angle, cephalic ones gradually shorter, longest about 1.5 in eye; fins moderate; origin of spinous dorsal over tips of pectorals, the rays weak and short, folded somewhat in a groove, the longest 2 in snout, the fin not connected to soft dorsal; soft dorsal long and low, anterior rays elevated, longest 2.9 in head, last ray equal to eye; last ray of dorsal finlet produced, its length 3.6 in head; distance between dorsal finlet and base of last dorsal ray 1 in eye; distance from last ray of dorsal finlet to base of caudal lobe 3.6 in head; origin of anal under about the fifteenth dorsal ray, the fin very low, anterior rays slightly elevated, the longest 4 in head; detached anal spines obsolete; caudal very deeply forked, lobes long and slender, their length equaling distance from snout to first third of pectoral; pectoral short, scarcely falcate, 2 in head; ventrals about equal to pectoral; scales small, numerous, cycloid; head naked, except cheek and postocular region; scales on cheek in about 7 series; scales on nape and antedorsal region smaller than elsewhere; lateral line well developed, continuous, forming a very low keel on last part of caudal peduncle.

Color in alcohol, dark blue or leaden above, becoming paler and yellowish below; under parts dirty white; fins dusky, yellowish, or olivaceous. In life 2 conspicuous blue bands on side of body, the upper beginning at orbit and passing to dorsal margin of caudal peduncle, its width about equal to that of eye, the other beginning at snout and passing along the lower margin of orbit across opercle and above pectoral fin to the caudal; caudal yellowish with a darker margin; ventrals and pectoral yellowish with some blue.

The above description based upon a specimen (No. 04446) 3 feet long obtained in Honolulu market, which is the only record of the species in these islands. It reaches a length of 3 feet and is found in all tropical seas, on the Atlantic coast straying as far north as Long Island. It was obtained by Poey at Havana and was originally described from the Keeling Islands.

Genus 110. DECAPTERUS Bleeker. The Mackerel Scads.

Body elongate, little compressed, almost perfectly fusiform; head short, pointed; mouth rather small; jaws about equal, the dentition feeble; maxillary rather broad, with a supplementary bone; premaxillaries protractile; scales moderate, enlarged for the whole length of the lateral line, but spinous and bony posteriorly only; second dorsal and anal each with a single detached finlet; free anal spines very strong; first dorsal well developed, persistent; pectorals comparatively short; abdomen rather shorter than anal fin; gillrakers long and slender. Species numerous. Only one known from the Hawaiian Islands.

139. Decapterus pinnulatus (Eydoux & Souleyet). "Opélu." Plate 30.

Head 3.9 in length; depth 5.5; eye 4 in head; snout 3; interorbital 4; maxillary 3.4; mandible 2.5; D. viii–i, 32–i; A. i–28–i; scutes 25; scales 116.

Body oblong, little compressed, almost perfectly fusiform; head moderate, pointed; mouth rather small, slightly oblique; jaws equal; a few very small teeth on palatines and tongue, no others evident; tongue long, narrow, rounded, free for almost entire length; eye slightly above axis, anterior; adipose eyelid covering nearly entire eye; interorbital wide, slightly convex; longest dorsal spine 2.2 in head, longest ray 3, origin of soft dorsal just over vent; caudal forked, lobes moderate; anal similar to soft dorsal, its longest ray 3.5 in head; ventrals 2.8 in head; pectoral scarcely falcate, 1.65 in head, base anterior to base of ventrals; lateral line nearly straight from origin to interdorsal space, thence gently descending until over about fifth anal ray, whence it continues straight to caudal fin; scales deciduous, enlarged for whole length of lateral line, minute on nape and forward to interorbital space; small embedded scales on cheek, opercle, preopercle and preorbital, rest of head naked.

Color in alcohol, bluish silvery above, lighter below, becoming white on belly; dorsal fins and caudal with dark punctulations, other fins pale; upper edge of opercle with a black spot; base of pectoral dusky.

The above description is based on a specimen (No. 03306) 12 inches long from Honolulu. It seems to be a common fish at times at Honolulu, where it is highly prized by the natives as food. It was first noticed by Eydoux and Souleyet. Jenkins's specimens were taken by Dr. Wood and Mr. McGregor. The identification of this species with Decapterus sanctæ-helenæ and Decapterus maruadsi as Steindachner has indicated, is apparently not correct. Our species is quite distinct in color in that it has no yellow or golden stripe or, in fact, no yellow anywhere.

Genus 111. TRACHUROPS Gill.   The Big-eyed Scads.

This genus is close to *Carangus*, differing in the more elongate form, and especially in the structure of the shoulder-girdle, which has a deep cross furrow at its junction with the isthmus, with a fleshy projection above the furrow.   Species few.   Found in all warm seas.

One species known from the Hawaiian Islands.

140. Trachurops crumenophthalma (Bloch).   "*Akule;*" "*Halalalu.*"   Fig. 71.

Head 3.4 in length; depth 3.5; eye 3.2 in head; snout 3.3; maxillary 2.3; interorbital 4.5; D. vii–i, 26; A. ii–i, 22; scutes 35.

Body oblong-elongate, little compressed, the back not much elevated; head long, rather pointed, the lower jaw somewhat projecting, maxillary reaching middle of pupil, slipping under the preorbital, exposed portion triangular, posterior portion somewhat wavy; eye very large, longer than the snout and greater than the interorbital width; adipose eyelid strongly developed; mouth moderate, somewhat oblique; a single series of small teeth in each jaw, very weak teeth on vomer and palatines; a small patch of teeth on tongue; shoulder-girdle near isthmus with a fleshy projection, in front of which is a deep cross furrow; an angle at lower posterior portion of opercular region as in *Clupea;* dorsal spines moderate, their length 2 in head, the fin folding in a groove; dorsal rays low, scaled at base, folding in a groove; anal low, resembling soft dorsal, longest rays 2.6 in head; free anal spines strong, their length 2 in eye; caudal small, forked, the lobes equal, 1.6 in head; pectoral moderately

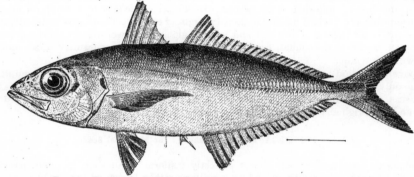

FIG. 71.—*Trachurops crumenophthalma* (Bloch); after Jordan and Evermann.

long and falcate, 1.25 in head; ventrals barely reaching vent, 2 in head; scales small; lateral line nearly straight, the scutes little developed except on caudal peduncle; cheeks and breast scaly.

Color in alcohol, bluish silvery above, paler below, with brassy reflections, under parts white; dorsal and caudal fins somewhat dusky; other fins pale.

The above description based upon a specimen (No. 02924) 12 inches long from Honolulu.

An abundant and well-known species, next to the *ulua* and the *amaama* the most important food fish of Honolulu.   It was obtained in 1889 by Dr. Jenkins, and has been recorded from the Hawaiian Islands by Günther, Steindachner, Fowler, and Snyder.   Numerous specimens were obtained by us at Honolulu, Kailua, Hilo, Hoopuloa, and Hanalei Bay, Kauai, varying in length from 5 to 12.25 inches.

The synonymy of this species is open to some question.   Our specimens probably correspond to *Trachurops torva* Jenyns, described from Tahiti.

Genus 112. CARANGUS Griffith.   The Cavallas.

"*Papiopio,*" small size; "*Pa'upa'u,*" medium size; "*Ulua,*" large size.

Body ovate or oblong, compressed, the back sometimes considerably elevated, sometimes little arched; head moderate or rather large, more or less compressed; mouth moderate or large, oblique; maxillary broad, with a well-developed supplemental bone extending to below eye; premaxillaries protractile; teeth developed in 1 or few series, unequal, or at least not in villiform bands; villiform teeth usually present on vomer, palatines, and tongue, wanting or deciduous in some species; gillrakers long; eye large, with an adipose eyelid; dorsal spines rather low, connected; second dorsal long, usually elevated in front, both fins depressible in a groove; anal fin similar to second dorsal and nearly as long, preceded by 2 rather strong spines, its base longer than the abdomen; caudal fin strongly forked, the peduncle very slender; ventral fins moderate; pectorals falcate; no finlets; preopercle entire in the adult, serrate in the young, usually with a membranaceous border.   Species very numerous in all warm seas, most of them valued for food.

About 9 species of this genus are now known from the Hawaiian Islands.

141. Carangus ignobilis (Forskål). "*Pauu'u.*" Fig. 72

Head 3.5 in length; depth 3; eye 5 in head; snout 3; interorbital 3.5; maxillary 2.1; preorbital 4.8; D. viii–i, 21; A. ii–i, 19; scutes 27.

Body short, stout, and compressed; head short and heavy; snout short and blunt, the anterior profile rising abruptly to nape, the dorsal outline strongly elevated from tip of snout to origin of spinous dorsal; ventral outline relatively straight; portion of body covered by soft dorsal and anal fins tapering rapidly to the short caudal peduncle, which is much depressed, its least depth about 2 in its least width; mouth large, nearly horizontal, the jaws equal; moderately strong, canine-like teeth in a single row in each jaw, sparsely set, especially on upper jaw, a patch of villiform teeth on vomer; palatines and tongue with granular or villiform teeth; maxillary reaching vertical at posterior edge of orbit; supplemental maxillary well developed and slipping under the broad preorbital; eye moderate, about 1.5 in interorbital; adipose eyelid strongly developed posteriorly; interorbital and nape strongly keeled; fins moderate, origin of spinous dorsal somewhat behind base of pectoral, the spines folding in a groove, the longest 3 in head; anterior dorsal rays produced, their length 1.8 in head, equal to that of longest anal rays; caudal widely forked; pectoral ray very long and falcate, tip reaching about to base of seventh anal ray, the length 2.8 in body and equaling base of soft dorsal; ventrals short, reaching vent, 2.1 in head; scales rather large, covering entire body, entire cheek, and upper part of opercle with fine series, rest of head and nape naked; breast naked, except a small central patch of scales; lateral line with a strong regular arch above pectoral fin joining the straight part over origin of anal, chord of arch part slightly shorter than length of straight part; scutes well developed on entire straight portion.

Color in alcohol, greenish olivaceous above, becoming paler on the sides and below; head green-

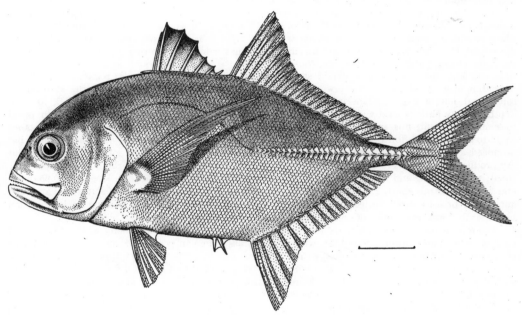

FIG. 72.—*Carangus ignobilis* (Forskål); from the type of *C. hippoides* Jenkins.

ish, silvery on cheek, lower jaw paler, the head with a yellowish or brassy tinge; axil black; no spot on opercle; dorsals, anal, and caudal dusky; more or less yellow in life; soft dorsal and anal each with a narrow, pale border; edge of free portion of caudal paler, upper part of caudal peduncle dusky; pectoral and ventrals somewhat dusky; no spot on lower pectoral rays.

The above description based upon a specimen (No. 04448) 22 inches long, from Honolulu. A much smaller example (No. 02918) 8 inches long, from Honolulu, may be described as follows:

Head 3.2 in length; depth, 2.4; eye 3.6 in head; snout 3.4; maxillary 2.25; interorbital 4; D. viii–i, 20; A. ii–i, 17; scutes about 30.

Body short and deep, greatly compressed, the back strongly elevated, the dorsal profile strongly and regularly convex from tip of snout to origin of spinous dorsal; outline from origin of anal to snout nearly straight; head as long as deep; snout short, very steep, bluntly rounded; jaws subequal, the lower heavy; bands of villiform teeth on vomer, palatines, and tongue, those on jaws in a single row, small, sharp, conic, and wide-set; tongue rather thick, rounded, and free for most of its length; maxillary reaching to posterior border of pupil; eye anterior, somewhat above axis of body; interorbital trenchant; spinous dorsal low and weak, 2.5 in head; origin of soft dorsal midway between tip of snout and fork of caudal, longest ray 1.5 in head; caudal deeply forked; longest anal ray 1.65 in head, origin of fin under about seventh soft dorsal ray; ventrals short, reaching past vent, 2.1 in head; pectoral long and falcate, reaching beyond arch of lateral line, slightly longer than base of anal; arch of lateral line dropping rather suddenly from under last dorsal spine to the straight part under third soft dorsal ray, chord of arch 1.4 in straight part; scutes on entire straight part; breast naked except a small patch of scales near center; cheek, postocular region, and upper part of opercle scaled, rest of head naked, body completely scaled; dorsal and anal fins scarcely sheathed.

Color in life, very pale olive, side white; head greenish; no opercular spot; no spot on pectoral; base of pectoral dark; both dorsals edged with blackish; upper lobe of caudal blackish, especially the edge, lower lobe bright yellow; anal bright, light yellow, the edge whitish; ventrals whitish with yellowish streaks along the rays; pectoral pale, the axil blackish.

Color in alcohol, slaty silvery, becoming lighter below, almost white on belly; spinous dorsal dusky; soft dorsal pale, edged with dark, other fins pale, inner axil of pectoral black.

This species is related to *Carangus hippos* of the Atlantic, with which it agrees in the small patch of scales on the otherwise naked breast, the character of the lateral line, and the teeth. It is, however, a much deeper fish, the snout is shorter, the anterior profile rises more abruptly, and there is no black spot either on the opercle or on lower rays of the pectoral. The yellow color of the anal fin seems to be constant and diagnostic, especially in the young. The species is common at Honolulu, from which place we have examined 13 specimens 2.5 to 22 inches in length.

142. Carangus elacate Jordan & Evermann.   Plate 31.

Head 3.6 in length; depth 3.4; eye 4.5 in head; snout 3.8; interorbital 3.8 in snout; maxillary 2.1; preorbital 8.5; mandible 1.9; D. vii–i, 19; A. ii–i, 16; scutes 28.

Body slender, compressed, not greatly elevated; snout rather short, profile ascending to nape in a gentle curve, slightly trenchant; mouth large, slightly oblique; lower jaw somewhat projecting; maxillary reaching posterior edge of orbit, its width at tip 1.5 in orbit; supplemental maxillary well developed, its width 3.25 in entire width; gape reaching vertical of posterior edge of pupil; villiform teeth on vomer, palatines, and tongue, those on jaws in a single row, small and somewhat canine-like; eye large, anterior; adipose eyelid strongly developed behind; supraocular region with 2 ridges, extending to humeral region, the lower the stronger; posterior half of body, beginning at origin of soft dorsal, long and gently tapering to caudal peduncle; caudal peduncle much depressed, its least depth scarcely half its least width; distance from base of last dorsal ray to origin of caudal fin equal to snout and pupil; fins small; origin of spinous dorsal posterior to base of pectoral by a distance equal to eye; longest dorsal spine slightly greater than snout; anterior rays of soft dorsal somewhat produced, about 1.8 in head; anal similar to soft dorsal, its origin under eighth soft dorsal ray, anterior ray produced, but scarcely equaling longest soft dorsal rays; caudal widely forked, lobes apparently equal; pectoral long and falcate, reaching past origin of anal, exceeding head in length by 0.65 diameter of eye; ventrals short, 2.4 in head; scales rather large, a low sheath at base of soft dorsal and anal anteriorly; breast entirely scaled; lateral line strongly arched above pectoral, joining straight portion under sixth dorsal ray, chord of arched portion 1.6 in straight part.

Color in alcohol, rusty olivaceous above, paler on side below lateral line; belly white; top of head dark olive, side and lower jaw lighter, with strong brassy tinge on postocular and on lower portions of opercle; lower jaw profusely covered with fine brown points; a black spot at upper end of opercular opening; axil black; vertical fins all more or less dark; produced part of soft dorsal almost black, low part of soft dorsal black at base, then lighter, narrowly tipped with dark; anal dark brown, with a subterminal stripe of yellowish white along edge of fin; pectoral and ventrals pale.

The above description based upon the type, No. 50638, U. S. N. M. (field No. 04452), a large example, 27 inches long, from Honolulu. This species somewhat resembles *Carangus marginatus*, from which it differs in the much more slender body, larger eye, and dark anal fin. The type is the only example obtained.

143. Carangus marginatus (Gill).   "*Ulua.*"

Head 3.4 in length; depth 2.8; eye 4 in head; snout 3.75; interorbital 4; maxillary 2; D. viii–i, 22; A. ii–i, 16; scutes about 34.

Body oblong, compressed, dorsal outline evenly arched to nape, rather steep thence to tip of snout; head slightly longer than deep; snout bluntly pointed; mouth moderate, slightly oblique, lower jaw prominent, slightly produced; villiform teeth on vomer, palatines and tongue, a single row of small, wide-set, sharp, conic teeth in each jaw; tongue rounded, rather thick, free for most of its length; maxillary reaching to posterior edge of pupil, its width 1.25 in eye, sheathed by preorbital for the greater part of its length; eye anterior, pupil above axis; interorbital slightly trenchant; dorsal spines weak, longest 2.75 in head; origin of soft dorsal midway between tip of snout and fork of caudal, longest soft dorsal 1.75 in head, 2 in base of fin; caudal deeply forked, anal similar to soft dorsal; ventrals reaching just beyond vent, 2.35 in head; pectoral long and falcate, reaching considerably beyond end of arch, slightly longer than head, equal to base of soft dorsal; arch of lateral line nearly straight to under sixth dorsal spine, then descending rather abruptly to straight part under about the fifth dorsal ray, making rather a sharp angle, arch 1.35 in straight part; scales on entire body, cheeks, and upper parts of opercle; breast scaly; scaly sheath of fins not greatly developed.

Color in alcohol, grayish silvery, with slight bluish reflection above, becoming light below and white on belly; spinous dorsal dusky, the produced part of soft dorsal black, rest of fin edged with dark; caudal edged with dark; anal pale, a row of about 10 spots at its base, these seeming to be produced by the bone showing through the membrane; other fins pale, the pectoral with a black spot at its axil; a small black spot on opercle at upper part of gill-opening.

The above description based on a specimen (No. 04052) 11.25 inches long from Honolulu. We have examined 7 others from Honolulu, 8 to 11.25 inches long. Comparison with specimens from Panama fails to show any differences.

144. Carangus forsteri (Cuvier & Valenciennes). *"Ulua."*

Head 3.3 in length; depth 2.5; eye 5.5 in head; snout 3.5; interorbital 3.8; maxillary 2.6; D. vii–i, 23; A. ii–i, 19; scutes about 35.

Body oblong, greatly compressed, dorsal outline arched, steeper anteriorly, straight from nape to tip of snout; ventral outline curved from caudal peduncle to origin of anal, straight thence to tip of snout; head subconic, longer than deep, greatly compressed; snout bluntly pointed, lower jaw slightly produced; mouth moderate, slightly oblique; small villiform teeth on vomer, palatines, and tongue, a single row of larger, wide-set conic teeth on each jaw; tongue rounded, thin, free for most of its length; maxillary broad, its width 1.2 in eye, reaching anterior edge of pupil, and slipping under preorbital for most of its length; interorbital very convex, trenchant; dorsal spines slender and weak, longest 2.8 in head; origin of soft dorsal midway between tip of snout and fork of caudal, just over second anal spine; longest dorsal ray 1.6 in head, 2 in its base; caudal deeply forked; longest anal ray 1.8 in head; ventral short, reaching past vent, 2.5 in head; pectoral long, falcate, 1.1 in head, reaching considerably beyond arch of lateral line; lateral line arched to under fifth dorsal ray, chord of arched part greater than head, 1.3 in straight part; scutes on entire straight portion, obscure anteriorly; entire body scaly; breast not naked.

Color in life, of specimen (No. 02998) from Honolulu, pale bluish above, changing to silvery white on side and belly; dorsals, anal, and caudal dusky; pectoral rich lemon-yellow, iris yellowish white. Color of another specimen when fresh (No. 03450), silvery with golden reflections; 5 transverse dark bands on side, one over caudal peduncle, about as wide as length of snout, and distinct above lateral line; an indistinct dark band over head through eye; fins colorless.

Color in alcohol, light grayish silvery with bluish reflections above, paler below, becoming white on belly; dorsal spines pale, produced part of soft dorsal dark, edge of rest of fin dark; caudal edged with dark; the produced part of anal dark; ventrals and pectorals pale; no dark opercular spot; axil dusky but not showing above fin.

This species may be known in life by the dusky anal and yellow pectoral. In *C. ignobilis* the yellow is brightest on the anal fin. The above description based chiefly on a specimen (No. 04046) 11 inches long, from Honolulu. The collection contains numerous specimens from Honolulu.

The most important food-fish of the South Seas, abundant in the markets, and unsurpassed as the basis of fish-chowder. It is of wide distribution, being found throughout the tropical Pacific. A closely related species, *Carangus latus*, abundant in the West Indies, occurs as far north on the Atlantic coast as Virginia and has been doubtfully recorded from the Pacific coast of Mexico. This species needs close comparison with the present one. The earlier name probably belonging here is *Carangus forsteri*. *Caranx heberi* is figured as colored differently from any species known to us. It most resembles *Carangus marginatus*.

The large series of specimens in our collections, ranging from 2 inches to nearly a foot in length, enables us to study very satisfactorily the variation in the species. Most of the young show evidences of broad dark bluish cross-bars, though some show them scarcely at all, the color being plain silvery. While the breast is always scaled, the scales are often so embedded and obscure as to be easily overlooked. A series of 51 specimens examined, 2.4 to 11.25 inches in length, from Honolulu, Hilo, Waialua, Hanalei Bay, and Puako Bay.

145. Carangus melampygus (Cuvier & Valenciennes). *"Omilu;" "Omilimilu."* Fig. 73.

Head 3.4 in length; depth 2.8; eye 6.5 in head; snout 2.4; interorbital 3.8; maxillary 2.4; mandible 2; gape 2.8; preorbital 4.5; D. vii–i, 24; A. ii–i, 18; scutes 35.

Body short, deeply compressed, the back much elevated; head rather short, the snout short and blunt; mouth moderate, little oblique; teeth small, sparse, in a single row in each jaw; jaws subequal; maxillary reaching anterior edge of pupil, triangular, its width at end 9.2 in its length, its edge slipping under the preorbital; interorbital narrow and very convex; the anterior profile very trenchant; eye moderate, in middle of head, entirely above axis of body, the adipose eyelid well developed posteriorly;

ventral outline nearly straight from tip of jaw to origin of anal, thence ascending obliquely to caudal fin; origin of spinous dorsal posterior to base of pectoral, the spines weak and short, folding into a groove, the longest 4.3 in head; distance between dorsals equal to eye, anterior dorsal rays elevated, their length somewhat greater than snout and eye, 1.8 in head; anal spines short and blunt; origin of anal posterior to that of soft dorsal, the anterior rays elevated, their length 2 in head; soft dorsal and anal each anteriorly slipping into a scaly sheath; caudal widely forked, the lower lobe somewhat the longer, 1.4 in head; pectoral very long and falcate, its tip reaching base of about fourth anal ray, its length 2.75 in body; ventrals short, 3.25 in pectoral or 2.6 in head; scales small, closely but irregularly imbricated; lateral line beginning at upper end of opercular opening, continuing nearly straight to under fourth dorsal spine, where it begins to curve gently downward until orgin of soft dorsal, where the downward curve is more abrupt; scutes of lateral line beginning under about the eighth or tenth dorsal ray and increasing in size to the fourth from last.

Color in life, general ground-color silvery, dusky above, lighter below; upper parts with numerous small black spots, intermingled with numerous bright dark-blue spots; interspaces with more or less golden reflections; golden band along the scutes; soft dorsal, anal and a narrow area along their bases bright ultramarine; indistinctly outlined areas of same color on side of head about the eye; pectoral and caudal dusky, with golden reflections; ventrals dusky with dark blue; no opercular spot; base of pectoral not dark.

Color in alcohol, dirty white above and on sides, profusely covered with small irregular darker spots and blotches, these also upon top of head and opercles; lower part of sides and under parts dirty yellowish white; fins all dusky, soft dorsal and anal almost black, white tipped.

The above description based upon a specimen (No. 03412) 24 inches long, obtained in the Hono-

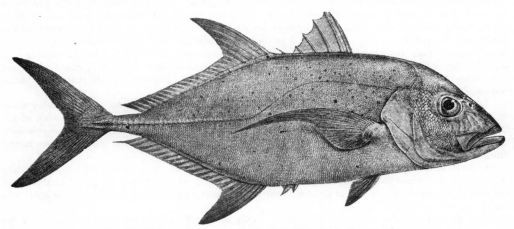

FIG. 73.—*Carangus melampygus* (Cuvier & Valenciennes); after Günther.

lulu market, July 18.   Two other examples 15 and 24 inches in length were obtained by us at the same place.   The species was also obtained by Streets and by the *Bonite*.   It is more common in Samoa, where it is known as *malauli*, and as a food-fish it is superior even to the *ulua*.

146. Carangus rhabdotus Jenkins.   Fig. 74.

Head 3.4 in length; depth 2.6; eye 3.75 in head; snout 3.8; maxillary 2.1; interorbital 3.3; D. VIII–I, 20; A. II–I, 16; scutes 32.

Body oblong, elliptical, compressed; dorsal outline evenly arched, ventral outline slightly straighter than dorsal outline; head compressed, its depth equal to length; snout bluntly rounded, lower jaw slightly produced; mouth moderate, slightly oblique; villiform teeth on vomer, palatines, and tongue, and a single row of small, conic teeth on each jaw; maxillary reaching to posterior edge of pupil, its greatest width about 0.75 in eye; center of eye slightly above axis of body, anterior; interorbital space convex; fins moderate; longest dorsal spine 2.5 in head; soft dorsal slightly concave, longest ray 1.75 in head; caudal forked, lobes moderate; anal similar to soft dorsal; ventrals short, 2.2 in head; pectoral long, falcate, reaching slightly beyond arch of lateral line, equal to head; body completely scaled; bases of soft dorsal and anal with low sheath of scales; cheek and upper part of opercle scaled, rest of head naked; breast scaled; lateral line strongly arched above the pectoral, tne arch joining the straight portion under fifth dorsal ray, the chord of the arch equaling length of head or 1.5 in straight portion; scutes rather strong, the largest 0.65 diameter of eye in width.

Color in alcohol, bright silvery, darker above, with 5 indistinct vertical bands nearly as wide as eye on upper three-fourths of body, a sixth band less distinct on caudal peduncle; no opercular spot; fins plain, except the elevated portions of soft dorsal and anal, which are tipped with black.

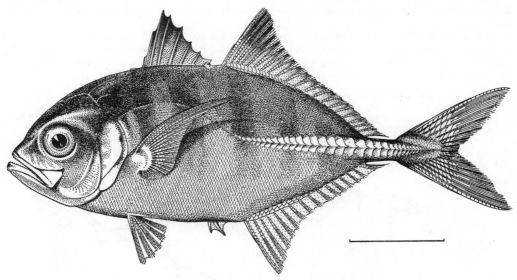

Fig. 74.—*Carangus rhabdotus* Jenkins; from the type.

This description is based upon the type (No. 50711, U. S. N. M.), a specimen 5.5 inches long. obtained at Honolulu by the *Albatross* in 1896. Another small example was obtained at the same time. This species was not seen by us at Honolulu. It resembles a species found in the estuaries of Samoa.

147. Carangus politus Jenkins. " *Maka;*" "*Makaa.*" Fig. 75.

Head 4 in length; depth 3; eye 4.1 in head; snout 3.5; interorbital 3.2; maxillary 3; D. VIII-I, 24; A. II-I, 19; scutes 40.

Body oblong, compressed, dorsal and ventral outline about equal; head subconic, longer than deep, compressed; snout bluntly pointed; lower jaw produced; small villiform teeth on vomer, palatines, and tongue, a single row of small canine-like teeth in each jaw, those in lower jaw almost obsolete; maxillary short, rather narrow, reaching anterior margin of eye; eye slightly above axis of body, anterior; interorbital moderately trenchant; fins moderate, longest dorsal spine 2 in head; caudal forked, lobes not greatly produced; anal similar to soft dorsal; ventrals reaching just past vent, 2.3 in head; pectoral long and falcate, tip not quite reaching to straight portion of lateral line, slightly longer than head, not quite equal to base of anal; arch of lateral line rather long, reaching to below eighth dorsal ray, and about equal to straight part; scutes on entire straight portion of lateral line.

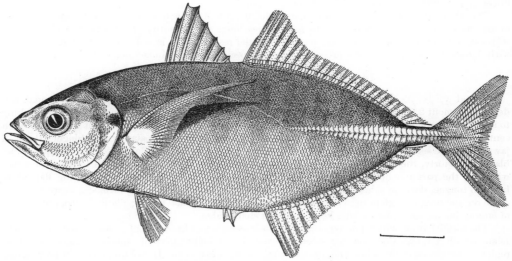

Fig. 75.—*Carangus politus* Jenkins; from the type.

Color in alcohol, grayish olivaceous above, lighter below, becoming white on lower sides and belly; 9 indistinct vertical dark bands on upper two-thirds of scales of body; fins all dusky; opercular spot present.

The above description, based upon the type (original No. 100), a specimen 8 inches long, obtained by Doctor Jenkins, at Honolulu, 1889. Another example, No. 327, 5 inches long, is in the same collection, and these agree very closely with specimens from the Philippines, which are determined as *Carangus hasselti*. *Carangus politus* is probably a synonym of the latter species.

148. Carangus affinis (Rüppell). *"Amuka;" "Púakahála."* Fig. 76.

Head 3.9 in length; depth 3.5; eye 4.1 in head; snout 3.6; interorbital 3.6; maxillary 3; D. VII-:, 23; A. II-I, 20; scutes 43.

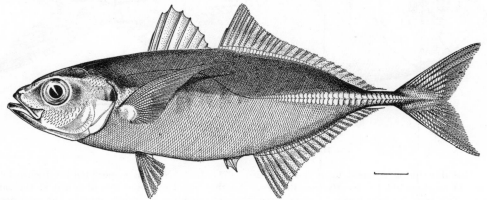

FIG. 76.—*Carangus affinis* (Rüppell).

Body fusiform, dorsal and ventral outlines about the same; head longer than deep; snout conic, its tip on a line with middle of eye; upper jaw bluntly rounded; lower jaw produced, rather pointed; series of small teeth on vomer, palatines, and tongue, a single row of minute canine-like teeth in each jaw; tongue rounded, thin, and moderately wide, free for most of its length; maxillary reaching anterior edge of orbit; dorsal spines weak and thin, longest 2.1 in head; soft dorsal sheathed, its longest ray 2.2 in head, its origin midway between tip of snout and last scute and directly over second anal spine; caudal forked; anal similar to soft dorsal and similarly sheathed, its longest ray 2.3 in head, spines very short, less than eye; ventrals short, just reaching posterior edge of vent, 2.1 in head; pectoral long, narrow, falcate, nearly reaching straight part of lateral line, its length 1.2 times the length of the head; lateral line with a long curve, whose chord nearly equals the straight part, the lateral line becoming straight under about the tenth soft dorsal ray; scutes on the entire straight part of the lateral line; in some examples a trace of a second lateral line under soft dorsal fin, continuing to posterior edge of dorsal spine.

Color in alcohol, bluish silvery above, becoming white silvery below lateral line; dorsal and caudal dusky, other fins pale, axil of pectoral black, a black spot on upper posterior edge of opercle, covering upper end of shoulder-girdle, slightly larger than pupil.

The above description from a specimen (No. 04030), 8.75 inches long, from Honolulu, where numerous examples were taken, 7.5 to 8.75 inches long. We identify these with *Caranx affinis* of Rüppell, with which they seem to agree in all essential respects. It is a deeper fish than *C. hasselti*, with lighter fins, and doubtless represents the same species which Steindachner had from Honolulu.

149. Carangus helvolus (Forster). Plate 32.

Dorsal v, 28; A. I, 22; head, including opercular flap, 3.3 in length to base of caudal fin; depth 2.5; snout 2.9 in head; lower jaw projecting somewhat beyond upper; maxillary 2.5, reaching to a vertical through anterior edge of pupil; eye 4.3, a horizontal from tip of snout passing through center of pupil; width of interorbital space 2.9. No teeth on vomer, palatines, or tongue, those of jaws in a single series. Tongue dead white in color; roof of mouth similar, becoming abruptly blue-black posteriorly, the white extending backward as a V-shaped prolongation; the membranous flap white on the part touched by tongue, black on sides; lower jaw below tongue dark, the flap white beneath tongue, dark on sides. Head with scales behind the eye and on the cheeks; a narrow, naked space on the occiput, extending backward to spinous dorsal; breast naked; plates in straight portion of lateral line 35, each plate with a keel forming a sharp ridge.

The locality from which Forster obtained this species is not known; but as he visited the Society Islands with Captain Cook on his second voyage, it is possible that his specimen came from that region. An example 15 inches long, obtained by the *Albatross* in the Honolulu market in 1902, agrees perfectly with the description of this species.

150. Carangus cheilio Snyder.   Plate 33, fig. 1.

Head, measured to end of opercular flap, 3 in length to base of caudal; depth 2.9; depth of caudal peduncle 6.7 in head; diameter of eye 7.1; width of interorbital space 3.3; length of snout 2.3; maxillary 2.9; pectoral fin 1.1; ventrals 2.5; height of first dorsal ray 3.1; anal ray 3.4; length of upper lobe of caudal 1.2; D. VIII–I, 24; A. II, 21; scales in lateral series about 116; between lateral line and spinous dorsal, counting upward and forward, about 23; plates in straight portion of lateral line about 38.   Snout pointed, anterior contour of head somewhat concave in the region of interorbital area.   Lower jaw slightly shorter than upper; maxillary not reaching a vertical through anterior edge of orbit by a distance about equal to diameter of pupil; lips very thick, the width of upper near its middle equal to half diameter of eye; teeth short and blunt, in a single series on the jaws, none on vomer and palatines; a few very short teeth on tongue; gillrakers 7+25, the longest equal in length to diameter of iris.

Scales on occiput, interorbital area, cheek, and upper parts of opercles; other parts of head naked; body, including breast and a sheath along base of dorsal and of anal, with small scales; scales of posterior part of body with minute ones along their edges; no scales on membranes of fins; lateral line a little more curved than contour of back, the straight part beginning below tenth articulated ray. Plates highest and broadest near middle of caudal peduncle, their width at that point equal to half the width of maxillary at posterior part.   First dorsal spine short and closely adnate to second; second spine longest, 3 in head; rayed portion of fin with a scaled sheath along its base, the height of anterior part of which is equal to diameter of pupil; posteriorly the sheath gradually grows lower, disappearing near end of fin; anal spines thick and strong, their height a little less than diameter of pupil; base of fin with a sheath similar to that of dorsal.   Caudal deeply forked, the lobes sharply pointed; pectoral falcate, sharply pointed; ventrals not reaching anal opening.

Color silvery, a little darker above than below; upper edge of opercular flap with a dark spot about half the size of pupil; axil dusky.

This species was based on a single specimen 30.3 inches long obtained by the *Albatross* in 1902 in the Honolulu market.

Genus 113. CARANX (Commerson) Lacépède.

This genus differs from *Carangus* mainly in the dentition, the teeth being very small, granular, and entirely lost with age; maxillary broad; body compressed; the fins without filaments.

Only one species known from Hawaii.

151. Caranx speciosus (Forskål).   "*Páopáo;*" "*Ulua Pauú.*"   Plate XII.

Head 3.25; depth 2.14; eye 5; snout 2.5; maxillary 2.75; D. VI–I, 20; A. I, 16; scutes weak, about 15.

Body broadly ovate, strongly compressed; back considerably elevated, the ventral outline less curved; caudal peduncle short; dorsal and ventral outlines approaching it at about equal angles; head rather small, short; snout short, the profile ascending rather abruptly; nape trenchant; mouth moderate, slightly oblique, the lower jaw included; maxillary reaching anterior border of pupil, its edge slipping under preorbital for its entire length; suborbital broad, about 2 in snout; mouth entirely toothless, tongue with small villiform teeth; interorbital space strongly convex; eye small, slightly above axis of body, slightly anterior; gillrakers moderate, about half diameter of eye, stout and blunt, about 20 below angle; dorsal spines weak, short, longest 3.2 in head; origin of soft dorsal midway between tip of snout and base of caudal; caudal deeply forked; anal similar to soft dorsal, its origin under seventh soft dorsal ray; ventrals short, reaching beyond vent, 2.5 in head; pectoral long and falcate, reaching beyond arch, its length equal to base of anal; arch of lateral line equal to straight part (in smaller examples the arch is less, sometimes 1.25 in straight part); cheek and upper parts of opercle scaly, breast scaly, no scales on snout and upper part of head.

Color in life, light dusky above with silvery and blue reflections, becoming white on belly; anterior part of belly and sides of face yellow; indistinct yellow blushes on other parts of body; yellow line on body at base of anal; 8 or 9 indistinct transverse bands on body; margin of caudal yellow; anterior anal yellow, bright toward tip of longest rays; ventrals white; pectoral translucent; dorsals dusky; irregular, blackish spots on back below base of soft dorsal.

Color in alcohol, dusky grayish, lighter below; soft dorsal brownish olivaceous, other fins slightly lighter, no bands evident on body, though these show in small examples.

The above description from a specimen (No. 03523) 18 inches long, from Honolulu, where the fish was also obtained by the *Albatross* in 1902.   Our collections contain an excellent series of this species, the specimens ranging from 8.5 to 20 inches in length.

Genus 114. CARANGOIDES Bleeker.

Teeth persistent, all small, in villiform bands on jaws, vomer, palatines, and tongue; lateral line scarcely arched in front; body oblong, not much elevated; otherwise essentially as in *Caranx*. Tropical seas.

152. Carangoides ferdau (Forskål). "*Omilu.*" Fig. 77.

Head 3.6 in length; depth 2.7; eye 4.5 in head; snout 3; interorbital 3; maxillary 2.5; D. vi–i, 29; A. ii–i, 25; scutes about 30.

Body elongate, elliptical, compressed, dorsal outline evenly arched, steep from above eye to tip of snout; head as deep as long; snout short, blunt, depressed in front of eye, steep anteriorly; mouth

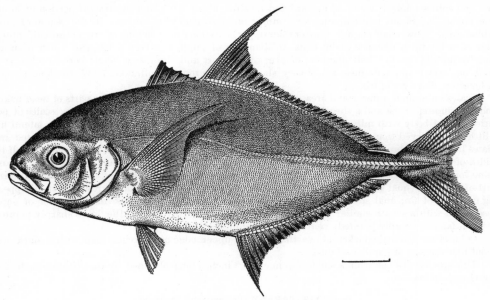

FIG. 77.—*Carangoides ferdau* (Forskål).

moderate, slightly oblique; teeth small, villiform on vomer, palatines, tongue, and jaws, those in jaws the larger and arranged in bands; tongue rounded, thin, and free for the most of its length; maxillary rather broad, its greatest width 2 in eye, extending to anterior edge of pupil; eye anterior, slightly above axis; interorbital very convex, the nape trenchant; spinous dorsal short, weak, and low; 6 or 7 rays of soft dorsal elevated anteriorly, the longest ray about 2 in base of fin, other rays even, slightly less than eye; origin of soft dorsal midway between tip of snout and base of caudal; caudal deeply forked, lobes equal; anal similar to soft dorsal, longest ray about 2 in its base; ventrals short, reaching past vent, 2.5 in head; pectoral long, falcate, equal to base of anal, the head contained 1.3 in pectoral, its lower base just anterior to base of ventrals; lateral line with a long, low arch, extending nearly to tip of pectoral.

Color in life, silvery, with dark-blue reflections over upper portions of back and head, several small lemon-colored spots with dusky centers on side, the number and position varying in different specimens, generally a group under curve of lateral line and one near beginning of straight portion; soft dorsal and anal blue, lower portion of these fins golden with blue outer margin; ventrals white with bluish shade, pectoral transparent, with golden shade; caudal bluish and golden with dusky margin.

Color in alcohol, purplish blue, lighter on sides and below, anterior portion of anal and soft dorsal dusky; pectorals pale; side with a few indistinct dark spots, usually below lateral line and posterior to middle of pectoral.

The above description based upon a specimen (No. 03413) 14 inches long, obtained in the market at Honolulu, July 19. Several other specimens were obtained at Honolulu and one is in the collection from Kailua. The fish is rather common about Hawaii, and equally so in Samoa.

153. Carangoides gymnostethoides Bleeker.

Head 3.3 (4) in length; depth 3 (3.6); D. vii–i, 31; A. ii–i, 26.

Body elliptical, compressed; profile convex from snout to nostril, thence regularly arched to caudal; ventral outline less convex, being almost straight from head to anal; head longer than deep; snout rather blunt, 3 in head; mouth low, somewhat oblique; maxillary 2.3 in head, extending opposite front of pupil; lower jaw little produced; teeth in villiform bands on jaws, vomer, palatines, and a patch on the tongue; eye large, 1.5 in snout, 4.4 in head; adipose eyelid little developed; cheeks and temporal regions with fine scales, head otherwise naked; scales rather small, those below pectoral smaller; a naked area on breast not widening forward from base of ventrals as much as in *C. ortho-grammus* Jordan & Gilbert; lateral line but little curved, arched above pectorals, and gradually becoming straight at their tips; greatest depth of arch about equal to pupil, the arched part of the line longer than the straight, plates developed only in the posterior half of the straight part; the plates small with low keels, their spines little prominent; 25 developed plates, including small ones; spinous dorsal rather weak, the highest spine 1.75 in snout (these spines probably varying according to the age); soft dorsal long and low, with slender rays; a well-developed scaly basal sheath anteriorly; the first articulate ray is 1.75 in base of fin and 1.25 in head; anal similar to soft dorsal; first free anal spine nearly obsolete, second small; caudal lobes moderate, equal, 1.2 in head, their length much less than the depth from tip to tip; pectorals falcate, their tips slender, reaching tenth ray of anal, their length 2.5 in body (from snout to base of caudal fin); ventrals 2.6 in head.

Color, in spirits, nearly plain olive, about as in *C. orthogrammus*. This species is recorded from Johnston Island by Smith & Swain. We have not seen it from elsewhere.

154. Carangoides ajax Snyder. Plate 33, fig. 2.

Head measured to end of opercular flap, 3.6 in length to base of caudal; depth 2.7; depth of caudal peduncle 7.7 in head; diameter of eye 5; width of interorbital space 3.5; length of snout 2.3; maxillary 2.3, D. 19; A. 16; plates in straight portion of lateral line about 32.

Anterior profile elevated, the contour rising abruptly to a point above posterior margin of orbit; lower jaw slightly longer than upper; cleft of mouth almost horizontal, maxilliary reaching a vertical passing through center of pupil; width of suborbital area 4 in head. Teeth villiform, in bands on jaws, vomer, palatines, and tongue; gillrakers on lower limb of first arch 14, the longest equal in length to width of posterior part of maxillary.

Head naked, except a small area behind and below eye, where there are small, deeply embedded scales; body mostly naked, there being an irregularly outlined area along lateral line with small, embedded scales; lateral line much more arched than dorsal contour, the highest point of curve just anterior to insertion of dorsal, the straight part beginning below base of twelfth dorsal ray; 3 or 4 posterior plates large, their length about half the depth of caudal peduncle; other plates growing smaller anteriorly, almost disappearing before curved portion of lateral line is reached; spinous dorsal not present; anal spines absent; anterior rays of both fins elevated, their height about 2.5 in head; caudal deeply forked, lobes of equal length, 1.2 in head; pectoral falcate, 1.1 in head; ventrals short, pointed, 2.3 in head.

Color silvery, darker above, indistinctly marbled with dusky along the back; base of pectoral colored on posterior side, upper half brownish black, lower dead white; dorsal fin with a dusky margin.

One specimen 38 inches long, from the market at Honolulu. Type, No. 50874, U. S. Nat. Mus.

Genus 115. ALECTIS Rafinesque. The Thread-Fishes.

Body rhomboid, deep, strongly compressed, more or less completely covered with minute embedded scales, sometimes apparently naked; scutes on the straight portion of the lateral line enlarged, bony, and spinous, as in *Carangus*, but much less developed; mouth moderate, with bands of villiform teeth on jaws, vomer, palatines, and tongue; first dorsal fin little developed, the spines short and rudimentary, mostly disappearing with age; soft dorsal and anal similar to each other; the first 5 or 6 rays of each fin elongate and filiform in the young, becoming shorter with age; ventral fins elongate in young, short in the adult; pectorals falcate; no finlets; caudal peduncle narrow, the caudal widely forked; gillrakers moderate, stout. This genus is not essentially different from *Carangus*, the great change in form arising from no important modification of the skeleton. The changes due to age are surprisingly great, as Dr. Lütken has shown, the characters of the nominal genera being chiefly stages in the growth of individuals. The young individuals are almost orbicular in form, with the filaments excessively long. Tropical seas.

155. Alectis ciliaris (Bloch). "*Ulua kihikihi.*" Fig. 78.

Head 3.2 in length; depth 1.9; eye 3.8 in head; snout 2.7; preorbital 3.6; interorbital 3.5; maxillary 2.5; gape 3.1; mandible 2; D. i, 22; A. ii, 17; scutes 18.

Body oval, much compressed, highest between the elevated bases of dorsal and anal; snout very short, the profile ascending abruptly in a straight line to front of eye, thence in a sharp curve to nape, from which point it is nearly straight to origin of dorsal fin; interorbital narrow and very trenchant; preorbital very deep; mouth moderate, very low, little oblique in adult, very oblique in young; the jaws equal; chin prominent; maxillary rather narrow, reaching vertical of anterior edge of pupil; teeth on jaws, vomer, tongue, and palatines in villiform bands; eye large, above axis of body, the adipose eyelid well developed before and behind; spinous dorsal obscure, the spines scarcely perceptible in adult; first rays of dorsal and anal filamentous, exceedingly long, in the young much longer than body, becoming somewhat shorter with age; lateral line with a wide arch, its summit under origin of dorsal, the chord of the curved portion about equal to straight part; scutes not strong, weak in the young; sheath of dorsal and anal fins little developed; ventrals moderate, about 2 in head; pectoral long, falcate, its length exceeding that of head, its tip reaching vertical of tenth anal ray.

Color in alcohol, bluish above, silvery on sides and below; head and middle of side with some yellow; a large dark blotch on opercle, a black blotch on orbit above; fins all pale, a large black blotch on base of the fourth to eighth dorsal rays, a smaller one on third and fourth anal rays; first 2 or 3 produced dorsal filaments pale, next 3 or 4 black for most of their length; ventrals dusky.   The above description based chiefly upon a specimen (No. 4039) 15 inches long from Honolulu.

A specimen 4.6 inches long, also from Honolulu, had in life 3 curved transverse bands on side of body, convex anteriorly, 1 on caudal peduncle, an indistinct trace of another in front of the 3, the most distinct one extending from just behind dorsal angle of body to just behind ventral angle; the next from about middle of soft dorsal to middle of soft anal; these 3 bands somewhat dusky above and showing very distinct when held at certain angles, but less so when held at others; black spot near

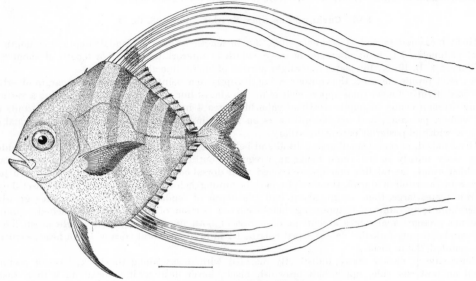

FIG. 78.—*Alectis ciliaris* (Bloch).

base on highest portion of dorsal; ventrals dusky for two-thirds their length; upper margin of opercle black; anterior dorsal and anal filaments white, the next ones black.

This interesting and beautiful fish is of wide distribution, being found on both coasts of tropical America, ranging northward to Cape Cod and Mazatlan.   It is generally common southward, especially about Cuba and the Florida Keys.   The many nominal species have been reduced by Lütken to 3 or 4—*gallus* and *ciliaris* of the East Indies, *alexandrinus* of North Africa, and *crinitus* of America.   We have not examined the East Indian forms, but we see no reason for doubting that *ciliaris* is the young of *gallus*, as has been supposed by Dr. Day and others.   The name *gallus* was, however, originally applied by Linnæus to *Selene vomer*.   Our young examples of *crinitus*, moreover, agree fully with the figures of *ciliaris*.   We think it therefore extremely probable that all the nominal species of this type are forms of *Alectis ciliaris*.   As has been shown by Lütken (Spolia Atlantica, 197), the nominal genera *Scyris*, *Blepharis*, and *Gallichthys*, are simply stages in the development of individuals, the characters assigned to these genera changing with age.

The species seems to be not uncommon among the Hawaiian Islands.   It was obtained by Dr. Jenkins in 1889, and our collection contains a fine series of examples, ranging in length from 4 to 15.5 inches.   The *Albatross* obtained specimens at Honolulu and at Hanalei Bay, Kâuai.

Family LVI. BRAMIDÆ.—The Pomfrets.

Body oblong, more or less elevated, strongly compressed, covered with firm adherent scales, large or small; scales firm, cycloid, lobate, or emarginate, or with a median ridge or spine, this character found in the young of all species but disappearing with age in some of them.   Mouth moderate, very oblique, maxillary broad and scaly, premaxillary protractile; jaws with bands of slender teeth; vomer and palatine teeth present or absent; preopercle entire or serrulate, serrate or spinous in the young; opercles well developed; dorsal and anal fins long, similar to each other, each with 3 or 4 anterior rays short and simple, developed as spines, the remaining rays all articulated; soft dorsal and anal scaly or with a sheath of scales; ventrals small, below the pectoral; axillary scale well developed, the rays I, 5; pectoral long; caudal peduncle slender, the fin lunate or forked, sometimes widely so; branchiostegals 7; pseudobranchiæ present; pyloric cœca few; air-bladder present or absent; supraoccipital crest large and high, extending forward to the snout; vertebræ numerous (16+23=39 in *Brama raii*); skeleton firm; shoulder-girdle thick and heavy, the hypocoracoid especially large and much dilated, entering the ventral outline, excluding the pubic bones from contact with the shoulder-girdle; pubic bones short and small; neurals and interneurals small and slender. Fishes of the open sea, widely distributed and often inhabiting considerable depths, subject to great changes with age.

Genus 116. COLLYBUS Snyder.

Body deep, ovate, greatly compressed; teeth in narrow bands, about 2 or 3 rows on jaws, none on vomer or palatines; 2 small fangs on each side of lower jaw near tip; teeth all small, weak, sharply pointed; gillrakers long and slender; pseudobranchiæ large; pyloric cœca 4, 2 of them about equal in length to diameter of pupil, the others nearly as long as stomach; vertebræ 38; mouth very oblique, nearly vertical; opercle, subopercle, interopercle, and preopercle smooth; scales short, very broad (vertically), the upper and lower edges sharply pointed, strongly ctenoid, each scale with a median, thickened, vertical ridge having a conspicuous tubercle in the center; number of scales in a lateral row between opercle and base of caudal about 50; no lateral line; dorsal inserted on a vertical passing just behind base of ventral, rays 34, the anterior 3 or 4 without articulations; anal 30, a row of scales along base of fin; caudal deeply forked; ventral inserted on a vertical through posterior half of base of pectoral.

Color silvery, dusky on head and back.

The genus *Collybus* differs from *Taractes* in not having teeth on the vomer and palatine bones, in having the caudal deeply cleft, the ventrals inserted posterior to the middle of the bases of pectorals, and in not having the opercular bones denticulated.

156. Collybus drachme Snyder.   Plate 34, fig. 1.

Head, measured to end of opercular flap, 3.3 in length (snout to base of caudal); depth 1.7; depth of caudal peduncle 3.6 in head; eye 2.8; snout 4.9; maxillary 2.2; interorbital space 3.3; D. 34; A. 30; scales in lateral series 51,—19

Body greatly compressed, its width at the widest part equal to length of maxillary; upper contour rather evenly curved from snout to caudal peduncle; lower contour much more convex, the base of anal not curved; mouth nearly vertical; lower jaw projecting somewhat beyond upper, posterior edge of maxillary reaching a vertical through anterior edge of pupil; teeth small, weak, sharply pointed, in narrow bands (2 or 3 rows) on jaws; 2 larger, fang-like teeth on each side of tip of lower jaw; no teeth on vomer and palatines; pseudobranchiæ large, the filaments equal in length to twice diameter of pupil; gillrakers 4+10, slender, long, and sharply pointed; edges of opercle, interopercle, subopercle, and preopercle smooth; lower jaw, snout, and interorbital area naked; other parts of head, including the maxillary and the body, closely scaled; scales strongly ctenoid, the ridges with minute tubercles; each scale with a high vertical ridge, on the middle of which is a prominent knob; the ridges of the scales hidden by the overlapping softer parts, the knobs projecting, lying in longitudinal rows; scales short, but very broad vertically, the upper and lower edges sharply pointed; scales of head, at base of pectoral and along the back much smaller than the others; no evident lateral line.

Dorsal inserted on a vertical passing behind base of pectoral a distance equal to diameter of pupil, rays 34, the anterior 3 or 4 without articulations; fin elevated anteriorly, the longest ray 1.4 in head; posterior rays 3.6. Anal rays, except first 1 or 2, articulated; length of anterior rays 3.6 of head; caudal deeply forked; pectoral pointed 3.2 of the length; ventrals inserted on a vertical passing through posterior half of base of pectoral.

Color bright silvery, dusky on upper part of head and along back; a silvery spot about the size of pupil at insertion of dorsal; upper and lower rays of caudal dusky; central part yellowish white; anterior rays of dorsal dusky.

The type, No. 50875, U. S. Nat. Mus., is a specimen 6 inches long, from station 4176, off Niihau, evidently near the surface. Other examples, among which are cotypes, 7737 L. S. Jr. Univ. Mus., were obtained from the stomach of a *Coryphæna* at Honolulu. Small squids and fishes were taken from the stomach of the specimen here described. A specimen seen in the Bishop Museum.

Family LVII. CORYPHÆNIDÆ.—The Dolphins.

Body elongate, compressed, covered with small cycloid scales; cleft of the mouth wide, oblique, the lower jaw projecting; cardiform teeth in the jaws and on the vomer and palatines; a patch of villiform teeth on tongue; no teeth in esophagus; opercular bones entire; skull with a crest which is much more elevated in adult than in young; a single, many-rayed dorsal fin, not greatly elevated, extending from nape nearly to caudal fin; anal similar, but shorter, each without distinct spines; pectoral very short and small; ventrals well developed, thoracic, I, 5, partly received into a groove in the abdomen; caudal fin widely forked; lateral line present; gill-membranes free from isthmus; branchiostegals 7; no pseudobranchiæ; no air-bladder; pyloric appendages very numerous; vertebræ about 30. A single genus with probably but 2 species. Very large fishes inhabiting the high seas in warm regions, noted for their brilliant and changeable colors.

Genus 117. CORYPHÆNA Linnæus.

Characters of the genus included above. The species are not well known, having been unduly multiplied by authors. According to Dr. Lütken they are probably reducible to 2; both known to occur among the Hawaiian Islands.

157. Coryphæna hippurus Linnæus. Common Dolphin. *"Mahihi;" "Máhimáhi."* Fig. 79.

Head 4.35 in length; depth 5; eye 6.2 in head; snout 3; interorbital 3; maxillary 2.1; D. 57; A. 27.

Body long and slender, deepest anteriorly; anterior profile in adult male nearly vertical; maxillary reaching posterior edge of pupil; mouth large, horizontal; bands of teeth on jaws, vomer, tongue, and palatines, the teeth all recurved, those in outer row larger, being wide-set, sharp, and conic; tongue rounded, free; eye low, anterior; a horizontal groove from eye to nostril; origin of dorsal over middle of eye in adult male, its tips extending to rudimentary rays of caudal, the twelfth or thirteenth ray being the highest; origin of anal nearer posterior than base of caudal; ventrals inserted slightly behind upper base of pectoral, 1.25 in head; pectoral 1.35.

Color in alcohol, bluish silvery above, lighter below, becoming white on belly; the sides, chiefly below lateral line, with many dark spots about size of pupil, these most numerous anteriorly; dorsal

Fig. 79.—*Coryphæna hippurus* Linnæus; after Jordan and Evermann.

fin dull purplish black; other fins color of corresponding parts of body except ventrals, which are dull purplish black on inner side; anal dull purplish on outer edge; peritoneum grayish black.

This description is from a specimen (No. 04450) 29.5 inches long, from Honolulu. Numerous other examples were seen by us and several were preserved. One from Hilo, when fresh, had the lower half of body yellowish; blue spots under pectorals; jet black spots all over the rest of the lower side, upper portion bluish with dark spots on silvery bluish ground; dorsal fin bright ultramarine blue; belly light; anal tinged with blue. The color of this fish in life is indescribably beautiful, but it undergoes very rapid changes while dying. After death only faint indications of the former colors remain. Our several specimens are 29 to 46 inches in length, from the largest of which the following measurements were secured:

	Inches.
Length of fish to end of cleft of caudal fin	46
Root of caudal to end of cleft	4.25
Body exclusive of head	33.25
Trunk	13.5
Height of dorsal	8.0
Height of anal	5.25
Height of ventral	7.75
Height of pectoral	7.5
Depth of body at vent	8.0
Caudal peduncle	2.5

158. Coryphæna equisetis Linnæus. Small Dolphin. Fig. 80.

Head 4.2 to 4.6 in length; depth 3.6 to 4; D. 51 to 55; A. 24 to 26; vertebræ 33; profile of head convex, but not nearly vertical, even in the adult; maxillary reaching front of pupil, 3.8 to 4.8 in head; insertion of dorsal behind eye; pectorals equal to half length of head; maxillary reaching middle of eye; profile of snout becoming nearly vertical with age; front of anal under middle of body. Colors brilliant in life, changing suddenly at death; brownish olive above, white or golden below, with bright-blue spots, which are largest on the back and head, forming bands on snout; dorsal purplish blue, with paler oblique lines, other fins tinged with blue; caudal yellow; in spirits pale, with blackish spots on the lower parts.

"Male with the front elevated, forming a crest, which projects a little beyond the upper jaw; female with blue spots along each side of tail, regularly arranged." (Poey.) Length 30 inches. Open Atlantic; rare in the West Indies; not recorded from coast of the United States.

FIG. 80.—*Coryphæna equisetus* Linnæus; after Günther.

Recorded by Bennett from the vicinity of Laysan (latitude 27° N., longitude 166° W.) and by Günther from between Tahiti and the Hawaiian Islands.

We are not sure that the specimens recorded by Bennett and by Günther were not the common species, *C. hippurus*, but the few dorsal rays in Günther's figure and his positive identification indicate that this species as well as the other occurs there. The position of the origin of the dorsal fin, however, is not, as Günther has thought, an important character, as it varies greatly with age, being much more anterior in the young than in the adult.

This species was not seen by us among the Hawaiian Islands.

Group PERCOIDEA.—The Perch-like Fishes.

A group of fishes of diverse habits and forms, but on the whole representing better than any other the typical *Acanthopterygian* fish. The group is incapable of concise definition, or, in general, of any definition at all; still, most of its members are definitely related to each other, and bear in one way or another a resemblance to the typical form, the perch, or more strictly to its marine relatives, the sea basses or *Serranidæ*. The following analysis gives most of the common characters of the group:

Body usually oblong, covered with scales, which are typically ctenoid, not smooth nor spinous, and of moderate size; lateral line typically present and concurrent with the back; head usually compressed laterally, and with the cheeks and opercles scaly; mouth variable, usually terminal and with lateral cleft, the teeth variable, but typically pointed, arranged in bands on the jaws, vomer, and palatine bones; gillrakers usually sharp, stoutish, armed with teeth; lower pharyngeals almost always separate, usually armed with cardiform teeth; third upper pharyngeal moderately enlarged, elongate, not articulated to the cranium, the fourth typically present; gills 4, a slit behind the fourth; gill-membranes free from the isthmus, and usually not connected with each other; pseudobranchiæ typically well developed; branchiostegals few, usually 6 or 7; no orbitosphenoid; no bony stay connecting the suborbital chain to the preopercle; opercular bones all well developed, normal in position, the preopercle typically serrate; no cranial spines; dorsal fin variously developed, but always with some spines in front, these typically stiff and pungent; anal fin typically short, usually with 3 spines, sometimes with a larger number, sometimes with none; caudal fin variable, usually lunate; pectoral fins well developed, inserted high; ventral fins always present, thoracic, separate, almost always with 1 spine and 5 rays; air-bladder usually present, without air-duct in the adult, simple, and generally adherent to the walls of the abdomen; stomach cœcal, with pyloric appendages, the intestines short in most species, long in the herbivorous forms; vertebral column well developed, none of the vertebræ especially modified, the number 10+14, except in certain extra-tropical and fresh-water forms, which retain the primitive higher numbers; shoulder-girdle normally developed, the post-temporal bifurcate, attached to the skull, but not coossified with it; none of the epipleural bones attached to the center of the vertebræ; coracoids normal, the hypercoracoid always with a median foramen, the basal bones of the pectoral (actinosts or pterygials) normally developed, 3 or 4 in number, hourglass-shaped, longer than broad; premaxillary forming the border of mouth, usually protractile; bones of the mandible distinct. Species very numerous, found in all seas except those of the Arctic regions. Many species inhabit fresh waters, especially in North America and Europe. These fresh-water forms are apparently nearer the primitive stock than the marine species are. The *Elassomidæ, Centrarchidæ,* and *Percidæ* are the most primitive, and apparently form, with the *Percopsidæ* and *Aphredoderidæ*, an almost continuous series. This series, however, we are compelled to break in a linear arrangement for the purpose of bringing in other series of transitional forms, which culminate in *Berycoids* and the *Scombroids*.

Family LVIII. KUHLIIDÆ.

Body oblong, strongly compressed; scales large, ciliated; lateral line complete, the tubes straight and occupying the anterior half of the exposed surface of the scale; mouth large, protractile; maxillary exposed, without supplemental bone; teeth in jaws in villiform bands; teeth on vomer, palatines, entopterygoids, and ectopterygoids; tongue smooth; head partly naked; preorbital and preopercle denticulate; opercle with 2 spines; gill-membranes separate; 6 branchiostegals; pseudobranchiæ large; gillrakers long and slender; dorsal fins connected at the base, with x, 9 to 13 rays, the spinous portion longer than the soft; anal as much developed as the soft dorsal, with III, 10 to 12 rays; dorsal and anal fins fitting in a well-developed sheath; caudal emarginate, pectoral obtusely pointed, with 14 or 15 rays, upper the longest; ventrals behind base of pectoral, close together, with a strong spine; posterior processes of the premaxillaries not extending to the frontals; supraoccipital bone extending forward to between the post-frontal processes, its crest not extending on the upper surface of the cranium; parietals short, without crest; precaudal vertebræ with transverse processes behind the fourth; ribs all but the last 2 to 4 sessile, inserted on the centrum behind the transverse processes. (Boulenger.) Vertebræ 25 (10 or 11 + 14 or 15). One genus with 7 or 8 species inhabiting the Pacific Ocean, especially fresh and brackish waters of East Africa, the islands of the Indian and Pacific oceans, and north Australia.

Genus 118. KUHLIA Gill.

Body oblong, much compressed; head compressed; mouth short, oblique; maxillary without supplemental bone; lower jaw projecting; no canines; teeth subequal; preorbital sharply serrate; angle of preopercle without strong spine; gillrakers slender; pseudobranchiæ large; scales large, not very rough; lateral line distinctly arched in front; top of head naked; dorsal fin deeply notched, but not divided to base, with 10 slender spines; caudal lunate; anal spines graduated, the fin short. Coloration bright silvery. This genus contains 2 groups of species, one strictly marine, the other ascending the rivers. The Hawaiian species, found in estuaries, is intermediate.

159. Kuhlia malo (Cuvier & Valenciennes). *"Ahólehóle."*

Head 3.4 in length; depth 2.6; eye 3.2 in head; snout 4; interorbital 3.3; maxillary 3; mandible 2.3; D. IX-I, 11; A. III, 11; scales 7–52–12; gillrakers 25 to 28.

Body oblong, strongly compressed, upper profile of head nearly straight; caudal peduncle compressed, its depth equal to length; head longer than deep; snout short, rather blunt; mouth oblique, lower jaw projecting; teeth minute, in bands on jaws, vomer, and palatines; tongue rather bluntly pointed, free anteriorly; maxillary reaching slightly beyond front margin of eye; eye very large, irregularly circular, its pupil slightly above axis of body, anterior; interorbital convex; 2 small, flat opercular spines, the lower the larger; origin of dorsal fin about over that of ventrals, behind that of pectoral, longest dorsal spine (fifth) 1.6 in head, longer than anterior soft rays; base of soft dorsal less than that of anal; caudal deeply forked, lobes pointed; anal spines graduated to the last, which is the longest, but shorter than the anterior or longest soft rays, longest spine 2.5 in head, longest ray 2.1 in head; ventrals reaching three-fourths distance to vent, 1.8 in head; pectoral 1.5 in head, not reaching as far as ventrals; scales ctenoid, 4 rows on cheek, those along bases of vertical fins very small; top of head naked, about 12 scales before dorsal; lateral line nearly concurrent with dorsal outline; caudal peduncle compressed, the least width 5 in least depth.

Color in life, bright silvery, bluish on back; fins dull whitish, the first dorsal and caudal narrowly edged with black; ventrals pure white; upper fins a little darker than lower; iris reddish silvery.

Young examples, when fresh, with top of head steel whitish with steel black reticulations and marblings which end in 2 dark stripes along side of back close to dorsal; soft dorsal with an intermaginal stripe of dusky; caudal pale, margined with dusky all round, the bulk of the fin white.

Color in alcohol, bluish brown above, more or less dusky, especially on top of head; lower surface of body white, washed with silvery; vertical fins dusky, the margins of caudal and dorsals blackish; margin of anal pale; pectoral dusky, with a median yellowish spot, axil dusky; ventrals whitish; inside of gill-opening and axil of pectoral dusky.

This beautiful fish was quite common in the streams and brackish water on the islands of Oahu and Hawaii. Numerous specimens are in the collections from Honolulu, Moanalua, Heeia, Waialua, Hilo, and Kailua, and numbers were obtained also by Dr. Jenkins and by the *Albatross* at Puako Bay, Hawaii; Hanalei Bay, Huleia River, and Waimea River, Kauai; Laysan Island; and at Station 3844 on the southern coast of Molokai.

The species attains a length of 8 to 10 inches, though most of the examples seen were smaller; a very attractive little fish, possessing many of the habits of our sunfishes and basses, dwelling by preference in the running fresh-water streams, where it may be found in numbers in the deeper pools. It is a good food-fish, takes the hook readily, and possesses game qualities of no mean order. As a pan-fish it ranks with our species of *Lepomis* and *Eupomotis*. The species is of very wide distribution, having been recorded from South Africa, the East Indies, Australia, many of the islands of the South Pacific, the Hawaiian Islands, and many other localities.

160. Kuhlia tæniura (Cuvier & Valenciennes)   Fig. 81.

D. x, 9 to 11; A. III, 10 or 11; scales 5–50 to 55–13 or 14; depth 2.75 to 3 in total length; head 3.5 to 3.66; snout 0.66 diameter of eye, which is 2.66 to 3.25 times in length of head, and equals inter-orbital width; lower jaw projecting; maxillary extending to below anterior border or anterior third of eye, the width of its distal extremity 0.25 to 0.33 diameter of eye; cheeks and opercles with large ctenoid scales; angle and lower border of preopercle finely denticulated; lower opercular spine strong; 25 or 26 gillrakers on lower part of anterior arch; dorsal originating just behind vertical of axilla; fifth or fourth and fifth spines longest, 0.6 to 0.66 length of head, longer than anterior soft rays; tenth spine longer than ninth, as long as third or a little shorter; pectoral 0.66 length of head; ventral a little shorter, reaching anus, or not quite so far; anal as long as or slightly longer than its distance from caudal; third spine a little longer than second, as long as tenth dorsal; caudal deeply forked, middle rays 0.33 to 0.4 length of outer. Silvery bluish gray on back; top of soft dorsal blackish; caudal with 5 black bands, one along the middle rays, and two pairs converging posteriorly.

This species, common among lava rocks in the south seas, was obtained in 1881 on Johnston Island, south of Hawaii, and recorded by Smith & Swain. It is common at Samoa.

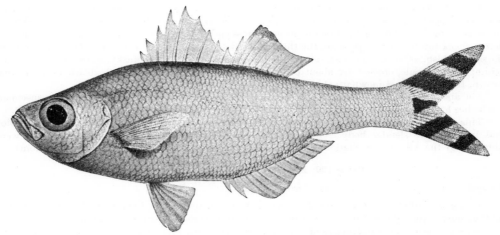

FIG. 81.—*Kuhlia tæniura* (Cuvier & Valenciennes) after Günther.

Family LIX. Apogonichthyidæ.—The Cardinal Fishes.

Body oblong or elongate, sometimes compressed and elevated, covered with rather large scales, which are striated and ctenoid, or sometimes cycloid; cheeks scaly, lateral line continuous; cleft of mouth wide, oblique; villiform teeth on jaws and vomer and sometimes on palatines; canines some-times present (teeth wanting in *Brephostoma*); preopercle with a double ridge, its edge entire or slightly serrated; opercular spine little developed; lower pharyngeals separate, with sharp teeth; pseudo-branchiæ present; branchiostegals 6 or 7; dorsal fins well separated, the first with 6 to 9 rather strong spines; no dorsal sheath or furrow; anal fin short, usually with 2 spines, sometimes with 3 or 4; ventral fins thoracic, I, 5, without axillary scale. Small fishes of the Tropics, especially abundant in the East Indies, some of them in fresh waters, most of them in rather deep waters. Color often bright red. Genera about 15; species about 130.

The family is represented in Japan by at least 8 species, and notwithstanding their small size they have great importance as food-fishes. In the Hawaiian Islands we know 9 species, all of them small and only 2 of any importance for food. These fishes are most abundant among the coral rocks about tropical islands. Many of our most interesting specimens obtained at Honolulu were secured by breaking apart masses of dead coral, in the interstices of which they take refuge.

Genus 119. MIONORUS Krefft.

This genus differs from *Amia* only in having the preopercle entire at all ages and the lateral line complete. The typical species (*lunatus*) has the body very deep and compressed and the dorsal spines elevated. Scales large (20 to 26) and weakly ctenoid; dorsal spines 7 in typical species, the soft dorsal and anal with 9 to 12 rays.

Small fishes, similar in habits to the species of *Amia*, *Foa*, and *Apogonichthys*, found in tropical seas in sandy bays or among corals. Several species known.

161. Mionorus waikiki (Jordan & Evermann).   Plate 35.[a]

Head 2.4 in length; depth 3; eye 3.2 in head; snout 4.6; interorbital 6; maxillary 2; D. vii–i, 8; A. ii, 7; scales 2–24–5.

Body short, stout, and compressed; dorsal outline strongly arched from tip of snout to posterior base of soft dorsal; ventral outline comparatively straight from tip of mandible to origin of anal; vent immediately in front of origin of anal; caudal peduncle deep and compressed; head rather large; mouth large, slightly oblique, jaws equal, maxillary reaching posterior edge of pupil; eye rather small, slightly above axis of body; interorbital space narrow, little convex; opercular and preorbital bones entire; a band of small villiform teeth in each jaw, and on vomer and palatines; fins moderate, origin of spinous dorsal nearer base of last soft ray than tip of snout; first dorsal spine very short, second about half length of third, which is equal to eye and snout; base of soft dorsal equal to depth of caudal peduncle; longest dorsal rays 2.25 in head; caudal rounded, its length 1.75 in head; origin of anal slightly posterior to that of soft dorsal, its longest rays 2.4 in head; pectoral slender, reaching past origin of anal, its length 1.5 in head; ventrals short, barely reaching origin of anal, their length nearly 2 in head; scales large, weakly ctenoid, firm, and somewhat deeper than long; lateral line strongly developed, following outline of back until under last dorsal ray, where it curves downward, following middle line of caudal peduncle to base of caudal fin.

Color in alcohol, head and body rather dark brownish, a lighter crossband around body at nape and across opercles; another light band surrounding body between the 2 dorsal fins; 3 dark-brown lines radiating from the eye, the first downward across cheek to tip of maxillary, the second backward across cheek toward base of pectoral, the third upward and backward to origin of lateral line; spinous dorsal blackish, especially on last spine; soft dorsal, anal, and caudal dusky, narrowly edged with white; pectoral pale, crossed by about 6 obscure brownish crossbars; ventrals black or very dark brown, the outer rays somewhat paler.

The above description is based upon the type, No. 50639, U. S. N. M. (field No. 20), a specimen 1.5 inches long, obtained from the coral rocks in front of Waikiki, near Honolulu, August 22, 1901.

This species is related to *M. alutus* of the coast of Florida, from which it differs markedly in color and in the more slender body. Only one specimen was obtained by us. Other specimens were obtained by the Albatross at Stations 3872 and 3876, between Maui and Lanai, in 28 to 43 fathoms.

Genus 120. FOA Jordan & Evermann, new genus.

Foa Jordan & Evermann, new genus (*Fowleria brachy grammus*).

This genus differs from *Amia* only in the character of the lateral line, which is developed only on the anterior part of the body. The preopercle, as in *Mionorus*, is without serration.

Several species occur in crevices of coral rock in the South Seas. All of them are of very small size and some are brightly colored, several of them with a conspicuous black ear-spot. This genus differs from *Apogonichthys* in having palatine teeth. *Fo* is the Samoan name for fishes of this family.

162. Foa brachygramma (Jenkins).   Fig. 82.

Head 2.5 in length; depth 2.5; eye 3.5 in head; snout 4.2; interorbital 4; maxillary 2; D. vii–i, 9; A. ii, 8; scales 2–22–3.

Body short, deep, and compressed, dorsal and ventral outlines symmetrical; head rather large, conic; mouth large, moderately oblique, jaws equal; maxillary reaching posterior border of pupil; eye large, slightly above axis of body; caudal peduncle compressed, twice as deep as thick; nape somewhat elevated, the profile slightly concave above and back of the eyes; opercles and preorbital entire, without teeth; minute villiform teeth on jaws, vomer, and palatines, none on tongue; vent immediately in front of origin of anal fin; scales large, weakly ctenoid, moderately firm, deeper than long; 2 scales in front of dorsal; lateral line incomplete, beginning at upper edge of gill-opening and ceasing under front of soft dorsal, number of pores about 10; pores rudimentary or absent altogether on posterior half of side; fins rather large; first dorsal spine very short, its base midway between tip of snout and base of last soft ray; longest dorsal spine about 2 in head; soft dorsal well separated from the spinous part, its rays about 1.9 in head; caudal rounded, its length 1.7 in head; anal immediately under soft dorsal, its rays 1.9 in head; pectorals small, equal to snout and eye; ventrals short, not reaching anal, a little shorter than pectoral.

Color in life, plain; pectoral, light rosy; dorsal, caudal, and anal yellow; ventrals dusky.

Color in alcohol, rusty yellowish brown, opercles and side with more distinct brownish blotches; spinous dorsal dark; ventrals dark; other fins pale.

---

[a] *Apogonichthys waikiki* on plate.

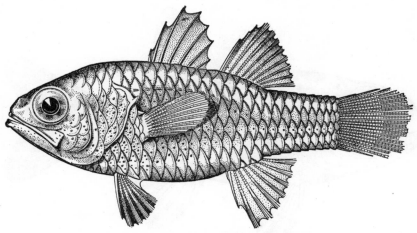

FIG. 82.—*Foa brachygramma* (Jenkins); from the type.

This species resembles *Apogonichthys auritus* of Cuvier & Valenciennes, which is the type of *Apogonichthys*. *A. auritus* has, however, a large black opercular spot bordered by a pale line, and the fins mottled and barred. Dr. Streets records it from Honolulu, which is doubtless an error.

Foa brachygramma reaches a length of about 2 inches. Three specimens were obtained by us from among coral rocks near the Moana Hotel at Waikiki and another at Hilo. A single specimen, the type of the species, was obtained by Dr. Jenkins at Honolulu in 1889, and others by the *Albatross* at Honolulu, at stations 3847 and 3849 on the southern coast of Molokai, and at stations 3872, 3873, 3875, and 3876, between Maui and Lanai, in 23 to 73 fathoms.

Genus 121. AMIA Gronow.

Body oblong, compressed, covered with large, ctenoid scales; lateral line continuous, with 20 to 30 scales; head large; mouth wide, oblique, the maxillary extending to below middle of the large eye; villiform teeth on jaws, vomer, and usually on palatines; no canine teeth; preopercle with a double ridge, the edge somewhat serrate, at least in the young, becoming entire with age in some species; opercle with a spine behind; gillrakers rather long; dorsal spines 6 or 7, strong; second dorsal remote, short; anal with 2 spines and 8 or 9 soft rays, the second much the longer, the soft part similar to the soft dorsal; pectorals and ventrals moderate; vertebræ 11+14=25. Warm seas; the species numerous.

The species are much alike in form, but differ greatly in markings, the ground color being usually bright red or reddish silvery. The principal groups differ in number of dorsal spines and in the form of the caudal. Most of the Pacific species belong to the subgenus *Ostorhinchus*, while all the Atlantic species belong in the subgenus *Apogon*.

163. Amia maculifera (Garrett). Fig. 83.

Head 2.5 in length; depth 2.75; eye 3.2 in head; snout 4.2; maxillary 2; interorbital 4; mandible 1.6; D. VII (-VIII)-I, 9; A. II, 8; scales 2-24-5; gillrakers about 6 + 15, long and compressed, filaments short, the longest smaller than the longest gillrakers.

Body short, deep, and moderately compressed, the greatest depth less than length of head; caudal peduncle rather deep, its least depth 2.5 in head; head pointed, longer than deep, eye and postocular part equal to its depth; eye very large, anterior, much greater than snout; interorbital flat with a low median ridge; upper rim of orbit not projecting above the profile of head; snout pointed; jaws subequal; maxillary extending nearly to posterior margin of pupil; teeth villiform, in bands on jaws, vomer, and palatines; tongue small, rounded, thin, and free; mouth large, oblique; bones of the head cavernous; posterior margin of preopercle and edge of suborbital finely serrate; anterior margin of preopercle simply rough; origin of spinous dorsal over base of pectoral, third spine enlarged, 2.4 in head; origin of soft dorsal slightly anterior to origin of anal, longest ray 1.7 in head; caudal deeply emarginate; longest anal spine 3 in head, longest ray 1.75 in head; pectoral long, reaching to above base of second anal ray, longest ray 1.6 in head; ventrals reaching nearly to origin of anal, 1.75 in head; scales large, finely ctenoid, deciduous, 4 in front of dorsal.

Color in life of an example (No. 5162) 5.6 inches long, body very pale purplish gray; belly pale orange; head dusky reddish orange, with purplish tinge; 6 or 7 rows of pale black spots longitudinally on body, the upper one over a part of lateral line; spinous dorsal orange-red, with rosy tinge, second spine delicate purple; second dorsal same color as first; caudal same color as dorsal, except its upper and lower edges blackish and its tip somewhat blackish; anal bright orange with

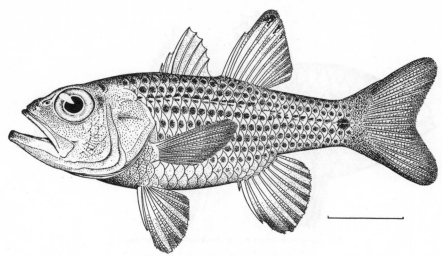

FIG. 83.—*Amia maculifera* (Garrett).

reddish shade, tip blackish; ventrals same as anal, but brighter and the tips blackish; pectoral same as dorsal, but uniformly paler; posterior third of iris bright yellow, with greenish reflections mottled with blackish-violet marks.

Color in alcohol, light brownish, paler below, side with a series of about 8 horizontal lines made up of a series of rather large, distinct dark-brown spots on the centers of the scales; the line immediately above lateral line and the third one below it most distinct; in some cases the spots coalesce, forming continuous lines; top of head dusky olivaceous; cheek, opercles, and lower jaw densely covered with fine brown punctulations, some of those on preopercle slightly larger and blacker; an obscure dark bar from eye to gill-opening; breast pale, with a few obscure brownish punctulations; base of pectoral dusky; a large black blotch at base of caudal peduncle; dorsals and caudal somewhat dusky, other fins pale.

This species attains a length of about 6 inches and appears to be common among the Hawaiian Islands. Our collections contain numerous specimens from Honolulu and Hilo, and the *Albatross* secured it at Station 3875, between Maui and Lanai in 34 to 65 fathoms.

164. Amia evermanni (Jordan & Snyder). Fig. 84.

Head, exclusive of opercular flap, 2.7 in length; depth 3.2; depth of caudal peduncle 2.7 in head; eye 3.5 in head; snout 3.5; maxillary 1.87; interorbital space 6.25; D. vi, i–9; A. ii, 8; pores in lateral line 25; Br. 7.

FIG. 84.—*Amia evermanni* (Jordan & Snyder); from the type.

Head conspicuously large; snout pointed; mouth large, the maxillary extending to a point midway between pupil and posterior margin of orbit; interorbital space concave, viewed either from the side or from before, its width equal to that of posterior edge of maxillary; edge of suborbital and lower edge of preopercle witn large, thin, membranous flaps; anterior edge of preopercle smooth; upper part of posterior edge finely serrated. Teeth villiform, in broad bands on the jaws, a V-shaped patch on the vomer, and in narrow bands on the palatines; gillrakers 5 + 16, the length of the longest contained 3 times in longitudinal diameter of eye; pseudobranchiæ present.

Head naked, except on interopercle, preopercle, and upper part of opercle, where there are a few large smooth scales; scales of body ctenoid, the number in a longitudinal series immediately above the lateral line 54, between lateral line and spinous dorsal 3, between lateral line and anal 15; lateral line complete, its curve closely following that of dorsal contour of body, located on middle of caudal peduncle posteriorly. Third and fourth dorsal spines longest, 2.7 in head; first and sixth of equal length, half as long as the third; a slight space between dorsals, the spines when depressed just reaching base of second dorsal; spine of second dorsal measuring 3.16 in head; longest ray 1.87; distance between soft dorsal and base of caudal equal to width of space between anterior margin of eye and posterior edge of opercle; first anal spine minute, the second 3.5 in length of head; longest ray 2; ventral reaching a point midway between anal opening and base of anal fin; pectoral fin rather pointed, its tip reaching a vertical through middle of anal; caudal forked.

In alcohol the color is very light (in life probably red), the body with 5 rather indistinct dark bands, none of which reaches the ventral surface; the first on nape, second triangular in shape, extending from base of spinous dorsal to near middle of body, third passing from base of second dorsal to a point near base of anal, the fourth located just behind the second dorsal, fifth at base of caudal; a narrow, dusky band passing from tip of snout to eye; a similar band from posterior margin of eye to edge of opercle.

A single specimen about 5.6 inches long from the market at Honolulu. The condition of the tissues indicates that the example came from deep water. Type, No. 51 87, U. S. N. M., collector E. L. Berndt.

165. Amia snyderi (Jordan & Evermann). Plate 36 *a* and Fig. 85.

Head 2.7 in length; depth 3.1; eye 3.7 in head; snout 3.7; interorbital 4.5; maxillary 2.2; mandible 2; gape 3; D. vii–i, 9; A. ii, 8; C. 17; P. 10; scales 2–25–5; Br. 6.

Body short and stout, moderately compressed, the dorsal and ventral outlines about equally curved; head rather large, conic; snout conic, the anterior profile very slightly curved from tip of snout to origin of spinous dorsal; mouth oblique, jaws subequal, the lower slightly included; maxillary long, reaching not quite to posterior edge of pupil, its width at tip 2 in eye, supplemental bone well developed; interorbital space rather broad, slightly convex, preorbital narrow, least width 3 in eye; teeth on vomer and jaws, the latter in villiform bands, none on palatines; gillrakers slender, 10 on lower limb of first arch; caudal peduncle compressed and deep, the least width about 4 in its depth; scales large, deep, closely imbricated, strongly ctenoid and loose; lateral

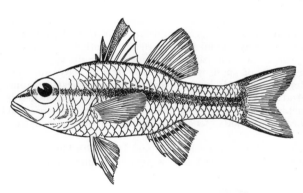

FIG. 85.—*Amia snyderi* (Jordan & Evermann); after Günther.

line beginning at upper end of gill-opening, nearly straight to base of caudal fin, 4 scales in front of spinous dorsal; nape with a striated shield; edge of opercle thin and smooth; both margins of preopercle and edge of interopercle serrate; teeth strongest at angles; a series of moderately strong teeth along lower edge of orbit; origin of spinous dorsal nearer snout than base of last dorsal ray; first dorsal spine very short, fourth longest, about 2 in head, second 2 in the fourth, seventh 2 in second; first soft rays longest, 1.8 in head; caudal deeply emarginate, longest rays about 1.6 in head; anal similar to soft dorsal, somewhat smaller, its origin under last rays of soft dorsal; ventrals pointed, scarcely reaching vent, 1.9 in head; pectoral reaching vertical at vent, 1.7 in head.

Color in alcohol, pale yellowish brown, darkest above; a darker brownish band extending from upper edge of opercle along side, just above lateral line, to posterior edge of soft dorsal; another broader, more distinct brown band from tip of snout through eye and along middle of side to base of caudal fin, covering lateral line on caudal peduncle; caudal peduncle at base of caudal fin with a broad dusky crossbar, usually darkest on upper half, sometimes obscure, sometimes with a darker blotch or spot in the upper portion; upper parts of head covered with fine dark brown punctulations; lower jaw similar, but somewhat paler; membranes of anterior 2 or 3 dorsal spines black, others finely punctulate; soft dorsal pale at base, above which is a broad indistinct dark crossband, the color confined chiefly to the interorbital membranes, this color extending to near tip of last rays; outer part of soft dorsal pale; anal similar to soft dorsal, the black bar narrower and nearer base of fin, rest

a Apogon synderi on plate.

of fin white; caudal dusky on membranes of outer 1 or 2 rays, the fin otherwise white, with a few fine punctulations on the interradial membranes; ventrals pale; distal parts of the first and second rays and their connecting membrane black; pectoral pale, axil and base of pectoral somewhat dusky.

Color in life (field No. 198, O. P. J.), pale red; 2 longitudinal pearly lines on body; first dorsal with a dusky olivaceous anterior border; white lines along fourth, fifth, sixth, and seventh spines, the membranes olivaceous; second dorsal with many white and some olivaceous spots; anal with a dusky line along base, the distal part red; base of caudal dusky, rest of fin pale red; ventral with a white spot near tip; pectoral pink; iris yellow.

Another example (field No. 03499) was coppery brown when fresh, with trace of dusky band along side; a faint black bar at base of caudal, forming a black spot above end of lateral line; some dusky on opercle; first dorsal dusky; second dorsal brownish red with some dark; anal same with a basal flesh-colored bar below it; caudal reddish brown; ventrals same, with first ray pinkish and dusky behind it; some dusky on opercle.

This species reaches a length of about 6 inches. It was obtained by Garrett in the Hawaiian, Society, and Paumotu islands. Our collections contain numerous specimens from Honolulu and Hilo. We have examined also 12 specimens in the collection made by Dr. O. P. Jenkins.

The species closely resembles *Amia menesema*, from which it differs chiefly in coloration; the black caudal crescent, which is such an excellent distinguishing mark in *A. menesema*, is wholly absent in this species; moreover, the 2 silvery lateral bands, which become dark brown in spirits, are not found in *A. menesema;* and the black on the anal and soft dorsal is less conspicuous in *A. snyderi.*

A fairly good figure of this specis is given by Günther in Fische der Südsee, under the erroneous name of *Amia frenata*. The species belongs to the subgenus *Pristiapogon* of Klunzinger, having both limbs of the preopercle serrate.

Our collections contain many specimens from Honolulu and Hilo, ranging in length from 3 to 5.5 inches.

166. Amia menesema (Jenkins). *"Upapálu."* Plate XIII and Fig. 86.

Head 2.5 in length; depth 2.8; eye 3.75 in head; snout 3.9; maxillary 1.9; interorbital 4; mandible 1.75; D. vii–i, 9; A. ii, 8; scales 2–25–5.

Body short, deep, moderately compressed, greatest depth less than length of head; caudal peduncle rather deep, its least depth 2.3 in head; head subconic, longer than deep, its depth slightly greater than eye and postocular part of head; snout bluntly rounded; jaws equal; mouth large, slightly oblique; bands of small villiform teeth on jaws, vomer, and palatines; tongue rather thick, narrowly pointed, free; maxillary reaching posterior margin of pupil, which is above axis of body, anterior; interorbital very slightly convex; longest dorsal spine 2.2 in head; preopercle sharply serrate on anterior as well as posterior margin; longest dorsal ray 1.8; caudal deeply emarginate; anal similar to soft dorsal, longest ray 1.8 in head; ventrals reaching nearly to anterior base of anal, 1.8 in head; pectoral reaching to origin of anal, 1.6 in head; scales large, weakly ctenoid, deciduous; lateral line complete, concurrent with dorsal outline.

Color in life, coppery purple, dull and clouded with grayish; sides and belly with bluish luster; first dorsal dull reddish, with membrane of first two spines jet black; second dorsal dirty pink, with a

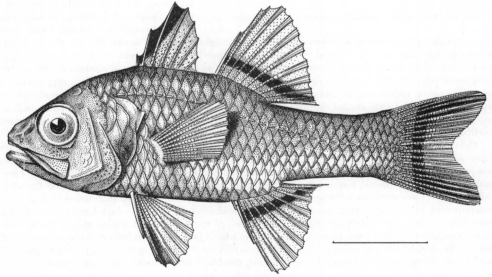

FIG. 86.—*Amia menesema* (Jenkins); from the type.

blackish bar near base, the tip blackish; anal same as soft dorsal; caudal dirty pink, with a broad blackish stripe along middle of each lobe, extending forward on median line of caudal peduncle above and below, these connected by a stripe; a curved black crossbar parallel with edge of fin; pectoral bright pink; ventrals pale pink, with black tips; body unmarked except a dusky shade across caudal peduncle connecting bases of the 2 caudal stripes.

Color of another specimen (No. 03439), when fresh, coppery, with blue and silvery reflection over body and head; fins, except the black areas, rosy.

Color in alcohol, light brown, becoming paler below and dusky grayish on belly; first 2 or 3 dorsal spines and their connecting membranes black, rest of fin pale with very light brown specks; soft dorsal and anal white, each with a broad, jet-black bar extending across the rays, the anterior end on lower fourth of rays, the bar gradually rising until on the last rays it is near their tip; caudal pale with a broad jet-black crescent across its base and extending to tips of fin on the 2 or 3 outer rays but one, the outer ray being white; between this crescent and caudal peduncle a lighter area, the color of the bar, confined chiefly to the membranes; rest of fin white, with obscure dusky specks; ventrals pale, with a few obscure dusky specks, tips of the longest 2 rays dark; pectoral pale, with obscure darkish punctulations; no trace of any streaks or bars on side of dark spot on caudal peduncle.

The above description is based chiefly upon a specimen (No. 02919) 6.25 inches long, from Honolulu.

This species is closely related to *A: snyderi*, from which it differs, however, in the smaller eye and the entire absence of the dark lateral stripe and the presence of a black crescent on the caudal fin; the black bar on the soft dorsal and anal is in each case farther up on the fin than it is in *A. snyderi*. This species reaches a length of at least 7 inches and appears to be abundant among the Hawaiian Islands. Besides the numerous specimens in our own collection from Honolulu, Hilo, and Kailua, we have examined 11 examples obtained by Dr. Jenkins and others collected by the *Albatross* at Laysan Island and on the southern coast of Molokai. We have also a specimen from Papeete, Tahiti.

167. Amia erythrina (Snyder). Plate 34, fig. 2.[a]

Head, including opercular flap, 2.5 in length; depth 2.5; depth of caudal peduncle 6; eye 2.7 in head; snout 4.9; maxillary 2.2; D. vi, i, 9; A. ii, 8; P. 14; scales 3–26–7, 5 in front of dorsal; width of body at pectorals about half the depth; caudal peduncle slender; distance between last anal ray and base of caudal 3.12 in length.

Head short, snout blunt and rounded, lower jaw included; interorbital space flat, with a slight median elevation, width equal to diameter of eye; mouth oblique, the maxillary extending to the posterior border of eye, the expanded portion with a slightly convex posterior border; both margins of preopercle weakly serrated; teeth on jaws, vomer,. and palatines, the latter covering a small anterior area of bones; gillrakers on vertical limb of arch mere papillæ, except a long slender one at angle; those on horizontal limb long and slender near the angle, gradually reduced in length to near middle of limb, where they are short and rudimentary; scales weakly ctenoid; cheeks and opercles with scales; first dorsal spine short and weak; second very strong, its length 1.67 in head, when depressed reaching base of second dorsal ray; remaining spines graduated in length to the last, which is about 3.3 in second; spine of soft dorsal very slender, equal in length to fourth spine of first dorsal; longest rays 1.58 in head; anal rays about equal in length to those of dorsal; caudal 0.3 of the length, its margin with a deep notch; pectoral 4.5 in length, ventrals 4.5.

Color reddish orange, scales edged with a narrow band of a somewhat deeper hue; occiput and a spot on opercle dusky; a small black spot at origin of spinous dorsal; minute dark specks on nape, along base of dorsals, at base of caudal, on breast and on opercles; fins immaculate.

Distinguished from the other Hawaiian species by the bright reddish color, the absence of large spots or bars on the body and fins, and by having the second dorsal spine largest.

Type, No. 50876, U. S. N. M., Puako Bay, Hawaii. Length 1.4 inches. Other specimens, among which are cotypes, No. 7733, L. S. Jr. Univ. Mus., are from Honolulu; Hanalei Bay, Kauai; and Laysan Island. The species was also abtained in Samoa.

Genus 122. ARIOMMA Jordan & Snyder.

Body not greatly compressed; head large; caudal peduncle slender, cylindrical; eyes large, with thin adipose lids; mouth small, the maxillary short, broad, rounded posteriorly; teeth on jaws, none on vomer and palatines; pseudobranchiæ present; preopercle smooth; head and body with scales, about 55 in lateral series; soft dorsal and anal elongate.

Only one species known.

168. Ariomma lurida Jordan & Snyder. Plate 37.

Head 2.9 in length; depth 4; eye 3 in head; snout 3.3; interorbital width 4; depth of caudal peduncle 7; D. x, 17; A. 15; P. 20; scales in lateral series 55 or more.

---

a Apogon erythrinus on plate.

Width of body a little greater than half its greatest depth; caudal peduncle cylindrical and markedly slender; interorbital space slightly convex; eye extremely large, with thin, transparent adipose lids, the posterior extending to edge of pupil, the anterior not more than one-fifth as wide; nostrils near tip of snout; lower jaw projecting a little beyond the upper; length of maxillary equal to interorbital width; jaws each with a single row of slender, minute teeth, those on lower jaw curved backward; no teeth on vomer or palatines; pseudobranchiæ large; gillrakers on first arch 9+19, those near the angle long and slender, the others growing successively shorter toward either end of arch; preopercle entire; scales probably between 55 and 65 in a lateral series, probably present on head, including upper part of snout and cheeks, scale-pits being present on occiput and below eye; lateral line probably developed, its anterior end below base of dorsal a distance equal to diameter of pupil; origin of dorsal above base of pectoral; soft dorsal and anal coterminous, the length of caudal peduncle measured to bases of upper and lower rays equal to length of maxillary; ventrals inserted on a vertical through second or third dorsal spine; caudal fin probably concave or forked. Whether the anterior rays of the anal are spinous or articulate can not be determined, but they are probably spinous. No distinctive color markings are apparent.

This species is represented by 2 small specimens, each about 7.5 inches long, in a very bad state of preservation, the scales having all been lost and the fins broken. The specimens were collected at Honolulu by Mr. E. L. Berndt, to whom we are indebted for them. Type, No. 51400, U. S. N. M. Cotype, No. 8441, Stanford Univ. Mus.

Genus 123. SYNAGROPS Günther.

Body rather elongate, covered with rather large, cycloid, deciduous scales, about 35 in lateral line; scales of head covered with very small scales; eyes large; jaws with a band of villiform teeth and with strong canines in front; small or villiform teeth on vomer and palatines; preopercle with its angle produced and with soft serrations; dorsal rays ix–i, 10; anal ii, 7; vent normal. Coloration black.

One species known from deep water in Japan and one from the Hawaiian Islands.

169. Synagrops argyrea (Gilbert & Cramer). Fig. 87.

Head 2.88; depth 3.75; D. xi–i, 9; A. ii, 7; P. 14 or 15; V. i, 5; lateral line 28 to 29 (+ 2 or 3 on tail); 2 scales in a transverse series between lateral line and origin of first dorsal fin; width of body at base of pectorals nearly 2 in the depth; least depth of caudal peduncle 2.25 in greatest depth of body; greatest width of head 1.5 in the greatest depth; orbit 3 to 3.25 in head; maxillary 2.25; ventral spine 2.5; snout 1.3 in orbit; distance from tip of snout to origin of first dorsal 2.67 in body; from tip of snout to origin of anal a little more than 1.5; from root of ventrals to origin of anal 3.13; base of first dorsal 5.5; base of second dorsal 8.3; distance between dorsals 10; base of anal 9.

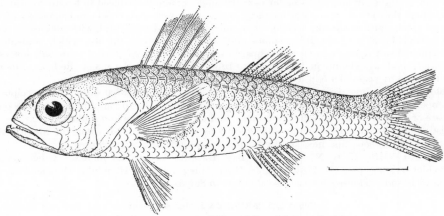

FIG. 87.—*Synagrops argyrea* (Gilbert & Cramer); from the type.

Body elongate, compressed; head compressed, dorsal and ventral profiles convex, similar; tip of snout about on a level with lower margin of pupil; orbit large; jaws equal, or the lower very slightly projecting, entering the steep profile; maxillary with a ridge along the middle, reaching to or a little beyond center of eye, much expanded behind, the end emarginate, lower posterior angle somewhat enlarged into a lobe; small teeth in bands on jaws, vomer, and palatines; a large canine tooth inside of band of small teeth near anterior end of each premaxillary, tip of lower jaw fitting between them; each ramus of lower jaw with 9 canine teeth in a single series, 2 very close together at each side of tip of lower jaw, just outside of these a depression in jaw into which fits canine of upper jaw, and behind this 7 nearly equidistant teeth, of which the most anterior is smallest and the fourth the largest, or as large as those behind it; small teeth outside of the row of canines, very few in number in lower jaw; canines sometimes as few as 5 in number on each side; posterior nares narrow, vertical slits close in front of rim of orbit and on a level with upper rim of pupil; anterior nares small, circular, and the distance between posterior and anterior nares 5 in orbit; interorbital space convex, its width a little less than orbit, divided into areas by a series of low, thin ridges, one of these, quite as long as snout, extending forward along median line of occiput to about the vertical from posterior margin of orbit; on each side of this, a little behind its anterior end, begins a curved ridge which runs forward and outward to about the vertical from the hinder edge of the pupil, and thence forward and inward to the median line between the anterior nares, these symmetrical ridges forming a pear-shaped figure with its pointed end directed forward; on each side, at the greatest convexity of the above ridges, at the vertical of the posterior margin of the pupil, begins another ridge which runs straight forward and outward close to the antero-dorsal margin of the orbit, then curves inward and forward inside of the nares to a point in advance of the anterior nares and not far from the middle one; suborbital ring narrow; posterior edge of preopercle nearly vertical and straight, directed a little downward and backward and very slightly curved backward near its posterior end, producing a prominent rounded angle, both edges closely serrated, the serrations strongest, almost in the form of small spines, at the angle and at the ridge of the opercle forming a rounded and obtuse but marked angle, with inferior edge serrated; opercle with slightly diverging ridges, the lower nearly horizontal and a little more strongly developed than the upper, both ending in small spines; gillrakers 13 on the anterior limb of first arch, the longest about 3 in eye; peritoneum black; scales large, thin, cycloid, very deciduous; interorbital space, snout, and lower jaw, and apparently the maxillary and opercles, scaleless; cheek with large, thin, embedded scales; second dorsal, anal, and caudal scaly on their basal parts; lateral line high up and continued on to basal part of dorsal fin; origin of first dorsal fin over root of pectoral, its third spine probably longest, at least half as long as head, the spines slender and weak; origin of second dorsal a little in front of origin of anal, the rays heavy; first spine of anal short, the second longer, 1.5 in orbit, the soft rays thick; caudal deeply forked, the longest rays at least half length of head, and (the ends of the rays of second dorsal, of anal, and caudal all injured); upper end of root of pectoral about on a level with lower edge of pupil, the width of the base less than half orbit, the longest rays (injured at tips) at least two-ninths of bony length; root of ventrals under root of pectoral; ventral spine with its outer edge densely serrate, the soft rays more than half as long as head.

Color in alcohol, though the scales are nearly all off, the back and upper part of side light brownish, with black lines at the edge of the fallen scales; top of head and snout dusky; sides of head and lower three-fifths of trunk and tail silvery; first dorsal fin blackish in the distal half, the other fins a little dusky; mouth cavity not dark, the gill-cavity a little dusky.

A second, smaller specimen differs from the type in having only 5 instead of 9 canines in each lower jaw, its depth a little greater, orbit larger, gillrakers a little shorter. Aside from some very slight differences in the proportions, it agrees in even minutest details with the type.

Length 3.75 and 5.5 inches. Described from examples dredged at stations 3472 and 3476, in 295 and 298 fathoms, by the *Albatross* in 1891 off the Hawaiian Islands. (Gilbert and Cramer.)

This species is said to be close to *Synagrops japonica* of Steindachner and Döderlein, differing from it, among other characters, in the serrated ventral spine, large number of canine teeth, greater length of second anal spine, in the color, the relative development of the 2 opercular ridges, and the absence of black color in the mouth cavity.

Family LX. SERRANIDÆ.—The Sea Basses.

Body oblong, more or less compressed, covered with adherent scales of moderate or small size, which are usually but not always ctenoid; dorsal and ventral outlines usually not perfectly correspond- ing; mouth moderate or large, not very oblique, the premaxillary protractile and the broad maxillary usually not slipping for its whole length into a sheath formed by the preorbital, which is usually narrow; supplemental maxillary present or absent; teeth all conical or pointed, in bands, present on jaws, vomer, and palatines; gillrakers long or short, usually stiff, armed with teeth; gills 4, a long slit behind the fourth; pseudobranchiæ present, large; lower pharyngeals rather narrow, with pointed teeth, separate (except in *Centrogenys*); gill-membranes separate, free from the isthmus; branchioste- gals normally 7 (occasionally 6); cheeks and opercles always scaly; preopercle with its margin more or less serrate, rarely entire; the opercles usually ending in 1 or 2 flat, spine-like points; nostrils double; lateral line single, not extending on the caudal fin; skull without cranial spines, and usually with- out well-developed cavernous structure; no suborbital stay; post-temporal normal; second suborbital with an internal lamina supporting the globe of the eye; entopterygoid present; all or most of the ribs inserted on the transverse processes when these are developed; anterior vertebræ without transverse processes; dorsal spines usually stiff, 2 to 15 in number; soft dorsal with 10 to 30 rays; anal fin rather short, its soft rays 7 to 12, its spines, if present, always 3, in certain genera (*Grammistinæ*, *Rypticinæ*) altogether wanting; ventrals thoracic, usually 1, 5 (1, 4, in *Plesiopinæ*) normally developed, without distinct axillary scale; pectoral well developed, the rays branched, with narrow base; caudal peduncle stout, the fin variously formed; vertebræ typically 10 + 14 = 24, the number sometimes increased, never more than 35; air-bladder present, usually small and adherent to the wall of the abdomen; stomach cœcal, with few or many pyloric appendages; intestines short, as is usual in carnivorous fishes. Genera 60 to 70; species about 400. Carnivorous fishes, chiefly marine, and found in all warm seas; several genera found in fresh waters. As here understood, the *Serranidæ* comprise the most of the family of *Percidæ* as understood by Günther and others, exclusive of those with imperfect pseudobranchiæ, those with 1 or 2 anal spines, those with the number of vertebræ increased, those in which the whole length of the maxillary slips under the preorbital, and those with the anal fin many-rayed and the cranium shortened behind. As here understood, the *Serranidæ* are essentially equivalent to the *Serraninæ* and *Grammistinæ* of Boulenger's Catalogue. Even after these eliminations, the family is considerably varied. Of the many recognized genera, only 3 are known to have representatives among the Hawaiian Islands.

Genus 124. PIKEA Steindachner.

Body elongate, the caudal peduncle robust; mouth moderate, the lower jaw projecting; maxillaries scaly; teeth small, uniform, the inner depressible; preopercle finely serrate; opercle with 3 flat spines; numerous pores on head; scales large; lateral line with a strong upward curve, as in *Anthias;* dorsal spines moderate, 8 in number, the third highest, the fin deeply notched; soft dorsal and anal short; caudal short, lunate; pectoral long, falcate; vertebræ 10+14. Few species known, mostly from deep water; only one thus far known from the Hawaiian Islands.

170. Pikea aurora Jordan & Evermann.   Plate XIV.

Head 2.5 in length; depth 3; eye 5 in head; snout 4; interorbital 6.2; maxillary 2.25; D. VIII, 13; A. III, 8; scales 5–55–22; Br. 7; gillrakers short and rather weak, about 9 + 5.

Body moderately stout, the back slightly elevated, head rather long and pointed; snout depressed, the anterior profile nearly straight from tip of snout to occiput; mouth large, maxillary reaching posterior margin of pupil, supplemental bone developed, the tip broad, 1.5 in orbit; mouth somewhat oblique, the lower jaw strongly projecting; teeth in broad villiform bands on jaws, vomer, and palatines; tongue naked; eye moderate, high up, chiefly above axis of body; anterior nostril in a short tubé at edge of prenasal; posterior nostril small, round, near upper anterior edge of orbit; edge of preopercle slightly dentate, especially on lower arm; opercle ending in a broad flap with a weak, flat spine; pseudobranchiæ rather small; interorbital low, very little convex; caudal peduncle stout, compressed, and very deep, the depth equaling snout and eye; fins rather small; origin of dorsal posterior to that of pectoral, slightly nearer base of last ray than tip of snout; dorsal spines low and weak, the third longest, 3.6 in head; soft portion of dorsal somewhat elevated and pointed, with longest ray 1.9 in head; anal similar to soft dorsal but smaller and somewhat posterior, fifth ray 2 in head; caudal truncate or slightly lunate; ventrals short, not nearly reaching vent, their length 1.75 in head; pectoral rather long and slender, reaching origin of anal, its length about 1.4 in head; scales rather small, finely ciliate, somewhat loose; entire head, except interorbital, snout, and under parts, scaled; lateral line well developed, complete, with a strong arch above the pectoral and distinctly decurved under last dorsal ray.

Color in life (field No. 03342), top of head, upper half of anterior part of body, and whole posterior half of body pale rosy; lower part of head and lower parts of anterior half of body white with faint rosy wash; top of head and back in front of dorsal vermiculated with greenish yellow lines; middle portion of upper jaw yellow with a broad sulphur-yellow stripe from it to eye, then back of eye to opercular opening; a narrow sulphur stripe on posterior edge of maxillary and continued interruptedly downward and backward across cheek to opercle; a few small yellow spots across cheek between the two stripes; tip of lower jaw yellow; yellow of back in about 6 indefinite lines; dorsal pale rosy, spinous part greenish yellow at base, this extending toward tip posteriorly and forming a submarginal yellow stripe on soft part, narrowly bordered above by rosy; rest of fin rosy; caudal dark rosy, paler toward tip, then with blackish red edge, a greenish yellow stripe along upper and lower margins narrowly edged with rosy; anal yellow anteriorly, rest of fin pale rosy; pectoral and ventrals pale rosy; yellow of lower jaw bounded by rosy, rest of jaw and chin whitish; some examples with posterior half of side with scattered small greenish yellow spots, these extending on caudal; eye with a broad brown bar through the middle, white above and below.

Color in alcohol, pale yellowish white, lighter below; body, especially posteriorly, caudal, and soft dorsal with numerous small distinct brown spots; head pale, a white line extending along upper edge of maxillary and across cheek to opercular opening, a similar but less distinct white line from eye to upper edge of gill-opening; between these 2 a few white specks; all the fins, except caudal and soft dorsal, plain yellowish white.

Four specimens of this interesting and handsome species were obtained by us, 2 at Honolulu and 2 at Hilo. Four others are in the collection made at Honolulu in 1898 by Dr. Wood, where it was also obtained by the *Albatross* in 1902.

Genus 125. CEPHALOPHOLIS Bloch & Schneider.

This genus is close to *Epinephelus*, from which it is distinguished mainly by the presence of 9 instead of 11 (or rarely 10) dorsal spines.

171. Cephalopholis argus Bloch & Schneider.   Fig. 88.

Head 2.75 to 3.25; depth 2.75 to 3; D. ix, 15 or 16; A. iii, 9; scales 9 or 10–100–33, 50 to 55 pores.

Body moderately elongate, the head rather pointed; mouth large, the lower jaw strongly projecting; maxillary extending considerably beyond eye, its tip rather wider than eye, its length 2 in head; preopercle very finely serrate, the serræ scarcely enlarged on the rounded angle; middle opercular spine never lower than upper, lower not so far back as upper; opercular flap pointed; scales of head cycloid, scales of body strongly ciliated; snout and maxillary scaly; teeth in broad bands, canines moderate; gill-rakers 8 or 9, besides rudiments below angle of arch, nearly as long as gill-fringes; third and fourth dorsal spines longest, about 3.5 in head, much shorter than soft rays; pectoral 1.8 in head; ventral 2.25, not reaching vent; second and third anal spines subequal, shorter than soft rays; caudal rounded.

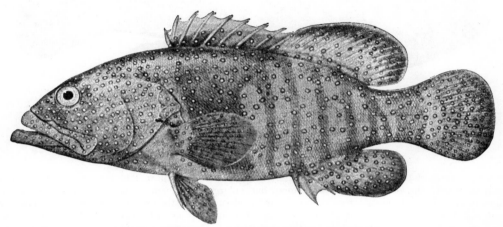

Fig. 88.—*Cephalopholis argus* Bloch & Schneider; after Günther.

Color dark purplish brown, paler posteriorly, with very faint paler and darker cross shades toward the tail; head, body, and fins covered with small blue spots ringed with black; anteriorly the spots form rows running backward and upward; below they form irregular longitudinal lines; spinous dorsal edged with bright orange; soft dorsal, anal, and caudal edged with whitish.

This species is common about the coral reefs in the south seas.   It is recorded from Hawaii by Quoy and Gaimard, but no later observer has found it about these islands.   Our description is taken from specimens from Samoa.

Genus 126. EPINEPHELUS Bloch.   The Groupers.

Body stout, compressed, covered with small, ctenoid scales, which are often somewhat embedded in the skin; scales of lateral line triangular, cycloid; soft parts of vertical fins generally more or less scaly; cranium narrow above; parietal crests not produced on frontals, which are without transverse ridge posteriorly; frontals with a process or knob on each side behind interorbital area; premaxillary processes fitting into a notch or cavity on anterior end of frontals; preopercle moderately serrate behind, its lower limb entire, without distinct antrorse spine; opercle with two strong spines; nostrils well separated; mouth large, maxillary large, with a well-developed supplemental bone, its surface usually with small scales; canine teeth few, large, in the front of the jaws; enlarged teeth of inner series of each jaw depressible; gillrakers short and rather few; dorsal spines usually 11, rarely 10, not filamentous, the last ones somewhat shorter than middle ones; anal spines 3, the second usually the larger; the number of soft rays 7 to 9; caudal fin rounded or lunate; pyloric cœca few (usually 10 to 20); pectoral rounded, shortish, nearly symmetrical, of 15 to 20 rays; ventrals moderate, inserted below pectoral, close together, each with a strong spine.   Species very numerous, most of them of large size, abounding in all the tropical seas, where they are valuable food-fishes.   This is the largest and most important genus of the *Serranidæ*, and its species are most widely distributed.

Only one species known to occur among the Hawaiian Islands.

172. Epinephelus quernus Seale.   "*Hapú'u pú'u.*"   Figs. 89 and 90 (juv).

Head 2.4 in length; depth 2.6; eye 7 in head; snout 3.6; maxillary 2; interorbital 4.65; D. xi, 15; A. iii, 9; about 130 scales in lateral line.

Body short, deep, and moderately compressed, back considerably elevated, the curve from tip of snout to caudal peduncle being quite uniform, somewhat more abrupt at origin of spinous dorsal; head large; snout moderate, pointed; mouth large at an angle of about 45° the lower jaw slightly projecting, the tip rounded; maxillary strong, reaching posterior edge of orbit; supplemental bone

FIG. 89.—*Epinephelus quernus* Seale.

present, width of tip about equaling diameter of eye; teeth in cardiform bands in jaws and on vomer and palatines, the outer row on jaws somewhat enlarged and canine-like, depressible, especially the inner series, 2 or more larger canines near tip of each jaw; tongue without teeth; eye small, in anterior half of head, and entirely above axis of body· interorbital space convex, rather broad, about half greater than eye; nostrils close together, the posterior the larger, vertically ovoid; preopercle serrate, strongest at the angle; opercle with a long, pointed soft flap and 3 flat spines, the middle the largest, closer to the lower than to the upper, lower edge of opercle serrate, branchiostegals 7; gillrakers short and stout, very blunt on short arm, 7+16; pseudobranchiæ well developed; tongue long and pointed, spoon-shaped, free along the sides and for a distance at tip greater than orbit; fins large; origin of dorsal from tip of snout about equaling length of head; dorsal spines strong, fourth and fifth longest, 2.6 in head; last dorsal spine slightly longer than snout, soft portion of dorsal somewhat elevated, rounded, the longest rays equaling snout and eye; caudal slightly rounded, the rays 1.9 in head; first anal spine short, second strong, third longest, about equaling snout; soft portion of anal

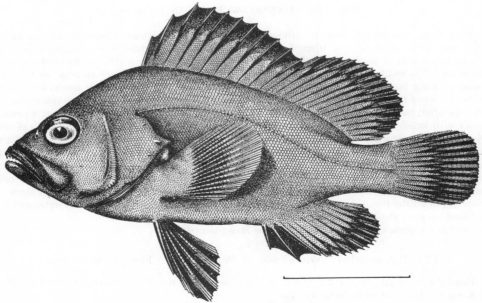

FIG. 90.—*Epinephelus quernus* Seale; from the young.

rounded, the longest ray 2.25 in head; ventrals scarcely reaching vent, 1.9 in head; pectoral broad, rounded, fan-shaped, about reaching vertical at vent, length of fin 1.75 in head; scales very small, and finely ctenoid; lateral line following curve of back, pores small; nape, opercles, and cheek densely covered with fine scales, anterior portion of interorbital and snout naked.

Color in life, nearly uniform dark-purplish brown, the fins darker on distal portions, the belly also darker; a dark shade above maxillary; irregular pearly white spots on side, arranged partly in vertical rows, the largest less than pupil, the smallest mere dots; head, nape, and whole dorsal fin more or less spotted; caudal broadly, soft dorsal and anal narrowly, edged with whitish; ventrals black; pectorals plain brown. In old examples the white spots become diffuse and disappear, the body becoming leather color, with paler blotches.

Color in alcohol, rich dark brown on head and body, sparsely covered with bluish white spots and specks; similar spots on spinous dorsal; anal and spinous dorsal narrowly edged with dirty white; caudal darkest distally, with a broad, pale border; ventrals blue-black; pectoral smoky, paler on distal portion.

This species is rather scarce in the Hawaiian markets, where very large examples, 2 to 3 feet long, are occasionally seen. Our collection contains 4 specimens, none of them full grown, from one of which—No. 03381, 15½ inches long—our life-color notes were made. This was obtained in the Honolulu market June 16, 1901, at which time 2 other specimens were obtained by us. We have 1 from Kailua, and there are 2 specimens in the collection of Dr. Jenkins obtained by Dr. Wood in 1898. The single specimen obtained by Mr. Alvin Seale, and upon which his description of the species is based, was secured by him August 9, 1901. The species was also obtained by the *Albatross* at Honolulu. Our specimens range in length from 3.75 to 16.5 inches.

There is a specimen of *Epinephelus* in the Philadelphia Academy (No. 13463, Coll. Dr. J. K. Townsend) that is probably this species. It was wrongly identified with *E. fuscoguttatus* (Forskål) by Mr. Fowler.

Genus 127. ODONTANTHIAS Bleeker.

Body strongly compressed; scales rather large, ciliated, smooth; lateral line complete, the tubes straight and extending along nearly the entire scale; mouth rather large, protractile; maxillary exposed; jaws with villiform teeth and curved canines; large, elongate patches of teeth on vomer, palatines, and tongue; head scaly, including the maxillary; preopercle serrated, without antrorse teeth on the lower border; opercle with 3 spines; gill-membranes separate; 7 branchiostegals; pseudobranchiæ present; gillrakers very long and slender; a single dorsal fin with x, 13 rays, the spinous portion a little longer than the soft; anal short, with iii, 7 rays; caudal emarginate; pectoral obtuse-pointed, subsymmetrical, rays 17; ventrals below pectorals, close together, each with a strong spine.

173. Odontanthias fuscipinnis (Jenkins). Plate XV and fig. 91.

Depth 2.5 in length; head 2.8; D. x, 17; A. iii, 7; scales, 4–47–15; P. 1.31 in head; V. about equal to head; eye 4 in head; interorbital slightly wider than eye; maxillary reaching to below middle of eye; narrowest part of preorbital a little less than 2 in eye; branchiostegals 7; gillrakers on lower arm of first branchial arch 34.

Mouth very oblique, lower jaw somewhat projecting, just entering profile; upper profile of head reentrant before the nostrils, thence to nape steep and almost straight, in one specimen rather prominently convex before the eyes; strongly bulging at nape in front of dorsal spines; profile of back straight from front of first dorsal to anterior rays of soft dorsal, from here descending to caudal peduncle, the upper edge of which is on a level with tip of snout; ventral profile less convex and less angular than upper; opercle with 2 flat spines, the upper the larger; lower part of edge of opercle serrated; angle of preopercle with 1 or 2 small spines; both vertical and horizontal margins of preopercle serrated; preorbital entire, edge of suborbital hidden by scales; teeth in sides of jaw minute, in villiform bands; 2 small canines in front of upper jaw, 2 to 6 in front of lower jaw; first dorsal spine short, less than eye; second more than twice as long as first; third nearly twice second, prominently longer than the succeeding spines; fourth spine 1.66 in the third; spines from fourth to tenth decreasing regularly in length, tenth 1.25 in fourth; soft dorsal somewhat rounded, longest rays equal to fifth spine; first anal spine a little shorter than first dorsal; third anal spine equal to second dorsal, slender and a little longer than second anal spine; soft anal short, medium rays longest, a little longer than longest rays of soft dorsal; caudal rather large, deeply forked, longest rays equal to length of head, longer than longest dorsal spine, lower lobe a little smaller than upper; ventrals longer than pectorals, about equal to head, acute, second ray longest; pectorals pointed, median rays longest; all parts of the head and body except the preorbital and jaws scaled; scales ctenoid and ciliated; lateral line strongly arched anteriorly, beginning above upper end of gill-cleft on eighth scale below the dorsal spines, the highest part on the fourth row from the back and on the twentieth from the ventral median line.

Color when fresh (No. 03461) orange-red, side and back nearly bright golden; tail and breast shaded pink; a golden stripe from eye to tip of snout, bordered all around by crimson, the crimson lines meeting across snout; lower lip crimson; chin golden; dorsal spines golden, their bases olive, the

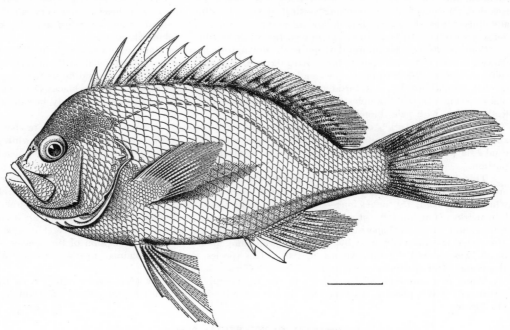

Fig. 91.—*Odontanthias fuscipinnis* (Jenkins).   Type of *Anthias fuscipinnis* Jenkins.

membranes mostly crimson; distal half of soft dorsal golden; a crimson stripe along base of dorsal, same shade covering most of lower half of fin except as replaced by dark olive-green, which forms a stripe above the crimson stripe and irregular blotches above that, leaving 2 irregular rounded spots of the crimson ground color within the green; an olive-green cross blotch at base of tail; caudal golden at tip, middle pink, outer rays bright crimson, basal half of fin mostly scarlet, the orange and red irregularly placed; pectoral shaded in gold and orange; ventrals and anal same, spines pinkish; iris golden, ringed by purple.

Color in alcohol, plain reddish yellow (red in life), dusky on scaly part of base of soft dorsal and of posterior part of spinous dorsal and about base of caudal.   Color in life pale orange-red, the dark areas clear olive-green.

This species was obtained at Honolulu (Jenkins, Wood, Jordan and Evermann, and the *Albatross*), Hilo, and Kailua.   It is taken in rather deep water, and is at times common in the Hilo market.   Our numerous specimens are 7.5 to 9.5 inches in length.

Genus 128. PSEUDANTHIAS Bleeker.

Scales small; jaws scaled; lateral line sharply angulated at base of caudal peduncle; no teeth on tongue.

174. Pseudanthias kelloggi (Jordan & Evermann).   Fig. 92.

Head 2.5 in length; depth 2.5; eye 4.5 in head; snout 3.6; maxillary 2; interorbital 5.4; D. xi, 15; A. iii, 7; P. 15; scales 4–36–10; gillrakers 16+4.

Body short, deep, and compressed; dorsal outline greatly arched, profile from origin of spinous dorsal to tip of snout nearly straight, being gently concave over interorbital space; ventral outline nearly straight; caudal peduncle compressed, its greatest depth 3 in head; head longer than deep; snout bluntly pointed, lower jaw prominent, slightly the longer; mouth large, nearly horizontal; a narrow band of small, sharp, conic teeth on palatines, a small patch on vomer, a band of cardiform teeth on upper jaw, a narrower band in lower jaw; several large canine teeth in each jaw anteriorly, 3 of these close together on middle of each side of lower jaw, these hooked backward; 6 or 8 large pores on lower side of mandible and several on upper part of snout; maxillary reaching to posterior edge of orbit, its greatest width 1.5 in eye; edge of preopercle above angle and edge of opercle below the upper middle of base of pectoral denticulate; 2 broad opercular spines, the upper the larger; eye anterior, its lower edge on line with upper base of pectoral; fins large, the second soft dorsal ray and upper rays of upper caudal lobe being produced each as a filament, the dorsal filament being produced half its length beyond rest of fin; dorsal spines stout and strong, the first spine 2.3 in third, the fifth being the highest, 2.5 in head; base of spinous dorsal 1.15 in head; base of soft dorsal 2.3 in head, its fourth ray 3.5 in head, the last ray 1.4 in fourth; caudal truncate, the lower rays produced slightly as a filament, but not nearly so long as the upper lobe; second anal spine longest, 2.5 in head; second soft ray longest, 2 in head; pectoral very long and large, reaching to origin of soft anal, the eighth and ninth rays from above the longest, 1.4 in head; scales large, finely ctenoid, in regular series; entire body and head scaled; basil portion of all fins except spinous dorsal with small scales; lateral line

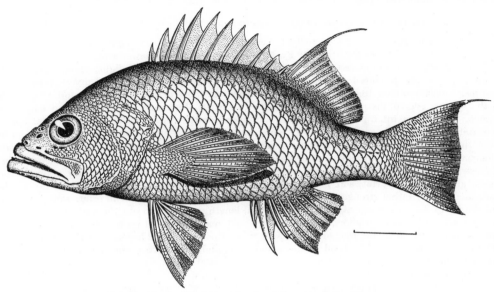

FIG. 92.—*Pseudanthias kelloggi* (Jordan & Evermann); from the type.

strongly convex, not concurrent with the dorsal profile, becoming straight on middle of caudal peduncle; one row of scales behind tip of last dorsal ray.

Color in alcohol, pale brown, the fins lighter; in life, red.

Only 3 specimens were obtained, all having been taken with the hook in deep water off Kailua, in southwestern Hawaii. They range in length from 7.75 to 8.5 inches. The species is allied to *Pseudanthias japonicus* (Steindachner & Döderlein).

Family LXI. PRIACANTHIDÆ.—The Catalufas.

Body oblong or ovate, compressed, covered with small, firm, rough scales; all parts of the body and head, even the snout and maxillaries, being densely scaly, each scale with a more or less developed plate on its posterior border, most developed in the young; head deep; mouth large, very oblique, the lower jaw prominent; villiform teeth on jaws, vomer, and palatine; none on the tongue; premaxillaries protractile; maxillary broad, without supplemental bone, not slipping under the very narrow preorbital, which is usually serrate; no suborbital stay; eye very large, forming about one-half length of side of head; posterior nostril long, slit-like, close to eye; preopercle more or less serrated, one or more strong spines at its angle; opercle very short, ending behind in 2 or 3 points; no barbels; gill-membranes separate, free from isthmus; pseudobranchiæ very large, extending along whole length of opercle; postorbital part of head very short, the opercle small; gills 4, a slit behind the fourth; gillrakers long; branchiostegals 6; lateral line continuous, not extending on caudal; dorsal fin continuous; x, 9 to 15, the spines depressible in a groove; anal II, 9 to 15; soft part long, similar to soft dorsal, spines strong, ventrals very large, thoracic, I, 5, close together, in advance of base of pectoral, joined to belly by a membrane which incloses a groove; no axillary process; spine strong; pectoral small, pointed, not symmetrical, of 19 or 20 rays, the upper longest; caudal fin truncate or lunate; spines of fins generally rough, with small serræ; air-bladder large; pyloric cœca few; vertebræ in reduced number, 9 or 10 + 13 = 22 or 23, the first vertebra being very small or absent; transverse process beginning on seventh (sixth) vertebra, the last 2 precaudal bridged across; ribs attached to the transverse processes; epipleurals absent on last 3 precaudal vertebræ; supraoccipital crest very low, continued forward to over front of orbit, where it is joined by the parietal crests; processes of premaxillaries moderate. Carnivorous fishes of the tropical seas, chiefly in deep waters; mostly rose-colored in life. The family is a sharply defined group, not close to any other, but the affinities on the whole seem to be nearest to the *Serranidæ* and their tropical allies. Genera 2, species about 10.

Only 1 genus, with 3 species, known from the Hawaiin Islands.

Genus 129. PRIACANTHUS Cuvier.

Scales very small, 80 to 100 in the lateral line; body oblong, more than twice as long as deep preopercle with a spine at angle; interorbital area externally transversely convex, the cranium itself transversely concave, the elevation being formed of flesh; a conspicuous foramen in the interorbital area; lateral line extending upward and backward from upper angle of gill-opening toward second dorsal spine, below which it changes its course, following outline of back to end of dorsal fin, thence direct to middle of caudal; anal fin rather long, its rays about III, 14; dorsal rays about x, 13. Species rather numerous in the tropical seas; 3 known from Hawaii.

175. Priacanthus alalaua Jordan & Evermann. *"Alalaua;" "Alalauwa."* Fig. 93.

Head 3.2 in length; depth 2.65; eye 2.4 in head; snout 3.6; maxillary 2; interorbital 3.8; D. x, 14; A. III, 15; scales 13–85 to 90–45, 70 pores; Br. 6; gillrakers about 22 on lower arm.

Body short, deep, compressed, ovate; upper profile of head nearly straight; snout very blunt; mandible prominent, produced; mouth very oblique; teeth small, sharp, in bands on jaws, vomer, and palatines; tongue rounded, free in front; maxillary reaching almost to front margin of pupil, its greatest width 2 in eye; edge of preopercle finely serrate, with a sharp, flat, serrated spine directed backward at angle; margins of interopercle, subopercle, and opercle entire; opercle with an obscure flat spine; interorbital space slightly convex; eye very large, its lower edge a little above base of pectoral and in line with axis of body; nostrils small, close together, the anterior with elevated rim; posterior nostril oblong, with broad flap; gillrakers rather slender, about 22 on longer arm of first arch, longest about 3 in eye; origin of spinous dorsal over upper base of pectoral; dorsal spines rather uniform, the longest about equal to orbit; soft portion of dorsal somewhat elevated, rounded, fourth ray 1.7 in head; anal spines rather stronger than those of dorsal, third the longest, 1.1 in orbit; soft portion of anal similar to that of soft dorsal, rays of about equal length; caudal truncate, the middle rays slightly greater than orbit; pectoral short, bluntly pointed, not reaching tip of ventral, length 1.4 in head; ventrals longer, just reaching base of second anal spine, their length 1.2 in head; ventral spine about 1.25 in longest ray, or 1.7 in head; scales small, firm, and rugose, those of lateral line somewhat enlarged; entire head, as well as body, densely scaled; lateral line rising abruptly for 6 or 7 pores from gill-opening, thence concurrent with back to caudal peduncle.

Color in life, silvery, light olive above, somewhat flushed with red in irregular blotches; chin red; spinous dorsal olive-yellowish, especially on edge; ventrals black, rays whitish; fins unspotted. Young of 4 inches in length are dirty gray, browner above, with no trace of red in life; some brown spots along lateral line; fins dusky, anal and ventral darkest; iris a little brownish-red.

Color in alcohol, plain yellowish-white; spinous dorsal and anal somewhat dusky; ventral mem-

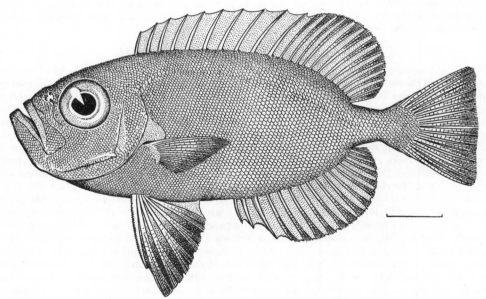

Fig. 93.—*Priacanthus alalaua* Jordan & Evermann; from the type.

branes black, the rays white, other fins pale yellowish-white. In some examples the color is much more flushed with red, especially above; the red paler and more evanescent than in the other species; fins red, unspotted; the spinous dorsal edged with golden; upper lip golden; ventral membrane black, pectoral pale.

There seems to be but little variation in this species; the younger individuals appear to be more brightly colored or with more evident wash of red than was shown in the type. We have 3 specimens, 6 to 8.25 inches long, from Honolulu; specimens were also secured by the *Albatross* at Honolulu and at Laysan Island.

173. Priacanthus cruentatus (Lacépède). "*Aweoweo*," adult; "*Alalaua*," young; "*Redfish*." Fig. 94.

Head 3 in length; depth 2.6; eye 2.4 in head; snout 3.4; maxillary 2; interorbital 3.4; D. x, 13; A. II, 14; scales 11–100–53, about 80 pores; gillrakers about 20 below angle.

Body oblong, deep, compressed, dorsal and ventral outlines evenly and similarly curved; head about as long as deep, subconic, compressed; snout bluntly pointed; lower jaw very prominent, strong and projecting; mouth moderate, oblique; bands of small, villiform teeth on jaws, vomer and palatines; gillrakers rather long and slender, about 1.5 in pupil, about 20 below angle; tongue broad, rounded and free; maxillary extending to anterior edge of pupil, its greatest width slightly more than 2 in eye; interorbital convex; eye large, its lower edge on a line with axis of body; fins moderate; origin of spinous dorsal over upper base of pectoral, the spines rather short, stout, and blunt, their anterior side rugose; last spine longest, 2.3 in head; soft dorsal rounded, longest ray 1.75 in head; caudal truncate; base of anal 2.75 in body, anterior edge of spines rugose; longest spine 2.6 in head, longest ray 1.9 in head; anterior edge of ventral spine rugose, its length 1.75 in head, longest ray slightly longer than spine, reaching to first anal spine; pectoral short, broad, longest ray 1.9 in head, not reaching as far posteriorly as the ventrals; scales small, very rough, the exposed portion triangular, with a re-entrant angle on anterior side, the posterior edges strongly toothed; lateral line complete, rising abruptly for 4 pores from gill-opening, then turning sharply, following approximately the curvature of the back, a little more distant under soft dorsal, turning in a broad angle at base of caudal peduncle, along the middle of which it follows to base of caudal; preorbital toothed or rugose on both edges; preopercle strongly toothed, with a strong rugose toothed sharp or blunt spine at the angle, this spine varying much in different individuals; lower edge of opercle toothed.

Another example was bright red in life, mottled with silvery white; dark red color forming about 6 vertical bars on side of back alternating with fainter bars; dorsal and caudal rosy, spotted with blood red, spots small, smallest and most distinct on caudal; pectoral and ventrals rosy; iris without dark spots or dark shading; iris and jaws deep red. In some examples the dark spots are large.

Color in alcohol, plain yellowish white, dusky above, silvery below, fins all yellowish white; spinous dorsal somewhat dusky; soft dorsal, anal and caudal with numerous small dark (blood red) spots on the membranes, their edges narrowly black.

The above description taken chiefly from a specimen (No. 03166) 10.5 inches long from Honolulu.

Color in life (note by Dr. Jenkins), head and body made up of mottlings of bright red and white; iris white with bright red blotches; dorsal mottled with red and white and covered on posterior portion with more or less distinct red; anal similar in color to dorsal; caudal red with rows of distinct darker red spots on membranes; pectoral pale red; ventral white, with red mottlings; inside of mouth white, with bright red blotches.

Color in life (Porto Rican specimens), body silvery, washed with rosy; back with 5 or 6 saddle-like blotches extending on side to below lateral line; under parts rosy; vertical fins with pale bases, brighter distally; caudal black-edged; pectoral and ventral rosy, the ventrals black-tipped.

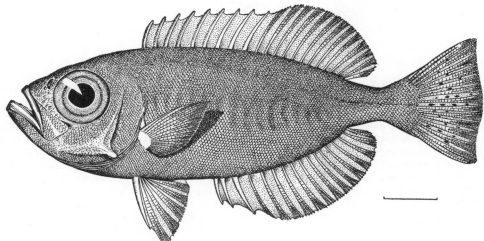

FIG. 94.—*Priacanthus cruentatus* (Lacépède).

We have compared our numerous specimens with others from the Galapagos and West Indies and can detect no differences. The Pacific species, *P. carolinus*, can not be distinguished from the West Indian species, *P. cruentatus*.

This is a species of wide distribution, having been recorded from St. Helena and the Canaries, the West Indies, the Galapagos, and the Hawaiian Islands. In the West Indies it is known as ojon, ojudo, and catalufa. Among the English-speaking people it is called big-eye. Streets says of the young:

"During the month of September, 1873, an immense shoal of the young of this species entered the harbor of Honolulu. The largest of them did not exceed 3½ inches in length. This shoaling, we were told, has occurred a number of times, but at uncertain intervals. The coming of the 'red-fish,' as they are called, foreshadows in the minds of the simple natives the sickness and death of some member of the royal family; and, on account of the pliant disposition of the Kanakas, the prophecy is usually fulfilled. But the fish are by no means unwelcome visitants to the common people, who are busy catching them night and day as long as they remain. They are dried and eaten without cooking."

This fish seems to be very abundant among the Hawaiian Islands and is represented in our collections by a fine series of 33 specimens, ranging in length from 4 to 11.75 inches; of these, 7 were collected by Dr. Jenkins at Honolulu in 1889. Specimens were obtained by us at Honolulu, Hilo, Napoopoo, and Kailua, but none was obtained by the Albatross.

177. Priacanthus meeki Jenkins. *"Ula lau au."* Fig. 95.

Head 3.4 in length; depth 2.8; eye 2.3 in head; snout 3.6; interorbital 4; maxillary 2; mandible 1.8; D. x, 14; A. iii, 15; scales 12–115–45; gillrakers 2+27.

Body oblong, compressed, the dorsal and ventral outlines about equally curved; head large, snout blunt, the anterior profile straight from tip of snout to nape; mouth large, very oblique, the lower jaw projecting, its anterior edge in line with profile from snout to nape; maxillary reaching anterior edge of pupil, its tip broad, nearly half eye; teeth on jaws, vomer and palatines in strong villiform bands, many of those on jaw somewhat enlarged; gillrakers rather long, about 2 in eye, their number

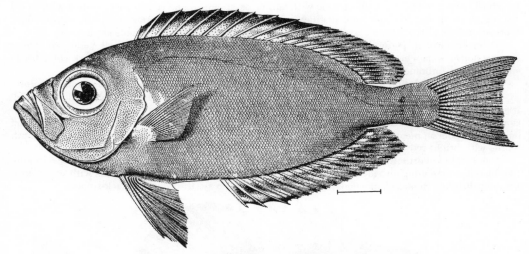

FIG. 95.—*Priacanthus meeki* Jenkins; from the type.

about 2+27; eye very large, its lower edge slightly below axis of body; interorbital space moderate, convex; opercle with a weak flat spine; preopercle serrate, without spine, weak and obscure except in young, where it is better developed; preorbital rough-edged; fins rather large, origin of spinous dorsal over base of pectoral; longest dorsal spine about 1.6 in head, soft portion of dorsal rounded, longest ray 1.5 in head; longest anal spine 1.8 in head, anal high, longest ray 1.3 in head; caudal rather deeply lunate, outer rays nearly equal to head, the middle ray 1.5 in the outer, upper lobe somewhat the longer; pectorals short, not reaching tips of ventrals, 1.5 in head; ventrals long, pointed, reaching base of third anal spine, 1 in head; scales small and rough, the free portion narrowly lunate, concave anteriorly, the posterior edge roughened; lateral line rising in a regular curve from gill-opening to about the tenth pore, then following contour of back to base of caudal.

Color in life, deep red, darker than any other species of *Priacanthus*, without trace of dark crossbands or round rosy spots; a row of about 15 roundish dusky spots, very faint along lateral line; fins deep red, unspotted, the dorsal and anal edged with dusky; caudal mesially dusky edged; ventrals with black membranes, pectoral paler rosy; inside of mouth deep orange red.

Color in alcohol, dusky silvery, darkest above, palest on belly; head dusky, snout and lower jaw blotched and spotted with darker; dorsal and anal fins pale, with dusky or black on some of the membranes and narrowly edged with black, in some specimens the black very marked; caudal pale, edged with black; ventrals black at tips; pectorals pale. Smaller examples 4 to 5 inches long are, in spirits, much darker, being dark brown covered with darker coffee-colored specks; all the fins except pectorals black.

The above description is based chiefly upon a specimen (No. 03396) 11.75 inches long, from Honolulu.

This species seems to be close to *Priacanthus hamruhr*, from which it differs chiefly in the greater depth of the body, the color, and much greater length of the dorsal and anal rays, and in the smaller scales. In current descriptions of *P. hamruhr*, the depth of the body is said to be nearly equal to the length of the head; in our specimens it greatly exceeds the length of the head.

This species appears to be an important food-fish at Honolulu and is fairly abundant. Our collections contain an excellent series of 9 specimens from Honolulu and 6 from Hilo. We have also examined the type, taken at Honolulu by Dr. Jenkins, and the 2 cotypes, collected also at Honolulu by Dr. Wood. These specimens range from 4 to 12.5 inches in length.

Family LXII. LUTIANIDÆ.—The Snappers.

Body oblong or more or less elevated, covered with moderate-sized adherent scales, which are more or less strongly ctenoid or almost cycloid; lateral line well developed, concurrent with the back, not extending on the caudal fin; head large, the crests on the skull usually largely developed; no suborbital stay; mouth moderate or large, usually terminal, low and horizontal; premaxillaries moderately protractile, their spines not extending to the occiput; maxillary long, without supplemental bone, for most of its length slipping under the edge of the preorbital, which forms a more or less distinct sheath, its form essentially as in the *Serranidæ;* teeth various, unequal and sharp, never incisor-like, some of them sometimes molar; vomer and palatines usually with villiform teeth, these sometimes molar, sometimes very small, sometimes wanting; lower pharyngeals separate; gills 4, a slit behind the fourth; pseudobranchiæ large; gillrakers moderate or long, slender; gill-membranes separate, free from the isthmus; preopercle serrate or entire; opercles without spines; sides of head usually scaly; dorsal fin single, continuous, or deeply notched, sometimes divided into 2 fins, the spines usually strong, depressible in a groove, the spines heteracanthous—that is, alternating, the one stronger on the right side, the other on the left, the spines 10 to 12 in number; anal fin similar to soft dorsal and with 3 spines; ventral fins thoracic, the rays i, 5, with a more or less distinct scale-like appendage at base; caudal fin usually more or less concave behind; air-bladder present, usually simple; intestinal canal short; pyloric cœca few; vertebræ usually 10+14=24; no distinct tubercles from the cranium for the articulation of the epipharyngeal bones; enlarged apophyses for the articulation of palatine and preorbital bones; anterior 4 vertebræ without parapophyses. This family comprises about 20 genera and some 250 species, chiefly inhabiting the shores of warm regions. All of them are valued as food, and all are active, carnivorous and voracious. The group is closely related to the *Serranidæ* on the one hand, and to the *Hæmulidæ* on the other.

Of the many genera of this family only 6 are known to have representatives in Hawaiian waters.

Genus 130. APSILUS Cuvier & Valenciennes. The Arnillos.

Body rather short and stout; teeth on palatines, vomer and jaws in villiform bands, those in outer series on both jaws enlarged and canine-like; no teeth on tongue, or very minute if present; last ray of dorsal and anal much or little produced; preopercle somewhat serrate; interorbital not flat; dorsal fin continuous; branchiostegals 7.

This genus has essentially the cranial structures of *Rhomboplites*, with the scaleless fins, peculiar squamation, and dentition of *Aprion*. The prefrontals have the posterior areas solid and somewhat tumid; the dorsal fin is short and scaleless.

178: Apsilus brighami (Seale). "*Ukikiki;*" *Kalikali.* Plate XVI.

Head 3 in length; depth 3; eye 4 in head; snout 2.75; maxillary 2.3; mandible 2; interorbital 4.1; preorbital 6.75; scales 7–67–15; D. x, 11; A. iii, 8; Br. 7; gillrakers short and broad, 11+4, those on shorter arm very blunt except lower one, longest a little greater than pupil.

Body rather short, stout, and moderately compressed; head large, bluntly conic; snout rather long, bluntly pointed; mouth large, slightly oblique; maxillary reaching anterior edge of pupil; lower jaw slightly the shorter; teeth on jaws, vomer and palatines in villiform bands, those in outer series on jaws enlarged and canine-like, the anterior ones largest; tip of maxillary greater than pupil, slipping under the rather broad preorbital; eye moderate, entirely above axis of body; interorbital smooth, convex; opercle ending in 2 flat, weak spines; preopercle serrate; preorbital smooth; caudal peduncle deep, compressed, its least width half its depth, which is equal to snout; fins rather large; origin of dorsal over base of pectoral, midway between tip of snout and base of fifth dorsal ray, first dorsal spine short, about 1.6 in second, fourth and fifth spines longest, a little greater than snout, last dorsal spine slightly shorter than second; last dorsal ray somewhat produced, about 2.25 in head, or a third longer than first ray; first anal spine short, about 1.9 in eye, or 2 in second anal; third anal spine slightly greater than eye; last anal ray equal to last dorsal; caudal moderately forked, lobes about equal, their length 1.25 in head; pectoral rather long, slightly falcate, the tip reaching origin of anal, the length nearly equaling that of head; ventrals long and pointed, reaching slightly past vent, their length 1.4 in head; scales rather small, firm, the lateral line well developed; cheek and opercles scaled; a row of modified plate-like scales from humeral plate to nape, in front of which is a patch of ordinary scales; soft dorsal and anal without scales; caudal finely scaled.

Color in life (from No. 03735), upper half of body with 4 broad yellow bands, last one extending to base of caudal, between these are 3 light red bands nearly as broad as the yellow ones; lower half of body yellow, the edge of scales here tinged with red; head and snout bright golden-red; opercles light red; jaw reddish; upper lip golden reddish, lower reddish; dorsal bright yellow, same as yellow bands on body; margin of soft dorsal tipped with reddish; caudal yellow, with reddish tinge, end yellow, upper and lower edges reddish; anal membrane faint golden red, rays faint red; ventrals pale, tinged with red; pectoral membrane pale, rays light yellow; axil golden reddish.

Color in alcohol, pale yellowish white, pale below, head slightly dusky, fins all pale yellowish white, tips of ventrals slightly dusky.

The life color of the type specimen, as given by Mr. Seale, was as follows: Ground color, pinkish white; 3 distinct wide yellow bands, as wide as interspaces, extending obliquely downward and backward on side of body, the first from the nape to a little posterior of axis of pectoral, the second from third to sixth dorsal spines ending above and anterior to vent on a line with lower base of pectoral, the third from eighth dorsal spine to third dorsal ray ending above and on a line with the fifth to eighth anal rays, behind this last band, above the lateral line, a wash of yellowish reaching to base of caudal; dorsal fin cadmium-yellow; caudal fin yellow, the upper lobe with pink tint; pectoral pinkish; ventrals and anal white; side of head and jaws with a few deeper splotches of pinkish, iris whitish, the pupil deep blue. In spirits the yellow bands fade so that the interspaces show more distinctly than the bands, the color becomes also a deeper pinkish, the fins whitish.

The above description is based chiefly upon a specimen (No. 04110) 15 inches long, obtained by us in Honolulu in the early part of August, 1901; 2 other specimens were obtained by Messrs. Goldsborough and Sindo at Kailua, August 10. A single specimen was obtained by Dr. Jenkins in 1889, and another by the *Albatross* in 1902.

The specimen described by Mr. Seale was obtained by him in Honolulu in October, 1901. The species is a typical *Apsilus*. Mr. Seale's error in placing it in the family *Serranidæ* instead of *Lutianidæ* was apparently due to his misinterpretation of the relation of the maxillary to the preorbital. The maxillary is well covered by the preorbital.

This species does not seem to be abundant, but is a good food-fish. It reaches a length of about 1.5 feet, and is an inhabitant of the deeper waters, 2 of the specimens that we have examined having the stomachs everted.

179. Apsilus microdon (Steindachner). *"Opakapaka."*

Head 3.1 in length; depth 3.5; eye 4 in head; snout 3; maxillary 2.6; mandible 2.1; preorbital 8; interorbital 3.1; Br. 7; gillrakers about 16 + 5; D. x, 11; A. iii, 8; scales 8–61–14.

Body moderately short, stout, and compressed; head large, longer than deep; snout bluntly conic; mouth rather large, slightly oblique, the maxillary reaching pupil, slipping for its entire length under the rather broad preorbital, its width at tip equal to diameter of pupil, jaws equal; bands of villiform teeth on jaws, vomer, and palatines, the outer series on jaws scarcely enlarged, scarcely canine-like, except a pair on front of upper jaw; no teeth on tongue; opercle ending in 2 flat, weak spines, the space between them deeply emarginate; preopercle somewhat serrate; eye moderate, its lower edge in line with axis of body; interorbital slightly convex, very broad; caudal peduncle short, its length from base of last dorsal ray to first supporting caudal rays 2.3 in head, its least width about 2.5 in its least depth, which is slightly greater than eye, or 3.6 in head; dorsal fin beginning over base of pectoral, its origin midway between tip of snout and base of fifth ray, distance from origin of dorsal to base of first supporting caudal rays twice length of head; first dorsal spine very short, about 1.7 in pupil, or 3.25 in second spine; fifth dorsal spine longest, about equal to snout; last dorsal ray produced, its length 1.5 times that of preceding ray; origin of anal under base of fourth dorsal ray; first anal spine short, its length about half that of second, anal spines all weak, the third longest, its length slightly less than diameter of eye; produced anal ray similar to that of dorsal; caudal deeply forked, the lobes about equaling length of head; ventrals moderate, not reaching vent, their length 1.6 in head; pectoral somewhat longer, its tip reaching slightly past tips of ventrals, its length 1.25 in head; scales rather small, firm, deeper than long; lateral line well developed, beginning at base of humeral plate and following contour of back to base of caudal; cheek and opercles scaled; a series of modified scales from bony opercular scale to nape, in front of which is a patch of normal scales.

Color in life (No. 03008), back and upper part of side violet brown, with bright reflections; lower part of side and belly silvery; faint brassy stripes separated by obscure bluish ones along middle of side; head color of back; cheek and suborbital silvery, with dusky wash; dorsal purplish, with 3 series of large yellow blotches forming 3 lines; caudal dusky and greenish, the middle rays yellowish; pectoral, anal, and ventrals white; iris greenish yellow.

Color in spirits, dusky or olivaceous brown above, paler on sides and below; belly somewhat dusky; each scale on back and upper part of side with a chocolate-brown triangular area, these forming indistinct longitudinal lines; membrane of dorsal fin dusky purplish, all other fins pale.

The above description based upon a specimen (No. 6081) 10 inches long, collected at Honolulu by Dr. Wood. We have 10 specimens from Honolulu, 1 from Hilo, and 1 from Kailua. Dr. Jenkins had 2 specimens obtained at Honolulu by Dr. Wood, and the species was also found by the *Albatross* at Honolulu. It is known only from the Hawaiian Islands, where it is a common food-fish in the markets, reaching a length of 2 feet.

Genus 131. APHAREUS Cuvier & Valenciennes.

Body long and slender; vomer, palatines, and tongue without teeth; teeth in each jaw in a narrow, villiform band, none enlarged or canine-like; last dorsal and anal rays much produced; preopercle entire; interorbital convex; dorsal fin not notched; branchiostegals 7.

This genus is related to *Apsilus*, from which it differs chiefly in the dentition.

180. Aphareus flavivultus Jenkins. Fig. 96.

Head 3.3 in length; depth 3.4; eye 4.4 in head; snout 3.1; maxillary 1.9; mandible 1.65; interorbital 3.2; preorbital 6.5; Br. 7; gillrakers 16 + 5; D. x, 11; A. iii, 8; scales 9–72–17.

Body long and slender, considerably compressed, the dorsal and ventral outlines beautifully curved from tip of snout to caudal peduncle, greatest depth at the origin of dorsal fin; head rather long, conic; snout long; mouth very large, somewhat oblique, the maxillary slipping for its entire length and most of its width under the broad preorbital, reaching posterior border of pupil; lower jaw long and strong, its tip projecting and entering into anterior profile; vomer, palatines, and tongue toothless; teeth in jaws in a narrow, villiform band, none enlarged; eye moderate, its lower border in line with axis of body; opercle smooth, without developed spines; preopercle not dentate, only slightly

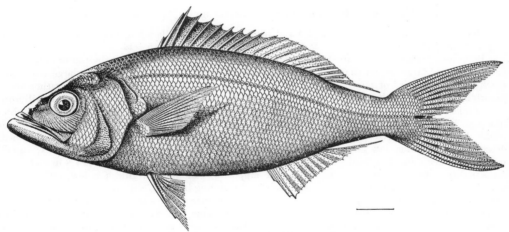

FIG. 96.—*Aphareus flavivultus* Jenkins; from the type.

crenulate; caudal peduncle long, its length from base of last dorsal ray to base of first supporting caudal rays equal to snout and eye, its least width about 2.5 in its least depth, which is slightly less than snout; fins small, the dorsal continuous, its origin slightly behind base of pectoral and equidistant between tip of snout and base of seventh soft ray; third dorsal spine longest, slightly greater than snout; last dorsal ray produced, its length about 2.4 times that of preceding ray; anal similar to soft dorsal, its origin under base of about fourth dorsal ray; third anal spine longest, slender, its length 3.8 in head; last anal ray much produced, its length equal to that of last dorsal ray; caudal widely forked, the lower lobe slightly the longer, its length somewhat greater than that of head; ventrals rather pointed, not nearly reaching vent, about 1.75 in head; pectoral long, somewhat falcate, upper rays produced, about 1.2 in head; scales small, moderately firm, covering entire body, nape, cheek, and opercles; a modified humeral scale from which a line of modified scales extends to occiput, in front of which is a patch of ordinary scales; scales on cheek in 6 rows, those on opercle in 9 rows; lateral line beginning at lower edge of humeral scale, very slightly arched, following closely curvature of back to base of middle caudal ray; soft dorsal and anal naked; caudal with fine scales.

Color in life, dirty violet, edges of scales brownish; lower side and under parts somewhat paler; head dirty violet or purplish; dorsal brownish red at base, yellowish olive and rosy on outer half; caudal greenish olive, edged with reddish purple; anal white at base, somewhat dusky, a large brassy yellow blotch on anterior part of fin, posteriorly dirty rosy; ventrals purplish and greenish yellow; pectoral pale rosy; iris yellowish rosy white.

This species is not common among the Hawaiian Islands, only 11 specimens having been obtained in that region by collectors.   It differs from *Aphareus furcatus* in form and otherwise.

According to Dr. Jenkins, the color of the top of the head was very distinct in life in the examples obtained by him in 1889.   None of our specimens showed any yellow on the face.   An examination of Dr. Jenkins's specimens shows that this color has entirely faded, so that no character remains by which his specimens can be distinguished from ours.

Besides the 5 specimens from Honolulu and Kona, Hawaii, in Dr. Jenkins's collection, we have 2 from Honolulu, 2 from Kailua, and 1 from Hilo.   One was also obtained by the *Albatross* at Honolulu. The species is known only from the Hawaiian Islands.

Length 4.5 to 15 inches.

Genus 132. BOWERSIA Jordan & Evermann.

Body long, rather slender and moderately compressed; top of head evenly rounded, the supra-occipital crest extending forward on cranium; jaws equal, lower not projecting; bands of villiform teeth on both jaws, the outer series somewhat enlarged and canine-like; villiform teeth on vomer, palatines, and tongue; maxillary slipping for its entire length under the rather broad preorbital; eye large; opercle entire, ending in 2 flat, obscure spines, the space between them deeply emarginate, but filled by soft membrane; preopercle scarcely dentate; dorsal fin continuous, the last ray produced, nearly twice length of preceding one.

This genus is related to *Apsilus*, with which it agrees in the presence of villiform teeth on the vomer and palatines, but from which it differs in having well-developed teeth on the tongue, and in the produced last dorsal and anal ray.   Two species are known.

"We take much pleasure in naming this new genus for the Hon. George M. Bowers, United States Commissioner of Fish and Fisheries, in recognition of his active and intelligent interest in promoting scientific work, especially the investigation of the aquatic resources of the Hawaiian Islands."

181. Bowersia violescens Jordan & Evermann.   "*Opakapaka.*"   Fig. 97.

Head 3.25 in length; depth 3.5; eye 4.4 in head; snout 3; maxillary 2.6; mandible 2; interorbital 3; preorbital 7.75; scales 8–60–15; D. x, 10; A. iii, 8; Br. 7; gillrakers 5+14.

Body long, rather slender, moderately compressed, tapering gradually into the rather long caudal peduncle; head large, longer than deep; snout moderate, rather bluntly conic; mouth large, maxillary reaching anterior third of pupil, slipping for its entire length under the thin edge of the rather broad preorbital, the width of its tip 2 in eye; mandible strong, but not projecting; broad bands of villiform teeth on jaws, vomer, palatines, and tongue, the outer series in the jaws slightly enlarged and canine-like; eye large, its lower edge in line with axis of body; interorbital broad, gently convex; anterior profile but slightly curved from tip of snout to nape, thence more strongly arched to origin of dorsal, descending in a long, low curve to caudal peduncle; ventral outline but slightly convex; caudal peduncle rather long, 2 in head, its least width about 1.6 in its least depth, which is 1.8 in its length, measured from base of last dorsal ray to base of supporting caudal rays; gillrakers few, rather strong and short, the longest about 2.6 in eye; opercle smooth, ending in 2 flat, obscure spines (more strongly developed in each of the cotypes); preopercle obscurely serrate at the angle (more distinctly so in the cotypes); fins moderately developed, the dorsal fin continuous, without notch, its origin over base of pectoral and equally distant from tip of snout and base of fourth ray, length of entire base of fin and

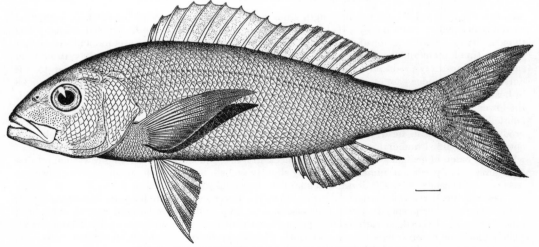

Fig. 97.—*Bowersia violescens* Jordan & Evermann; from the type.

to tip of last ray twice length of head; first dorsal spine moderately short, closely bound to the second, whose length exceeds it by about one-half; seventh dorsal spine longest, its length equal to that of snout; last dorsal ray produced, its length about 1.7 times that of the preceding; anal similar to soft dorsal, its origin under base of third or fourth dorsal ray; first anal spine very short, third longest and strongest, its length equaling diameter of eye; last anal ray produced, its length equaling that of produced dorsal ray; caudal rather widely forked, lobes about equal, their length, measured from base of first supporting ray, equaling head; ventrals pointed, their tips not reaching vent, length 1.4 in head; pectoral long, slightly falcate, the tip about reaching tips of ventrals, its length about 1.2 in head; scales large, deeper than long and rather loose; cheek and opercles scaled, 5 rows on cheek; a large bony humeral scale, from which extends to nape a series of somewhat modified scales, in front of which is a patch of ordinary scales; lateral line complete and well developed, beginning at lower edge of humeral scale and following curvature of back to base of middle caudal rays; the pores little or not at all branched.

Color in life (field No. 03404), light rosy olive, with violet shades, pale below; center of each scale of back shining violet; dorsal reddish flesh-color, its base anteriorly yellowish olive; caudal flesh-color, rosy along the edges; anal similar, its edge light lavender gray; ventrals pale, shaded with light orange; pectoral flesh-color, violaceous at base; snout violet, iris light yellow. A flesh-colored violaceous fish without color markings anywhere. Another specimen (field No. 03417) freshly dead, had the body, head, and caudal light rosy; ventrals white; outer margin of spinous dorsal golden, the membranes with irregular golden areas; pectoral and anal not distinctly colored; iris yellow.

Color in alcohol of type (field No. 03018), above dusky silvery, bases of scales brown; sides and under parts silvery, with pale greenish-yellow tinge; top of head somewhat olivaceous, sides rusty silvery; axil of pectoral dusky; fins all pale or yellowish-white.

This species reaches a length of about 2 feet and is an important food-fish.

Our 4 specimens, all from Hololulu, are each about 2 feet in length.

182. Bowersia ulaula Jordan & Evermann. *"Ulaula;" "Koá'e."* Fig. 98.

Head 3.6 in length; depth 3.8; eye 3.8 in head; snout 3.8; maxillary 2.9; mandible 2.4; interorbital 3.6; preorbital 10; scales 8–68–14; D. x, 11; A. iii, 8; Br. 7; gillrakers 21 + 5.

Body long and slender, the dorsal outline in a low, gentle curve from tip of snout to base of caudal, the ventral outline but gently convex; head moderate, bluntly conic; snout rather short; mouth moderate, somewhat oblique, the jaws equal; maxillary moderate, slipping for its entire length under the narrow, thin preorbital, its width at tip 2.8 in eye; bands of villiform teeth on vomer, palatines, tongue and jaws, those of outer series in the latter scarcely enlarged; opercle ending in 2 obscure, flat spines, the space between them deeply emarginate but filled by membrane; preopercle rather distinctly serrate, the teeth very short; eye rather large, its lower border in line with axis of body; preorbital very narrow, much narrower than in *B. violescens;* interorbital space narrower than in the preceding species, slightly convex; caudal peduncle long, its length from base of last dorsal ray to first supporting rays of caudal 1.7 in head, its least width about 2.1 in its least depth, which is 2.1 in its length; gillrakers rather numerous, close-set, the longest about 2.2 in eye; fins moderately developed, the dorsal continuous, without notch, its origin slightly behind base of pectoral and equally distant between tip of snout and base of fifth or sixth dorsal ray; head 2 in distance from origin of anal to middle of last dorsal ray; first dorsal spine rather short, about 1.9 in length of second; fifth dorsal spine longest, its length equal to distance from tip of snout to pupil; last dorsal ray produced, its length about 1.8 times that of the preceding; anal similar to soft dorsal, its origin under base of third dorsal ray; first anal spine very short, the third longest, its length 1.2 in diameter of eye; soft anal similar to soft dorsal, the last ray

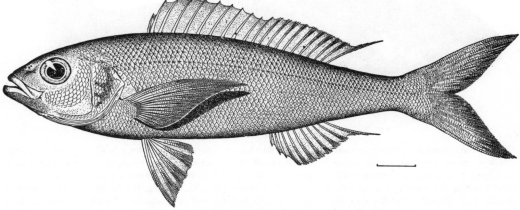

FIG. 98.—*Bowersia ulaula* Jordan & Evermann; from the type.

produced and of equal length with that of dorsal; caudal densely scaled and widely forked, lobes equal, their length, measured from base of first supporting rays equaling that of head; ventrals not pointed, their tips not reaching vent, their length 1.6 in head; pectoral long, slightly falcate, its tip reaching vent and much beyond that of ventral, its length equaling that of head; scales rather small, closely imbricated, deeper than long, their edges finely ciliated; cheek and opercles scaled, 6 rows on cheek; a large bony humeral scale from which extends a series of modified scales to nape, and in front of which is a patch of ordinary scales; lateral line complete and well developed, beginning at lower edge of humeral scale and following contour of back to base of middle caudal rays, the tubes little branched.

Color in alcohol, brownish or purplish olivaceous above, paler on side; under parts nearly plain white; each scale of back and upper part of side with a darker brown spot, these forming indistinct rows, about 6 above lateral line; side below lateral line with less distinct horizontal lines; upper parts of head olivaceous brown, lower parts paler, spines of dorsal fin purplish, the membranes white, purplish at tips; soft dorsal with rays whitish, membranes purplish; caudal slightly dusky, other fins plain whitish.

This species is related to *B. violescens*, from which it differs chiefly in the shorter snout, larger eye, shorter maxillary, shorter mandible, narrower interorbital space, decidedly smaller scales, more numerous gillrakers, and more posterior insertion of dorsal fin. Only one specimen known, type No. 50661, U. S. N. M. (field No. 04104), 14.25 inches long, from Hilo, Hawaii Island.

Genus 133. APRION Cuvier & Valenciennes.

Body oblong or elongate, compressed; scales large; mouth rather small; villiform teeth on vomer, palatines and jaws, outer series on jaws somewhat enlarged and canine-like; no teeth on tongue; preopercle entire; interorbital flat; last ray of dorsal and anal somewhat produced; dorsal continuous, not notched; skull essentially as in *Etelis*, the flat interorbital area separated from the occipital by a transverse line of demarcation by which the median as well as the lateral crests are limited; frontals wide in front, and not cavernous; supraorbital margin crenate; periotic region much swollen outward and with the bones thin and polished; frontals behind with funnel-shaped foramina; preorbital moderate.

Aprion has essentially the form of *Lutianus* with the skull of *Etelis*. The single American species (*A. macrophthalmus*) belongs to the subgenus *Chætopterus*, which agrees with *A. virescens* in the form of the skull, differing chiefly in the specific characters of deeper body, weaker teeth, and narrower preorbital. Species few; only one known from the Hawaiian Islands.

183. Aprion virescens Cuvier & Valenciennes. "*Uku.*" Fig. 99.

Head 3.2 in length; depth 4.1; eye 5.4 in head; snout 2.2; maxillary 2.45; mandible 2; preorbital 4.8; interorbital 3; Br. 7; D. x, 11; A. ii or iii, 8; scales 8–49–13.

Body long, slender, and moderately compressed, the dorsal and ventral outlines gently curved; head large, much larger than deep: snout long and bluntly conic; mouth large, somewhat oblique, the maxillary reaching orbit, slipping for its entire length under the broad preorbital, its width at tip about 1.75 in eye; jaws co-terminous, the lower projecting somewhat in the young; eye rather high up, considerably above the axis of the body; interorbital space broad and flat; opercle ending in one

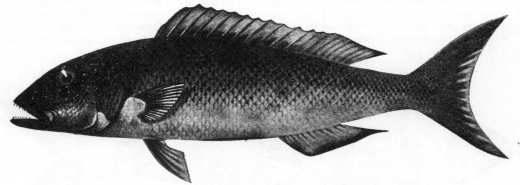

FIG. 99.—*Aprion virescens* Cuvier & Valenciennes; after Bleeker.

broad, flat, obscure spine; preopercle smooth; caudal peduncle long, its length slightly greater than that of snout, its least width about 1.75 in its least depth, which is 4 in head; dorsal fin continuous, not greatly notched, its origin behind base of pectoral, and midway between tip of snout and base of third dorsal ray: distance from origin of dorsal to base of first supporting caudal rays twice length of head; first dorsal ray short and slender, its length not exceeding diameter of pupil, fourth or fifth dorsal ray longest, about 3 in head, last dorsal ray produced, about one-third longer than preceding;

first anal spine small, obscure, or entirely absent in large examples; third anal spine weak, its length less than diameter of eye; soft portion of anal similiar to that of dorsal: caudal widely forked, the lower lobe sometimes the longer, its length a little shorter than that of head; ventrals short, reaching scarcely half way to origin of anal, 1.9 in head; pectoral very short and broad, the length about 2.75 in head; scales loose, large, somewhat deeper than long; lateral line fully developed and concurrent with the back; cheek and opercles scaled, 5 rows on cheek; anal and soft dorsal naked; caudal scaled

Color in life (No. 03411), uniform light gray, the upper parts tinged with blue, which, on top of head to snout and about eye, becomes distinct dark blue, without distinct outline, gradually disappearing toward lower parts; lower parts much lighter, becoming almost white on ventral line; 3 indistinct dusky spots on membranes of dorsal between seventh and tenth spines (one between each two); no other distinct markings on dorsal, but a tinge of yellow over the whole; ventral rays white, membranes yellow; anal whitish; caudal unmarked.

Color in alcohol of some specimens, dusky-bluish above and on sides, whitish below; head with some purplish; spinous dorsal with the membrane dusky at tips, 3 black spots on membranes between seventh and tenth spines; soft dorsal, caudal and anal dusky, ventrals white, dusky at tips; pectoral dusky.

This fish is common about Honolulu, being brought into the market almost every day. It is one of the best of food-fishes. The above description, based chiefly upon (No. 03411) a specimen 2 feet long, obtained in the Honolulu market. We have 17 excellent specimens from Honolulu, Hilo, and Kailua, and others were obtained at Honolulu by Dr. Jenkins and the *Albatross*. This species is known not only from the Hawaiian Islands, but also from the Society Islands, Macassar, Celebes, Ternate, and Amboyna. Length 7 to 24 inches.

Genus 134. ETELIS Cuvier & Valenciennes.

Body elongate, covered with large scales; eye very large; preopercle ending in 2 short, flat lobes, hardly points; preorbital very narrow; mouth moderate, the lower jaw projecting; canines in upper jaw only, villiform teeth on vomer and palatines; no teeth on tongue or pterygoids; gillrakers long and slender; dorsal fin deeply notched, rather short, its spines 10 in number, its soft rays not scaly; caudal very deeply forked; head naked above, skull with the interorbital area flat, separated from the occipital area by a transverse line, limiting the median and lateral crests also; frontals wide in front, not cavernous, simply normally perforate; supraorbital margins crenate; periotic region little convex, and with the bones thick, unpolished; prefrontals behind, with funnel-shaped foramina; caudal deeply forked; dorsal spines 10, the last shortest, the membrane falling far short of the ray following. In spite of the difference in the form of its dorsal, the relations of *Etelis* with *Aprion* are very close. The skulls in the 2 are almost identical, as has already been noticed by Poey and Gill.

184. Etelis marshi (Jenkins). "*Ulaula.*" Plate XVII and Fig. 100.

Head 3 in length; depth 3.5; eye 4 in head; snout 3.4; preorbital 7; maxillary 2; mandible 1.8; interorbital 3.9; D. x, 11; A. iii, 8; scales 6–51–11; Br. 7; gillrakers 3+9.

Body rather long, tapering, moderately compressed; the dorsal and ventral outlines gently convex; head rather large, bluntly pointed; snout bluntly pointed, slightly greater than eye; jaws subequal, the lower slightly projecting, its tip entering into the anterior rounded profile; maxillary long, reaching past middle of orbit, its width at tip equal to vertical diameter of pupil; mouth rather large, somewhat oblique; teeth on jaws, vomer, and palatines, those on jaws in villiform bands; an outer series of enlarged, sparse-set canines in each jaw, the one in front on each side longest, those of upper jaw somewhat stronger than those in the lower; tongue without teeth; eye large, its horizontal diameter slightly the greater; interorbital space flat, with a broad median groove, the ridges on each side somewhat roughened; preorbital thin, its edge smooth; opercle ending in 2 broad flat spines; preopercle finely dentate, teeth strongest at the angle, but no spines especially enlarged; gillrakers few, moderate in length, the longest about 3 in eye, the number about 3+9; fins moderately developed; dorsal fin deeply notched, almost divided into 2 fins; origin of spinous dorsal posterior to base of pectoral, its distance from tip of snout equal to distance to base of fifth dorsal ray; first dorsal spine short, about equal to diameter of pupil, third and fourth dorsal spines longest, about 2.4 in head, ninth dorsal spine short, about 2 in second; dorsal rays subequal, the last about 1.25 in third dorsal spine; origin of anal under about fourth dorsal ray; first anal spine very short, third longest, about 1.75 in third dorsal spine; last anal ray about equal to last one of dorsal; caudal rather widely forked, the lobes about equal, their length equal to distance from tip of snout to edge of preopercle, their outer rays not especially produced; ventrals rather short, reaching but slightly more than half distance to origin of anal, their length about 2 in head; pectoral longer, the upper rays somewhat produced, the fin slightly falcate, the length 1.2 in head; scales moderately large, firm, deeper than long; cheek and opercle scaled, the former with 6 rows; a large modified humeral scale; lateral line beginning at humeral scale and following contour of back, ceasing at base of caudal.

Color in life, rose-red, not quite so brilliant as in *Etelis evurus*; a golden stripe along lateral line, mouth not red inside; axil deep red; belly silvery, but less abruptly so than in *E. evurus* and some-

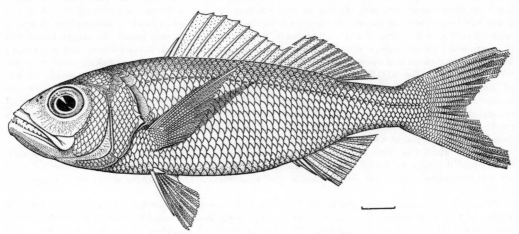

FIG. 100.—*Etelis marshi* (Jenkins).   Type of *Eteliscus marshi* Jenkins.

what shaded with rose; fins rose-colored, the first dorsal and caudal brightest, ventrals and anal almost white; a faint whitish stripe along side below golden one.   Another specimen (No. 03378), 2 feet long, from Honolulu, nearly fresh, was very bright red, silvery below, the center of each scale on back golden, these forming streaks; lateral line golden; upper fins bright red; lower fins pale red.

Color in spirits, light dusky, yellowish above, paler on the sides, whitish below; top of head dusky yellowish; fins all uniform whitish.

The above description based chiefly upon a specimen (No. 04148) 16.75 inches long, from Hilo.

This species reaches a length of at least 2 feet, and is a common and important food-fish both at Honolulu and Hilo.   The spawning time seems to be in the middle of the summer, several of the examples obtained by us in July being full of ripe spawn.   It is close to *E. evurus* from which it differs, however, in the smaller eye, much stronger teeth, somewhat shorter body, and in not having the caudal lobes markedly produced.   It is rather common in deep water, especially off Hilo.   The type (No. 50714, U. S. N. M.) was obtained by Dr. Wood at Honolulu.   Our collection contains 4 specimens from Honolulu, 9 from Hilo, and 1 from Kailua, ranging from 10 to 26 inches long.

185. Etelis evurus Jordan & Evermann.   *"Ulaula."*   Plates XVIII and 38.

Head 3.2 in length; depth 3.6; eye 3 in head; snout 3.9; maxillary 2.2; interorbital 3.6; D. x, 11; A. iii, 8; scales 5–50–11; Br. 6; gillrakers 15 + 6, longest about 2 in eye.

Body rather long, tapering, moderately compressed; dorsal outline slightly convex, ventral outline nearly straight; head considerably longer than deep, compressed, subconic, snout bluntly pointed, less than eye, equal to portion of eye anterior to posterior edge of pupil; mouth large, oblique; small bands of villiform teeth on vomer, palatines, and anterior part of each jaw; a single row of small wide-set, slender canine teeth on the outer edge of each jaw, those in upper jaw slightly larger and more wide-set; a single larger canine tooth on the side of each jaw in front, those in the upper jaw the larger; maxillary extending to middle of pupil; eye very large, its lower edge slightly below axis of body; preopercle finely serrate; opercle with 2 broad, flat spines, not produced, the upper rather obscure; fins moderately developed; origin of spinous dorsal slightly posterior to base of pectoral, its distance from tip of snout equaling that to base of sixth dorsal ray; dorsal fin deeply notched, almost divided; first dorsal spine short, its length but slightly greater than diameter of pupil; third dorsal spine longest, 2.1 in head; ninth spine short, its length 2.75 in third; soft dorsal not elevated, the rays about equal, the last 1.75 in third spine; anal similar to soft dorsal, the first spine very short, the third about 1.8 in third dorsal spine, last anal ray about equal to last dorsal ray; caudal deeply notched, the lobes much produced, the upper the longer, its rays greatly exceeding length of head, or about 2.4 in body; ventrals long, but not reaching vent by a distance equaling half diamater of pupil, their length 1.5 in head; pectoral long, reaching vent, the upper rays somewhat produced, their length 1.2 in head; scales moderate, firm, covering body, nape, opercles, and breast; a large humeral scale; lateral line beginning at lower edge of humeral scale and following contour of back to base of caudal fin.

Color in life, of a specimen (field No. 03481) 14 inches long, brilliant rose-red, the side from level of eye abruptly silver, with rosy shades; snout, jaws, eye, and inside of mouth red; fins all rose-color, the dorsal and caudal bright; ventrals and anal pale, the former washed with red on center; axil pale pink; pectoral pale rosy

Color in alcohol, uniform yellowish white, paler below; fins all pale yellowish white, the caudal lobes somewhat dark.

This species is related to *Etelis oculatus* of the West Indies, from which it differs in the somewhat larger scales, much longer caudal lobes (9.5 times length of middle rays instead of 4 times, as in *E. oculatus*), and larger eye. From *E. carbunculus* Cuvier & Valenciennes, from Isle of France, it seems to differ in the coloration, and in having only 16 instead of 20 scales in a transverse series. It is one of the handsomest of all Hawaiian fishes, thus far known only from Hilo, Hawaii, in the market of which we obtained 13 fine examples, and from Honolulu, where it was obtained by the *Albatross*.

Length 11 to 16.5 inches.

Family LXIII. SPARIDÆ.—The Porgies.

Body oblong or more or less elevated, covered with rather large, adherent scales, which are never truly ctenoid; lateral line well developed, concurrent with the back, not extending on caudal fin; head large, the crests on the skull usually largely developed; no suborbital stay; mouth small, terminal, low, and horizontal; premaxillaries little protractile; maxillary short, peculiar in form and in articulation, without supplemental bone, for most of its length slipping under the edge of the preorbital, which forms a more or less distinct sheath; preorbital usually broad; teeth strong, those in front of jaws conical, incisor-like or molar; lateral teeth of jaws always blunt and molar; no teeth on vomer or palatines; posterior nostril largest, usually more or less oblong or slit-like; lower pharyngeals separate; gills 4, a large slit behind the fourth; pseudobranchiæ large; gillrakers moderate; gill-membranes separate, free from the isthmus; preopercle entire or serrulate; opercle without spines; sides of head usually scaly; dorsal fin single, continuous, or deeply notched, the spines usually strong, depressible in a groove; spines heteracanthous, that is, alternating, the one stronger on the right side, the other on the left, the spines 10 to 13 in number; anal fin rather short, similar to the soft dorsal, and with 3 spines; ventral fins thoracic, the rays I, 5, with a more or less distinct scale-like appendage at base; caudal fin usually more or less concave behind; air-bladder present, usually simple; pyloric cœca few; vertebræ usually 10 + 14 = 24; intestinal canal short.

Carnivorous shore-fishes of the tropical seas, especially abundant in the Mediterranean, Red Sea, and West Indies. Genera about 12, species about 90, most of them much valued as food.

Only one species thus far known from the Hawaiian Islands.

Genus 135. MONOTAXIS Bennett.

Jaws each with several conical, canine-like teeth in front, and with a single series of molars on the sides; cheek scaly; dorsal fin with 10 spines, depressible in a groove; anal spines 3; scales moderate; branchiostegals 6; pyloric appendages few. Species few.

186. Monotaxis grandoculis (Forskål). *"Mu;" "Mamámu."* Fig. 101.

Head 3.1 in length; depth 2.5; eye 4 in head; snout 2.2; preorbital 3.1; interorbital 2.75; D. x, 11; A. III, 10; scales 6–46–12.

Body oblong, deep, compressed, back not much elevated; profile from nape to tip of snout nearly straight, being steeper from the prominence in front of eye to tip of snout; head slightly deeper than long, compressed; snout bluntly rounded; mouth large, horizontal; jaws equal, maxillary entirely

Fig. 101.—*Monotaxis grandoculis* (Forskål); after Bleeker.

concealed except for its lower edge; teeth large, wide, and irregularly set, conic teeth in anterior part of each jaw, lateral teeth on each jaw large and molar; preorbital very broad; preopercle entire; eye anterior, high, upper edge of pupil on line with lateral line; dorsal fin continuous, its origin slightly in advance of pectoral, its distance from tip of snout equal to its distance from base of ventrals, longest spine 2.1 in head, first spine short and weak, .6 height of second; soft dorsal rounded, rays much longer than spines, longest 1.75 in head; anal similar to soft dorsal, longest spine 2.5 in head, ray 1.75; caudal broad and strong, rather deeply forked, its lobes short and strong; pectoral broadly falcate, its tip reaching as far as those of ventrals, nearly 1 in head; ventrals falcate, reaching past vent, nearly to base of anal, 1.2 in head; scales rather large, much deeper than long, cycloid; top of head, snout, mandible and cheek naked; 3 rows of large scales on upper and 6 on lower part of preopercle, 6 rows on opercle; soft dorsal and anal moderately sheathed; a single row of small scales on each caudal ray, extending nearly to tip; lateral line concurrent with dorsal outline.

Color in life, scales below lateral line pale silvery with a purplish tinge; margin of scales on middle of body and on the upper part of opercle greenish yellow, those on back darker, with margin blackish yellow; belly pale, margin of scales on belly darkish; a blackish band on nape; head and snout purplish gray; cheek with a dark dirty purplish blotch tinged with yellow; lips darkish yellow; inside of mouth reddish, spinous dorsal pale purplish silvery, margin of the membranes with a wide deep cardinal stripe; soft dorsal blackish claret, rays paler; caudal dirty claret, somewhat paler than soft dorsal, rays paler, margin reddish; anal same as soft dorsal, spines dark reddish, black blotches at root of third to sixth membrane inclusive; pectoral pale reddish, axil black; ventrals very pale purplish, tips darkish; iris silvery-yellow, the upper border blackish silvery, this border with a deep cardinal border ventrally; root of pseudobranchiæ purple.

A smaller example (No. 03241), 9 inches long, from Honolulu, showed the following colors in life: Olive-gray, silvery below, each scale above with a bluish white center; traces of 4 narrow, whitish, yellowish cross-bars on back; one at nape, one under first dorsal spines, one under last dorsal spines, and one under last dorsal rays; head paler and more yellowish; a black spot on upper part of eye; inside of jaws bright red; spinous dorsal dirty gray, the pale band of back extending on it; soft dorsal with a large black central blotch, the last rays reddish white; caudal reddish gray, the rays mostly grayish, the membranes deep red; anal gray, blackish mesially, the rays tipped with dirty red; ventrals whitish, tipped with dirty red; pectoral light rusty red, the color fading on lower rays; a small black axillary spot with yellowish shade below it. Smaller examples show yellowish on fins and head rather than red; a dusky bar on cheek below eye; pale bars more distinct, the interspaces more clearly black.

Color in alcohol, grayish brown above, lighter below, margin of scales darker; top of head and cheek darker brown; a black blotch on upper edge of the yellow iris; spinous dorsal pale brown with a darker blotch on the anterior part of each membrane; membrane of soft dorsal, anal, and caudal dark; pectoral pale, black at axis; ventrals pale, tipped with dark brownish.

The above description based chiefly upon (No. 04140), a specimen 20.5 inches long from Hoopuloa, Hawaii.

Our collection contains 22 specimens 5 to 20 inches long, the localities represented being Honolulu, and Kailua and Hoopuloa, Hawaii.

This fish reaches a length of about 22 inches. It is fairly abundant and highly prized as a food-fish, always commanding a high price. It has a very wide distribution among the Pacific islands.

Family LXIV. MÆNIDÆ.—The Picarels.

Body oblong or elongate, covered with moderate or small ciliated scales; mouth moderate or small, extremely protractile, the spines of the premaxillaries extending backward to the occiput; teeth small or wanting, all pointed; no incisors or molars; dorsal continuous or divided, the spines very slender; preopercle entire; intestine short, with few pyloric cœca. Carnivorous shore-fishes, chiefly of the Old World. In the form of the mouth they present analogies to the *Gerridæ*, in other regards they closely resemble the *Hæmulidæ*. Genera 4 or 5; species about 25.

Genus 136. ERYTHRICHTHYS Temminck & Schlegel.

Body elongate; caudal peduncle long; snout rather sharply conic; mouth very protractile, the processes of the intermaxillaries extending to occiput; dorsal fins 2, scarcely, if at all, connected, the spines all slender and feeble; no detached dorsal spines; caudal widely forked, the lobes long and pointed; no teeth on jaws, vomer or palatines; lower pharyngeals separated from each other, and like the upper ones, armed with cardiform teeth; preopercle entire; scales rather small, ciliated; branchiostegals, 7; pseudobranchiæ present.

This genus is distinct from *Emmelichthys*, differing chiefly in having no detached dorsal spines.

187. Erythrichthys schlegelii Günther.   Plate XIX and Fig. 102.

Head 3.4 in length; depth 4; eye 3.4 in head; snout 3.6; maxillary 2; mandible 2; preorbital 7; interorbital 3.75; D. x–1, 11; A. III, 10; scales 10–75–17; Br. 7; gillrakers 24+6, the longest about 2 in eye.

Body long and slender, deepest at vertical of pectoral, thence gradually tapering to the long caudal peduncle, not much compressed, the back not much elevated; head moderate, conic; snout rather sharply conic; mouth rather large, somewhat oblique, the maxillary reaching anterior edge of pupil; vomer, palatines, tongue, and jaws toothless, the latter sometimes with a few very small villous teeth; premaxillaries greatly protractile; lower jaw projecting, its tip rounded, entering into dorsal profile; eye very large, its center scarcely above axis of body; interorbital broad and convex; preorbital very narrow; opercle smooth, 2 weak flat spines on its upper portion, the bony portion between these deeply emarginate; preopercle slightly crenate or fluted, not serrate, the angle rather broadly rounded; origin of spinous dorsal slightly posterior to base of ventrals, a little nearer tip of snout than base of last dorsal ray; dorsal spines all slender, the first short, about 2.5 in second; third longest, about 2 in head, the

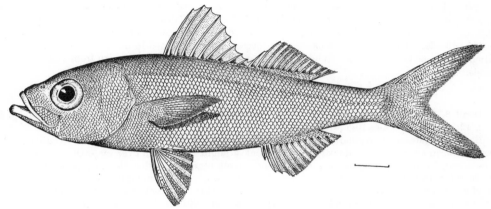

FIG. 102.—*Erythrichthys schlegelii* Günther.

tenth shortest, rather remote from the ninth but connected with it by a membrane, scarcely or not at all connected with the eleventh, which is somewhat longer, 1.6 in eye; soft dorsal with a scaly-sheathed base, the rays approximately equal, 1.1 in eye; anal similar to soft dorsal, the first spine short, about 2.5 in second, the third longest, about equal to eye, second anal ray slightly longer; caudal widely forked, lobes equal, long and pointed, about equaling head; ventrals short, reaching about two-fifths distance to vent, their length a little shorter than snout and eye; pectoral short, not reaching tips of ventrals, the length 1.6 in head; scales small, very finely ctenoid, deeper than long, firm, covering base of caudal and forming a scaly sheath at base of anal and dorsal fins; head completely scaled, 6 rows of scales on maxillary; mandibles scaled.

Color in life of an example (No. 03491) from Hilo, pinkish olive, pinkish silvery below; back with golden luster; faint yellowish cross-bands spreading from lateral line, these being muscle marks; faint darker streaks above middle of side; head orange-red, yellowish on side, red below; jaws red; sheath of scales of dorsal salmon-color; dorsal translucent, the spinous part orange-tinted, the rest light crimson; lower fins red; pupil orange within, silvery without; middle of side distinctly yellowish, the general effect orange.

Color in alcohol, pale yellowish orange, deepest above and on head; under parts whitish; faint brownish or orange streaks along the rows of scales; fins all whitish, tinged with orange.

This species reaches a length of something more than a foot. It does not appear to be very common, as our collection contains only 5 specimens, all from deep water off Hilo. It was described originally from Japan.

Family LXV. KYPHOSIDÆ.—The Rudder Fishes.

Herbivorous fishes with incisor teeth only in the front of the jaws; body oblong or elevated, with moderate or small scales, ctenoid or not; mouth moderate, with incisor-like teeth in the front of each jaw; no molars; teeth on vomer and palatines present or absent; premaxillaries moderately protractile; preorbital rather narrow, sheathing the maxillary; gillrakers moderate; pseudobranchiæ well developed; opercles entire; gills 4, a slit behind the fourth; gill-membranes separate, free from the isthmus; dorsal fin continuous or divided, with 10 to 15 rather strong spines, the soft dorsal naked or scaly; anal with 3 spines; ventrals thoracic, the rays I, 5, an accessory scale at base; caudal lunate or forked; pectoral fin with all its rays branched; intestinal canal elongate, with a few or many pyloric cœca; air-bladder usually with 2 posterior horns; vertebræ in ordinary or slightly increased number, 24 to 28; post-temporal of normal percoid form, the stout forks not adnate to the cranium. Herbivorous shore fishes, feeding largely on green or olive algæ; chiefly of the Mediterranean Sea and the Pacific Ocean; most of them valued as food. Genera 20, species about 70.

Genus 137. KYPHOSUS Lacépède. The Chopas.

Body elongate-ovate, regularly elliptical, moderately compressed; head short, with blunt snout; eye large; mouth small, horizontal; maxillary barely reaching front of eye; each jaw with a single series of rather narrow obtusely lanceolate incisors, implanted with compressed conspicuous roots posteriorly; behind these a narrow band of villiform teeth; fine teeth on vomer, palatines, and tongue; branchiostegals, 7; gillrakers long; preopercle obsoletely serrate; preorbital narrow, covering but little of the maxillary; squamation very complete, the space between and about the eyes being the only naked part; scales smallish, thick, ctenoid, 60 to 70 in the lateral line, which is continuous; similar scales entirely covering the soft parts of the vertical fins, and extending up on the paired fins; dorsal fin low, with about 11 spines, which are depressible in a groove of scales, the fin continuous but the last spines low, so that a depression occurs between the 2 parts of the fin, the bases of the spinous and soft parts about equal; soft dorsal rather low in front, not falcate, pointed behind; pectoral fins small, ventrals well behind them; intestinal canal long; pyloric cœca very numerous; vertebræ 9 or 10+15 or 16=25. This genus contains some 10 species, chiefly confined to the Pacific Ocean, and most of them valued as food; 2 species found in the West Indies. Two species known from the Hawaiian Islands.

188. Kyphosus sandwicensis (Sauvage). *"Nenue paiii."*

Head 3.75 in length; depth 2.15; eye 4.3 in head; snout 2.9; maxillary 3.25; interorbital 2.3; D. xi, 12; A. iii, 11; scales 10–72–17.

Body elongate-ovate, regularly elliptical, moderately compressed; dorsal outline evenly curved, nearly uniform from origin of dorsal to tip of snout, a slight depression over eyes, thence steeper to tip of snout; head deeper than long, compressed; snout bluntly rounded; jaws equal, the upper lip very broad, maxillary slipping under preorbital for most of its length, not quite reaching eye; a single row of moderately broad and strong incisor teeth on each jaw, their roots with very conspicuous backward parallel prolongation; behind these a narrow band of villiform teeth, similar villiform teeth on vomer and palatines; tongue very inconspicuous; eye entirely above axis of pectoral, anterior, with a prominence on snout above and in front of it; preorbital entire; interorbital broad and convex; caudal peduncle short, its length 2.5 in head; origin of dorsal slightly behind origin of ventrals; distance from origin of dorsal to tip of snout slightly less than depth; dorsal spines moderately strong, longest spine much higher than soft dorsal, 1.9 in head; first spine half as long as second; caudal broad, not deeply forked, its upper lobes slightly the longer, the length, measured from base of first supporting ray to tip, slightly longer than head; anal similar to soft dorsal, its base equal to that of soft dorsal, each about 1.2 in head; pectoral broadly falcate, 1.5 in head, not reaching nearly as far as ventrals; ventrals resembling pectoral, slightly longer, 1.35 in head; scales moderate, ctenoid, larger on the sides of body, deeper than long, entire body and head scaled, except snout from upper front of eye to tip, scales on head small, small scales on entire soft dorsal, anal, and caudal, and most of pectoral and ventrals; lateral line concurrent with dorsal outline.

Color in life (No. 05044, paper tag 3510), 23 inches long, body above lateral line silvery blue, with 5 or 6 greenish-yellow stripes which diffuse at the region of nape imparting to the back a greenish reflection; below the lateral line 10 greenish-yellow stripes along the intersection of scales on pale silvery-blue ground; margin of scales blackish; belly pale silvery blue; throat slightly reddish; head and top of nape dark-bluish emerald green, margin of scales blackish; a blue bar across occiput; snout blackish blue; cheek pale silvery blue; a golden-brown bar from angle of mouth toward angle of preopercle, another but wider bar of same color posteriorly from eye; anterior edge of opercle golden brown, a greenish-brown blotch on upper corner, a dark blotch on middle, posterior edge dark, dirty golden brown; anterior edge of shoulder-girdle and axis of pectoral darkish golden brown; iris silvery, anterior and posterior edges golden brown, upper edge dark blue, lower edge pale silvery blue; spinous dorsal dark ashy gray, the spines dirty greenish yellow, margin blackish; soft dorsal darkish; caudal dark gray, edges blackish, base and root with silvery reflections; anal silvery, margin darkish; ventrals pale, darkish silvery, margin blackish, inner side with dark brownish streak along the rays; pectoral silvery, margin pale, upper edge blackish, inner side burnt ochre or blackish brown.

Color in alcohol, brownish olivaceous becoming lighter below, the posterior edge of each scale being darker; dorsal slightly darker than the body, edge darker; caudal and anal similar to dorsal; pectoral palish brown; ventrals brownish, tips darker on lower side, the front of rays scaled, the scales being white, speckled with brown.

The above description based chiefly upon a specimen (No. 03012) 17.5 inches long, from Honolulu, where we obtained 5 specimens 11 to 23 inches long. The species was also taken by the *Albatross* at Laysan Island. It attains a length of 1 to 2 feet and is a good food-fish.

On comparison of our specimens with *Kyphosus elegans* from Mazatlan, we find very little difference, and we adopt *Kyphosus sandwicensis* as a distinct species only provisionally.

189. Kyphosus fuscus (Lacépède). *"Mânaloa;" "Nenue."*

Head 3.5 in length; depth 2.4; eye 4 in head; snout 3.1; maxillary 3.5; interorbital 2.6; D. xi, 12; A. iii, 11; scales 12–82–21, about 70 in series just below lateral line.

Body oblong, deep, compressed, dorsal outline more convex than ventral, the latter being nearly straight from origin of anal to before base of ventrals; dorsal outline from origin of dorsal to tip of snout nearly evenly arched, becoming slightly steeper over snout, the prominence in front of eye not very evident; head deeper than long, compressed, much broader through the middle; snout very short, bluntly conic; mouth small, horizontal, upper jaw slightly the longer, maxillary reaching slightly beyond anterior edge of eye; a single row of moderately broad and strong incisor teeth on each jaw, their roots with very conspicuous backward parallel prolongations; no villiform teeth back of these evident; bands of villiform teeth on vomer and palatines; eye entirely above axis of pectoral, anterior; preopercle entire; interorbital broad and convex; caudal peduncle 1.8 in head; origin of dorsal slightly in advance of origin of ventrals; distance of origin of dorsal from tip of snout equal to depth of body; dorsal spines moderately strong, longest spines much higher than soft dorsal, 2.2 in head, first spine two-thirds as high as second; caudal broad, not deeply forked, its lobes broad and equal, their length, measured from the first supporting ray to tip, slightly longer than head; anal similar to soft dorsal, its base equal to that of soft dorsal, about 1.25 in head; pectoral rather broadly rounded, 1.6 in head, not reaching ventrals; ventrals not reaching vent, shaped like pectoral, 1.6 in head; scales rather small, weakly ctenoid, much deeper than long, larger on side of body; entire body and snout scaled, except anterior part of snout; scales on head small, small scales on entire soft dorsal, anal and caudal fins and most of pectoral and ventrals, a large humeral scale on which is a patch of smaller scales; lateral line concurrent with dorsal outline.

Color in alcohol, grayish brown, with bluish silvery reflections, becoming lighter below, almost white on belly, narrow, dark bands on the side between the rows of scales, a narrow silvery band under eye; snout dark brown, membrane of spinous dorsal with some brownish; soft dorsal, anal and pectoral color of body; caudal brownish olivaceous, tips lighter; ventral membranes purplish brown, rays lighter.

The above description based chiefly upon a specimen (No. 04480) 8.75 inches long, from Honolulu. This fish reaches about a foot in length and is valued as a food-fish. It was obtained only at Honolulu, whence we have 4 good specimens 5 to 9 inches long.

Genus 138. SECTATOR Jordan & Fesler.

This genus is very close to *Kyphosus*, from which it differs in its smaller incisor teeth, which have very inconspicuous roots, and in the deeply forked caudal.

Only 2 species known—*Sectator ocyurus* from Panama and *S. azureus* from Oahu.

190. Sectator azureus Jordan & Evermann. Plate XX.

Head 4 in length; depth 3; eye 5 in head; snout 3.65; maxillary 4; interorbital 2.4; D. xi, 15; A. iii, 13; scales 14–81–20.

Body elongate, ovoid, greatest depth about at tip of pectoral; head slightly longer than deep, compressed; snout very bluntly convex; jaws about equal, maxillary not reaching front of eye; mouth small, horizontal; teeth very small, compressed, in a single series in each jaw; minute villiform teeth on vomer, palatines and tongue; tongue broad, rounded and free in front; preopercle entire, posterior edge very oblique; lower edge of eye on a line with upper base of pectoral, posterior margin well in front of middle of head; interorbital broad, strongly convex, a deep groove in front of eye to nostril; caudal peduncle rather long, 1.9 in head; origin of spinous dorsal slightly in front of base of ventrals, well behind pectoral, its distance from tip of snout slightly greater than depth of body; longest dorsal spine 3 in head, last dorsal ray elongate, being one-fourth longer than other rays, its length 3.4 in head; third anal spine longest, 4.9 in head; first anal ray longest, 3.4 in head; base of anal 1.8 in base of dorsal; caudal deeply forked, lower lobe the longer, 3.5 in body; pectoral short, slightly longer than ventrals, 1.8 in head, the spine more than half length of longest ray; scales cycloid, present on head except on jaws and in front of eye, very minute on all the fins except ventrals; lateral line concurrent with dorsal outline; peritoneum dark gray.

Color in life, dark steel-blue, becoming paler below; a definite deep blue stripe from snout below eye widening on opercle, and thence straight to center of base of caudal; below it a narrow bright golden stripe from angle of mouth to lower part of caudal, and then a fainter blue stripe below this; a blue stripe from eye to upper part of gill-opening, interspace golden shaded with green; a deep blue stripe, not sharply defined, from upper part of eye along each side of back to base of upper caudal lobe; upper fins dusky golden or olivaceous; ventrals yellow; anal and lower lobe of caudal dirty golden; pectoral translucent.

Color in alcohol, deep steel-gray, brown above, each scale with a very pale spot, the edge pale, lower surface whitish silvery; a pale streak of gray behind eye to edge of opercle; dorsal fin gray-brown like the back; caudal and pectoral whitish; inside of ventrals dusky orange; ventrals and anal dusky; inside of pectoral blackish brown.

Type, No. 50664, U. S. Nat. Mus. (field No. 03363), a specimen 15.25 inches long, taken off the shore near Heeia, Oahu Island.

This species must be very rare, being unknown to the fishermen and only the single specimen having been obtained by us.

Family LXVI. MULLIDÆ.—The Surmullets.

Body elongate, slightly compressed, covered with large scales which are usually slightly ctenoid; lateral line continuous, the pores often branched; large scales on the head; upper profile of head more or less parabolic; mouth small, low, subterminal; teeth mostly small, variously placed; no canines, incisors, nor molars; premaxillaries somewhat protractile; maxillaries thin, nearly as broad at base as at tip, without supplemental bone, partly hidden by the broad preorbital; preopercle entire or slightly serrate; opercle unarmed or with a single spine; eye moderate, placed high; branchiostegals 4; pseudobranchiæ present; 2 long, unbranched barbels at the throat, attached just behind the symphysis of the lower jaw; dorsal fins 2, remote from each other, both short, the first of 6 to 8 rather high spines, which are depressible in a groove; anal short, similar to the soft dorsal, with 1 or 2 small spines; ventrals thoracic I, 5; air-bladder usually present, simple; vertebræ 9+14=23; stomach siphonal; pyloric cœca about 20. Species about 40, referable to 5 closely related genera, found in all tropical seas, some species straying northward. Many of the species are highly valued as food, especially the European *Mullus barbatus* and *Mullus surmuletus*.

Genus 139. MULLOIDES Bleeker.

This genus differs from *Upeneus* only in the dentition, the teeth in both jaws being in narrow villiform bands, none on vomer or palatines. Species numerous, chiefly of the Pacific Ocean.

191. Mulloides auriflamma (Forskål). *"Weke;" "Weke ula."* Fig. 103.

Head 3.6 in length; depth 3.6; eye 3.5 in head; snout 3.1; interorbital 3; maxillary 3; shortest distance between maxillary and eye 1.67 in longitudinal diameter of eye; D. VII–9, longest dorsal spine 1.4 in head; A. 7, longest anal ray 2 in head; scales 3–40–6, 42 pores; gillrakers 24 + 8, the longest 2.5 in eye, serrate, those on longer limb becoming short and blunt.

Body oblong, compressed, deepest through anterior base of spinous dorsal; head moderate, compressed, its upper profile not straight, the line being slightly concave above eyes, the part anterior to nostrils rather steep; snout blunt; lower jaw slightly included; mouth rather small but oblique; tongue short, rounded anteriorly, not broad, thick, nor free anteriorly; teeth in a villiform band in each jaw; maxillary 1.3 in snout, not quite reaching anterior edge of orbit, rather large, covered anteriorly by a sheath; eye moderate, high, median; adipose eyelid slight, not nearly halfway to pupil anteriorly; barbels reaching to posterior edge of preopercle; pseudobranchiæ well developed; spinous dorsal high, its posterior edge nearly truncate, its base equal to longest spine, distance from anterior base to tip of snout equaling distance from anterior base across body to anterior base of anal; soft dorsal slightly concave; caudal deeply forked; anal similar to soft dorsal, inserted slightly behind it; ventrals

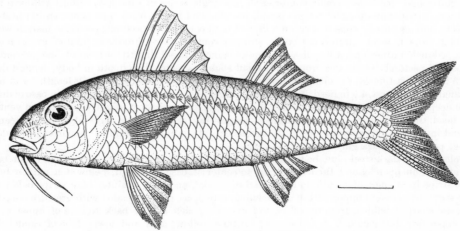

FIG. 103.—*Mulloides auriflamma* (Forskål).

reaching slightly beyond pectoral, the rays equal in length, and equal to longest dorsal spine; lateral line concurrent with the back; scales large, slightly ctenoid; entire body and head scaly.

Color in life, upper half of head, nape and back rosy red, richest on head; lower half of head white with very light rosy wash; side with a pale yellow band a scale wide, from eye to base of caudal, most distinct anteriorly; lower two-thirds of side white, with a light rosy wash; fins all pale rosy, except pectoral, which has a slight lemon-yellow wash; iris white with narrow inner rosy ring. Color in alcohol, dusky gray, fins all pale, except slight indications of black on upper posterior edge of dorsal spines. This description based chiefly on No. 02986, an example 8.5 inches long, from Honolulu.

Another specimen, No. 03479, from Hilo, had in life back violet red with some slight yellowish edging to scales; a broad yellow stripe from eye to base of caudal; a yellow streak horizontally below eye; lower part of side pale rosy; barbels white; fins all light orange, rosy and golden shaded, without marking; first dorsal darkest; iris red.

The collection contains 8 other examples from Honolulu and 4 from Hilo. We have also examined a specimen 10 inches long, collected by Dr. Jenkins at Honolulu, and others obtained at that place by the *Albatross*.

This fish is rather common in the market of Honolulu, being taken inside the reef. The 28 specimens we have are 3.25 to 14 inches long.

192. Mulloides erythrinus Klunzinger.

Head 3.5 in length; depth 3.75; eye 3.33 in head; scales 42 or 43; eye large, .66 of snout, equaling the length of postorbital part of head and somewhat more than the width of interorbital; barbel reaching to under posterior edge of preopercle; first and second dorsal spines of equal length, flexible, .75 as high as head. Color in life, deep rose-red, back darker; a broad golden band from eye along middle of body to caudal; oblique yellow lines; fins scarlet to orange-red. Recorded from Laysan Island by Steindachner; not seen by us.

193. Mulloides pflugeri Steindachner.

Head 3.6 in length; depth 3.6; eye 6 in head; snout 1.9; maxillary 2.6; interorbital 2.9; preorbital 3.8; D. vii–1, 8; A. i, 6; scales 3–40–7.

Body moderately slender, not greatly arched; head large; snout long, slightly decurved; mouth moderate, slightly convex; maxillary not reaching front of orbit; teeth on jaws in villiform bands, none on palatines; eye small, high up; interorbital space broad, convex; preorbital oblique; scales deeper than long, moderately firm; lateral line following contour of back, the pores with few branches; origin of spinous dorsal posterior to base of pectoral, length of longest dorsal ray 1.6 in head; base of spinous dorsal 1.25 in longest ray, and slightly greater than interdorsal space, the latter being equal to base of soft dorsal.

Color in life, body, head, and barbels uniform bright red; dorsals, ventrals, and pectoral red, with tinge of yellow; caudal red but with yellow predominating; no yellow lateral band and no blue spot on side below spinous dorsal. Color in spirits, uniform dusky olivaceous and yellowish, with blotchings of rosy on head and lower part of side.

This species does not appear to be common, as only 2 examples were secured by us, No. 03529, 23 inches long, on August 4, 1901, and No. 04113, 21 inches long, both from the market at Honolulu.

These specimens seem close to what we have called *M. samoensis*, but differ in having 40 instead of 35 scales in the lateral line, and in the uniform red coloration, there being no evidence of a yellowish lateral band as in the other species. These specimens can not be *M. samoensis* because of the absence of a black lateral spot. They do not seem to be *M. preorbitalis* because of the smaller scales and different coloration. They are not *M. ruber* (*erythrinus*) as described by Günther in Fische der Südsee, because of the much larger eye and the presence of yellow bands in the latter species, which is also said to have no yellow on the fins.

194. Mulloides flammeus Jordan & Evermann. "Weke ula ula." Fig. 104.

Head 3.6 in length; depth 4; eye 4.3 in head; snout 2.25; interorbital 3.5; maxillary 2.6; mandible 2.1; shortest distance from eye to upper edge of maxillary 1 in eye; D. vii–9, longest dorsal spine 1.75 in head, longest dorsal ray 2.6; A. 7, longest ray 2.7; scales 3–41–6; pectoral 1.5; ventral 1.4.

Body oblong, not much compressed; head heavy, broad, the interorbital space broad and slightly convex; snout rather long and pointed, not abruptly decurved; mouth rather large, somewhat oblique, the lower jaw but slightly included; maxillary broad, slipping for most of its length under the thin preorbital, its tip not reaching orbit by diameter of pupil; eye rather large, high, slightly posterior; gillrakers 18 + 7, the longest about 2 in eye, serrate; opercular spine obscure in adult, more plainly developed in the young; origin of dorsal a little nearer posterior base of soft dorsal than tip of snout; distance between dorsals considerably less than snout, about 2.6 in head; anal similar to soft dorsal, its origin somewhat more posterior; ventrals rather long, reaching slightly beyond tip of pectoral; caudal deeply forked, the lobes equal, about 1.2 in head.

Color in life (field No. 03459), bright rose-red, with 5 broad crossbands of darker clear rose, which vanishes very soon after death; a very faint yellow lateral streak, with yellow shades on scales below; lower side of head rose, snout and lips very red; 2 wavy golden streaks from below eye to angle of mouth, lower conspicuous; first dorsal clear red; second dorsal deep red on the lower half, fading above; caudal deep red at base, fading outward; anal pink, pectoral light yellow; ventral creamy red; barbels red, paler toward tip; iris silvery.

A color note on specimens bearing field Nos. 03054 and 03055 says that they were rosy in life.

Color in alcohol, pale dirty olivaceous above, yellowish white on sides and belly; head yellowish olive above, pale on cheek and below; a yellowish band from snout under eye; fins all colorless, the

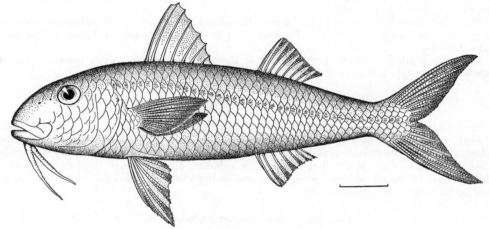

FIG. 104.—*Mulloides flammeus* Jordan & Evermann; from the type.

spinous dorsal slightly dusky, all with slight yellowish tinge; ventrals with the middle membranes blackish. Smaller examples show considerable rosy on the sides, indicating that the fish in life was probably red or rosy in color.

This species somewhat resembles *Mulloides auriflamma*, from which it differs in the smaller eye, larger, more oblique mouth, longer maxillary, the longer less decurved, more pointed snout, and fewer gillrakers. It bears some resemblance to *M. pflugeri*, but has the eye larger and the snout longer and more pointed. Compared with *M. samoensis*, it has a much larger and more oblique mouth, and a considerably longer maxillary, as well as a different coloration. It does not agree with any of the plates of Day, Günther, or Bleeker, nor with any current descriptions. In life its banded coloration gives it a very handsome appearance. It is found in deeper water than most of the other species.

M. flammeus seems to be fairly abundant, and is represented in our collections by 9 specimens from Honolulu, Hilo, and Kailua, ranging from 6 to 11.25 inches long.

195. Mulloides samoensis Günther.   "*Weke;*" "*Weke a'a.*"   Fig. 105.

Head 3.5 in length; depth 4; eye 4 in head; snout 2.35; interorbital 3.2; maxillary 3.4, shortest distance between maxillary and edge of eye 1.25 or less in eye; D. vii–9, longest spine 1.5 in head; A. 7, longest ray 2.5 in head; pectoral 1.5; ventral 1.6; scales 3–35–6, 37 pores; gillrakers 18+7.

Body oblong, compressed, deepest through anterior base of spinous dorsal; head moderate, compressed, the profile evenly arched from anterior base of spinous dorsal to tip of snout; snout bluntly pointed; lower jaw included; mouth small, slightly oblique; tongue short, rounded anteriorly, not broad or thick and not free anteriorly; teeth in a villiform band in each jaw, no teeth on vomer or palatines; maxillary short, 1.5 in snout, maxillary broad, slipping under a sheath for more than half its length; eye moderate, high, slightly posterior, adipose lid somewhat developed; barbels reaching gill-opening, 1.5 in head; pseudobranchiæ well developed; longest gillrakers nearly equal to diameter of pupil, finely serrate, the last 5 or 6 on longer limb very blunt and short; spinous dorsal high, posterior edge nearly truncate, its base equal to highest spine; origin of spinous dorsal midway between tip of snout and origin of anal measured across body; distance between dorsals 1.25 in snout or slightly less than base of soft dorsal; dorsal slightly concave; caudal deeply forked; anal similar to soft dorsal, inserted slightly behind it; ventrals reaching slightly beyond pectorals, the rays equal in length, these slightly less than longest spinous dorsal; lateral line concurrent with dorsal outline; scales large, finely ctenoid; entire body and head scaly.

Color in alcohol, above bluish-olivaceous, the sides becoming yellowish white; borders of the

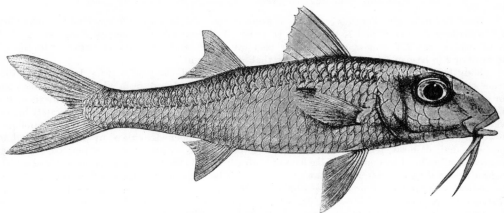

FIG. 105.—*Mulloides samoensis* Günther; after Güuther.

scales dusky; under parts white, a yellowish line under eye; preopercular edge yellowish; an obscure darkish blotch sometimes present on middle of side under spinous dorsal; fins all pale, colorless.

Color in life (No. 02987), back greenish olive; middle of side with a broad (one scale) pale yellow band from eye to caudal peduncle, where it gradually fades out; cheek with 2 or 3 faint yellow lines; side below yellow band white with 2 very faint yellow lines, belly white; fins all whitish, the spinous dorsal yellow on anterior part; soft dorsal and caudal washed with yellow.

A young example from Hilo had body greenish olive, with a broad golden stripe which is blackish in life; a quadrate black spot under first dorsal; lower fins and barbels white like belly; upper fins pale olive; no trace of red on body in life.

This species is very abundant inside the reefs of Oahu, and in bays between the rocky promontories about Hilo, being often taken for bait, but it is known only from the Hawaiian Islands and Samoa. Our collections contain a fine series of 152 specimens, from 3 to 13 inches long.

196. Mulloides vanicolensis (Cuvier & Valenciennes).

Head 3.8 (4.75) in length; depth 4.33 (5.25); D. VIII–I, 8; A. II, 6; scales 2.5–36–6.

Body rather slender; ventral outline almost as much curved as dorsal; profile gently and nearly evenly curved from snout to first dorsal fin; caudal peduncle tapering evenly from dorsal and anal to the caudal fin, and nearly equaling length of head, its least depth 2.33 in its length; snout short, bluntish, 2.75 in head; mouth small, maxillary reaching posterior nostril, 2.8 in head; the bands of villiform teeth very narrow; in front 2 series in each jaw, on the sides only one; eye large, 1.25 in snout, 3.5 in head; interorbital space moderately convex, 3 in head; upright limb of preopercle straight; opercular spine small; gillrakers slender, 2.5 in maxillary, 7 in head, about 25 on lower limb of arch; barbels 1.66 in head, extending beyond posterior margin of eye; scales moderate, ctenoid; preorbital smooth; dorsal fins moderate; spines of first dorsal rather weak, depressible into a groove; first spine very minute, second and third longest, 1.33 in head, those following evenly decreasing in height to the eighth spine, which is 3 in head; first ray of second dorsal fin unbranched, showing no articulations, having the appearance of a true spine, slightly shorter than last soft ray, 4 in head; second articulate ray contained 1.8 times in the highest dorsal spine; caudal well forked, its longest rays 1.25 in head; anal with 2 spines, the first of which is very minute, otherwise similar to soft dorsal, though a very little higher; pectorals 1.6 in head; ventrals 1.33 in head; air-bladder moderate; peritoneum black.

Color in spirits, grayish green above lateral line, lighter below, with yellow metallic luster; minute black punctulations on scales above lateral line, none below.

Genus 140. PSEUDUPENEUS Bleeker. The Goat-Fishes.

Body oblong, compressed; mouth moderate, nearly horizontal, low, the jaws subequal; eye large, high, posterior; opercle short, deep, with a posterior spine; both jaws with rather strong unequal teeth, in 1 or 2 series in each jaw; no teeth on vomer or palatines; lips well developed; the bone which forms a hook over the maxillary less developed than in *Mullus;* interorbital space concave and narrow; opercle ending in 1 spine; barbels nearly as long as head; scales very large, somewhat ctenoid; lateral line continuous, its tubes ramifying on each scale; head covered with large scales; first dorsal with about 7 spines; anal with 2, the first very short; caudal fin forked. Species numerous in the tropical seas.

197. Pseudupeneus chryserydros (Lacépède).   *"Moano kea."*   Fig. 106.

Head 3.25 in length; depth 3.7; eye 6.5 in head, in snout 3.5; snout 1.9; interorbital 3.5; maxillary 2.4, maxillary to eye 4.3, or 1.75 times eye; D. VIII–9; A. 7; scales 3–30–6; longest dorsal spine 1.5 in head, longest ray 2.6; longest anal ray 2.3; pectoral 1.5; ventral 1.4; distance between dorsals 4.4 in head or 2 in base of spinous dorsal or 1.9 in that of soft dorsal.

Body long, tapering posteriorly; back considerably elevated, the profile rising in a straight line from snout to occiput, thence gently curved to origin of spinous dorsal, from which point it descends in an approximately straight line to caudal peduncle; ventral outline nearly straight, the axis of the body much below median line; head rather large, compressed; interorbital space moderately broad, very convex; snout long and bluntly pointed; mouth very low, moderate in size, somewhat oblique; lower jaw slightly included; maxillary very broad at tip, the upper edge curved upward; eye small, in posterior half of head; teeth on both jaws, rather large, none on vomer or palatines; barbels long, nearly equaling head and just reaching base of ventrals; fins moderate, origin of spinous dorsal a little nearer posterior base of soft dorsal than tip of snout; distance between origins of dorsals equal to distance from snout to edge of preopercle; caudal moderately forked, lobes equal, length slightly less than distance between origins of dorsals; gillrakers 20 + 7, serrate, longest two-thirds diameter of eye, last few on each limb short and blunt, merely rudiments; scales large, firm, deeper than broad, the mar-

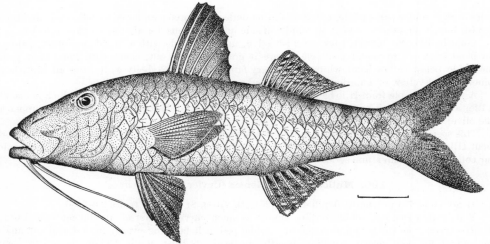

FIG. 106.—*Pseudupeneus chryserydros* (Lacépède).

gins finely toothed; lateral line following curve of back, the pores each with 3 to 6 branches; 3 scales between dorsal fins, 3 rows on cheek; a series of long mucous canals extending downward from eye and forward across snout to maxillary, these profusely branched anteriorly.   The above description based chiefly on a specimen (No. 03850) 12 inches long, from Honolulu.

Color in life (No. 02920) dark leaden purple shaded with red on side; nape yellowish; a large conspicuous orange-yellow blotch on caudal peduncle above; violet stripes radiating from eye, with orange and olive-yellow interspaces; cheek with bluish and yellowish stripes, iris red with yellow ring; barbels grayish, dusky at base, the tips yellow; fins all blue-black; soft dorsal and anal with sky-blue streaks between rays, then turning obliquely upward and backward, olive shades between the blue streaks; first dorsal blackish blue, with violet between the rays; pectoral blackish at the base, the tip purplish-red; ventrals blue-black, paler than caudal.   Specimen No. 03425 was in life very dark brown; each scale dark blue at base, golden on posterior portion; blue lines radiating from eye, with golden interspaces; side of head with blue and golden lines; dorsals and ventrals very dark, with golden markings on membranes; pectoral light rosy; anal crossed by golden bands parallel with body; caudal nearly black, an orange saddle on upper side of caudal peduncle.

No. 03356 (somewhat faded), from Honolulu, 7 inches long, in life was purplish olivaceous; upper parts darker, lower parts palest; 2 short blue lines above eye, 3 paler blue ones extending backward from eye to posterior edge of opercle, 3 similar lines extending forward from eye, the lower one longest, all these separated by brassy yellow lines of similar width and length, a brassy yellow line from upper end of premaxillary to lower edge of eye, where it is slightly interrupted by blue, then continuing across opercle; below this a broader bluish stripe, below which is another brassy yellow one, followed by an indistinct blue stripe and that by a faint yellow one on middle of cheek; tip of premaxillary brassy; side above lateral line with 2 series of small blue spots; below lateral line 2 or 3 indistinct series of yellowish spots, these plainest above pectoral; rich reddish orange saddle on anterior portion of caudal peduncle reaching lateral line on each side, the lower series of blue spots faintly evident through its base; opercle mixed purplish, brassy, bluish, and brownish, edge bluish below, brownish above; spinous dorsal with rays purplish, membranes pale dusky; soft dorsal dark purplish at base, the outer third with about 5 curved narrow brassy lines, separated by similar purplish ones; caudal dark purplish; anal pale purplish with about 4 greenish yellow stripes; pectoral dull rosy; ventrals with rays pale purplish or bluish, membranes slightly yellowish; barbels grayish, tips yellow; iris yellow. A specimen (No. 03466) from Hilo had in life the ground-color purplish rose inclining to red rather than to the usual livid purplish lead-color; about 9 faint violet crimson streaks along the rows of scales, these streaks separated by orange radiating from eye; barbels flesh-color, then livid bluish, then whitish; back of tail bright golden shaded with orange; dorsal livid purplish, rays violet; second dorsal blackish purple at base with oblique stripes of golden olive on violet above; caudal dirty violet, the membranes olive, the rays violet; anal pale violet with oblique streaks of golden olive; ventrals light violet and olive; pectoral reddish flesh-color, a curved darker bar at base; iris red. Another large specimen from Hilo in life was very bright violet gray blue; the caudal brilliant blackish violet.

Color in spirits (No. 3850), dirty white or light olivaceous on back and upper part of side; lower part of side and belly clearer white; head rusty, evidence of a dark bar across caudal peduncle and one under soft dorsal; top of caudal peduncle with a large white area; spinous dorsal, pectoral and ventrals, uniform pale; soft dorsal pale, crossed by about 5 narrow oblique darker bands; anal similar, the markings more obscure; caudal somewhat yellowish.

Color in spirits of another example (No. 02920), head and body rather uniform olivaceous brown, darkest on back, palest on belly; tip of snout dark, cheeks somewhat lighter; caudal peduncle anteriorly with a large white saddle; dorsal, caudal, and anal fins all blue-black; ventrals somewhat paler; pectorals pale.

Our collection contains 18 specimens of this species 3 to 15 inches long, and we have examined 6 specimens collected by Dr. Jenkins and Dr. Wood. This species is generally abundant in the markets, where its livid purplish colors contrast strongly with those of the other species.

198. Pseudupeneus multifasciatus (Quoy & Gaimard). "*Moano.*" Plate XXII.

Head 3.2 in length; depth 3.5; eye 6.25 in head; snout 1.8; interorbital 3.75; maxillary 2.4, maxillary to eye 4.4; D. viii–9; A. 7; scales 3–29–5.

Body rather short and deep, much compressed; the back little elevated, the ventral outline comparatively straight; head rather large; snout long and projecting; mouth large, slightly oblique, lower jaw included; maxillary very broad at tip; teeth rather large, wide-set in a single row in each jaw, none on vomer or palatines; eye small, in posterior half of head; barbels long, reaching nearly to base of ventrals, 1.25 in head; interorbital space high and very convex; opercular spine small, flat; fins large, interspace between dorsals .3 greater than diameter of eye; origin of spinous dorsal nearer last dorsal ray than snout by a distance equal to two-thirds diameter of eye; longest dorsal spine 1.4 in head; base of spinous dorsal 1.5 in longest ray; third dorsal ray 2 in longest spine; last dorsal ray much produced, nearly reaching base of caudal, 1.3 in longest dorsal spine; caudal peduncle rather short, scarcely exceeding snout; anal similar to soft dorsal, its origin somewhat posterior, its third ray 2 in longest dorsal spine, last anal ray produced, its length half greater than that of third ray; caudal moderately forked, the lobes a little greater than longest dorsal spine; pectoral short, about 1.5 in head, not reaching tips of ventrals; ventrals longer, 1.2 in head, their tips not reaching origin of anal by a distance slightly greater than diameter of eye; scales large, not very firm, the edges finely and obscurely ctenoid, lateral line parallel with the back, the pores not numerously branched, the branches numbering 5 to 8.

Color in life, body with alternating bands of pale rosy red and darker red; the snout and head to beyond eye smoky red, then a broad dark red band covering body from eye to origin of spinous dorsal, this with some black blotches, 3 or 4 in front of dorsal, one on humeral region, and one on salient angle of opercle, a pale red band as broad as base of spinous dorsal around the body under the base of spinous dorsal, behind this a double dark red band around body from last dorsal spine to eighth dorsal ray, this band with much black above, but scarcely any below lateral line; next a pale band around anterior end of caudal peduncle and under last dorsal ray, followed by a dark band around middle of caudal peduncle; posterior part of caudal peduncle with a pale ring; spinous dorsal rosy at base, black on distal portion, a little yellowish in center; soft dorsal greenish yellow at base, the outer three-fourths blackish, with 5 or 6 narrow pink lines parallel with the border; anal similar, the pink lines brighter and separated by olivaceous lines; pectoral always yellow, rosy on base and in axil; ventrals rosy with cross lines of whitish, the anterior border blackish; caudal dull rosy, edges black.

Other examples from Hilo were, in life, deep rose red, the old ones becoming darker or dark purplish cherry-red; dark bands of black with red over the black; pale band under first dorsal whitish and shaded with golden; the one under soft dorsal similar but fainter; scales of all upper parts veined with deeper red, first some bright red shaded with orange; second dorsal black, the rays red with longitudinal red streaks above; anal blackish above with longitudinal streaks above and irregular broad lines of violet; caudal violet red, the outer ray violet black with a slight pale edging; pectoral golden crimson at base; ventrals dark red, with wavy streaks of olive and violet; barbels pink with cream colored tips; iris scarlet; young with the tips of barbels bright yellow.

No. 02988, a young individual 6.5 inches long, differs markedly in color. It showed in life a general color of dirty white with scarcely a trace of rosy; body with 6 half-bars of black, the first across nape and down to lower edge of eye on each side; the second at origin of dorsal and down to base of pectoral; the third indistinct from under spinous dorsal to pectoral; fourth across back between dorsals and reaching two-thirds down side; the next from anterior half of soft dorsal; the last and blackest across caudal peduncle and down side; none of these makes a complete ring; fins resembling those of adult in color, but paler; iris pinkish.

The above description based upon a specimen (No. 02985) 10.25 inches long, from Honolulu. Some of the specimens are shorter and deeper. The species is one of the most abundant of the Hawaiian fishes, always found in the markets and conspicuous for its bright color. Our collections contain 85 specimens, ranging in length from 4.5 to 10.25 inches, from Honolulu, Hilo, Kailua, Laysan Island, and Puako Bay, Hawaii.

199. Pseudupeneus chrysonemus Jordan & Evermann.   Plate XXI.

Head 2.8 in length; depth 3.4; eye 5.3 in head; snout 1.7; interorbital 3.5; maxillary 2.3; D. viii–9; A. i, 7; scales 3–30–7.

Body slender, not greatly compressed, the back gently and rather uniformly elevated from tip of snout to dorsal; ventral outline slightly convex; head moderate; snout long, bluntly pointed; mouth moderate, slightly oblique, the lower jaw included; maxillary broad at tip, falling short of vertical of orbit by diameter of pupil; interorbital space convex; eye small, in posterior half of head; teeth rather large, in a single band in each jaw; barbels long, 1.2 in head, reaching nearly to base of ventrals; opercular spine small; fins rather large; third dorsal spine longest, 1.5 in head, or equal to distance from tip of snout to middle of pupil, third ray longest, 3.2 in head; base of spinous dorsal 1.4 in third spine; base of soft dorsal 1.4 in longest spine; origin of spinous dorsal nearer last dorsal ray than tip of snout by longitudinal diameter of pupil; distance between dorsals 1.5 in eye; length of caudal peduncle 1.5 in head; pectoral long, pointed, slightly falcate, 1.4; ventrals slightly longer, 1.3; last anal ray 2.9, equal to base of fin; caudal shallowly forked, lobes 1.3 in head, middle rays 2.75 in upper lobe; scales finely ctenoid and obscurely dendritic; lateral line concurrent with the back, the pores with few branches, the number usually not exceeding 5 or 6; 2 scales between the dorsals, 8 on dorsal side of caudal peduncle; peritoneum somewhat silvery.

Color when fresh, deep scarlet red, especially a shade from snout through eye toward tail; first dorsal plain scarlet, second paler golden with oblique stripes of scarlet and yellow edge; caudal orange, reddish at base, yellowish at tip; anal like second dorsal; pectoral pale orange; ventrals deep red; barbels bright yellow; iris red. In life, a pale streak backward from eye to middle of side parallel with back; side with 2 blotches of deep red; a row of dark spots along bases of both dorsals; young of 3 inches, from the rock pools, in life, dark olive-green above with a dark olive streak along lateral line and 3 dark shades under first dorsal, second dorsal, and back of caudal peduncle; tip of first dorsal cherry-red, edged with white; second dorsal and caudal translucent, scarcely reddish; ventrals and anal bright cherry-red, former mesially dusky; barbels golden.

Color in alcohol, pale yellowish; each scale below dorsal with brownish edgings, generally most distinct in young and often entirely disappearing with age; a series of smaller obscure spots along median line from opercle to tip of pectoral; sides and under parts with faint traces of rosy.

This species may be known by the series of dusky blotches along each side of the dorsal fin and by the simple structure of the lateral line. In life it is at once known by its golden barbels.

The above description based upon a specimen (field No. 03929) 8 inches long, obtained at Honolulu, in 1898, by Dr. Wood. We have examined 4 other specimens of approximately the same size obtained at the same time, and numerous examples collected by us at Honolulu and Hilo, which range in length from 4 to 8.5 inches.

200. Pseudupeneus bifasciatus (Lacépède).   "Munu." Fig. 107.

Head 3.2 in length; depth 3; eye 5 in head; snout 1.9; interorbital 3.25; maxillary 2.5; D. viii–8; A. 7; scales 3–31–6; gillrakers 29 + 8, serrate, longest 1.5 in eye, no blunt rudiments, but all fairly well developed.

Body short, stout, considerably compressed, back elevated; profile concave before the eye, strongly arched thence to spinous dorsal; ventral profile comparatively straight; head moderate, much compressed; snout moderate, somewhat projecting, bluntly rounded; mouth low, nearly horizontal, lower jaw included; maxillary very broad at tip, not reaching orbit; eye small, high up, in posterior part of head; interorbital very convex; teeth rather large, unequal, in a single series in each jaw, none on vomer or palatines; cheek deep; opercular spine moderate, flat; barbels moderate, reaching gill-opening, a little shorter than snout; fins rather large; spinous dorsal slightly nearer last dorsal ray than tip of snout; longest dorsal spine 1.5 in head, slightly greater than snout and pupil; base of spinous dorsal 1.2 in longest spines; longest dorsal ray 1.65 in longest dorsal spine, or 1.25 in base of soft dorsal; interspace between dorsals greater than eye or 2.6 in longest dorsal spine; length of caudal peduncle equal to longest dorsal spine; origin of anal slightly posterior to that of soft dorsal, its longest ray about equal to that of soft dorsal, its base 1.6 in that of soft dorsal; caudal broad, not deeply forked, its lobes 1.6 in head; pectoral rather short, equaling longest dorsal spine; ventrals considerably longer, 1.2 in head; scales large, moderately firm, slightly rivulate, the edges weakly ctenoid; pores of lateral line profusely branched, the branches usually about 10 to 12 in number, fewer posteriorly, the number as low as 5 or 6.

Color in alcohol, rusty black; body crossed by 2 broad dark bars, the first under anterior half of spinous dorsal, second under posterior half of soft dorsal, each of these bars about equal to snout and eye in width and separated by a broader pale interspace; head dark; caudal peduncle pale; vertical fins dark; the spinous dorsal darkest on its anterior portion; soft dorsal and anal dark, crossed by numerous narrow wavy pale streaks; caudal yellowish white, dark edged; ventrals pale, dark on inner surface and on edge; pectoral pale; in larger specimens the caudal fin shows somewhat the markings of soft dorsal and anal.

A large specimen, No. 03465, 12 inches long, from Hilo, had in life body purplish cherry-red, rather dull and dusky, with obscure dark cross bands (one at nape, one under first dorsal, one under front of second, one under last rays, and one at base of tail); snout darker than body; barbels blackish; no

FIG. 107.—*Pseudupeneus bifasciatus* (Lacépède); after Günther.

golden or clear red anywhere; first dorsal deep dull red; second red olive, mottled and streaked with crimson, edge blackish; caudal deep dull red, finely spotted with crimson, edge blackish with a faint pale edging; anal like soft dorsal; ventrals purplish black, with pale edge; pectoral light purplish red; iris red.

The above description based chiefly upon a specimen (No. 03911) 11 inches long, from Honolulu.

This is an excellent food-fish of fine, delicate flesh. The collection contains other specimens from Honolulu, Hilo, and Kailua.

201. Pseudupeneus crassilabris (Cuvier & Valenciennes).

Head 3 (3.66) in length; depth 3 (3.66); D. viii–9; A. i, 7; scales 2–31–6.

Body oblong, compressed, robust; head and anterior part of body heavy; profile concave from snout to a point midway between the nostrils, thence regularly curved to first dorsal; snout long, blunt, 1.66 in length of head; ventral outline little curved; caudal peduncle two-thirds length of head, its least depth almost twice in its length; mouth moderate, little oblique, the lower jaw included; maxillary 2.33 in head, terminating between the nostrils; strong, blunt, but conical teeth in one series in each jaw, the teeth more or less widely separated; eye 2.75 in snout and 5 in head; interorbital space very convex, 3.66 in head; preopercle with upright limb slanting obliquely forwards; opercular spine strong; gillrakers 2 in eye, 4.5 in maxillary, about 28 on lower limb of arch; barbels two-thirds length of head, reaching posterior margin of subopercle; scales large, ctenoid; dorsal fins well developed, third and fourth spines longest, 1.33 in head, twice the height of soft dorsal, the last rays of which are scarcely longer than the first; soft dorsal two-thirds as high as long, its length 2 in head; caudal moderate, well forked, upper lobe more rounding, 1.37 in head; anal differs from soft dorsal in having its first branched rays one-fourth longer than the last, the unbranched ray also slightly exceeding the last ray; the greatest height of the fin 2.6 in head; the membrane of the first soft ray envelops a small spine, which, being thus covered, might easily be overlooked; the first articulate ray of anal, as in soft dorsal, not branched; ventral fins large, 1.33 in head, about reaching tip of pectoral; air-bladder large.

Color in spirits, olivaceous, lighter below, the fish as a whole having a smutty appearance; exposed part of each scale punctulate with brown; first dorsal and caudal dusky; base of soft dorsal dusky, upper half irregularly light and dark; anal with irregular dusky bars; soft dorsal, caudal, and anal tipped with black; ventrals yellowish, spine and connecting membrane smutty; pectorals yellow, their base, the preorbital, and upper part of head purple; barbels very dark; branchiostegal membrane purple; peritoneum light.   Known from Johnston Island, but not found among the Hawaiian Islands.

202. Pseudupeneus pleurostigma (Bennett).   Fig. 108.

Head 3.35 in length; depth 3.6; eye 5 in head; snout 1.9; interorbital 3.6; maxillary 2.65; D. VIII-9; A. 7; scales 3-28-5.

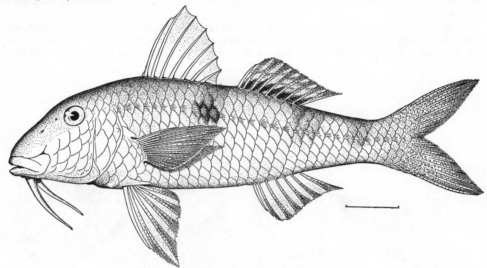

FIG. 108.—*Pseudupeneus pleurostigma* (Bennett).

Body oblong, compressed, profile evenly arched from origin of spinous dorsal to tip of snout, except a slight depression on snout; snout bluntly rounded, lower jaw included; mouth moderate, horizontal; a single row of wide-set, small, conic teeth in each jaw, none on vomer or palatines; maxillary not reaching vertical from eye by a distance equal to three-fourths diameter of eye; barbels reaching slightly beyond posterior edge of preopercle; longest dorsal spine 1.3 in head or from posterior base of spinous to posterior base of soft dorsal, last soft dorsal ray equal to second, each 2.5 in head; distance between dorsals equal to 3 rows of scales or one-fourth of head; second anal ray equal to last, each equal to base; origin of soft dorsal slightly in advance of anal, tips of last rays of each extending to same line posteriorly, the spinous dorsal extending nearly an eye diameter beyond tip of pectoral; pectoral not reaching quite as far posteriorly as ventrals, which are 1.2 in head; pectoral 1.3; caudal peduncle 1.3, its least depth 2.7; scales large, finely and distinctly ctenoid and strongly rivulate; lateral line parallel with back, pores usually with 8 to 12 branches anteriorly, fewer posteriorly.

Color in life, dirty whitish, darkest on back; scales narrowly edged with yellowish olive; under parts white, with slight rosy wash; head obscure rosy, snout and maxillary clearer rosy; side with some olive; a large black blotch on lateral line just under and behind last dorsal spine; spinous dorsal greenish on membranes, the spines rosy; soft dorsal greenish, with a few small dark spots crossed by about 7 narrow pale streaks; caudal pale yellowish, edge of lower lobe red; anal pale with 3 pale yellowish green streaks; pectoral pale; ventrals pale rosy.

A fresh specimen from Hilo had the body bright rose-red with a little yellow shading, more crimson on opercle; a black spot on side opposite space between dorsals, behind this spot a large paler oblong area of pink; first dorsal red, with yellow olive on membranes; second with basal half blood red (black washed with red), above this 5 oblique violet lines alternating with olive-yellow; caudal with outer rays crimson, the fin mottled red and reddish olive; anal with 4 oblique violet stripes alternating with golden; pectoral light reddish; ventral deeper red; barbels white; iris scarlet.

Color in alcohol, side and upper parts dull plumbeous, an irregular broad pale bar across side under anterior portion of soft dorsal, this usually appearing as a large white blotch; a broad darker area under posterior portion of soft dorsal; a large black spot, 2 or 3 scales in diameter, on lateral line under last dorsal spines; under parts yellowish white; dorsal, caudal, anal, pectoral, and ventrals pale yellowish white; the caudal and spinous dorsal somewhat dusky; soft dorsal black at base, paler on distal portion, the color made up of a number of closely placed black bars, obscure at the base.

The above description based chiefly upon a specimen (No. 02984) 10.25 inches long, from Honolulu. We have 27 specimens 5 to 11.25 inches long, from Honolulu and Hilo.

203. **Pseudupeneus fraterculus** (Cuvier & Valenciennes). Fig. 109.

Head 3.75 to 4 in total; depth 4.75 to 5; eye 5 in head, 1.35 to 1.5 in interorbital portion of head, 2.35 to 2.5 from end of snout, 1.25 in interorbital space; D. VIII–9; A. I, 7; scales 2 or 3–31–7.

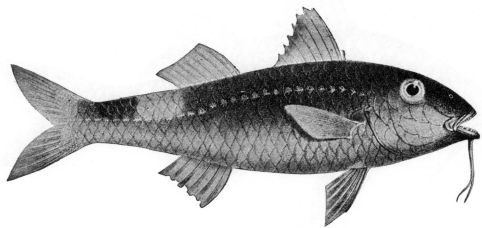

FIG. 109.—*Pseudupeneus fraterculus* (Cuvier & Valenciennes); after Playfair.

Snout pointed, compressed, maxillary reaching rather more than halfway below front edge of orbit; barbels reaching below hind margin of preopercle; interorbital width slightly convex; opercular spine of moderate strength; fourth dorsal spine rather the longest, equal to three-fourths the height of body below it; 3 rows of scales between 2 dorsals; front portion of second dorsal equal to two-thirds height of first dorsal; pectoral as long as head, anterior to hind edge of orbit, anal commencing slightly behind origin of second dorsal; caudal deeply forked, lobes pointed; scales on snout and head, including most of preorbital bone, and uncovered portion with some rather large pores.

Color reddish, the edges of the scales slightly darkest; a broad purplish band, having a light silvery edge, passes from in front of eye to snout; 2 more narrow silvery lines, formed of short oblong spots, proceed from hind edge of orbit for a short distance; 2 rows above lateral line, and generally 3 below, have a golden yellow spot in the center of each scale; a light golden band over free portion of tail; first dorsal marbled with brown, second with 4 and the anal with 3 reddish bands; caudal reticulated with light-gray markings. Length 8.5 inches. (Day.)

This species is recorded from Honolulu by Steindachner. It was not recognized by us.

204. **Pseudupeneus porphyreus** Jenkins. "*Kumu.*" Fig. 110.

Head 3.2 in length; depth 3.5; eye 4.7 in head, slightly nearer tip of snout than edge of opercle; snout 2.2; interorbital 3.5; maxillary 2.6; orbit to maxillary equal to eye; D. VIII–9; A. 7; scales 3–31–5.

Body rather short, stout and somewhat compressed, the back gently elevated, the ventral outline comparatively straight; profile from snout to eye very slightly concave, thence gently convex to origin of spinous dorsal; head moderate; snout moderate, blunt at tip; mouth small, low and horizontal; maxillary somewhat curved upward at extremity; lower jaw included; no teeth on vomer or palatines, those on jaws moderate, in a single row; eye moderate, slightly anterior; caudal peduncle somewhat compressed, the least depth 2.5 in head; fins moderate; longest dorsal spine equal to snout and pupil, the longest ray slightly shorter than snout; origin of spinous dorsal exactly midway between tip of snout and base of last soft dorsal ray; base of spinous dorsal slightly less than longest spine or equal to distance from tip of snout to middle of pupil; base of soft dorsal equal to longest dorsal ray; space between dorsals less than half longest dorsal spine, or 3.6 in head; length of caudal peduncle equal to snout and eye; pectoral slightly greater than snout and eye, about 1.4 in head; ventral pointed, slightly longer than pectoral, not reaching anal opening, about 1.25 in head; anal somewhat posterior to soft dorsal, its base 1.25 in its longest ray, which is 2.6 in head; caudal moderately forked, the lobes equal, and equal to eye and snout; scales large, firm, very finely ctenoid; most of the scales obscurely dendritic; lateral line concurrent with the back, the pores very profusely and widely branched, the number of branches usually about 10 to 12, sometimes as few as 6 or 7; two and a half scales between dorsal fins and 7 on dorsal edge of caudal peduncle); suborbital and side of snout with numerous branched pores; peritoneum pale; gillrakers 25+7, serrate, the longest about 2.2 in eye.

Another specimen (No. 03851), 14.5 inches long, gives the following description:

Head 3.1 in length; depth 3.4; eye 4.6 in head; snout 2.3; interorbital 3.5; maxillary 2.45, maxillary to eye 4 in head or 1.25 times eye; D. VIII–9; A. 7; scales 3–30–6; longest dorsal spine 2 in head, longest ray 2.25; longest anal ray 2.3; pectoral 1.65; ventral 1.65.

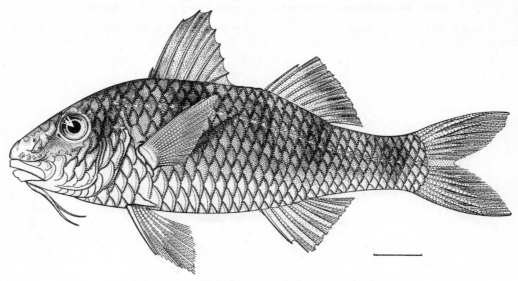

FIG. 110.—*Pseudupeneus porphyreus* Jenkins; from the type.

Body stout, back elevated anteriorly, sloping gradually posteriorly to caudal peduncle; anterior profile slightly concave between snout and eye, convex from eye to origin of dorsal; ventral outline nearly straight; head large; interorbital broad, convex; snout long, somewhat projecting, blunt at tip; mouth low, nearly horizontal; lower jaw short, decidedly included; maxillary somewhat expanded at tip, not quite reaching vertical of orbit; teeth strong, in a single series in each jaw, none on vomer or palatines; eye large, in posterior half of head; barbels short, not reaching vertical of preopercular edge, 2.5 in head; preopercular spine broad, flat, not strong; caudal peduncle somewhat compressed, slender, its least depth 2.8 in head; fins moderate; origin of spinous dorsal midway between snout and posterior base of soft dorsal; interspace between dorsals slightly greater than eye, 1.75 in base of spinous dorsal, nearly 2 in base of soft dorsal; anal similar to soft dorsal, its origin somewhat posterior to that of the latter, its base a little more than 3 in head; caudal not widely forked, lobes somewhat rounded, about 1.8 in head; scales large, finely ctenoid, some of them faintly dendritic, 2.5 scales between dorsals and 3 rows on cheek; lateral line concurrent with the back, the pores profusely branched.

Color in life (No. 02983), rich rosy on back and top of head, paler on side; about 5 rather distinct lines, made up of broken marks along center of scales; lower part of side and underparts whitish, with slight rosy wash; edges of scales on upper half of body yellowish olive; opercles rosy; fins all rosy, the dorsal and anal brightest, outer edge of ventral white; lips white; iris silvery, rosy above.

A fresh example from Hilo had body very bright rose-red; back olive; a whitish streak from eye backward to front of second dorsal; a broader pinkish white band from tip of snout below eye to below middle of spinous dorsal; a faint darker red cross shade below spinous dorsal; another narrower one between dorsals and a broad one under second dorsal, most distinct under its posterior part; a blackish shade on caudal peduncle, before which is a quadrate blotch of pinkish white. The most distinct marks are the olive of back and its 2 pale streaks and the pink and olive on tail; fins all clear red; the dorsals paler edged; ventrals and anal broadly pale edged; barbels white; iris silvery.

Color in alcohol, dirty yellowish white, pale olivaceous on back, head with some traces of orange; fins all uniform white or whitish, probably yellowish in life; anterior upper part of caudal peduncle with a large whitish blotch.

This species is abundant at Honolulu and Hilo, whence we have 38 specimens 5 to 14.5 inches long. It is one of the best food-fishes, ranking with the surmullet of Europe.

205. Pseudupeneus preorbitalis (Smith & Swain). Fig. 111.

Head 3.4 (4.16) in length; depth 4.16 (5.12); D. viii–9; A. i, 7; scales 2–37–5.

Body more slender than in *Mulloides vanicolensis* (Cuvier & Valenciennes); ventral outline almost straight, dorsal outline well curved; profile from snout to dorsal regularly curved; caudal peduncle 1.33 in head, its least height 3.25 in head; mouth nearly horizontal, maxillary 3 in head, terminating behind anterior nostril; lower jaw produced; the band of villiform teeth moderate in both jaws, in a patch in front, narrowing posteriorly; eye moderate, 2.5 in snout, 4.33 in head; interorbital space slightly concave, 4.25 in head; preorbital very deep, 2.25 in head; gillrakers short and rather slender, 4.5 in maxillary; 19 on lower limb of arch; barbels 1.5 in head, reaching posterior margin of preopercle;

scales large, ctenoid; dorsal fins medium; spinous dorsal depressible into a groove, first spine rudimentary, scarcely perceptible, second and third spines longest, 1.66 in head, eighth spine 4 in second; first ray of soft dorsal unbranched but evidently articulate, shorter than the first branched ray, which is 2.33 in head, the rays thence about regularly decreasing in height; caudal well forked, its longest

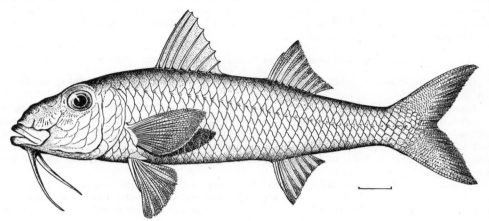

FIG. 111.—*Pseudupeneus preorbitalis* (Smith & Swain); from the type.

rays 1.33 in head; anal similar to soft dorsal, its spine very minute and first ray unbranched but plainly articulate; ventrals 2 in head; pectorals 1.66 in head; air-bladder moderate.

Color in spirits, nearly uniform yellowish; snout dusky, fins plain; peritoneum dark.

Known only from Johnston Island.

Genus 141. UPENEUS Cuvier.

This genus differs from *Mulloides* and *Pseudupeneus* in having teeth in both jaws and on the vomer and palatines.

206. Upeneus arge Jordan & Evermann.   *"Weke"* or *"Weke Puéo;" "Weke pahúla."*   Plate 39.

Head 3.75 in length; depth 4.1; eye 5 in head; snout 2.25; interorbital 3; maxillary 2.3; shortest distance between maxillary and eye 1.25 in longitudinal diameter of eye; D. VIII–9, second spine 1.5 in head; A. II, 6, longest anal ray 1.9 in head; pectoral 1.5; ventrals 1.45; scales 3–40–7.

Body oblong, compressed, deepest through the anterior base of the spinous dorsal; head moderate, compressed, profile arched from origin of the spinous dorsal to tip of snout, steepest on snout; snout bluntly rounded; lower jaw included; mouth moderate, slightly oblique; tongue short, rounded anteriorly, not broad nor thick, and not free; teeth in villiform bands on each jaw and on vomer and palatines; maxillary moderate, reaching anterior edge of eye, moderately broad and sheathed for more than half of its length; eye rather small, high, median, adipose eyelid well developed; barbels not reaching edge of gill-opening; pseudobranchiæ well developed; gillrakers 16+6, finely serrate, last 5 or 6 on longer limb very blunt and short, pupil of eye contained 1.5 in longest; spinous dorsal 1.5 in depth, first 2 spines even, longer than the others and longer than base; distance from snout to origin of spinous dorsal one-third distance from snout to last scale on caudal; distance between dorsals slightly less than base of soft dorsal; soft dorsal slightly concave; caudal deeply forked, upper lobe longer; anal similar to soft dorsal, inserted slightly behind the latter; ventrals reaching slightly beyond pectoral, rays of pectoral slightly the longer; lateral line concurrent with dorsal outline; scales large, finely ctenoid; entire body and head scaly.

Color in life, pale green, changing to white below; edges of scales on back and down to lateral line purplish brown, giving the appearance of 3 rather distinct stripes of purplish brown, with greenish centers on the scales; side with 2 broad yellow stripes, the upper beginning on opercle at level of eye and running to caudal just above lateral line, which it crosses under soft dorsal; second beginning on base of pectoral and running to base of caudal just below lateral line, this stripe less distinct and narrowing posteriorly; opercle bright rosy; top of head dusky; cheek white with some rosy; lower jaw white; barbels yellow; dorsal fins pale, each crossed by 2 or 3 brownish rosy bars; caudal white, upper lobe with 4 broad brownish red bars running downward and backward, 1 at base narrow; lower lobe with similar but much broader black bars running upward and backward, 2 of them more distinct than the others, 2 longish dark spots on inner rays; anal, ventrals, and pectoral pale, ventrals rather pale yellowish; iris yellowish, pink above.

Color in alcohol, above bluish olivaceous, the side becoming lighter, almost white on belly; borders of scales dusky; first dorsal spine with 3 or 4 dark spots, and the upper posterior edge of membranes with dark spots; soft dorsal with 3 dark spots on anterior edge and similar spots on upper part of fin; caudal fin with dark bands, upper lobe with about 6, those on lower lobe 4, much broader, other fins pale.

This species resembles *Upeneus vittatus* (Forskål), described from Djidda, Arabia, but the latter has the belly abruptly deep yellow in life. It is an abundant and important food-fish at Honolulu, where we obtained 10 specimens and where 4 others were collected by Dr. Jenkins in 1889. It is equally common at Hilo and in Pearl Harbor, living in shallow water along quiet shores.

Our specimens are 8 to 12.5 inches long.

207. Upeneus tæniopterus Cuvier & Valenciennes. "Weke."

Head 5 in total length; depth 5; eye 5 in head, 1.65 in snout, 1.5 in interorbital space; D. VII–I, 7; A. 7; scales 3–38–7.

Interorbital space flat, a very slight rise from snout to base of first dorsal, a slight swelling over the snout in front of eye; barbels reaching to first third of orbit; teeth villiform in jaws, vomer, and palatines; first spine of dorsal fin the highest, and equal to two-thirds height of body, the second very nearly as long; 6 rows of scales between bases of dorsal fins; pectoral equal in length to first dorsal spine; caudal deeply forked; tubes of lateral line very arborescent posteriorly; air-bladder large; branchiostegals 4; pyloric cœca 2.

Color, back reddish, becoming white on the abdomen; a large reddish spot said to have existed on the free portion of tail, but not now apparent; first dorsal fin with 3 brownish longitudinal bands, second dorsal likewise banded; caudal with 6 oblique streaks across either lobe. Length 12 inches. (Day.)

The above description was taken from Cuvier and Valenciennes's type in the Paris Museum.

We know of no record of this species from the Hawaiian Islands other than that of Steindachner, who refers 2 examples, obtained at Honolulu, to this species. It was not seen by us and it is probable that *Upeneus arge* has been mistaken for it.

Family LXVII. POMACENTRIDÆ.—The Demoiselles.

Body short, deep, compressed, covered with ctenoid scales of varying size; lateral line wanting posteriorly; mouth small, usually with rather strong teeth, either conic or incisor-like; vomer and palatines toothless; nostril single on each side, nearly round; preopercle with its posterior edge largely free, serrate, or entire; preorbital sheathing the small maxillary; dorsal fin single, with numerous strong spines, the spinous portion longer than the soft, which is similar to the soft anal, both fins scaly at base; anal spines 2; ventral fins thoracic, I, 5, the anterior rays longest, usually filamentous; a scaly appendage at base of ventral; lower pharyngeals fully united; branchiostegals 5 to 7; gills 3.5, the slit behind the last gill very small or obsolete; gillrakers rather long and slender; no labyrinthiform appendage; air-bladder and pseudobranchiæ present, well developed; pyloric cœca 2 or 3; gill-membranes free from the isthmus; vertebræ 12+14=26. Fishes of the tropical seas, similar in mode of life to the *Chætodontidæ*, feeding on small marine animals and plants in the coral reefs. Most of them are too small to be used as food. They are very active in life, and the coloration is usually brilliant, sometimes changing much with age. The family shows strong affinities with the *Labridæ* in gill-structures and pharyngeals. In other respects it approaches the *Kyphosidæ*, while the unique character of the simple nostril is shared with the *Cichlidæ* only, from ancestors of which group the *Pomacentridæ* are probably descended.

Genus 142. DASCYLLUS Cuvier.

Preopercle and sometimes preorbital serrated; teeth small, villiform, in a narrow band, with an outer series of somewhat larger ones; dorsal fin with 12 or 13 spines, anal with 2; scales of moderate size, in fewer than 30 transverse series; lateral line ceasing below the soft dorsal fin; branchiostegals 5; gills 3.5; pseudobranchiæ present; air-bladder large; pyloric appendages 2 or 3. Coral reefs of the Pacific.

208. Dascyllus albisella Gill. Fig. 112.

Head 3.35 in length; depth 1.5; eye 2.3 in head; snout 3.35; maxillary 3; interorbital 2.75; D. XII, 16; A. II, 15; scales 6–27–12.

Body deep, short, greatest depth over base of pectoral; head much deeper than long, the anterior profile nearly vertical; snout short, vertical; mouth small, oblique; jaws subequal, protruding very little beyond anterior profile of head; teeth in jaws with an enlarged outer series, conic, pointed; behind these several series of small teeth in each jaw; maxillary small, reaching little beyond anterior margin of orbit; interorbital width broad, convex; nostril circular, small; margins of preopercle and preorbital finely serrate; second dorsal spine longest, 1.4 in head; base of soft dorsal 2 in spinous dorsal, fourth ray longest, 1.2 in head; second anal spine 1.35 in head; seventh anal ray longest, 1.2 in head; caudal slightly emarginate, lobes rounded and upper longer than lower; pectoral pointed, upper rays longest, 2.1 in base of dorsal; ventrals large, pointed, 2.6 in body; caudal peduncle deep, 1.65 in head; scales large, ctenoid. The above description chiefly from an example (No. 543), obtained at Honolulu in 1889, by Dr. Jenkins.

Color in life (Nos. 03445 and 03549), each scale with a blackish border and whitish base, except in the white area in middle of dorsal part of body, where dark borders of each scale are almost absent; nuchal spot blue when present; all fins dark, almost black, except the whitish scales on dorsal fin.

One example (No. 03355) shows general color whitish, blue darkest on head and breast; scales enveloping bases of dorsal and anal whitish blue; snout and anterior part of head dark brownish blue; dorsal pale bluish, blackish toward tip; caudal, anal, and ventrals bluish black; pectoral pale blue; iris bluish brown.

Color in alcohol, uniform brown, margin of each scale with darker; a large white blotch on middle of back above; lips, margins of vertical fins, base of pectoral above, and ventrals, dusky blackish. Young examples are very deep brownish black with pearly white blotch extending down on side of body pronounced, the pectoral pale, and soft dorsal whitish above. Some also show margins of anal and caudal whitish and a white nuchal spot.

FIG. 112.—*Dascyllus albisella* Gill; after Bleeker.

Our collections contain 40 specimens ranging in length from less than half an inch to 4.75 inches, all from Honolulu except one, which was collected at Waikiki Beach. This pretty little fish is rather common in crevices of the coral reefs. Apparently the Hawaiian species, *albisella*, is different from the common *trimaculatus* of the South Seas.

Genus 143. CHROMIS Cuvier.

Body oblong or ovate, the depth two-fifths to two-thirds the length of body without caudal; pre-opercle entire, or nearly so; lateral line wanting on tail; mouth small; teeth conical, in 2 or more series, the outer series enlarged and blunt; scales rather large, 24 to 30 in a longitudinal series; sub-orbital and lower jaw scaly; dorsal fin with 12 to 14 spines and 9 to 14 soft rays; caudal more or less forked, the lobes rounded or acute; branchiostegals normally 5; pyloric cœca 2; gillrakers long and slender. Tropical seas; species numerous, varying considerably in form, perhaps divisible into smaller genera.

209. Chromis elaphrus Jenkins.   Fig. 113.

Head 3.4 in length; depth 2.25; eye 3 in head; snout 3.75; maxillary 3.75; interorbital 2.5; D. XII, 15 or 16; A. II, 12; P. 18; scales 4–27–9, 20 pores.

Body short, deep, ovate and compressed, the dorsal outline of body more convex than ventral outline; snout short and bluntly conic; anterior outline a little more convex in interorbital region than on nape; caudal peduncle about 2 in head; snout shorter than eye; suborbital, preopercle, and opercle entire, the preopercle somewhat crenulate; opercle ending in 2 small flat spines, the upper

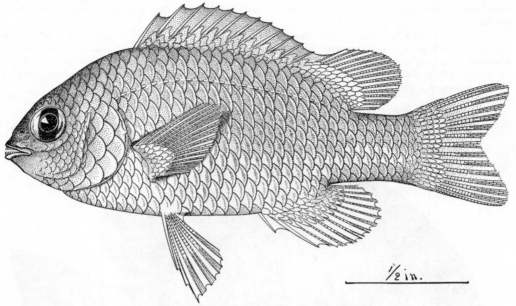

FIG. 113.—*Chromis elaphrus* Jenkins; from the type.

obscure; teeth conic, close-set in a single series in each jaw; third dorsal spine longest, 1.8 in head; soft dorsal somewhat higher than spinous portion, slightly rounded, longest rays about 1.7; anal rounded, similar to soft dorsal, 1.4; caudal deeply emarginate, the upper lobe slightly the longer, about equaling head; ventrals nearly reaching vent, 1.3; pectoral broad, rather truncate, 1.3; scales large, regular, slightly ctenoid, densely covering entire body and head except snout anterior to nostril and tip of lower jaw; lateral line well developed, beginning at upper edge of gill-opening, gently arched, following contour of back to within 3 scales of base of last dorsal ray, where it ceases; bases of all the fins scaled, those on spinous dorsal largest.

Color in alcohol, brown above and on top of head, paler below; opercle dusky; fins all plain or dusky, without markings; no black spot or blotch upon anterior portion of spinous dorsal, and none at base of pectoral.

The above description based chiefly upon a specimen 2.25 inches long from Hilo, where several specimens were obtained in Henshaw's pool, in lava rocks 2 miles to the southward of Hilo. The species seems to be fairly common, though it was obtained by us only at Hilo, where we secured 9 specimens. Nine specimens, including the type, were obtained by Dr. Jenkins from among the coral rocks at Honolulu in 1889. This is one of the most agile of fishes.

210. Chromis ovalis (Steindachner).   Fig. 114.

Head 3.5 in length; depth 2.3; eye 3.2 in head; snout 4.2; maxillary 3; interorbital 3; D. XIV, 11; A. II, 13; scales 3–28–8.

Body oblong-ovate, deepest through base of ventrals, compressed; dorsal outline steepest from origin of dorsal fin to tip of snout, slightly concave over interorbital region; head deeper than long, compressed; snout subconic; lower jaw slightly included; maxillary reaching anterior edge of eye; mouth small, nearly horizontal; a single row of small distinct conic teeth in each jaw, 1 or 2 short indistinct rows back of the outer row in the anterior part of jaws; opercle and preopercle entire, no opercular spine; eye anterior, its lower edge on line with upper base of pectoral; interorbital slightly convex, almost flat in some examples; fins rather large, origin of dorsal slightly anterior to origin of pectoral, fourth to eighth spines about equal and the longest 1.85 in head; first spine slightly shorter than last; middle rays of dorsal longest, 1.8, the soft part being rounded; anal rays nearly all equal, the last 2 or 3 slightly the shorter, longest 1.9; second spine rather stout and strong, 2; first spine very short; caudal deeply forked, upper lobe slightly the longer, longest ray about 3 in body; ventrals reaching vent,

1.25 in head; pectoral large, pointed, upper rays longest, 3 in body; scales large, very finely ctenoid, covering entire body and head except lips, small scales at bases of all the fins, those on soft dorsal and anal and caudal small and covering most of the fin; lateral line concurrent with dorsal outline, on first 20 rows of scales, then dropping 3 rows and very obscurely extending on middle of caudal peduncle to base of dorsal fin.

Color in alcohol, brownish or dusky olive above, below silvery yellowish; base of pectoral black, color not extending to axil; about 8 indistinct longitudinal dusky streaks along side of body below dorsal region, following rows of scales; membranes of spinous dorsal black; soft anal and dorsal dusky; caudal dusky brown.

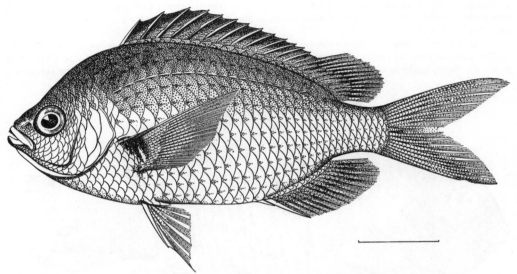

FIG. 114.—*Chromis ovalis* (Steindachner). Type of *C. velox* Jenkins.

We have seen only 4 specimens, all from Honolulu, 3 obtained by Dr. Jenkins and one by Dr. Wood. Each is 6 inches long.

Genus 144. POMACENTRUS Lacépède.

Body ovate, or oblong, compressed, the profile steep, usually rounded; head moderate, nearly as deep as long, the snout scaly, the lower jaw scaly or naked; mouth quite small, terminal, the jaws equal; each jaw armed with 1 or 2 close-set series of compressed, immovable teeth, which are truncate or rounded at tip, sometimes a few small teeth behind these; gillrakers long; preopercle more or less serrate; preorbital serrate; scales large, strongly ctenoid, the lateral line running parallel with the back to near end of dorsal fin, at which point it ceases; dorsal fin continuous, with 12 or 13 low stout spines; membrane of spinous dorsal usually not deeply incised nor lobed, the soft part more or less elevated, its last rays gradually shortened; lower limb of preopercle usually more or less scaly; preorbital narrow, without deep notch; anal fin similar to soft dorsal, with 2 spines, of which the second is much the larger; soft rays 12 to 16; dorsal spines with a sheath of large scales, the membranes of both dorsal and anal covered high up with small scales; caudal fin more or less forked, the lobes rounded; lower pharyngeals triangular; branchiostegals 5 or 6. Species numerous in the tropical seas; extremely variable in form and color, the brilliant coloration apparently dependent on surroundings.

211. Pomacentrus jenkinsi Jordan & Evermann. Fig. 115.

Head 3.4 in length; depth 1.8; eye 3.3 in head; snout 4; maxillary 3.2; interorbital 2.75; D. XIII, 16; A. II, 13; scales 4–29–11; Br. 4.

Body ovate, deep, compressed, dorsal outline rather steep, evenly curved from tip of snout to soft dorsal, following edge of scales on spinous dorsal; head deeper than long, compressed, subconic; snout bluntly conic, jaws equal; maxillary reaching anterior edge of eye; mouth small, horizontal; a single row of close-set, incisor teeth in each jaw; posterior edge of preopercle roughly serrate; opercle ending in 2 short flat spines, the upper very obscure; interorbital wide, strongly convex; fins rather large; origin of dorsal over ventral, origin of each equally distant from tip of snout; first 2 or 3 dorsal spines shorter than others; others about of equal length, shorter than the longest dorsal rays, the median rays being longest, 1.5 in head; caudal forked, lobes rounded, upper the longer; anal rounded, longest ray 1.5 in head, second spine rather stout and strong, 2.2 in head; ventrals long, reaching vent, 1.1 in head;

pectoral broad, upper rays the longer, 1.2 in head; scales large, finely ctenoid; body and head, except lower jaw and snout, scaled, scales on top of head small; bases of all the fins except ventrals well covered with fine scales, those on spinous dorsal larger; lateral line concurrent with dorsal outline to a line under base of third or fourth dorsal ray, where it drops 3 rows of scales to middle of caudal peduncle, thence continuing to base of caudal fin, the detached portion little developed.

Color in life, ground dark drab; central portion of scales olivaceous, each one with black on lower part of posterior edge forming vertical bands on body; axil black; outer border of dorsal fin, above scaled part, black; pectoral dusky olivaceous, black at base; ventral and anal black; caudal dusky with posterior border lighter; iris bright yellow.

Color in alcohol, dark brown, edges of scales darker; a dark stripe on upper edge of membranes of spinous dorsal, broadest and most distinct anteriorly; rest of dorsal, and caudal and pectoral dark brownish; ventrals and anal dark, almost black; a black blotch at upper base of pectoral, continuous with the black axil.

This is a very abundant species among the Hawaiian Islands. Numerous specimens were obtained at Honolulu in 1889 by Dr. Jenkins, and others by Dr. Wood in 1898 and Dr. Jordan in 1900. Our own collections, made in 1901, contain numerous specimens, the localities represented being Honolulu,

FIG. 115.—*Pomacentrus jenkinsi* Jordan & Evermann. Type of *Eupomacentrus marginatus* Jenkins.

Hilo, and Kailua, and specimens were taken by the *Albatross* in 1902 at many different places among the Hawaiian Islands.

The above description is based chiefly upon a specimen (field No. 04526) 4.8 inches long, obtained by us at Honolulu. The length varies from 3.75 to 5.25 inches.

Genus 145. ABUDEFDUF Forskål.

Body deep, compressed, covered with large ctenoid scales; snout without scales; preopercle and preorbital entire, the lower limb of preopercle scaleless; 3 to 4 rows of scales between lateral line and dorsal; teeth compressed, fixed, more or less distinctly emarginate, in one series in each jaw, those below occupying most of the free edge of the jaw; jaws subequal. Dorsal usually with 13 spines, the last slightly shorter than the medium ones; branchiostegals 5 or 6; pyloric cœca 3; lower pharyngeals triangular. Species numerous, often brightly colored, found about coral reefs in the tropical seas. We exclude from this genus all species with rounded, biserial teeth.

212. Abudefduf sindonis (Jordan & Evermann). Plate 40.*a*

Head 3.5 in length; depth 1.75; eye 3.4 in head; snout 3.5; maxillary 3.4; interorbital 2.8; D. XII, 19; A. II, 15; scales 4–28–9, 22 pores.

---

a Glyphisodon sindonis on plate.

Body short and deep, dorsal outline evenly arched from tip of snout to soft dorsal; head deeper than long, compressed; snout short and conic; mouth small, horizontal, lower jaw slightly shorter; maxillary reaching to anterior edge of orbit; a single row of small, rather blunt, slightly compressed teeth on each jaw; preopercle entire, opercle ending in 2 small flat spines, upper very small and obscure; eye anterior, high, its lower edge above upper base of pectoral; interorbital broad, steep, and convex; fins large, origin of dorsal over base of ventrals, its distance from tip of snout equal to distance from base of last ray to tip of upper caudal lobe; spines strong and long, first 0.7 of fourth, which is 1.9 in head and of same length as following spines; middle dorsal rays produced, longest ray 1.25 in head; anal similar to soft dorsal, longest ray 1.25 in head, second spine longest, 2 in head; caudal forked, upper lobe the longer; ventrals reaching past vent, outer rays longest, about equal to head; pectoral broad, upper rays longest, equal to head; scales large, ctenoid, covering entire body and head except lower jaw and snout anterior to eye; lower limb of preopercle scaled; large scales covering nearly all of dorsal spines, smaller scales covering as much of soft dorsal and anal and nearly all of caudal; very minute scales on base of pectoral, none on rays of ventrals; lateral line concurrent with dorsal outline, on 22 scales, ending 3 rows of scales short of posterior base of dorsal, then dropping 3 rows of scales and continuing obscurely on middle of caudal peduncle to base of caudal fin.

Color in alcohol, uniform very dark brown, nearly black; 2 narrow wavy bands of white on side, first beginning about under fourth dorsal spine and extending under about middle of pectoral, thence curving slightly backward toward vent, rather indistinct below pectoral; second band beginning under last dorsal spine and first ray, extending toward middle of anal, rather obscure, indistinct for 2 or 3 scales before reaching anal; fins all black, pectoral slighty lighter than others; a large black ocellated spot with a narrow white border on back and lower part of soft dorsal, larger than eye, just back of last white bar.

The above description based on the type, No. 50669, U. S. N. M. (field No. 04524), a specimen 3.75 inches long, from Honolulu.   One other specimen obtained and taken as a cotype, No. 2727, Bureau of Fisheries reserve series (field No. 03732).   It is 2.75 inches long, and was taken at Kailua where the species was first discovered by Mr. Michitaro Sindo, for whom it is named.

This species agrees with typical *Abudefduf* in all respects except that none of the teeth appears to be emarginate.   It agrees with *Chrysiptera* in the entire preopercle and preorbital and naked snout, but differs from the type of that genus in having the teeth in a single series.

213. Abudefduf abdominalis (Quoy & Gaimard).   "*Maomao.*"   Fig. 116.

Head 3.5 in length; depth 2; eye 3.75 in head; snout 3.4; maxillary 3.5; interorbital 2.8; D. XIII, 14; A. II, 14; scales 5-30-11.

Body oblong, deep, compressed, much longer in adult than in young; head small, its depth equal to its length; upper profile concave over eyes; snout short, obtuse, rounded: mouth small, oblique, jaws equal; lips fleshy; teeth in jaws small, uniserial, compressed, incisor-like, their margins notched; no teeth on vomer, palatines, or tongue; tongue elongate, pointed, free in front; eye anterior, superior, less than snout; preopercle oblique, its margin smooth; interorbital width broad, convex; nostril small, circular; third dorsal spine 2 in head; longest dorsal ray 1.4; fourth anal ray 1.5; pectoral long, pointed, 3.1 in body; ventrals pointed 3.6, the spine 1.4 in first ray; scales large, rounded, ctenoid; lateral line arched, not continued beyond soft dorsal; tubes of lateral line arborescent; no scales on snout, in front of eye, or on lips and chin; scales on infraorbital, vertical fins, and base of pectoral minute.

Color in life (No. 3007), body, pale brassy green, with 5 narrow bluish black vertical bars, the first from front of dorsal to base of pectoral, the second from third to fifth dorsal spines to beneath middle of pectoral, the third from eighth or ninth spine toward origin of anal; the fourth from last spines to middle of anal and the last, which is faint, from last dorsal rays across caudal peduncle; head dusky; belly white; black spot on base of pectoral above, axil black; dorsal brassy, mottled with dark, the edge of membrane black, the projecting spines white; black blotch on base of last dorsal rays; caudal and anal dusky yellowish; ventrals white, dusky at tips; pectoral pale yellowish; breast dusky; iris silvery, black above and below.   Another example was steel-blue when fresh, olive-green on back with 4 broad cross bars; spinous dorsal, base of soft dorsal, caudal and base of anal black; a black spot at base of pectoral; ventral black; soft dorsal, caudal and anal pale, except base.

Color in alcohol, purplish brown above; side below lateral line with dull light green longitudinal bands; lower surface of body whitish; 5 blackish vertical bands on side of back, indistinct on lower half of body, and extending up on fin; first band begins at origin of spinous dorsal, second at fourth and fifth dorsal spines, third at ninth and tenth spines, and fourth at last dorsal spine and first 2 rays; dark brown blotch on caudal peduncle above; a deep black blotch on basal portion of posterior rays of soft dorsal and anal; vertical fins dusky grayish; pectoral and ventrals grayish, the latter with whitish streaks between rays; blackish spots at base of median caudal rays.

Described from an example (No. 4488), from Honolulu.

This species is close to *Abudefduf saxatilis* of India, from which it is distinguished by the large black spots at bases of posterior dorsal and anal rays, and the fourth blackish vertical bar beginning at

FIG. 116.—*Abudefduf abdominalis* (Quoy & Gaimard); after Günther.

last dorsal spine and first 2 or 3 soft rays.   The Atlantic form, *Abudefduf marginatus*, is distinguished by the shorter, more orbicular body and the absence of black blotches on soft dorsal and anal.

We have examined 55 specimens of this species, all from Honolulu except 1 from Hilo and 4 from Kailua.   They range in length from 3.4 to 9 inches.   Specimens were also found by the *Albatross* at numerous places among the Hawaiian Islands.

214. Abudefduf imparipennis (Sauvage).

Head 4 in total length; depth 3; eye 3.5 in head; D. xii, 16; A. ii, 11; scales 2–28–8.

Head longer than high; interorbital equaling snout, which equals orbit; infraorbital almost as long as preorbital; teeth long and compressed; scales of head extending on snout nearly to tip; caudal scarcely forked, a little shorter than head; second dorsal spine as long as soft rays.   Honolulu.

Not seen by us; known only from the description by Sauvage.

215. Abudefduf sordidus (Forskål).   "*Kupipi.*"   Fig. 117.

Head 3.2 in length; depth 1.75; eye 4.6 in head; snout 2.8; maxillary 3.2; interorbital 2.5; D. xiii, 16; A. ii, 15; scales 6–29–12.

FIG. 117.—*Abudefduf sordidus* (Forskål); after Rüppell.

Body short, deep, compressed, back rather trenchant in front; head small, deep; snout round, blunt, a little longer than eye, mouth small, slightly oblique, the jaws equal; lips fleshy; teeth compressed, uniserial in jaws; eye small, anterior and superior; preopercle very oblique, its margin entire; interorbital width broad, strongly convex; nostril small, circular, in front of middle of eye; longest dorsal spine 2 in head; longest dorsal ray 1.5; second anal spine 2.1; longest anal ray 1.4; caudal broad, forked, lobes rounded; pectoral 1 in head; ventrals 1.2, reaching origin of anal; caudal peduncle broad, 1.75 in head; scales large, ctenoid, except those on fins which are very small; snout, preorbital, and jaws naked.

Color in alcohol, dull brown, a little darker on back; side with 6 broad dark brown vertical bands, deep on back; scales over and behind eye, a row over nape with black centers; a black spot on caudal peduncle above, at base of last dorsal rays; vertical fins blackish; pectoral pale brown; ventrals blackish.

Described from an example (No. 04511) taken at Honolulu.

This species is easily distinguished by the presence of the black spot on caudal peduncle, which is present at all ages. The young have also a black spot at base of pectoral.

We have examined 39 specimens of this common species, 6 collected by us at Kailua, 5 at Hilo, 10 at Waianae, 1 at Moanalua, and 8 at Honolulu; 1 obtained by McGregor at Lahaina, Maui, and 8 by Dr. Jenkins at Honolulu. Specimens were also collected by the *Albatross* at Honolulu; Puako Bay, Hawaii; Napili Bay, Molokai; Necker Island, and Laysan Island. Our examples are one-half to 8.25 inches long.

Family LXVIII. MALACANTHIDÆ.—The Blanquillos.

Body more or less elongate, fusiform, or compressed; head subconical, the anterior profile usually convex; suborbital without bony stay; the bones not greatly developed; cranial bones not cavernous; opercular bones mostly unarmed; mouth rather terminal, little oblique; teeth rather strong; no teeth on vomer or palatines; premaxillary usually with a blunt posterior canine, somewhat as in the *Labridæ;* premaxillaries protractile; maxillary without supplemental bone, not slipping under the edge of the preorbital; gills 4, a long slit behind the fourth; pseudobranchiæ well developed; gill-membranes separate, or more or less united, often adherent to the isthmus; lower pharyngeals separate; scales small, ctenoid; lateral line present, complete, more or less concurrent with the back; dorsal fin long and low, usually continuous, the spinous portion always much less developed than the soft portion, but never obsolete; anal fin very long, its spines feeble and few; caudal fin forked; tail diphycercal; ventrals thoracic or subjugular, I, 5, close together; pectoral fins not very broad, the rays all branched; vertebræ in normal or slightly increased number (24 to 30); pyloric cœca few or none. Fishes of the temperate and tropical seas, some of them reaching a large size.

Genus 146. MALACANTHUS Cuvier.

Body elongate, slightly compressed; cleft of mouth horizontal, with the jaws equal; eyes lateral; scales very small, minutely ciliated; one continuous dorsal, with the first 4 to 6 rays not articulated; dorsal and anal very long; pectoral rays all branched; jaws with villiform teeth; an outer series of stronger teeth, some of them canine-like, and with a canine at the posterior extremity of the intermaxillary; no teeth on the palate; preopercle entire; opercle with a spine; gillrakers little developed; vertebræ in small number, 10 + 14 = 24.

216. Malacanthus parvipinnis Vaillant & Sauvage. "*Maká'a.*" Fig. 118.

Head 5 in length; depth 6.8; snout 3 in head; eye 4.7; interorbital 2.9; maxillary 2.6; D. v, 57; A. 53; P. 16; V. I, 4; scales 8–175–24.

Body very elongate, compressed, greatest depth about middle of belly; head elongate, compressed, its depth 1.7, width 2; upper profile of head evenly convex; snout elongate, convex, rather blunt; jaws nearly equal, rather large· mouth large, slightly inclined, end of maxillary reaching almost to front of pupil; eye small, high, posterior margin of pupil nearly midway in length of head; nostrils formed as horizontal slits in a groove in front of middle of eye, well separated, the anterior placed in about last third of snout; interorbital space very broad, convex; lips rather broad, fleshy; teeth sharp pointed, somewhat unequal, in broad bands in jaws; opercle with a large strong spine with a fleshy flap; gill-opening rather large, the isthmus broad, gill-membrane forming a broad fold across; scales very small, ctenoid, those in the lateral line very small, and with posterior margin deeply scalloped; head naked except on postocular region, occiput, cheek, and opercle, which are covered with small finely ctenoid scales; dorsal very long, of more or less uniform height; dorsal spines short, flexible; rays flexible, seventh 2.5; anal long, similar to dorsal, twelfth ray 2.5; the fin beginning at tip of pectoral; pectoral broad, 1.35 in head; ventrals small, close together, 2.5; caudal expanded, truncate, 1.6; caudal peduncle short, compressed, its depth 3.75; lateral line slightly irregular, superior at first, then running down on middle of side of trunk at its last third.

Color in life of a specimen 12 inches long, from Honolulu, light olive green; belly silvery; side with about 20 faint short bands of the back color; dorsal flesh-color, a little rosy, a narrow edge of yellow; caudal lobes gray; iris deep blue, a little golden above.

Color in alcohol, pale brown on upper surface and forming about 20 pale slightly inclined cross bars along side, fading out in the pale color beneath; side and lower surface very pale straw-color washed with silvery; fins, with the exception of caudal, pale straw-color; caudal pale straw-color,

Fig. 118.—*Malacanthus parvipinnis* Vaillant & Sauvage; after Günther.

middle rays whitish, 2 jet-black horizontal bands beginning on the upper and lower rudimentary caudal rays and running to edge of fin; a spot on lower part of iris.

Described from an example (No. 04128) taken at Honolulu.

We have from Honolulu 20 examples 7.25 to 11.75 inches long and 1 from Hilo 8.75 inches long.

Specimens were obtained by Dr. Wood at Honolulu and by the *Albatross* at Honolulu and at Lahaina, Maui.

Suborder PHARYNGOGNATHI.—The Labroid Fishes.

Lower pharyngeals fully united; nostrils double; gills 3.5, with no slit behind the last; ventral fins thoracic, each with 1 spine and 5 rays; dorsal and anal spines not very strong; scales weakly ctenoid or cycloid; in other respects essentially as in the *Percoidea*. Species mostly of the tropical shores; most of them large fishes of strong dentition and bright colors.

Family LXIX. LABRIDÆ.—The Wrasse-Fishes.

Body oblong or elongate, covered with cycloid scales, lateral line well developed, continuous or interrupted, often angularly bent; mouth moderate, terminal; premaxillaries protractile; maxillaries without supplemental bone, slipping under membranaceous edge of the preorbital; anterior teeth in jaws usually very strong and canine-like; teeth of jaws separate or soldered together at base, not forming a continuous plate; no teeth on vomer or palatines; lower pharyngeals completely united into one bone, without median suture, this bone T-shaped or Y-shaped, its teeth conical or tubercular; lips thick, longitudinally plicate; nostrils round, with 2 openings on each side; dorsal fin continuous, the spinous portion usually long, its spines rather slender, 3 to 20 in number; anal similar to soft dorsal, with 2 to 6 spines; ventrals thoracic, I, 5, inserted below the pectorals or slightly in advance of them; branchiostegals 5 or 6; pseudobranchiæ well developed; gills 3½, the slit behind the last arch small or obsolete; gill-membranes somewhat connected, sometimes joined to the narrow isthmus; air-bladder absent; no pyloric cœca. Species chiefly of the tropical seas, living among rocks, coral reefs, or kelp. Many of them are brilliantly colored, and some are valued as food-fishes. Most of them feed upon mollusks, the dentition being adapted for crushing shells.

Genus 147   LEPIDAPLOIS Gill.

Body compressed, oblong, covered with large scales, 30 to 35 in the lateral line; snout pointed; mouth large, the lateral teeth in both jaws in a single series coalescent at base; 4 canine teeth in front and a posterior canine tooth; cheeks and opercles with imbricated scales; dorsal and anal scaly at base; lateral line not interrupted; preopercle usually finely serrated; soft dorsal and anal not falcate anteriorly; caudal fin lunate. Dorsal rays usually XII, 10; anal rays III, 12. Tropical parts of the western Pacific from Hawaii through Polynesia to Japan and Africa.

217. Lepidaplois albotæniatus (Cuvier & Valenciennes). "*A'awa*." Plate XXIV.*a*

Head 2.9 in length; depth 2.9; snout 3 in head; eye 6; mouth 3; interorbital 3.5; D. XII, 10; A. III, 12; scales 8–34–13.

Body oblong, compressed; head longer than deep, upper and lower profiles evenly weakly convex; snout rather long, pointed, rounded above; jaws produced, pointed, about equal; mouth rather large,

---

a Lepidoplois bilunulatus on plate.

maxillary reaching front of eye; teeth strong, conic; 4 large canines in front of each jaw, the outer on each side of mandible enlarged; lips rather thin, fleshy; eye moderately large, its posterior margin about middle of length of head; posterior margin of preopercle finely serrated; interorbital width broad, convex; nostrils in front of eye, anterior in short. fleshy tube; last dorsal spine 2.7 in head; seventh dorsal ray 2.25; third anal spine 2.5; fifth anal ray longest, 2.2; dorsal and anal rather broad, rounded; caudal truncate, broad at base; pectoral small, 1.7 in head; ventrals pointed, 1.5; caudal peduncle broad, compressed, 1.75; scales large, thin, small upon back in front of dorsal fin and along base of dorsal and anal; scales smaller on chest than on sides of body; interorbital width, snout, space in front of eye, and mandibles without scales, head otherwise scaly; scales on cheeks very small; lateral line concurrent with back and running posteriorly along middle of side of caudal peduncle. Described chiefly from an example (No. 04288) from Hilo.

Color in life (No. 122 O. P. J.), pinkish shades on white ground-color; numerous horizontal brown stripes crowded together along top of head and back; a brown stripe from angle of mouth to angle of preopercle; chin and throat white, covered with red spots; colors of body posteriorly gradually give way to yellow, which becomes bright yellow on caudal fin; a black blotch at base of posterior part of soft dorsal extending on caudal peduncle; a black spot nearly as large as eye on first dorsal between first and third spines; iris black, with red inner margin; tips of dorsal spines yellow, the soft dorsal and anal bright yellow; pectoral rosy; ventrals white, with rosy and yellow shadings.

Specimen No. 02976 in life had upper half of head and anterior portion of upper part of side dull rosy; side mostly dirty yellowish, with about 10 pale bands made by pale areas on centers of scales; caudal peduncle fading gradually into rosy anteriorly; a broad dark reddish band from snout through eye to gill-opening, below this pale rosy, with small blotches of brown and pale red; a bluish wash from angle of mouth to gill-opening; lower jaw and throat pale rosy; a large deep black blotch on side under last dorsal rays, connecting with its fellow across caudal peduncle; spinous dorsal with rosy spines, membranes bluish-black, and a large blue-black blotch on membrane between second and third spines; soft dorsal bright yellow; caudal and anal bright yellow, the latter somewhat smoky anteriorly; pectoral rosy; ventrals pale bluish, rosy on margin.

Specimen No. 02977 was in life dark purplish red, becoming ashy below; upper parts of head rosy; cheek ashy, washed with rosy; 2 or 3 obscure dark blotches on preorbital; a dark postocular bar ending in a rather distinct opercular spot; 2 or 3 black blotches at angle of preopercle; subopercle also with several black blotches; lower jaw bluish gray, blotched with rosy and dusky; a very pale reddish blotch under last rays of soft dorsal, in center of which is a black spot covering 1 scale; spinous dorsal bluish gray, a large black blotch on membrane between second and third spines; soft dorsal pale red with a yellow border, the last rays orange near tips, which are yellow, a more or less distinct patch of pale pinkish brown below them; caudal pale rosy, membranes smoky blue, outer rays darker, and with a narrow pale yellow border; anal very pale rosy, the border pale yellow, narrowly bordered with bluish; pectoral rosy, base darkest; ventrals pale smoky bluish; iris red.

Another example in life was deep purple red, fading to livid purplish. Old examples were distinctly striped, caudal dull purplish red, not yellow, besides pale blotch below dorsal.

Color in alcohol pale brown; back a little darker, lower surface whitish; head with dark-brown lines above, lowest 2 broadest, running from snout to eye and back along side of head; streak from corner of mouth and several spots at same place dark brown; narrow brown lines along back and broader ones on side; a black blotch on spinous dorsal in front between second and third spines; a large black blotch below last dorsal rays on back; fins all pale or whitish, except ventrals, which are grayish in middle.

We have several small examples (the smallest 4.2 inches in length) which are marked exactly like the adults.

This species is very common about Hawaii, appearing daily in the markets. Our collections contain 33 examples (31 from Honolulu and 2 from Hilo), 4.4 to 14 inches in length. Specimens were obtained at Honolulu also by Dr. Jenkins, the Fur Seal Commission, and by the *Albatross*.

218. Lepidaplois modestus (Garrett). Fig. 119.

Head nearly 4 in total length; depth 4; eye nearly 6 in head; scales ?–33–12; Br. 6; D. xii, 10; A. iii, 12; V. i, 5; P. 17; C. 2, 1, 6, 6, 1, 2. Head presents a slight concave depression above eyes; preopercular serrations very small; eyes subcircular; maxillary reaching to center of eye; scales of lateral line slightly branched.

Dorsal fin extends over a base equal to half length of fish without caudal, base of soft portion slightly less than one-third the fin; anal nearly half as long as dorsal, its posterior base slightly posterior to dorsal; ventrals nearly reaching anal; edges of caudal fin pointed and prolonged.

Color, purplish brown, passing into bluish gray beneath, and obsoletely lineated longitudinally with darker; a large oblong pale diffuse spot beneath the posterior end of the dorsal fin, which is

---

a Misprinted *Lepidoplois*.

FIG. 119.—*Lepidaplois modestus* (Garrett); after Günther.

directed obliquely downward and forward; irides silvery, tinged with yellow; dorsal fin pale grayish, marked anteriorly with a large diffuse bluish-black spot, its soft portion tinged with reddish and margined above with yellow; anal, ventral, and caudal bluish gray, the former posteriorly tinged with faded red and edged with yellow; pectorals nearly colorless.   (Garrett.)

219. Lepidaplois strophodes Jordan & Evermann.   *"A'awa."*   Plate XXIII.

Head 2.75 in length; depth 2.75; eye 4.65 in head; snout 3.25; mouth 3.1; interorbital 4; D. xii, 10; A. iii, 12; scales 7–34–13.

Body oblong, compressed; head longer than deep; upper and lower profiles evenly and slightly convex; snout long, pointed, rounded above; jaws produced, pointed, about equal; mouth large, maxillary reaching beyond front of eye; teeth strong, forming a sharp cutting edge on sides of jaws, front of each jaw with 4 large canines; eye rather large, anterior, high in head; posterior margin of preopercle very finely emarginate; interorbital space rather broad, convex; nostrils small, anterior in short tube; dorsal spines pungent, longest 3 in head, last 3.5; third anal spine longest, 2.8; third anal ray 1.9 in head; pectoral rounded, 1.7; ventrals pointed, 1.4; caudal broad at base, truncate; caudal peduncle broad, compressed, its depth 2; scales large, thin, those on front of dorsal, along its base and that of anal, small; lateral line concurrent with back, sloping down at caudal, then running straight to its base.

Color in life, pale rosy white; upper parts of the snout, nape, and side to base of about ninth dorsal spine, lemon-yellow, extending down on side to level of upper edge of pupil; side of head very pale rosy, 2 irregular broken lines of wine-colored spots across snout and through eye to posterior edge of opercle, a similar row of 4 oblong spots from angle of mouth downward and backward to edge of opercle; cheek and side of lower jaw with numerous small irregularly placed orange spots; side with about 16 brighter rosy longitudinal lines, those above less distinct on account of the deeper rosy ground color, those below more distinct, the ground color being more white; side between anal and soft dorsal fins with a broad sooty black spot extending irregularly upon both fins and fading out upon body anteriorly, the posterior edge being nearly vertical and well defined; caudal peduncle and base of the caudal fin whitish, with a slight tinge of rosy, a pale rosy band separating this from the black lateral area; region in front and below the pectoral with about 4 series of small reddish-brown spots; pectoral region and the under parts somewhat bluish; dorsal fin rich lemon-yellow, the tips of the soft rays whitish, and a small, round, black spot on middle of membrane of second spine; base of soft rays and last dorsal spines rosy from intrusion of the rosy wash on side of body; last dorsal rays sooty black at the base from extension of the black spot on the side; caudal pale lemon-yellow; anal pale rosy in center, lemon on spines and along tip of fin, base of fin sooty black from intrusion of black spot on side of the body, the black extending farthest down on the interradial membranes; pectoral very pale rosy; ventrals pale rosy, the membranes bluish, the tip of second ray blackish.

Color in alcohol (field No. 04291), gray-brown, gradually darker posteriorly; space between soft dorsal and anal abruptly black, the color extending forward in darker streaks along the rows of scales and forming a large black blotch on soft dorsal and anal; top of head and space before dorsal abruptly pale; posterior part of caudal peduncle also abruptly pale; a black blotch on dorsal between second and third spines, not involving third and fourth, as in *L. bilunulatus;* dorsal and caudal otherwise pale; a pale blotch at base of posterior dorsal rays; side with narrow dark brown longitudinal lines, coalescing posteriorly with the black blotch; 2 narrow brown streaks from lip to front of eye, then

---

back across side of head above, edged with narrow, darker, wavy lines; a wavy streak from corner of mouth toward base of pectoral; lower side of head with small brown spots or blotches; ventral fin mostly dusky.

This species is very close to *Lepidaplois bilunulatus*, differing chiefly in the dark zone on posterior part of body and in the smaller size of the dorsal spot. Our specimens are all young, but we have the young of *L. bilunulatus* scarcely larger and showing the markings of the adult.

Our collection contains 5 specimens 3.75 to 4.7 inches long, all from Honolulu.

Genus 148. VERRICULUS Jordan & Evermann.

Body elongate, subfusiform, compressed, with rather long pointed snout; mouth rather large, with anterior canines strong, ¼ to ⅜; posterior canines present; lateral teeth short, confluent in a serrated cutting edge; cheeks and opercles scaly; preopercle entire, both limbs more or less scaly; scales moderate, about 40 in lateral line; lateral line continuous; D. xii, 10; A. iii, 10; dorsal spines low, pungent; soft dorsal and anal not elevated, their bases without scales; caudal subtruncate; pectoral short. This genus is allied to *Verreo* and *Nesiotes*. From its nearest relative, *Nesiotes*, it differs in the presence of a posterior canine tooth. The single species is brilliantly colored.

220. Verriculus sanguineus Jordan & Evermann. Plate XXV.

Head 2.9 in length; depth 3.5; eye 6.2 in head; snout 3.1; mouth 2.8; interorbital 4.75; D. xii, 10; A. iii, 12; scales 5–40–13.

Body elongate, compressed oblong; head long, pointed, conic, its depth 1.7 in its length; eye small, its posterior margin in middle of length of head; snout long, pointed, rounded; jaws produced, equal; mouth large, nearly horizontal, corner reaching below front rim of eye; lips thick, fleshy; teeth strong, those on sides short, close-set, forming a sharp cutting edge on side of jaw; 5 canines in front of upper jaw, 4 in front of lower, a posterior canine on each side of upper jaw; tongue long, pointed, free in front; preopercle not serrate; interorbital space broad, convex; nostrils small, anterior in short tube; dorsal spines strong, sharp-pointed, longest in middle and posteriorly; last dorsal spine 4 in head; anal spines strong, last spine longest, 3.75; seventh anal ray 3; caudal rounded; dorsal and anal fins scaled at base; pectoral rounded, 1.9 in head; ventrals short, spine strong, pointed, two-thirds longest ray, which is 2 in head; caudal peduncle broad, deep, 2.2 in head; scales small, thin, cycloid; head with very small thin cycloid scales on occiput, cheek, greater part of opercle, behind eye, and on opercles, otherwise naked; lateral line slightly curved in front, then obliquely down to base of caudal.

Color in life, deep red, edge of upper jaw and lower lip golden; a long stripe below eye pure golden; a long stripe from eye along back to base of caudal golden, with a red shade, a vertical black bar edged with golden above, on opercular region; a long blackish area covering it from eye to above pectoral, with some blackish before, behind, and above; a black spot at base of caudal; dorsal and caudal golden, first dorsal edged with violet and with the lower half violet; anal entirely deep blood-red; ventrals golden; pectoral reddish, golden at base.

Color in alcohol, very pale brown; a dusky band from snout across back of head and on side, fading out indistinctly posteriorly; a blackish spot at middle of base of caudal; opercle posteriorly with black vertical blotch; fins all pale or light brown.

Described from the type, No. 50677, U. S. N. M. (field No. 03489), an example 7.5 inches long, taken at Hilo with hook and line, in deep water with *Etelis evurus*, *Eteliscus marshi*, *Erythrichthys schlegeli*, *Antigonia steindachneri*, and *Anthias fuscipinnis*. Only the type thus far known.

Genus 149. VERREO Jordan & Snyder.

This genus differs from *Lepidaplois* in having the teeth in 2 series, the outer ones canine-like, growing smaller posteriorly, the inner ones coalesced into a narrow, blunt-edged plate; a large straight posterior canine projecting forward from hinder part of upper jaw. Large fishes, similar in appearance to *Lepidaplois*.

221. Verreo oxycephalus (Bleeker). Fig. 120.

Head 2.9 in length; depth 3.35; eye 7 in head; snout 2; mouth 3.75; interorbital 4.1; D. xii, 11; A. iii, 12; scales 6–35–13.

Body elongate, compressed, oblong; head elongate, compressed, pointed, its depth 1.5 in its length; snout and jaws produced, pointed, the latter about equal; lips very thick, broad, fleshy, plicate; maxillary not reaching anterior rim of orbit; nostrils small, close together, anterior in very short tube; mouth rather large, nearly horizontal; teeth in 2 series in jaws, the outer canine-like growing smaller posteriorly, the inner coalesced into a narrow blunt-edged plate; 2 enlarged canines in front of each jaw, those in lower with 2 small teeth between them at symphysis; posterior margin of preopercle very finely serrate; a posterior canine; interorbital width broad, slightly convex; gill-opening large; gillrakers short, thick, conic; dorsal spines strong, thick, pointed, the membranes deeply incised between; seventh spine longest, 3.4 in head; seventh dorsal ray longest, 2.3; anal spines stout, strong, third longest, 2.75; ninth anal ray longest, 3; pectoral rather short, broad, rounded, 1.9; ventral spine strong, 3.4 in head, fin 2; depth of caudal peduncle 2.75; scales large, thin, cycloid; lateral line concurrent with back, running along to base of caudal; head with small scales on top, on cheeks, and on opercles, otherwise naked.

Color in life, 2 straight longitudinal stripes from eye, lower one continuous to root of caudal, but becoming somewhat faint at places, the upper breaking up into 3 elongated blotches over the lateral line; 5 red blotches on back, first 2 under spinous dorsal, third under anterior part of soft dorsal, fourth at posterior end of soft dorsal, fifth forming a saddle above end of tail; ground color above lateral line faintly pinkish; 4 faint reddish streaks from nape to caudal, the upper 2 running through the red blotches on back; body below dirty white with a purplish tinge; 13 faint, dirty reddish-yellow stripes from axil and throat to caudal, the uppermost running together at a point above vent, the 5 lowermost ones terminating at base of anal, fourth and fifth from above border red stripe; head and snout faint reddish; a cluster of yellowish spots on a red ground on interorbital; a yellow patch on each scale on head, except those on subopercle; cheek and jaw paler; frenum and throat faintly purplish; a jet-black blotch covering the lower half of sixth to ninth spinous dorsal membranes; a small blotch at root of tenth spine; anterior half of soft dorsal yellow, reddish at root and tip, membrane of posterior half pale, rays orange, lower half of last 4 red; caudal yellow, middle of membrane and rays

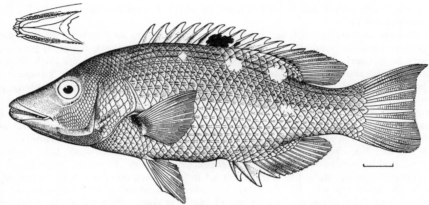

FIG. 120.—*Verreo oxycephalus* (Bleeker); after Jordan and Snyder.

reddish orange, edges reddish, a red spot at upper and lower base of fin; a small red blotch at ventral side of tail, another above posterior end of anal; anal spines and membranes faintly purplish; soft anal yellow, root and margin reddish, tip white, faint purplish streaks on membrane; ventral pale, faintly tinged with purple, spine tinged with red; membrane of pectoral very faintly purplish, rays faint orange, root reddish, axil faintly purplish, a reddish yellow bar at base of fin; the outer edge of iris red, inner yellowish.

Color in alcohol, very pale brown with longitudinal pale lines; basal portion of dorsal fin from sixth to tenth spines black.

Described from one example (No. 04134) from Kailua, which agrees fairly well with specimens from Japan described and figured by Jordan and Snyder (Proc. U. S. Nat. Mus. 1902, 619), and doubtless belongs to the same species. The identity of the Australian pig-fish (*Verreo unimaculatus*) with this species is not proved, but it is not unlikely. Apparently the species is subject to considerable variation in the number and position of the pinkish spots.

Genus 150. STETHOJULIS Günther.

Body oblong, compressed, covered with large scales, 25 to 30 in lateral line, those of the thorax enlarged, larger than those of rest of body; head scaleless; lateral line not interrupted; mouth small; canines small, close set, those of upper jaw very short, those of lower jaw forming a cutting edge; large posterior canines present; fins low; D. IX, 11; A. III, 11, the spines short and pungent. Small fishes of the coral reefs allied to *Halichœres*, but the anterior canines much less developed and the posterior canine wanting. Coloration always exquisite.

222. Stethojulis axillaris (Quoy & Gaimard). "*Omaka.*" Fig. 121.

Head 3 in length; depth 3.2; eye 5.4 in head; snout 2.6; preorbital .5; interorbital 5; D. IX, 11; A. III, 11; scales 3–26–8.

Body rather short, deep and moderately compressed; head longer than deep and pointed; snout sharp pointed; jaws each with a series of close-set bluntly conic teeth; no enlarged anterior canines, posterior canine not developed in any specimen examined; preorbital oblique; opercle ending in a broad thin flap; eye small, the lower edge of orbit in axis of body; dorsal and ventral outlines about equally curved; caudal peduncle moderate, its depth about 2.2 in head; fins moderate; dorsal spines short, the rays slightly longer; caudal slightly rounded; ventrals short; pectoral longer, 1.5 in head;

FIG. 121.—*Stethojulis axillaris* (Quoy & Gaimard); after Günther.

scales large, those on breast and nape not reduced in size; head entirely naked; lateral line complete, curving downward; 3 rows of scales under posterior portion of dorsal.

Color in life of example (No. 03441) taken in coral rocks, olive, with irregular white areas irregularly placed over body; dorsal and anal fins golden with series of pink dots on rays; on one side of caudal peduncle 2, on other side 3 black spots; black spot with yellow margin at bases of last 2 rays of soft dorsal, similar one in same position on anal; golden spot just above axil of pectoral; yellow from tip of snout following horizontal straight line backward just below eye to preopercle; yellow below this line to ventral aspect of head, fading to a light color in alcohol.

A young example 2.5 inches long when fresh, clear olive-green, sanded above with very faint gray points; lower half of head from snout abruptly golden, the upper lip orange; axil orange; a black streak across base of pectoral; 3 indigo-blue spots bordered with paler blue on caudal peduncle, the middle one largest, the third not ocellate and above median line; dorsal orange, finely barred with darker and with olive at base, its edge whitish; anal orange with whitish edge, obscurely green at base; a large ocellus on last rays of dorsal and anal; caudal plain reddish; pectoral and ventrals greenish gray.

Example No. 3077, somewhat faded; back greenish brown with very fine white sand-like specks; head violet brown, dotted above; belly and lower half of side abruptly purplish red, with traces of 4 red streaks along rows of scales; 2 very small black ocelli surrounded with blue on tail, the second larger, both on lateral line; a large yellowish white spot in axil of pectoral, base blackish; dorsal brown, everywhere finely speckled, edge darker; caudal plain dusky; anal same color, yellowish at base; ventrals dirty white; pectoral pale.

Another example, in life was olivaceous, thickly covered with very small bright green dots; throat and belly greenish silvery; base and axil of pectoral with brown spot; a bright orange spot just above pectoral, fading to white in alcohol; 2 or 3 small black spots on lateral line on posterior part of caudal peduncle, the last, if present, on base of caudal fin; dorsal fin olivaceous, with brownish spots, a black spot at the base of last 2 rays; anal olivaceous, the base green.

In alcohol the small green specks become white. In the very young there is a small black spot on the last rays of anal; spots on caudal peduncle almost invariably 3 or 4, the black dorsal spot nearly always present; in examples a little larger the anal spot has disappeared and the number on the caudal peduncle is reduced to 2, rarely 3; in still larger examples the spots on caudal peduncle are reduced to 1 or 2; the anal spot is absent, and that on the dorsal is usually absent. In young examples the yellow or white axillary spot is not evident. Our collection contains a good series of specimens exhibiting these characters, and consists of a fine series of 64 specimens, one-half to 4.7 inches long, 18 from Hilo, the others from Honolulu. Of the latter, 3 were secured by Dr. Wood and 14 by Dr. Jenkins. Specimens were also obtained by the *Albatross* at Honolulu, Puako Bay and Hilo, Hawaii; off the southern coast of Molokai at stations 3829, 3834, and 3837 in 20, 8, and 13 fathoms, respectively. This species, originally described from Maui, is known also from Pelew, Solomon, Fiji, Navigator, Society, New Hebrides, Ponape, and Bandao islands. Individuals were frequently attracted by an electric light of the *Albatross* hung just below the surface of the water.

223. Stethojulis albovittata (Kölreuter). Plate XXVI.

Head 3 in length; depth 3; eye 6 in head; snout 2.7; premaxillary 4; interorbital 4; D. ix, 11; A. iii, 11; scales 4–27–9.

Body rather short, stout and moderately compressed; head longer than deep; snout moderately long, conic; dorsal profile rising in a regular gentle curve from tip of snout to caudal peduncle; ventral outline somewhat less convex; mouth small, each jaw with a series of close-set, bluntly conic teeth, decreasing regularly in size posteriorly; no canines; eye small, slightly anterior, lower border of orbit in line with axis of body; interorbital space rather broad, gently convex; caudal peduncle not deep, its depth equal to snout; lower posterior edge of opercle very oblique, extending upward and backward; opercular flap high, broadly rounded; scales large, those on breast and nape not reduced; a series of smaller scales at base of dorsal and anal and on base of caudal; lateral line complete, following curvature of back to middle of soft dorsal, where it curves downward 3 scales and continues to base of caudal; fins low, longest spines of dorsal about 2 in snout; dorsal rays a little longer; anal similar to soft dorsal; caudal slightly rounded; ventrals short, reaching halfway to origin of anal, their length less than snout; pectoral longer, 1.4 in head, reaching base of anal.

Color in life, upper half of side grayish olive, lower grayish white with purplish wash; a purplish blue-red line along body at base of dorsal, beginning on snout, curving downward to include upper margin of eye, then upward to occiput, thence along base of dorsal to last dorsal ray; a similar line from eye backward under lateral line to vertical from base of third dorsal spine; a third from snout under eye to middle of base of caudal, curving upward over base of pectoral and then broadly down on middle of side; a fourth beginning on lower jaw, curving upward across cheek, then running upward and backward on shoulder-girdle, passing over base of pectoral, thence parallel with third line to base of caudal; these lines at first bright purple-red but soon fading to white; dorsal pale orange, slightly dusky along border; caudal orange, dusky at base and along margins; anal pale bluish; pectoral pale yellow at base, dusky toward tip; ventrals smoky; iris yellow.

Color in alcohol, bluish purple above, paler below; a narrow white line from tip of snout to base of caudal; below this a similar line beginning on lower jaw, curving upward across cheek to edge of opercle, then ascending margin of shoulder-girdle to base of pectoral, then across base of pectoral and along lower part of side to lower base of caudal fin; a similar line backward from eye under lateral line, ceasing above pectoral, another from forehead across upper edge of eye, crossing upward to nape, thence along base of dorsal to caudal peduncle; side of head washed with bluish, the under part with bluish and Chinese white; breast pale bluish with brighter bluish spots; fins all pale or dusky white.

Above description based upon a specimen (No. 05748) 4.6 inches long, obtained at Honolulu; life color taken from specimen (No. 03031) 4.25 inches long, obtained at Honolulu, June 7. Our collection contains one other specimen (No. 03231) 4.1 inches long, obtained at the same time and place. In addition to these, we have examined 21 specimens collected by Dr. Jenkins, and others obtained by the *Albatross* at Honolulu, where the fish appears to be common. The length varies from 4 to 5 inches.

Original type locality unknown. The species has been recorded from Maui and Honolulu.

Genus 151. HALICHŒRES Rüppell.

Body oblong, compressed, not elevated, covered with large scales, 25 to 30 in the lateral line, which is not interrupted, but bent abruptly behind; scales on breast a little smaller; head scaleless, compressed conic; preopercle entire; teeth large, 2 to 4 strong canines in front of each jaw, a posterior canine tooth; fin rays usually D. ix, 11; A. iii, 11; fins low; caudal lunate, truncate or rounded; ventrals inserted under axil of pectoral; gillrakers short and feeble; gill-membranes slightly joined to the narrow isthmus; no scaly sheath at base of dorsal; vertebræ $10 + 15 = 25$. Species numerous, of rather small size and gay coloration, the typical species (with canines $\frac{4}{4}$) all belonging to the East Indies and Polynesia, those with canines $\frac{2}{4}$ (*Ichthycallus*) being all American.

224. Halichœres lao Jenkins. "*Lao.*" Fig. 122.

Head 3.4 in length; depth 3.4; eye 5.5 in head; snout 3; preorbital 5; interorbital 4.25; D. ix, 12; A. iii, 12; scales 4-28-8.

Body short, slender and greatly compressed; dorsal outline rather straight from tip of snout to occiput, thence gently arched in a long curve to base of caudal; ventral outline a longer lower curve; head small, much longer than deep; snout long, sharply conic, jaws each with a pair of strong canine teeth anteriorly, and a row of close-set shorter teeth on the sides; eye small, lower edge of orbit on axis of body; interorbital convex, the nape trenchant; caudal peduncle moderately deep, 2 in head; preorbital oblique; preopercle and opercle smooth, the latter ending in a long pointed flap; scales large, thin, their edges soft, surface delicately striate; scales on breast and nape much reduced; head entirely naked; lateral line complete, following curvature of back for 20 scales, then descending 3 rows and continuing to base of caudal; spinous dorsal low, its spines weak, about equal to snout, dorsal rays somewhat longer and about equal to distance from tip of snout to posterior edge of pupil; anal similar to soft dorsal; caudal slightly rounded, the outer rays slightly produced; ventrals long, the outer rays produced, reaching vent, 1.6 in head; pectoral small, slender, as long as ventrals.

Color of a fresh example, side brick-red, with about 6 series of green spots, the upper 3 brightest; belly pale blue; the upper blue stripe continued anteriorly, running across humeral region and above eye to just above nostril, a broad green stripe across opercles and below eye to mouth, this narrowly bordered by blue, and on anterior part of opercle, broadening and running downward, somewhat yellowish and bordered by blue; opercular flap green, purplish above; an oblong triangular purple area bordered anteriorly by blue, below opercular flap; a broad, oblong purple spot on lower part of cheek from lower jaw to posterior edge of preopercle; a broad, brick-red stripe from eye to upper lip, where it is broken by blue, then ending in a red spot on upper lip; above this is a narrow green stripe, then a broader brick-red one, connecting with this a broad brick-red stripe running across head and along side at base of dorsal; median line of head with a narrow green stripe, bluish on snout; chin, throat and belly pale blue, some rosy at base of ventrals; a blood-red crescent in front of pectoral, with a rosy wash in front and on side behind it; dorsal with a series of round bright green spots along base, separated by reddish brown connecting with a broad median band of dark reddish brown, above which is a narrow bright olive-green stripe, then a broader deep-red stripe, the extreme edge of the fin whitish blue; a black or dusky spot on membrane between first and second spines, a similar but larger black spot on membrane between second and third rays; anal brownish red at base, then a narrower greenish-yellow band with zig-zag upper edge, next a broad brownish-red band narrowly bordered with white; caudal brownish red, crossed by 3 irregular series of green spots, bordered by blue, the posterior series yellowish green, bordered by bluish white, the fin tipped with bluish white; pectoral pale rosy, greenish yellow at base; ventrals bright green, dusky on outer ray; iris pale blue.

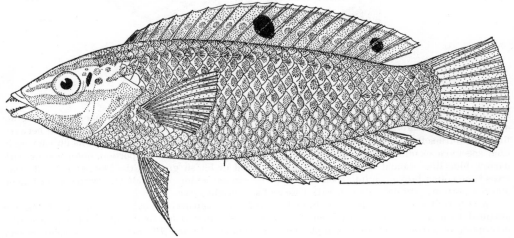

Fig. 122.—*Halichœres lao* Jenkins; from the type.

Color in alcohol, pale dusky greenish, paler below, the green stripes on head faded to brownish green, the purplish and red stripes now pale green; dorsal and anal purplish and bluish green; dark spot on first dorsal membranes and a larger one between second and third rays; dark spot on last dorsal rays obscure; base of caudal blue green, the tip whitish, with a thin subterminal black line; a small black postocular spot.

The above description is based upon a single specimen (No. 03314) 5 inches long, obtained by us at Honolulu, June 13. Two specimens were obtained by Dr. Jenkins, 3.8, and 4.25 inches long.

225. Halichœres ornatissimus (Garrett). "*Ohua paawela.*" Fig. 123.

Head 3.5 in length; depth 3.16; eye 5 in head; snout 3.2; preorbital 4.9; interorbital 4.1; D. ix, 12; A. iii, 12 or 11; scales 4–27–8.

Body elliptical, compressed, the dorsal and ventral outlines about equally curved; head longer than deep; mouth small, each jaw with 2 strong canines in front, followed by a series of smaller conic teeth laterally; a strong posterior canine on each side in upper jaw; eye small, its lower edge on axis of body; opercular flap long and narrowly rounded; caudal peduncle compressed; its depth at middle 2 in head; vertical fins high; dorsal spines about 2.5 in head, the rays a little longer, about 1.8 in head; anal similar to soft dorsal but somewhat lower, the rays 2.4 in head; caudal slightly rounded, the rays 1.5 in head; ventral long, the outer ray produced, nearly reaching origin of anal, 1.4 in head; pectoral moderate, reaching vertical at vent, 1.4 in head; scales large, their edges soft, the surface finely striate, scales of nape and breast much reduced; head naked; lateral line complete, following contour of back to line of fourth dorsal ray from last, where it curves downward 3 rows of scales and continues to base of caudal; pores of lateral line with 3 to 7 or 8 branches.

Color in life, each scale with a dark red crescent spot, convex anteriorly, bordered posteriorly with blue; head bright red, with a bright green stripe on median line from snout to base of caudal, another of same color along upper margin of eye on to the body, where it continues more or less distinctly just above lateral line about half length of body; a narrow green line from snout to middle of anterior margin of eye; a bright green stripe from near angle of mouth along lower margin of lower limb of preopercle and on subopercle and opercle, this green gradually shading into blue on throat and belly; a black spot behind eye surrounded by bright green, with red spots in some specimens; dorsal fin dark red, with a row of dark green oblong spots on proximal border, one spot on each interspinous

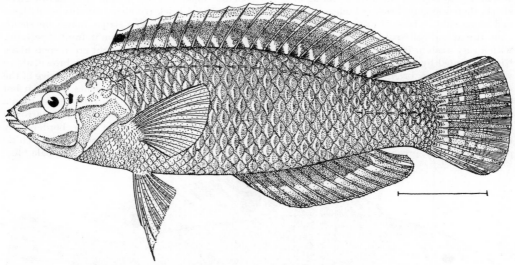

FIG. 123.—*Halichœres ornatissimus* (Garrett). Type of *H. iridescens* Jenkins.

membrane, a green longitudinal band on outer portion, with a very narrow outer margin of light blue; a black spot on membrane between first and second spines; in one example a double blotch between first and third soft rays, and a median row of green spots, the detail of markings of this fin varying in each specimen examined; anal dark red with a green band along central portion, outer margin with narrow blue line; caudal dark red, with a cross band of bluish green at the base, and 2 or 3 other cross bands often broken up into spots of green with orange centers; ventrals blue with a dark line on anterior portion; pectoral pale red, with base and axil bright green.

A very brilliant little fish taken from the coral reefs, apparently not very common. It was not obtained by us and is known only from the 3 examples collected by Dr. Jenkins in 1889, the earlier description of Garrett, and from examples taken at Honolulu by the *Albatross*. These specimens vary in length from 5 to 6 inches.

Genus 152. MACROPHARYNGODON Bleeker.

This genus is allied to *Halichœres*, differing in the deeper body and in the presence of but few large pharyngeal teeth. Coloration very brilliant and varied. Coral reefs of the Tropics.

226. Macropharyngodon geoffroy (Quoy & Gaimard). "*Hinalea aki-lólo.*" Fig. 124.

Head 3.1 in length; depth 2.6; eye 4.6 in head; snout 3.1; preorbital 4.75; interorbital 4; D. ix, 11; A. iii, 11; scales 3-28-10.

Body short, deep and compressed; head short and blunt; snout short, conic; mouth small, horizontal, 4 front teeth in each jaw strong, the second on each side of upper jaw turned backward; a prominent posterior canine on upper jaw near the angle, this sometimes duplicated; caudal peduncle deep, 2 in head; eye small, wholly above axis of body; interorbital space rounded; opercular flap rather long and rounded; fins well developed; origin of dorsal anterior to upper end of gill-opening, its distance from tip of snout equal to length of head; dorsal spines soft and flexible, their length about 2.5 in head, rays about equally high, outline of fin gently rounded; anal rounded, its origin under base of second or third dorsal ray, its height equaling that of soft dorsal; caudal truncate or very slightly rounded; outer rays of ventrals produced, reaching origin of anal, their length 1.4 in head; pectoral broad, the upper rays somewhat lengthened, equal to length of ventrals; scales large and firm, the surfaces finely striate; head entirely naked; nape naked; scales of breast scarcely reduced; lateral line following curve of back curving downward 3 rows of scales under last dorsal ray and continuing on 4 scales to base of caudal, the tubes with 2 or 3 branches.

Color in life, olive, with broad stripes along the rows of scales, these made up of a large, bright steel-blue spot on each scale and a black bar behind it, the spots smaller, closer, and brighter on breast; head with many curved blue stripes, throat with similar ones; first 3 dorsal spines tipped with golden, rest of dorsal, anal, caudal and ventrals golden olive with bluish-black edged ocelli; a narrow black edge on dorsal, anal, and caudal, followed by a still narrower whitish one; pectoral light orange, its base deep bluish.

Color in alcohol, grayish brown, side of body with about 10 irregular pale stripes separated by darker ones; cheek and opercles with narrow wavy brownish or bluish lines; breast and belly with

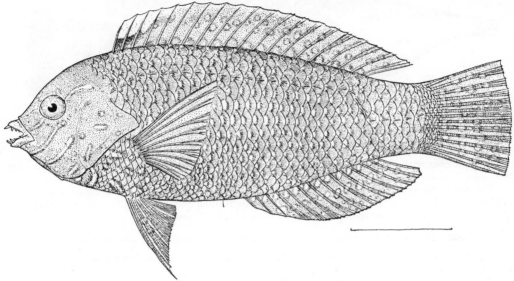

FIG. 124.—*Macropharyngodon geoffroy* (Quoy & Gaimard).   Type of *M. aquilolo* Jenkins.

round bluish spots; dorsal brownish, with a median series of large round bluish spots, above which is a similar series of smaller spots; base of membranes of anterior dorsal spines black, white at tip; anal similar to soft dorsal, somewhat darker, a series of blue spots along its base in addition to the second series distally, edge of fin paler, narrowly tipped with dark; caudal grayish, with narrow, vertical darker lines, the fin narrowly tipped with darker; ventrals whitish with 5 or 6 cross series of bluish spots; pectoral pale.

We have examined 7 specimens of this species—one collected by us at Honolulu in 1901, 5 obtained by Dr. Jenkins at the same place in 1889, and one sent us by Mr. Berndt. They are 3.5 to 5.4 inches in length and agree well with the original of *M. geoffroy*, which was described from Maui. Quoy & Gaimard's plate has the body and fins all blue; blue spots on all the fins save pectoral; yellowish on base of pectoral and tip of caudal; spots on ventrals distinct. The species is rare about the reefs. In life it is very handsome.

Genus 153. GOMPHOSUS Lacépède.

Body rather elongate, compressed, covered with moderate-sized scales, 25 to 30 in the lateral line; lateral line not interrupted; head scaleless; snout abruptly produced, a long tube, which bears the rather long jaws at the end; canines small; no posterior canine; gill-membrane attached to the isthmus; D. VIII, 13; A. III or II, 11.

Small fishes of brilliant colors, allied to *Thalassoma*, but distinguished from all other *Labridæ* by the prolonged snout.

227. Gomphosus varius Lacépède. "*Akilolo.*" Fig. 125.

Head 2.5 in length; depth 3.5; eye 10 in head; snout 1.8; mouth 4.5; interorbital 5.5; D. VIII, 13; A. II, 11; scales 4–27–9.

Body elongate, compressed, deepest about middle of pectoral; head long, upper profile straight; snout very long, upper jaw slightly the longer, and produced into a long beak, its depth equal to eye; lips thick, fleshy; teeth strong, ends rounded, forming a cutting edge in sides of jaws; canines 2 in front above, 4 on front of mandible, all conic; eye small, anterior margin behind middle ot length of head; margin of preopercle undulate; interorbital width broad, convex; nostrils small, posterior nearly over front margin of eye; dorsal spines pungent, much lower than soft rays, the longest of which is 3.75 in head; second anal spine longest, 3.6 in snout; longest anal ray 3.75 in head; caudal obliquely truncate, the lowest rays the longest; pectoral 2 in head; ventrals small, 3.2; scales large, cycloid; lateral line descending abruptly below posterior dorsal rays, tubes branched.

Color in alcohol, anterior half of body below white, shading into deep brown above pectoral; top of head dusky; each scale on trunk with black median spot; blackish streak in front of eye, 2 broken blackish streaks from behind eye; dorsal, anal, and caudal blackish brown, former 2 fins narrowly white, caudal broadly white; anal with median row of rounded pale spots; pectoral and ventrals pale

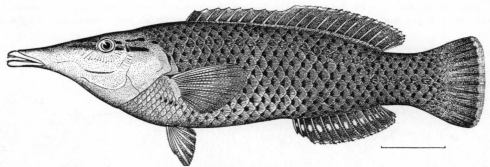

FIG. 125.—*Gomphosus varius* Lacépède.

brownish, former with blackish spot at base above.   Described from an example (No. 04276) taken at Honolulu.

The species is rather common in the markets of Honolulu and Hilo, and is represented in our collections by 27 specimens—21 from Honolulu, 3 from Kailua, and 3 from Hilo.   It is smaller than *G. tricolor*, the length of our specimens ranging from 5 to 9.2 inches.

228. Gomphosus tricolor Quoy & Gaimard.   "*Hinalea iiwi*."   Plate XXXVI.

Head 2.5 in length; depth 3.8; eye 11 in head; snout 1.7; mouth 4.6; interorbital 6; D. VIII, 13; A. II, 11; scales 4–27–9.

Body elongate, compressed, deepest about base of pectoral; head long, upper profile straight; snout very long, jaws equal, produced into a long beak, its depth equal to eye; lips thick, fleshy; teeth forming cutting edge in sides of jaws, 2 curved canines in front of upper jaw, 4 canines at front of mandible; eye small, its anterior margin much nearer gill-opening than tip of snout; margin of preopercle undulate; interorbital width broad, convex; nostrils small, the posterior nearly over front rim of orbit; dorsal spines pungent, the longest much shorter than longest ray, which is 4.8 in head; anal spines pungent, second longest, 4.5 in snout; first anal ray 4.65 in head; caudal emarginate, lobes pointed; pectoral 2.1 in head, reaching above origin of anal; ventrals short, 1.7 in pectoral, sharply pointed; caudal peduncle deep, its depth 4 in head; scales large, cycloid; lateral line descending abruptly below posterior dorsal rays, the tubes branched.

Color in life (No. 03256), indigo-blue with a greenish shade becoming distinctly green on back and belly; edge of each scale dull violet, the violet shades continuous on belly, but restricted on back to a brownish-red spot on each side, the form and shade of violet markings varying considerably; head green above, deep blue on cheeks and opercle, light blue on jaws, indigo-blue at throat, otherwise varying shades of greenish and dark purple; light-red streaks radiating from eye; a bright yellowish-green bar behind gill-opening covering basal fourth of pectoral fin; a jet-black spot in this on base of first rays of pectoral; dorsal reddish brown at base, then bright blue, the upper part golden green; anal similar; caudal light bluish green, its scaly base dull violet; ventrals dull blue, other rays black; pectoral golden green at base, otherwise pale violet washed with blackish above; iris green with a scarlet ring.   Another example was dark blue in life, with a golden-green patch behind pectoral; scales of body each with a vertical bar of dull purplish red.

Color in alcohol, blackish shaded with deep blue-green; lips, dorsal, anal, median caudal rays, and blotch above base of pectoral pale blue-green; pectoral blue-green basally; black spot at base of upper caudal rays, outer portion of fin black.

Described from (No. 04192) an example from Hilo.   Our collections contain 47 excellent specimens, varying in length from 5.75 to 12.5 inches—39 from Honolulu, the others from Hilo.   Of these, 10 were collected by Dr. Jordan, 3 by the *Albatross* in 1896, and 4 by Jordan and Snyder in 1900. Specimens were collected by the *Albatross* in 1902 at Honolulu and Puako Bay, Hawaii.

This handsome species is common in the markets at Honolulu and Hilo, whither it is brought in quantities from its native reefs.

Genus 154. ANAMPSES Cuvier.

Body oblong, rather deep, compressed, covered with moderate or large scales (25 to 30 in the lateral line, about 50 in subgenus *Ampheces*); lateral line continuous; head scaleless; preopercle entire; teeth uniserial; 2 anterior canines in each jaw prominent, turned forward, compressed, with cutting edges; no posterior canines; D. IX, 12; A. III, 12.   Species of rather large size and showy colors, of the East Indies and Polynesia.   The group is naturally divisible into 2 groups distinguished by the size of the scales.   The Japanese species constitute the subgenus or probably distinct genus *Ampheces*, distinguished from *Anampses* by the small scales.

229. Anampses cuvier Quoy & Gaimard. *"Opule;" "Hilu."* Fig. 126.

Head 3.3 in length; depth 2.8; eye 8 in head; snout 3.1; preorbital 4.2; interorbital 4; D ix, 12; A. iii, 12, scales 4–28–9.

Body oblong, deep, and compressed; dorsal and ventral outlines about equally convex; head short, snout obtusely conic, the anterior profile a little concave in front of eye; mouth small, 2 pairs of flat projecting canines in the jaws anteriorly; eye small, entirely above axis of body; interorbital high, convex, nape trenchant; caudal peduncle compressed, its least depth 2 in head; fins moderate; dorsal spines nearly as long as snout, rays somewhat longer, fully equaling snout; anal similar to soft dorsal and equally high; caudal squarely truncate, rays 2 in head; ventrals short, not reaching vent, 2.4 in head; pectoral longer, 1.9 in head; scales large, deep, the edges soft; scales on nape and breast much reduced; a row of small scales at base of dorsal and anal and some on base of caudal; lateral line normal, following curvature of back until under base of third dorsal ray from last, where it curves downward for 3 rows of scales and continues to base of caudal; head entirely naked.

Color in life, grayish olive, under parts brick-red; edges of scales somewhat darker; back along base of dorsal fin with numerous, irregularly arranged, small round white spots; below these about 13 or 14 series of larger roundish white spots, with smaller white blotches between, forming stripes from head to caudal, these most broken above, the lower 5 or 6 continuous white lines; among these spots are a good many small yellowish or orange specks; the red below pectoral in 5 or 6 definite stripes; small white specks along base of anal; upper half of head pale brownish, with numerous small round white dots, a number of narrow pale blue wavy lines forward and downward from eye and 1 or 2 short ones back of it; lower parts of head bluish white with numerous small round red spots; breast, throat, and lips reddish white, with a few red spots; snout above lip and preorbital region dusky; 2 small bluish spots on side of caudal peduncle and a few smaller bluer ones on under edge; dorsal orange-red, most pronounced in the outer band, mottled with darker and greenish elsewhere, crossed by about 6 narrow irregular or broken greenish blue lines, the lower one broadest anteriorly, the 3 lower ones more or less broken up into spots posteriorly, the fin with a broad rich blue border; anal rich blood-red, with 6 rich blue lines running full length of fin, the inner and outer ones broadest; caudal dusky orange in center, the outer rays dark blood-red, the edge blackish, green toward tip, extreme tip of fin whitish; pectoral orange on upper half, the lower half pale; ventrals with the rays sky-blue, the membranes blood-red; iris dull orange.

Color in alcohol, dark brownish; side with about 13 or 14 series of round bluish white spots on the centers of the scales, coalescing in the lower 5 or 6 rows so as to form more continuous lines; under parts yellowish-white, with purplish-blue line; top and sides of head to below level of eye profusely covered with small roundish bluish-white specks; lower jaw and lower parts of cheek pale bluish with numerous round pale orange spots; dorsal dusky olive, the spinous portion crossed by wavy lines of blue-green, the soft portion covered with small bluish white specks, the border of the fin dark green; anal yellowish and bluish-green crossed by 5 or 6 wavy deep blue lines; anal dusky; pectoral plain

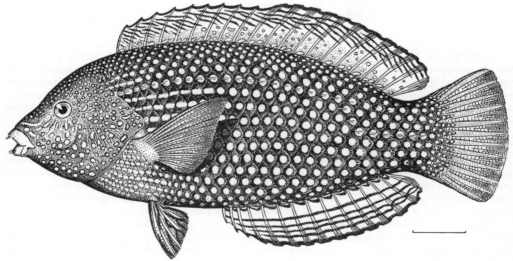

Fig. 126.—*Anampses cuvier* Quoy & Gaimard.

dusky yellowish, ventral rays indigo blue, the membranes yellowish white. Young examples, about 3 inches in length, show in alcohol, a large black spot more or less ocellated, on the last 4 rays of dorsal fin.

This species is common about the reefs at Honolulu and is one of the most brilliantly marked of the many bright-colored fishes seen among the Hawaiian Islands. Our collections contain 29 specimens, all from Honolulu except 1, which is from Hilo. Of those from Honolulu, 8 were collected by Dr. Jenkins, 2 by the *Albatross* in 1891 and 1 in 1896, and 1 by Jordan and Snyder in 1900. It was also obtained at Honolulu by the *Albatross* in 1902.

Our specimens are 3.2 to 11.5 inches long.

230. Anampses evermanni Jenkins.   *"Opule lauli."*   Fig. 127.

Head 3.25 in length; depth 2.6; eye 8 in head; snout 2.9; preorbital 4; interorbital 4; D. ix, 12; A. iii, 12; scales 4–27–10.

Body short, oval, deep, and compressed, deepest anteriorly; anterior profile rather straight from tip of snout to nape, thence in a long curve to caudal peduncle; ventral contour evenly curved from tip of snout to origin of anal, thence in a long low curve to base of caudal peduncle; head short, nearly as deep as long; snout short, evenly conic; mouth very small, in line with axis of body; jaws anteriorly each with 2 prominent canines, flattened and curved forward, with cutting edges; eye small, above axis of body; interorbital high, somewhat trenchant; caudal peduncle greatly compressed, its least depth 2 in head; scales large, deep, the edges thin and soft; scales of breast and nape much reduced; scales with a few thin striæ or lines; lateral line following contour of back until under fourth dorsal ray from last, where it curves downward 3 rows of scales and continues to base of caudal; a row of small scales at base of dorsal and several series on base of caudal; head entirely naked; fins rather large; origin of dorsal above upper end of gill-opening; longest dorsal spines shorter than snout, the rays a little longer; anal similar to soft dorsal, the rays about equally long; caudal truncate, about 2 in head; ventrals very short, 2.5 in head; pectoral longer, 1.7 in head.

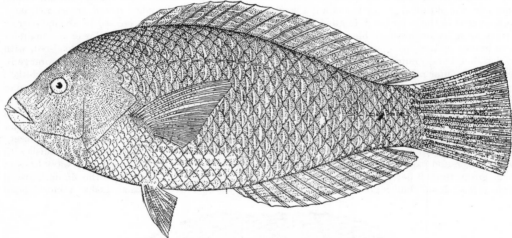

FIG. 127.—*Anampses evermanni* Jenkins; from the type.

Color in life, brownish red, with a narrow vertical blue line on each scale; snout blue; chin, throat, and sides of head with blue reticulations; dorsal fin brownish red, the outer margin blue, the fin with 7 or 8 longitudinal wavy blue lines and rows of dots, some running into each other and making reticulations; ground-color of anal red, the outer margin blue, the fin with 4 or 5 distinct longitudinal lines; ventral fin red with blue lines and dots and blue on anterior margin; pectoral olive, anterior margin blue; caudal red with longitudinal blue lines.

Color in alcohol, bluish brown on head and body, lower jaw blue and green, the sides purplish, breast and belly purplish and bluish; scales of side each with a narrow vertical pale bluish streak, these forming irregular vertical bars; dorsal purplish, the edge bluish green, the membranes with irregular pea-green lines and spots in about 5 series, these sometimes coalescing and reticulate; anal purplish, the edge pea-green, the membranes crossed by 5 narrow blue-green lines, parallel and continuous; caudal brownish at base, paler distally, the membranes with some greenish; ventrals dusky, greenish on anterior margin; pectoral brownish white, dusky at base and anteriorly.

This species appears to be related to *Anampses godeffroyi* Günther, from which it differs markedly in the coloration and in the larger scales. Günther states that his specimen had 30 scales in the lateral line, but his figure shows 37, and his species is described as bluish gray in color, whereas the present one is brownish red. The markings on the dorsal, anal, and caudal fins are also quite different.

This species was first described by Dr. Jenkins, from Honolulu, where he obtained 4 specimens. Another was obtained by the *Albatross* in 1896, 2 in 1891, and 1 by Jordan and Snyder in 1900. Others were obtained at Honolulu by the *Albatross* in 1902. The specimens examined are 10.5 to 12.5 inches long.

A beautiful and interesting species, moderately common about the coral reefs.

231. Anampses godeffroyi Günther.

Head 3.3 in length; depth 2.6; eye 8 in head; snout 2.6; preorbital 3.75; interorbital 3.75; D. ix, 12; A. iii, 12; scales 4–27–10.

Body short, oval, deep, and much compressed; dorsal and ventral outlines about equally curved; head short, but longer than deep; mouth small, each jaw provided with 2 flat, projecting canines; eye small, above axis of body; interorbital space rather narrow and very convex; caudal peduncle deep, 2 in head; fins rather high, the soft portion of dorsal somewhat higher; caudal truncate, 1.9 in head; ventrals short, not reaching vent, 2 in head; pectoral longer, nearly equal to distance from base of ventrals to origin of anal; scales large, thin, much deeper than long, the edges soft; scales on breast and nape much reduced; a row of small scales at base of dorsal and anal and several series on base of caudal; head entirely naked; lateral line following curvature of back until under fourth dorsal ray from last, where it curves downward 3 scales and then continues to base of caudal; pores of lateral line little branched.

Color in life essentially that of *A. evermanni*, except that the bluish vertical lines on the scales are broader and more spot-like in the center, especially on the caudal peduncle, where they assume the form of oval or roundish blue-green spots; side with about a dozen pale horizontal stripes, made up of the series of spots on the rows of scales; anterior part of side under pectoral with 8 or 9 rather distinct bluish horizontal lines composed of a series of spots on the rows of scales, the upper 3 or 4 extending from shoulder-girdle, curving upward and backward to base of pectoral; back along base of dorsal with 3 or 4 irregular series of small bluish-white specks, these usually quite distinct; blue-green stripes on anal broader, more wavy, and more oblique than in *A. evermanni;* dorsal spotted and reticulated with bluish green.

This species is related to *A. evermanni* and *A. cuvier*, differing from the former as already described, and from the latter chiefly in the less spotted coloration. It is possible that these specimens are extreme forms of the common species called *Anampses evermanni* and that the proper name of all is *Anampses godeffroyi*.

We have 3 specimens of this species, 10.25 to 12 inches long, obtained by us at Honolulu.

Genus 155. PSEUDOJULIS Bleeker.

Body elongate, compressed, covered with large scales; lateral line continuous; each jaw with 2 strong canines in front, no trace of posterior canines; dorsal with 9 pungent spines, anal with 3.

General characters of *Halichœres*, from which genus *Pseudojulis* differs in the absence of posterior canines and in having 3 anal spines. Species of small size occurring about rocky islands of the Pacific. Only 1 species known from the Hawaiian Islands.

232. Pseudojulis cerasina Snyder.

Head, measured to end of opercular flap, 3.1 in length; depth 4.3; depth of caudal peduncle 8; length of snout 2.8 in head; eye 5; interorbital space 5.26; D. ix, 11; A. iii, 12; pores in lateral line 28; scales in lateral series 26; between lateral line and dorsal fin 1; between lateral line and anal 7; body notably long and slender, head conical, snout pointed; mouth very small, the cleft smaller than eye; 2 canines in each jaw, the upper pair wide apart, allowing the lower ones to fit between them; canines but little longer than the other teeth, which grow gradually smaller posteriorly; no posterior canines; preopercle not serrated; head naked; scales of breast smaller than those of body; lateral line abruptly bent downward below ninth dorsal ray; dorsal low, the longest (eighth) spine equal in length to snout, the rays about a tenth longer; longest anal ray 3.1 in head; spines slender, the third with a short cutaneous filament; caudal slightly rounded, 1.54 in head; pectoral 2.1 in head; ventral pointed, 2 in head.

Color in spirits (perhaps somewhat similar in life), head pale orange, upper part of opercle with a purple tint, the lower part silvery; nape purple; a narrow dorsal area, reddish orange fading ventrally to light orange; a rather indefinitely outlined, broad, pinkish stripe from opercle to base of caudal; lower part of body light orange; a reddish orange spot somewhat smaller than the pupil at lower edge of base of pectoral; each scale row with a narrow line of a darker shade than the color area on which it occurs; fins orange, the spinous dorsal suffused with red; scaled portion of caudal reddish orange.

One specimen, the type, measuring 3.5 inches long, was collected at Honolulu by Mr. Berndt. No. 50877, U. S. Nat. Mus. No other specimens known.

Genus 156. THALASSOMA Swainson.

Body oblong or elongate, moderately compressed, covered with large scales; lateral line continuous; head scaleless; a slight sheath of scales along base of dorsal; no posterior canine; dorsal spines slender, the number always 8; anal spines 3, the first very small; lower pharyngeals essentially as in *Halichœres*. Beautiful fishes of the coral reefs and warm currents, the coloration largely deep green or blue.

233. Thalassoma purpureum (Forskål).

"*Olani;*" "*Olale;*" "*Palaea*" (very small); "*Awela*" (small); "*Hou*" (large).

Head 3 in length; depth 3.4; eye 9 in head; snout 2.6; preorbital 3.2; gape 3; interorbital 3.7; D. viii, 12; A. iii, 9; scales 3–29–10.

Body short and stout, heavy forward and not greatly compressed in the adult; head heavy, longer than deep; snout short, bluntly conic; mouth small, slightly oblique, the gape not nearly reaching anterior edge of orbit; jaws each with a pair of very strong blunt canines in front and a series of shorter, close-set conic teeth laterally; eye small, slightly anterior, high above axis of body; anterior profile in a gentle uniform curve from tip of snout to origin of dorsal; ventral outline similarly curved from tip of lower jaw to edge of gill-opening; fins low; dorsal beginning over base of pectoral, its distance from tip of snout equaling length of head, or 1.6 in base of dorsal; dorsal spines short and weak, their length 5.5 in head; soft portion of dorsal slightly elevated, the rays 4.5 in head; anal similar to soft dorsal, its origin under base of third or fourth dorsal ray, its spines obscure, its rays equal to those of dorsal; caudal short, doubly lunate, the outer rays slightly produced, their length equal to distance from tip of snout to middle of pupil, or exceeding the shortest rays by an eye's diameter; middle caudal ray slightly longer than the next one on either side; ventrals short, reaching halfway to vent, their length less than that of snout by a pupil's diameter; pectoral short, broad, rhombic, the upper edge being longest, the free edge but little shorter, the upper rays longest, 1.6 in head, the lowermost ray 3.5 in the upper; scales large, thin and leathery, those on breast considerably reduced; head entirely naked; lateral line nearly straight from origin to vertical of last dorsal ray but 3, where it curves downward and proceeds to the base of caudal on the third series below; pores of lateral line beautifully and numerously branched, the branches ranging from 4 to 8 or 10 in number.

Color, nearly fresh, very brilliant, bright grass-green, the belly abruptly bright blue, top of head livid purplish, lower part of head deep blue, cheeks and opercle green, edged with blue; salmon-scarlet dash across cheek; blotches on side of back livid violet lavender; 2 stripes on side and some odd scales a peculiar dull scarlet red, same as head markings; 2 similar stripes across base, or in front of pectoral, the stripes edged with blue; dorsal lavender at base, the upper half blue; caudal blue, with lavender streaks and blotches; anal like the dorsal, greenish at edge; ventrals plain blue; pectorals blue, blackish above; the axil red; upper lip pale edged; lateral bands not serrated; no black dorsal spot.

Color of same specimen in spirits, pale bluish green; top of head and snout with a broad purplish area extending from nape over interorbital to near tip of snout, and extending down on side of snout in an irregularly pointed angle to near gape, dull purplish; in front of this on snout, a narrow pea-green stripe uniting on sides with the color of the cheeks; in front of this a narrow purplish line, partly upon skin of premaxillaries and extending on side to posterior angle of mouth, rest of skin of premaxillaries pea-green; under parts of head, lower jaw, and a broad band extending upward on the cheek, narrowly enveloping the eye except for a narrow space on the supraorbital and extending in a narrow point toward the occiput, pale pea-green; a large irregular yellowish-white marking from eye broadening downward across cheek and opercle, bifurcating on opercle, the lower branch extending downward to edge of subopercle, the other backward toward base of pectoral and terminating at edge of opercle; above this the opercle and humeral region are unicolor with the cheek and lower parts of head; edge of opercle above pectoral with a narrow dusky yellowish border, dark on anterior line; upper part of side at base of dorsal with a narrow irregular green line, outside of which is a greenish-purple line about 2 scales in width, extending from nape to posterior end of dorsal fin; side below this pale bluish green with broad yellowish-white lines, the upper extending from above base of pectoral to middle of base of caudal, the lower from lower base of pectoral along lower part of side to caudal, these 2 lines approximately parallel and 2 scales apart; a few odd scales of same color; another line of same color from gill-opening under base of pectoral, terminating under tip of short pectoral rays; a more narrow, but similar, bar across base of pectoral; breast and belly bluish green; upper edge of caudal peduncle bluish purple; lower edge of caudal peduncle whitish; basal half of dorsal fin pale slaty olive or bluish purple; lower edge of caudal peduncle whitish; basal half of dorsal fin pale slaty olive or bluish purple; outer half of dorsal bright pea-green, the 2 colors separated by a narrow wavy black line, the lower band increasing abruptly at last dorsal ray, about three-fourths of which it covers; anal same color as dorsal; caudal irregularly bluish and greenish at base, the distal portion dusky yellowish, a bluish mark extending to tip of fin on produced portion above and below; edge of basal portion of outer ray, above and below, pale greenish; ventrals greenish white; pectoral greenish yellow, darker above, especially on outer ray, which is purplish black; axil somewhat dusky.

The above description is based upon a specimen (No. 03390) 16 inches long, obtained at Honolulu July 8.

Another specimen (No. 03731) 16 inches long, obtained at Kailua August 5, was described as follows, as it appeared in life after having been placed in a small pool: Two bright coral-red stripes on body, one along middle of side, the other from lower base of pectoral to lower portion of caudal fin; body below this line bright cobalt-blue; between the 2 stripes, green above and blue below, blending in center, the upper edge of scales in middle of these stripes with a coral-red patch; back emerald green, with 5 deep cardinal blotches on upper part of back, those nearest nape being largest, the size diminishing posteriorly; nape and snout darkish cardinal red, the patch on snout expanding laterally and forming a triangle in front of eye, the ventral angle of which terminates near posterior end of gape; tip of snout blue, with a dark cardinal bar in middle; suborbital region blue, overlaid with green; a short blue bar dorsally from eye; an irregular darkish cardinal patch downward and backward from eye across cheek and opercle; upper portion of opercle blue, middle of opercle green; jaws and throat bluish green; rest of pectoral with a red bar; upper angular part of opercular flap red; base of scales on back red; lower half of dorsal fin deep coral-red, upper half cobalt-blue; caudal blue, with 8 stripes of darkish cardinal color, only outer 2 of which reach to the end of fin, the others extending about two-thirds length of fin; margin of caudal fin greenish; anal same color as dorsal; ventrals blue; upper half of pectoral deep blue, the lower paler, edge darkish purple; axil coral-red; inner part of lips deep cardinal-red; iris green, with red border. As this fish died the darkish cardinal-red on head, snout, nape, back, and stripes on caudal fin became darkish brown and the bright coral-red on body and fins bright brick-red; the green assumed a darker shade, and the blue faded noticeably. Generally at death that indescribable luster of the fish entirely disappears.

Another specimen (No. 03460) 8 inches long, from Hilo, was in life clear green with various marks of bright creamy red; head green with radiating red stripes of the same shade; fins also red and green, the edge of dorsal and anal purplish black; a deep purple edge to the lower red band of dorsal and upper of anal; caudal tipped with dull yellowish; throat verging on blue.

This latter specimen in spirits shows the dorsal and anal fins each with a broad dusky purplish base, beyond which is a somewhat narrower bright bluish-green band, bordered distally by an equally broad pale yellowish-white band, the fin in each case tipped with thin scallops of purplish, the bluish-green line with a thin wavy black border proximally. While the color of the dorsal and anal fins in this specimen differs considerably from that in our larger examples, it does not differ as greatly from the smaller ones, and we hesitate to regard it as representing a different species.

Although the markings of this species are quite distinct and diagnostic, it has been frequently confused with related species, particularly with *Thalassoma fuscum*. This is evidently the species described by Forskål under the name *Scarus purpureus*, which was later described by Lesson and by Cuvier & Valenciennes as *Julis quadricolor*, recently by Mr. Fowler as *Thalassoma immanis*, and still more recently by Seale as *Thalassoma berendti*. Bleeker had 4 specimens which he identified as *Julis quadricolor;* one of these possessed irregular markings on the head and was doubtless *T. purpureum*. The 3 other specimens, without distinct markings on the head, and one of which he figured (Pl. 34, fig. 3) as *Julis quadricolor*, were doubtless what we have identified as *T. fuscum*. From *T. fuscum* the present species may be distinguished by the presence of broad, irregular markings on the head; the more distinct wavy blue line separating the 2 colors of the dorsal and anal, as seen in spirits, and the somewhat longer, more pointed snout.

Two specimens of this interesting species were obtained by Dr. Jenkins, 1 by the *Albatross* in 1896, 1 by Jordan and Snyder in 1900, and 7 by us in 1901. It was also obtained at Honolulu by the *Albatross* in 1902. Of the 7 specimens collected by us, 5 are from Honolulu and 1 each from Hilo and Kailua, the length ranging from 8.5 to 16 inches. Not rare in Samoa.

234. Thalassoma ballieui (Vaillant & Sauvage). "*Hinalea luahine.*" Fig. 128.

Head 3 in length; depth 3.4; eye 6.9 in head; snout 2.4; preorbital 3.2; interorbital 4.6; D. vii, 13; A. ii, 11; scales 3–27–9.

Body long, moderately slender and compressed; head considerably longer than deep, the snout long and bluntly pointed; mouth moderate, horizontal, the gape not nearly reaching eye; jaws equal; lips thick, the lower with a broad loose fold on each side; each jaw with a series of small conic canines on each side, a longer pair in front of upper jaw and 2 pairs in lower jaw; premaxillary broad and oblique; interorbital moderate, high and convex; anterior profile gently curved from tip of snout to origin of dorsal, thence in a low curve to caudal peduncle; ventral outline less convex than dorsal; caudal peduncle very deep, nearly equal to one-half greatest depth of body; eye small, anterior, entirely above axis of body; origin of dorsal fin over base of pectoral, the spines all low, their length about 4 in head; soft portion of dorsal slightly higher, the rays 3.25 in head; anal similar to soft dorsal, its origin equally distant between tip of snout and tip of produced caudal rays; anal rays as high as those of dorsal; caudal deep, short, the middle rays a little longer than length of snout, the outer rays produced a distance a little greater than diameter of orbit; ventrals short, reaching only half the distance to origin of anal, their length 2.4 in head; pectoral longer, 1.5 in head; scales large and thin, their size quite uniform except on nape, where they are somewhat reduced; head entirely naked; lateral line not strongly developed, the pores often branched, following contour of back until under base of fourth dorsal ray from last, where it drops 2 rows and continues to base of caudal; base of caudal with small scales.

Color in alcohol, dark, purplish brown, each scale on side with a narrow bluish-black vertical

---

a Misprint for *berndti*.

stripe, these forming about 45 more or less distinct discontinuous vertical bars; head uniform purplish or olivaceous, paler below and without markings; dorsal, anal, and ventrals purplish or bluish black, the edges lighter; caudal bluish black, the base and produced rays darkest; in some specimens the caudal is throughout uniform bluish black excepting a very narrow paler margin on middle rays, in other cases only the base and produced rays are dark, all the rest of fin being light yellowish white or

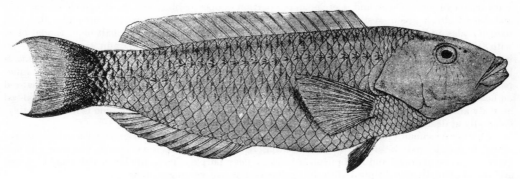

FIG. 128.—*Thalassoma ballieui* (Vaillant & Sauvage); after Günther.

dusky; pectoral uniform bluish black with lighter edge, or more or less yellowish white with dusky at base or middle and dusky on inner side.

There is considerable variation in the extent of prolongation of the outer caudal rays; in the smallest individual they are scarcely produced and the caudal is practically truncate. In the largest individuals the outer rays are produced beyond the tips of inner rays a distance equal to half length of latter. There is also considerable variation in the color of the caudal fin. In some of the larger examples, probably old males, it is uniform bluish black, while in others the large lunate pale area covers most of the fin. We are convinced, however, after an examination of a large series of excellent specimens, that the specimen from Johnston Island described by Smith and Swain as *Julis verticalis* and Günther's *Julis obscura* are identical with *Julis ballieui* Vaillant & Sauvage.

This species is extremely abundant at Honolulu, where it is constantly seen in the market. Of the 63 specimens examined by us, 19 were obtained at Honolulu by Dr. Jenkins, 4 by the *Albatross* in 1896, 5 by Jordan and Snyder in 1900, 32 by us at Honolulu, and 3 at Hilo. In 1902 the *Albatross* obtained specimens at Honolulu and Laysan.

235. Thalassoma fuscum (Lacépède). "*Awela.*"   Plate XXXIV.[a]

Head 3.4 in length; depth 3.2; eye 6.8 in head; snout 3; preorbital 4.25; interorbital 3.25; D. VIII, 13; A. III, 11; scales 4–27–8.

Body short, moderately deep and compressed; dorsal and ventral outlines about equally convex; head short, slightly longer than deep; snout short and bluntly conic; mouth small, in line with axis of body, little oblique, jaws equal; a pair of strong canines in front in each jaw, and a series of close-set conic teeth on the sides; eye small, scarcely anterior; interorbital space high, broadly convex; caudal peduncle deep, 1.8 in head; fins rather small, origin of dorsal over middle of base of pectoral, its distance from tip of snout one-third distance to base of caudal fin; dorsal spines short, their length 5.2 in head; soft portion of dorsal somewhat higher, the longest rays about 2.9 in head; anal similar to soft dorsal, the rays of about equal length, caudal somewhat lunate, the outer rays produced, their length 1.9 in head or a fourth longer than middle rays; ventrals short, 2 in head or reaching halfway to origin of anal; pectoral longer, broad, 1.3 in head; scales large, thin, and firm, those on breast and belly somewhat reduced; head wholly naked; lateral line nearly straight for 19 scales, or under the fourth dorsal spine from last, where it curves downward 2 rows, continuing to base of caudal on median line of peduncle.

Color in spirits of some specimens, head and nape dusky bluish above; cheek light brownish; opercle blackish; under jaw and throat pale bluish; upper part of side dark brownish and bluish; middle of side with a pale whitish band somewhat dusky, extending from opercular flap to base of caudal; above and below this 2 broad bluish-green bands somewhat greater than a scale in width, made up of oblong or quadrate vertical spots separated by intrusion of the central paler band, these bluish-green areas suggesting the openings in the French harp; under part of side and belly colored like the median line; dorsal bluish green at base, bordered above by a broad purplish band, beyond which is a somewhat narrower blue-green band indistinctly bordered with paler; membranes among first 3 dorsal spines blackish; anal similar to soft dorsal, the blue-green border somewhat wider; lines separating the blue-green and purplish not blackish; ventrals pale at base, light greenish on distal

a *Thalassoma purpureum* (Forskål) on the plate.

portion; pectoral pale yellowish at base, dusky on outer half, the axil and upper margin black; head without markings.

The above description is based upon a specimen (No. 03526) 9.5 inches long obtained at Honolulu, from which the accompanying colored plate was made.

Another specimen (No. 03021), 8 inches long, from Honolulu, had side with 3 broad pale brick-red stripes separated by 3 bluish or yellowish-blue ones, these extending from opercle to caudal; upper stripe about 3 scales wide, narrowly bordered above at base of dorsal by greenish blue, and crossed by about 6 narrow vertical greenish or yellowish bars connecting with the first yellowish-blue stripe, which is about one scale wide, begins at upper edge of opercle and ends at base of caudal, a narrow saddle of same passing over caudal peduncle at posterior end of dorsal fin, third stripe brick red, running from opercular flap to middle of base of caudal, fourth stripe like the second but better defined, fifth like the first and third, the sixth along side of belly ill-defined, yellowish green; head reddish olive, lower jaw and breast the same; opercular flap bluish olive; dorsal orange red at base, then a narrow bright blue stripe, broadly edged with green on posterior two-thirds, the membranes with faint yellow blotches; anal pale brick red at base, then a broad bright blue border, the outer half of membranes between ninth and eleventh rays white; the last ray brick red to tip, a little blue at base and on tip; caudal dusky orange with reddish wash at base, greenish in center, the outer half with alternating blue and orange lines, the blue lines more or less greenish at anterior end, upper and lower margins bright blue, with some green; pectoral yellow at base, bluish dusky along anterior edge and outer two-thirds; ventrals pale bluish; iris greenish brown.

A specimen (No. 05754) obtained at Hilo had the following colors when fresh:

Body darkish coral-red (modified brick-red); shoulder and belly light yellowish brown; back claret, rather darkish; 2 longitudinal rows of elongated squares of bright emerald-green with cobalt-blue border on body; the upper one beginning on fourth scale and terminating on the upper part of caudal peduncle; the lower one beginning on seventh scale and terminating at base of caudal, where the upper edge of the row touches the lateral line; from the upper row issue 5 green bars dorsally at regular intervals, these connecting with the green stripe at base of dorsal; ventral side of tail slightly greenish; nape greenish on claret ground; head greenish on dark dirty purple; cheek darkish brown, angle of opercle blackish; chin pale reddish brown, throat same as belly; iris green; lips greenish dark; dorsal light claret, margin cobalt-blue, the latter wider on soft dorsal; caudal emerald-green, edges and half of end cobalt-blue, half of membrane orange-brown; anal same as soft dorsal; ventrals pale cobalt-blue; proximal half of pectoral emerald-green, distal half deep Prussian blue, edge Prussian blue.

This same specimen, in spirits, is dusky purplish brown above and on upper part of sides, the head most purplish; side with 3 irregular greenish lines; dorsal with purplish-black on the first 2 membranes, the basal three-fifths of the fin dusky purplish, a few small bright blue spots on the base; distal two-fifths of the fin bluish green bordered irregularly by pale yellowish white; anal similar to soft dorsal, the blue-green border a little broader, the edge not paler; caudal with the rays dusky at base, blue-green distally, the central membranes whitish, the outer ones more dusky, a dusky purplish stripe extending to tip of outer rays both above and below, upper and lower edges of caudal bluish green; pectoral blue-black, paler at base; ventrals greenish white.

In young individuals the dorsal and anal are more decidedly tricolor, there being a broad blue-green stripe through the middle, above a somewhat broader purplish proximal stripe, and below a narrower but distinct paler stripe, the rays tipped again with greenish blue; the median stripe on side as well as the back more brownish.

This species may be readily distinguished from all others by the absence of distinct markings on head and the presence on the side of 2 series of vertically oblong or quadrate bluish green areas bordered by whitish, suggesting the 2 rows of openings in the harmonica; aptly compared by Lacépède to 2 rows of Chinese characters. Of the 4 specimens possessed by Bleeker and which he identified as *Julis quadricolor*, 3 (including the one which he figured) evidently belonged to this species. They are said to have had no markings on the head, and his figure (pl. 34, fig. 3) clearly shows the harmonica markings. Other species have the unmarked head and still others may possess the peculiar body markings, but we know of none other possessing both.

This species is fairly common about the coral reefs of the Hawaiian Islands, and is not rare in Samoa. Our collection contains a series of 16 specimens: 9 from Honolulu, 3 from Kailua, and 1 each from Honuapo and Hilo. In length they vary from 5.25 to 11.5 inches.

236. Thalassoma umbrostigma (Rüppell). Fig. 129.

Head 3.6 in length; depth 3.6; eye 6.6 in head; snout 2.8; preorbital 4; gape 3; interorbital 3.5; D. VIII, 13; A. III, 11; scales 4–27–8.

Body moderately long and compressed, the dorsal and ventral outlines moderately convex; head but slightly longer than deep; snout moderate, bluntly conic; preorbital oblique; jaws each with a pair of stout canines in front and smaller close-set conic teeth laterally; eye small, slightly anterior, entirely above axis of body; interorbital rather low, convex, the profile from tip of snout to nape evenly convex; least depth of caudal peduncle slightly greater than half head; origin of dorsal slightly posterior to base of pectoral, its distance from tip of snout greater than head by diameter of orbit; dorsal spines short, their length about 2 in snout; dorsal rays longer, 1.3 in snout; anal similar to soft dorsal, of about equal height; caudal shallowly lunate, the outer rays but slightly longer than middle one, which is equal to snout and eye; ventrals short, reaching somewhat more than half distance to vent, length 2.4 in head; pectoral longer, reaching vertical at vent, its length 1.3 in head; scales large, thin, but firm, those on breast somewhat reduced; head entirely naked; lateral line parallel with dorsal outline to below fifth dorsal ray from last, where it curves downward 3 scales and then continues to base of caudal, the pores with 3 to 6 or 7 branches; small scales on base of caudal.

Color in life (No. 03022, 7 inches long, from Honolulu), side pale greenish with 3 irregular broad rosy stripes, the upper one darkening into Indian red; median dorsal line at base of dorsal fin green, next a broad Indian red stripe, the edges of the scales red, the centers pale greenish, a few smaller red specks; next a broad greenish stripe with greenish bars connecting with the median stripe and with narrow rosy bars crossing it connecting the rosy stripes above and below; rosy stripes along middle of side with 3 or 4 brownish blotches; the next stripe greenish, crossed by numerous narrow rosy or purplish bars; next stripe rosy, narrower than the other 2; belly whitish, top and sides of head greenish, vermiculated with rosy or purplish lines; humeral region with several roundish red spots; base of dorsal greenish, and with Indian red from invasion of body-color; middle line of dorsal rosy, with purple upper border, followed by a somewhat narrower yellow stripe, then a rosy or orange stripe, followed by a narrow white border; anal with rosy band at base, then a green band with bluish edges, then a broad pale rosy band with narrow white edge, the green band not on last 2 rays; caudal rays and membrane alternating greenish yellow and orange; pectoral dusky, greenish at base, rosy in center; ventrals pale yellow; iris brownish.

The same specimen in spirits faded to a creamy white, with 5 irregular broken dusky cross-bars; black spot on membrane of first 3 dorsal spines; soft dorsal and anal white with faint trace of greenish; top of head and nape with faint traces of dark spots and lines.

Specimen No. 03240, from which the above general description was taken, is in alcohol dusky greenish on back and top of head, the sides somewhat paler, under parts greenish white; side with about 4 or 5 irregular broken, vertical cross-bars of dark brownish or black; membranes of first 3 dorsal spines blue-black; base of dorsal narrowly pea-green, followed by a broad greenish yellow band,

FIG. 129.—*Thalassoma umbrostigma* (Rüppell); after Bleeker.

bordered above by a narrower pea-green band, which is followed in turn by an irregular border of pale yellowish and purplish; anal scallopy green at base, followed by a broad white band, beyond which is a nearly equally broad blue-green band, which in turn is followed by a narrower yellowish white stripe, the edge of the fin pale pea-green; caudal greenish, yellowish and creamy white, dusky at base; ventrals pale creamy white; pectoral dusky yellowish at base, dusky at tip.

A smaller specimen (No. 05256), 6.25 inches long, agrees essentially with the larger ones, except that the blue-green of the head is profusely covered with small round black or brownish spots and a few lines or reticulations of the same color. Another specimen (No. 05263) shows the dark spots on the head very plainly, but ordinarily specimens of that size have those colors obscure or indistinct in spirits. In all of our numerous examples the markings are quite distinct. The species is rather abundant about the coral reefs.

Dr. Jenkins obtained 11 specimens at Honolulu, and our own collection contains 10 specimens from Honolulu, 8 from Kailua, and 2 from Hilo. These range in length from 1.5 to 10.25 inches.

237. Thalassoma duperrey (Quoy & Gaimard).   Plate XXXV and Fig. 130.
"*Hinaléa lauwili;*" "*A' alaíhi.*"

Head 3.5 in length; depth 3.4; eye 6 in head; snout 3; preorbital 4.5; interorbital 3.6; D. VII, 13; A. II, 11; scales 3–28–9.

Body rather slender, compressed, the dorsal and ventral outlines nearly equally and regularly curved from tip of snout to base of caudal peduncle; head rather small; longer than deep; mouth small, horizontal, the gape scarcely exceeding orbit, in line with axis of body; cheek oblique, not deep; interorbital space high, convex; a pair of strong canines in front of each jaw, those above usually stronger; a series of short, bluntly conic teeth on each side of jaws; fins low; origin of dorsal slightly behind base of pectoral, its distance from snout 3.2 in head; dorsal fin continuous, the anterior spines not detached nor elevated; longest dorsal spine about equal to snout, the rays equally long; anal similar to soft dorsal, their heights equal; caudal with the 3 or 4 outer rays produced, their length equal to head or nearly twice that of middle rays; scales smooth and thin, of about uniform size; a row of somewhat smaller scales sheathing bases of dorsal and anal and on base of caudal; produced caudal rays with fine scales at base; head entirely naked.

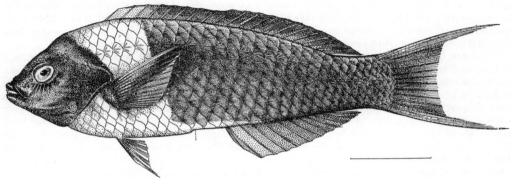

FIG. 130.—*Thalassoma duperrey* (Quoy & Gaimard).   Type of *T. pyrrhovinctum* Jenkins.

Color in life of a nearly fresh specimen, 6.5 inches long, taken at Honolulu, June 15, side bright green, with numerous (about 40) very narrow purplish-red vertical bars, the green interspaces about twice as wide; a broad band of reddish-orange, in width from nape to third dorsal spine, extending downward and backward on side behind the pectoral and widening out below, enveloping whole under parts from gill-openings to origin of anal, this area somewhat paler below, purplish behind ventrals; head rich bright blue, a small rusty-orange spot on upper edge of opercle; lips paler, lower jaw greenish; dorsal green along base, then a narrow greenish-blue line, next a broad reddish-brown or purplish-red band widening posteriorly, the fin narrowly bordered by pale blue; a jet-black spot with blue border on second dorsal membrane, this sometimes extending to first and third membranes; caudal blue, the produced rays reddish, a little greenish-blue on outer edge; anal greenish at base, rest of fin purplish blue; pectoral pale blue, dusky at tip, deeper blue at base; axil blue and green.

A specimen (No. 02939) somewhat faded, had the head and body and fins deep violet; chin bluish; a black spot on front of dorsal and a violet-black area on pectoral; area behind head violet-gray, scarcely contrasting with body; caudal violet.

Another specimen had the head violet, blue on lower jaw; area behind head orange-brown; body behind light green with a vertical orange-brown line on each scale; first dorsal spines violet with a black spot; pectoral pale with black area and black axil; dorsal behind first spines orange-brown with violet edge; caudal violet-gray, with the lobes bright orange-brown; anal violet-black.

Still another specimen (No. 03525) differed from typical examples in the entire absence of a paler bar on body at pectoral region.

Color in alcohol, head dark bluish or bluish-black; a broad, pale, bluish-white band around body under nape and first part of spinous dorsal; rest of body dusky brown washed with bluish-green; dorsal and anal greenish-blue; caudal dark with some bluish, in some cases with the distal portion, except produced rays, almost white; pectoral pale on base, the outer half dark; belly pale; chin rich blue.

The young have a black stripe, about as wide as the eye, extending from the snout to the upper half of the base of caudal, where its end is slightly broadened and rounded. Below and parallel with the dark stripe is a pinkish-white one of about equal width. Some specimens have a narrow, short, indistinct, dusky stripe below the latter. With increasing age the stripes become indistinct and disappear, the general color grows darker, while the broad, light band behind the head appears. The caudal is at first rounded, later becoming concave, the upper and lower rays being much produced in the adult.

This species is the most abundant of the labroids inhabiting Hawaiian waters. Numerous specimens were obtained by Dr. Jenkins, and a yet greater number is in the present collection obtained by us at Honolulu, Hilo, and Kailua; and by the *Albatross* at Honolulu, Laysan Island, station 3881 between Maui and Molokai, and at Puako Bay, Hawaii. The fish is not known to occur in Samoa.

238. Thalassoma lunaris (Linnæus).

Head 3.5 in length; depth 3.7; eye 5 in head; snout 3.2; preorbital 4.8; interorbital 4; D. VIII, 13; A. II, 12; scales 4–27–8.

Body greatly compressed, elongate; caudal peduncle deep; dorsal outline evenly curved; vertical outline slightly less convex; head small, much longer than deep; snout rather long, conic; jaws each with a pair of stout canines in front and a series of shorter canine-like teeth laterally, growing successively shorter posteriorly; no posterior canine; preorbital moderately deep, oblique; opercle and preopercle smooth, the former ending in a broad low flap; scales large, thin, and leathery on edges, the surface finely striate, the spaces between the striæ with cross-markings, giving the appearance of being covered with minute scales; scales on breast and nape somewhat reduced; a patch of 8 rather large scales on upper end of opercle, rest of head entirely naked; lateral line following curvature of back for 19 or 20 scales, then bending downward 2 rows and continuing to base of caudal; pores with 3 to 6 or 7 branches; a low sheath of scales at base of dorsal and anal; small scales on base of caudal; fins moderate, origin of dorsal slightly posterior to base of pectoral; dorsal spines rather short, the longest about equal to distance from tip of snout to middle of pupil, dorsal rays slightly longer; anal similar to soft dorsal; caudal lunate, the outer rays produced, their length nearly twice that of middle rays; ventrals short, reaching half way to origin of anal; pectoral rather long; equal to distance from base of ventrals to vent, or 1.4 in head.

Color in life, greenish, the body crossed by numerous narrow, vertical broken orange bands; side of head and snout with 4 broad bright-green bands, separated by golden interspaces; the first green band extending from eye to upper end of gill-opening; the second from eye across cheek and opercle to base of pectoral; the third from median line of mandible upward and backward across cheek to edge of opercle; the fourth branching from this at its anterior end and extending backward to lower edge of gill-opening; a pair of less distinct greenish lines on median line of throat; an orange band across side of snout from mouth to eye, continued under eye with the third orange band; dorsal fin with a yellow band distally, bounded below by a narrow blue line, beneath which is a broader orange band; anal orange at base, bounded by a narrow blue line, beyond which the fin is greenish-yellow; caudal yellow, the produced rays orange; pectoral dark blue, almost black distally, the base orange, 2 narrow blue stripes on breast below pectoral, separated by an orange interspace.

In alcohol these colors mostly disappear, the green stripes on the head becoming pale blue and the orange interspaces purplish brown; dorsal pale distally, a faint median dark line beneath which the color is pale yellowish; anal similar, the basal portion more greenish; pectoral with an oblong black bar from middle of middle rays to tip of longest rays, rest of fin yellowish or dusky-white.

We identify with this species a single specimen (No. 03429) 6 inches long, obtained at Honolulu July 20. It agrees well with Bleeker's description and plate of *Julis lunaris* (90, pl. 33, fig. 5). Jordan and Snyder had a specimen from Japan which they identified with *Labrus lutescens* Solander, and they expressed the opinion that that species might be the same as *Labrus lunaris* Linnæus. The original description of *L. lunaris* is not sufficiently full to enable us to settle this question with certainty. Jordan and Snyder expressly state that the head of their specimen was naked; ours has a patch of well-developed scales upon the upper limb of the opercle, which may indicate specific distinction. Moreover, we are able to find but 2 anal spines, a character in which it differs from other species of *Thalassoma*.

239. Thalassoma aneitense (Günther). Plate 41.

Head 3.7 in length to base of caudal; depth 3.4; snout 2.8 in head; eye 5.3; interorbital space 4; scales 26–11; D. VIII, 13; A. II, 11.

Teeth in both jaws growing gradually shorter from before backward; no enlarged teeth or canines; head smooth; scales smaller on breast and belly than on sides and back; lateral line extending along fourth row of scales to below base of eleventh articulated ray, where it bends downward across 3 rows of scales and passes along middle of caudal peduncle; first dorsal spine equal in length to about two-thirds diameter of orbit, the others successively longer, the last being 1.6 times diameter of orbit; articulated rays higher, about twice diameter of orbit; anal spines rather strong, the first equal in height to third dorsal spine, the second equal to last dorsal spine; dorsal and anal rays about equal in height; pectoral 1.4 in head; caudal probably truncate; ventral 2 in head.

Color in spirits, pale brownish, the head dusky above; 2 dusky bars passing backward from eye, the lower of which extends toward angle of opercle; a broad semicircular bar extending from chin toward eye and bending downward toward lower edge of opercle; a smaller semicircular bar below the latter; scales with small white spots; distal half of pectoral blackish, the color fading out toward the lower edge; dorsal with a dark spot about the size of pupil on membrane of second and third spines. Known to us from the Hawaiian Islands by only one specimen, 5.2 inches long, obtained at Honolulu by Mr. Berndt.

Genus 157. JULIS Cuvier.

This genus as here understood differs from *Coris* chiefly in the more elongate body and especially in the smaller scales, which are 75 to 95 in lateral series. In most species the anterior dorsal spines are slender and prolonged. Brilliantly colored fishes of the coral reefs, some of the species burying themselves in the sand. The name *Julis*, originally based on the Girelle of the Mediterranean (*Julis julis*), has been wrongly transferred to the genus *Thalassoma* by Bleeker and by Günther.

240. Julis gaimard Quoy & Gaimard. "*Lolo.*"

Head 3.3 in length; depth 3.4; eye 8 in head; snout 2.75; mouth 4; interorbital 4; D. ix, 12; A. iii, 12; scales 6–76–27.

Body oblong, elongate, deepest about origin of anal; head longer than deep, pointed; snout long, profile above straight, pointed; mouth horizontal; jaws equal, produced, pointed; lips thick, fleshy; teeth large, conic; upper jaw with 2 canines in front, mandible with 2 large canines fitting in between, all projecting forward; eye small, anterior high, margin of preopercle nearly forming a right angle; interorbital space convex, elevated; nostrils small, close, anterior in short fleshy tube; first 2 dorsal spines longest, anterior 1.5 in head; longest dorsal ray 2.2; caudal rounded; pectoral 1.4 in head; ventrals long, pointed, 3.7 in body; scales small, thin, cycloid, extending well out on basal portion of caudal; lateral line high along back, falling below last dorsal rays to middle of side of caudal peduncle, then straight.

Color in life (No. 252, O. P. Jenkins) bright red, bands on head and chin green; a greenish vertical band behind tip of pectoral; axil of pectoral dark blue with green and yellow border. Another specimen was (No. 03477) reddish brown, rather dark; a deep green cross brand from dorsal to vent; stripes on head clear green, the lowest from lower jaw to base of ventral interrupted in certain places; middle line of chin and throat whitish; snout flesh-colored; axil of pectoral black, broadly edged with green; posterior half of body with small blue-edged violet spots which grow larger and more crowded behind, but are still smaller than in *pulcherrima;* dorsal scarlet, crimson at base with fine dots of violet here and there, violet stripes above the last at edge, the middle one broadening and becoming green anteriorly; caudal golden, orange below; anal dark crimson with a blue and violet line; small violet dots below, and larger ones on orange distal part of fin; pectoral crimson, its tip orange; ventrals dull orange, edged in front with dark violet, the third (long) ray green.

Color in alcohol, dull purplish brown; head pale greenish brown, snout pale or dull brown; several lines and spots down middle of forehead; a brown line from side of snout to eye, continued, broken above, to origin of dorsal; brown streak behind eye to corner of opercular flap; a dull blue-green streak from upper lip toward eye, then down across opercle below; a deep blue band from mandible along side of breast to base of ventral; chin to space between ventrals deep blue; round dark-edged blue spots, small, very numerous .on trunk, especially posteriorly; dorsal and anal bordered with gray brown, with 3 narrow dark marginal lines parallel with edges of fins; small spots on dark bases of each dorsal and anal; a blue-green spot at base of each dorsal spine and most soft rays; caudal and pectoral whitish or pale brown; ventrals broadly dusky on outer portion; axil of pectoral deep blue black, edged with blue and blue green.

Described from an example (No. 625) taken at Honolulu by the Fur Seal Commission in 1896.

This species is common about the reefs of Honolulu, burying itself in the sand when at rest, with only the snout and eyes visible. For this reason it is called *lolo,* lazy.

Three examples were obtained by Dr. Jenkins, 1 by the *Albatross* in 1896, and 3 by us, 1 of them from Hilo.

241. Julis pulcherrima (Günther). "*Hinalea loló.*" Plate XXVII.

Head 3.35 in length; depth 3.4; eye 7 in head; snout 3; mouth 4.4; interorbital 3.8; D. ix, 12; A. iii, 12; scales 6–82–25.

Body elongate, deepest about origin of anal; head longer than deep, pointed; snout long, pointed; mouth horizontal, jaws produced, equal; lips thick, fleshy; teeth conic, directed forward; 2 large canines in front of upper jaw directed forward; 2 large canines in front of mandible, directed forward, fitting in between upper pair; eye small, anterior, high in head; margin of preopercle a thin fleshy flap; interorbital width convex, elevated; nostrils close together in front of eye, anterior in short fleshy tube; first 2 dorsal spines elongate, first longest, 1.4 in head; longest dorsal ray 2; caudal rounded, 4.25 in body; pectoral 1.4 in head; ventrals long, pointed, 3.75 in body; scales small, thin, cycloid, extending well out over basal portion of caudal; lateral line high along back, falling below last dorsal rays to middle of side of caudal peduncle, then straight.

Color in life (No. 03475) brownish orange, the posterior half shaded blackish violet, the anterior half shaded on salmon; snout bright salmon, median line deep violet; line before eye and above, extending in dots to front of dorsal bright violet, the lines bordered with crimson, especially before eye; a broader crimson band behind eye edged with paler; a curved band below, similar; throat and middle of breast violet black; axil of pectoral jet black with a crescent of bright green above; sides of body with violet blue spots, each ringed with darker violet and about alike in size, these sparse on anterior half, crowded behind; dorsal bright salmon-orange with violet-crimson edged spots, violet lines and dashes, and steel-blue edges; caudal clear golden; anal salmon-orange, very bright blue spots at base; edge blue with black line, the middle stripe muddy blue; pectorals bright orange; ventrals orange, edged with violet blue.

Color in life of another example (No. 03380), cinnamon-brown, rather darker posteriorly, bright on head; middle line of throat and breast livid blue-brown, with a broad green-brown band on each side; a curved brown band edged with red from angle of mouth to edge of subopercle, another from eye to opercular flap; a dark blue-black streak from eye backward toward front of dorsal where it breaks up into spots; a dark median stripe on front of head; side of body with round violet spots edged with blue, much more numerous and brighter posteriorly; tail golden yellow, unspotted; dorsal orange-red, violet spots at base, then a violet line, then a shade of lighter orange with a blue-black margin; a dusky blotch at base of first dorsal spine; anal colored like dorsal with a row of curved violet streaks instead of the stripe; violet spots at base very distinct; pectoral red, fading to yellowish; axil of pectoral black with green edge; ventrals yellowish green, the long rays orange, spines violet.

Color in alcohol, dull purplish brown; head pale brown, snout very pale or whitish; several lines and spots in single series down middle of forehead; a brown line from side of snout to eye, continued, broken above, to origin of dorsal; a brown streak behind eye to corner of opercular flap; a pale brown streak from upper lip toward eye then down across opercle below; a brown band from mandible along side of breast to base of ventral; chin to space between ventrals with blackish streak; round, dark-edged blue spots on trunk, most numerous posteriorly and on tail; dorsal and anal whitish, margins narrowly blackish with many dark-edged bluish spots, and dusky tinge basally; outer portions of soft dorsal and anal each with a narrow dusky line parallel with margins of fins; caudal and pectoral whitish, latter blackish inside at base; ventrals whitish with dusky edges.

Described from an example (No. 05345) from Honolulu. This species is abundant, found with the preceding about the reefs at Honolulu and elsewhere among the Hawaiian Islands, specimens having been obtained by about every collector who has visited those islands. The localities represented in our very large series of specimens (45) are Honolulu, Hilo, and Kailua. These examples range in length from 5.4 to 11.25 inches. Occasional in Samoa.

242. Julis lepomis (Jenkins). *"Hilu lauwili;" "Úhu."* Fig. 131.

Head 3.35 in length; depth 3.35; eye 8 in head; snout 2.9; mouth 4.5; interorbital 4; D. ix, 12; A. iii, 12; scales 8–92–35.

Body ovoid, elongate, deepest about pectoral; head elongate, much longer than deep, the upper profile convex, swollen in front of eye above; snout long, blunt, convex; mouth horizontal, small; lips thick, fleshy, broad; teeth large, powerful, conic; 2 large canines in front of each jaw, the lower fitting in between those above; eye small, well anterior, high in head; nostrils small, anterior in very

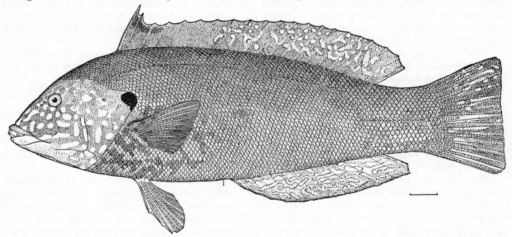

FIG. 131.—*Julis lepomis* (Jenkins). Type of *Coris lepomis* Jenkins. Figure not quite accurate in proportional measurements.

short tube; opercle with well-developed flap posteriorly; interorbital space high, convex; first 2 dorsal spines elongate, flexible, the first longer, 1.8 in head; third anal spine longest, 4; longest anal ray 2.3; caudal slightly rounded posteriorly; pectoral rather short, 1.5; ventral 1.7; scales small, thin, those on occiput very small, head otherwise naked; lateral line rather indistinct, running down on side of caudal peduncle below posterior dorsal rays.

Color in life, green with blue shades; opercular spot deep blue, blackish before and behind; about 8 blackish vertical bars behind pectoral; back very green, middle and along lateral line tinged with olive brown; head olive gray with spots and radiating lines of clear blue; throat and breast blue with drab olive spots; fins greenish sky-blue marked with olive; pectoral olive tinged with bluish; ventrals similar, more blue.

Another nearly fresh example (No. 03344) with general color bright blue; side back of pectoral with 7 or 8 darker short cross-bars; head pale blue with numerous bluish-white spots about size of pupil; opercular flap bright blue with pale margins, yellow posteriorly, brown in front; dorsal vermiculated or blotched with olive, greenish, and bright blue; caudal dirty blue; anal with irregular spots and blotches of bright blue separated by greenish-yellow; pectoral bluish-olive; ventrals pale olive; iris yellowish. One example when fresh had the black opercular spot shaded with deep bluish, palest in center; golden markings on head bright yellowish-brown.

Color in alcohol, dull purple brown; head and chest marked with broad pale short lines, spots, and blotches; opercular flap blue-black behind; short blackish oblique lines on side beyond tip of pectoral; vertical fins grayish, marked with pale bluish blotches and spots, most numerous on rayed portions of fins; a large blackish blotch behind second and third dorsal spines; pectoral and ventral grayish, the former variegated with indistinct lighter markings.

Described from an example (No. 04099) from Honolulu.

This is the largest and one of the handsomest of the many shore fishes of this group. It is often seen in the markets of Honolulu. We have 11 examples from Honolulu and 1 from Hilo, ranging in length from 13.75 to 18.75 inches.

243. Julis flavovittata Bennett. Plate XXVIII.

Head, measured to end of opercular flap, 3.12 in length; depth 4; snout 3.3 in head; eye 5.5; D ix, 12; A. iii, 12; scales 7–88–27.

Color in alcohol, white with black longitudinal stripes. A black stripe, pointed anteriorly, broken and irregular posteriorly, extends from middle of snout to end of dorsal; a second runs from tip of snout through eye to base of caudal, where it is connected with the one on opposite side by a band passing over the caudal peduncle; a third extends from lower jaw over base of pectoral to base of caudal; a fourth passes from throat to end of anal; breast and belly dusky; dorsal black, edged with white, a few white blotches along middle of fin; caudal white at base and on margin, middle of fin with a black lunate band; anal black, bordered with white; pectorals white; ventrals dusky at base; a posterior canine tooth present.

This species, described originally from the Hawaiian Islands, was not obtained by us, but 1 specimen, 1.8 inches long, was taken by the *Albatross* at Laysan Island.

244. Julis greenovii Bennett. Plate XXX.

Head 3.4 in length; depth 3.7; eye 5 in head; snout 3.5; D. ix, 12; A. ii, 12; P. 12; V. i, 5; C. 14; scales 6–78–21.

Body short, compressed, and fusiform; dorsal outline regularly and evenly arched from tip of snout to origin of dorsal fin, thence very slightly convex to base of caudal; ventral outline about evenly convex throughout; caudal peduncle compressed, the least depth less than snout and eye; head small, thin, and pointed; snout pointed; mouth small, nearly horizontal, the jaws equal; maxillary short, not reaching orbit, its distal end wholly concealed under the broad, thin preorbital; upper jaw with a pair of slender, projecting canines in front, and a series of short, close-set teeth on side, the anterior one somewhat enlarged and canine-like; no canine at angle of mouth; teeth of lower jaw similar to those of upper; eye small, wholly in anterior half of head; interorbital space moderately wide, convex; gill-membranes united to the isthmus; opercle ending in a long thin flap. Origin of dorsal fin in vertical at base of pectoral; dorsal fin low, the rays and spines of approximately equal length, the last spine about 3.2 in head, the last ray about 3; caudal rounded, the middle rays about 1.7 in head; anal similar to dorsal, its origin under base of first dorsal ray; pectoral about 1.7 in head; ventral pointed, its length 1.6 in head. Scales very small and smooth; head entirely naked; lateral line strongly arched above the pectoral, then closely following outline of back until under tenth dorsal ray, where it bends downward to median line of side and continues thence to base of caudal.

Color in life, rich blood-red, faintly tinged on lower parts of head, at base of pectoral, and slightly on middle of side with yellowish or orange; top of snout with an ovate or oblong white area surrounded by a narrow black border; a similar white saddle across nape at posterior border of eyes; a diamond-shaped white spot on side and base of dorsal, extending upon lower part of fourth to sixth membranes of spinous dorsal; another roundish white spot on side, extending from just below lateral line upward upon seventh and eighth interradial dorsal membranes, about one-half the spot being upon the fin; a white saddle on middle of caudal peduncle; these 5 white spots each with a distinct black border, the one on caudal peduncle not well defined; caudal peduncle with a large diffuse brownish-black area, breaking up into small specks at the edges, especially anteriorly, and overlaid with small sky-blue spots, largest and most distinct in the center and posteriorly; dorsal fin rich red, the spines with slight yellow tinge, the rays bluish-white, a narrow black border full length of fin, slightly broader posteriorly; a large oblong bluish-black spot on last 2 dorsal membranes, the 2 white spots on side involving lower portions of membranes between fourth and seventh spines and between seventh and ninth rays; caudal fin brownish-yellow, lightest toward tip, reddish at base, and crossed near the middle by 2 series of oblong black spots on the membranes, those of the inner series the larger, the 2 series parallel and curving distally; anal similar to dorsal, with a narrow black border, but without spots anywhere; pectoral lemon-yellow, washed with reddish on basal portion; ventral yellowish, washed with reddish on proximal portion, the outer two-fifths sky-blue, darkest at tip.

In alcohol the bright colors all fade; general color grayish-yellow, darkest on nape; jaws and lower parts of head pale; breast and isthmus dark; the 4 white saddles on back and spot on nose plain white, each with black border; side of caudal peduncle rusty black, the blue faded; dorsal and anal fins white, each with a narrow black border, the former with an oblong black spot on last 2 membranes; caudal white, rusty at base, crossed near the middle by 2 parallel series of black spots, those of inner series largest and practically continuous; pectoral and ventrals pale.

The above description is from a specimen (No. 2743) 3.5 inches long, taken in 1902 by Dr. Jordan at Apia, Samoa. The colored painting by Kako Morita is from color notes and sketch from the live fish by Dr. Jordan. The original type specimen came from Hawaii, but none has since been reported from those islands.

245. Julis eydouxii Cuvier & Valenciennes. *"Hilu."* Plate XXIX.

Head 3.1 in length; depth 3.2; eye 8.2 in head; snout 2.8; mouth 3.6; interorbital 4.7; D. ix, 11; A. iii, 12; scales 8–81–31.

Body elongate, compressed, greatest depth at beginning of anal; head elongate, pointed, its depth 1.4 in its length; upper profile of head slightly convex; snout compressed, 2.8 in head; mouth rather long, horizontal, the corner slipping under preorbital sheath; lips thick, fleshy; teeth powerful, conic; 2 produced strong canines in front of each jaw, those on mandible largest and fitting in between upper pair; jaws pointed and produced; eye small, anterior, high in head; preopercle with thin convex edge; interorbital width convexly elevated; nostrils close together in front of eye, anterior in short, fleshy tube; last dorsal spine 3.3 in head; longest dorsal ray 2.5; anal spines graduated to last, which is longest; anal rays longer than spines, longest 2.4 in head; caudal broad, margin a little convex, 1.4 in head; pectoral with upper rays longest, 1.6; ventral pointed, not reaching anus, 2; scales small, cycloid, rather thin; head, except on occiput, naked; small scales only on base of caudal, none on vertical fins; lateral line high, concurrent with back till below last dorsal rays, then running down and along middle of side of caudal peduncle.

Color in life (No. 02964), upper half of side with a broad lake-purple stripe, divided for its anterior two-thirds into 2 by a narrow pale lemon stripe, which begins on snout and extends across head just above eye to beneath fifteenth dorsal ray; a narrow stripe of lake-purple at base of dorsal separated from the broad stripe by a somewhat wider pale lemon stripe, which begins on nape just above posterior rim of eye and unites with the yellow of caudal peduncle, the broad lake purple stripe narrowly bordered below by rose-pink, below which is a narrow yellowish-white line, narrowest and best defined on cheek, broadest and most yellow on posterior third of body; lower half of side rose-pink, whitening below and somewhat yellowish on caudal peduncle; a broad brick-red stripe from snout through eye to upper edge of opercle; opercular flap light greenish anteriorly, then black, then pale on posterior border; cheek and lower half of head reddish, mixed with lemon; dorsal black and brownish-red, with narrow white border, and a series of large roundish chrome-yellow spots; a black ocellus on second dorsal ray and its membrane; base of caudal yellowish-white, followed by a broad purplish-black lunate bar, anteriorly with a yellowish streak and posteriorly by white, which is broadest at the outer angles; anal lake-red with yellow spots at bases of spines; the last ray yellow, fin becoming blacker toward edge and bordered narrowly with white; pectoral pale, slightly yellowish at base; ventrals white, anteriorly edged with vermilion.

In another example (No. 05325) there is an indistinct brown band along middle of side from pectoral to base of lower caudal rays.

Color in alcohol, pale brownish white; back with 3 blackish brown longitudinal bands, first beginning on side of snout, narrow, running along base of dorsal, and continued as broad crescent across caudal; above and behind eye it gives out a second band which joins the lowest near descent of lateral line; lowest or third band broadest, beginning on side of snout, running through eye across opercle above to base of upper caudal rays; black spot on opercular flap; dorsal and anal blackish brown with narrow white edges, the former with median series of whitish spots; anal blackish brown with median longitudinal dark band; pectorals and ventrals pale like belly.

This large and brilliant species, described originally from these islands, is very common in the markets of Honolulu and Hilo, from which places we have numerous specimens 5.8 to 15.75 inches long.

Genus 158. CORIS Lacépède.

Body compressed, oblong, covered with moderate or small scales, 50 to 60 in the lateral line; head scaleless; lateral line not interrupted; posterior canine tooth absent or not; dorsal ix, 12; anal iii, 12; anterior dorsal spines usually produced and flexible; caudal rounded.

Polynesia, the species few; deeply colored fishes of the coral reefs.

246. Coris ballieui Vaillant & Sauvage. Plate XXXII.

Head 3.5 in length; depth 3.4; eye 6.4 in head; snout 2.8; mouth 5; interorbital 5.2; D. ix, 12; A. iii, 12; scales 5–53–18.

Body elongate, oblong, deepest about middle of pectoral; head longer than deep, pointed; snout long, pointed; mouth horizontal, upper jaw slightly produced; lips thick, fleshy; teeth strong, conic, directed forward; 2 large canines in front of each jaw directed forward, those on mandible fitting in between upper pair; eye rather large, posterior rim about middle of length of head; preopercular flap thin; interorbital width elevated, convex; nostrils close together in front of eye, anterior in short tube; first dorsal spine elongate, filamentous, 3.7 in body; longest dorsal ray 2.2 in head; third anal spine longest, 4.3; longest anal ray 2.25; caudal rounded, 1.6; ventrals long, pointed, 1.7; scales rather large, thin, cycloid; lateral line high along back, descending below last dorsal rays to middle of sides of caudal peduncle.

Color in life (No. 03260) light olive-brown, with a silver streak on each row of scales, about 22 in number, some scales with a light bluish-green central spot forming irregular stripes, the one above lateral line most distinct, the interspaces forming golden stripes; behind tip of pectoral about 5 short vertical irregular bars of golden, alternating with violet, behind these faint violet stripes alternating with 3 golden ones; base of anal violet; breast and belly white; head golden olive, with blue dashes and stripes, 2 across lower jaw meeting to surround a white area, 2 behind these across pre- and subopercle; first dorsal spine dusky, a jet black blue-edged spot behind it; dorsals with 1 broad and 3 wavy narrow stripes of sky blue, with golden interspaces; caudal golden yellow, with 5 sky-blue wavy crossbars; anal like dorsal, the bands interiorly parallel with the margin, posteriorly running upward and backward; pectoral pale yellowish, the base dusky; ventrals reddish, the outer ray dusky; iris orange pink.

Color in alcohol, dull brown, side with narrow longitudinal dull purplish brown lines, broadest on back; head brown with leaden streak from corner of mouth to eye, another from corner of mouth back over preopercle; and still others below eye, on opercle, and mandible; vertical fins pale grayish, dorsal with blackish spot at bases between first 2 spines; spinous dorsal gray with 3 narrow pale or light gray lines on outer portion, below which are gray blotches and longitudinal streaks of gray; anal gray with oblique whitish crossbars; caudal gray with darker blackish edged vertical cross bands; pectoral and ventrals pale, the latter with dusky edges.

Described from an example (No. 05326) from Honolulu.

Rather common. Dr. Wood's Honolulu collection contained 1 specimen, and we obtained 13 at Honolulu and 3 at Hilo. The *Albatross* also secured specimens at Honolulu. The numerous specimens examined range in length from 6.5 to 11.5 inches.

247. Coris rosea Vaillant & Sauvage. "*Malamalama.*" Fig. 132.

Head 3.35 in length; depth 2.75; eye 5.4 in head; snout 2.8; mouth 4.7; interorbital 4.6; D. IX, 12; A. III, 12; scales 5–53–18.

Body elongate, oblong, deepest about middle of pectoral; head longer than deep, pointed; snout long, pointed; mouth horizontal, jaws produced, equal; lips thick, fleshy; teeth conic, strong, directed

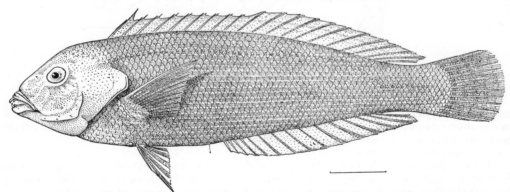

FIG. 132.—*Coris rosea* Vaillant & Sauvage. Type of *Hemicoris keleipionis*. Figure not quite accurate in proportional measurements.

forward; 2 large canines in front of upper jaw directed forward; 2 large canines in front of mandible directed forward, fitting in between upper pair; eye rather large, high, a little before middle of head; preopercular flap rounded, the margin thin; interorbital width elevated, convex; nostrils close together, anterior in short tube; first dorsal spine longest, 2.8 in head; longest dorsal rays about middle, 2.1; third anal spine 3.75, longest; middle anal rays longest, 2.3; caudal rounded, 1.6; pectoral pointed, 1.6; ventral pointed, 1.8; ventral spine weak, 2.3 in longest or first ray; scales rather large, thin, cycloid; lateral line high along back, descending below posterior dorsal rays, then running along middle·of side of caudal peduncle.

Color in life (No. 03268), bright brownish pink, a large golden area above pectoral; side with about

24 curly white streaks running along rows of scales, these yellow in the golden area, the streaks above lateral line most distinct; head golden olive, with vague bluish shades; upper part of opercle bright yellow, bluish shades placed much as in *C. ballieui;* a bluish streak from eye to first dorsal spine; no black spot on front of dorsal; iris red; dorsal with a row of bluish spots at base, a broad blue band just below the middle, a narrow blue band above it, the fin otherwise golden; caudal golden with 3 narrow pale bluish bands; anal violet at base, then golden, then a violet stripe, otherwise golden; behind middle of anal violet streaks run obliquely; pectoral pale yellowish; ventrals reddish.

Another example (No. 03310) is richer red, the yellow or golden area above pectoral absent, the curly white stripes most distinct on under part of side; only tips of first dorsal membrane black, edge of fin with dashes of bluish purple.

Color in alcohol, dull brown, many narrow brown lines longitudinally along side; head uniform dull brown with indistinct darker colored pattern shown in figure of *C. ballieui* by Steindachner; fins pale brown, marginal or outer portion of dorsal with 4 narrow pale brown longitudinal lines; anal uniform pale brown; caudal pale brown with 3 or 4 indistinct pale crossbars at base; pectorals and and ventrals pale uniform brown.

Described from an example (No. 2552) taken at Honolulu.

This species is near *Coris ballieui.* It differs in having the first dorsal spine short, the color paler, and the marks on anal and caudal indistinct. Rather common at Honolulu.

We have 20 specimens, 17 from Honolulu and 3 from Hilo, 6.5 to 10.4 inches long.

248. Coris venusta Vaillant & Sauvage. Plate XXXI and Fig. 133.

Head 3.5 in length; depth 3.4; eye 5.7 in head; snout 3.2; mouth 5; interorbital 5; D. ix, 12; A. iii, 12; scales 5–52–17.

Body elongate, compressed, deepest about origin of anal; head much longer than high, pointed; snout long, jaws produced, equal; mouth small, horizontal; lips thick, fleshy; teeth strong, directed forward; 2 canines in front of each jaw directed forward, the lower fitting in between upper; eye small,

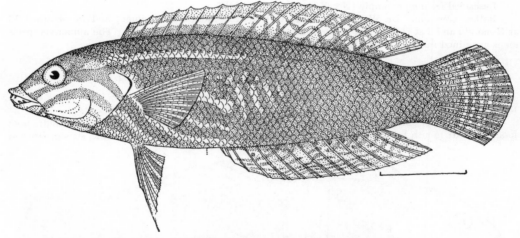

FIG. 133.—*Coris venusta* Vaillant & Sauvage. Type of *Hemicoris remedius* Jenkins.

its posterior rim in center of length of head; interorbital space broad, convex; nostrils small, anterior in very short tube; posterior dorsal spines longest, last 2.8 in head; longest dorsal ray about 1.8; third anal spine 3.2 in head; longest anal ray 2; pectoral 1.5; ventrals long, pointed, 1.2.

Described from an example (No. 4569) from Hilo.

Color in life, brown (No. 6133, L. S. Jr. Univ. Mus.), dark above, light below; a bright red band from eye along lateral line to its downward bend; a bright red band from opercular flap extending backward to tip of pectoral, from which it is broken up into a series of short oblique crossbars on every alternate row of scales, becoming less distinct toward caudal peduncle; a bright red band curving downward just below anterior portion of middle line of body, becoming indistinct about below vertical from twelfth dorsal spine; another bright red band from axil curving downward and extending backward to about second anal ray; a bright red band from angle of mouth curving upward to lower margin of eye and down to edge of opercle just below flap; a bright red band from a short distance behind symphysis curving upward over cheek and downward across middle of posterior margin of opercle on to breast to a point just behind base of ventrals; a bright red band on each side of middle line of throat; a short red bar at symphysis; a red spot just above and back of eye; anterior portion of opercular flap scarlet, bordered posteriorly first with black then with bright yellow; spinous dorsal with a longitudinal band of red on middle portion, which on soft portion is broken up into small wavy lines and reticulations.

Another example (No. 03351) with greenish-olive side; a pink-red band along lateral line from back of eye to middle of length, then fading and running above lateral line to caudal peduncle; another similar but broader band from gill-opening just above pectoral to middle of length, where it breaks up into spots; between these 2 a series of 5 or 6 small red spots; a narrower red band from axil along lower part of side; head greenish-olive, a broad bluish white bar from eye forward and downward to lip, a similar one under eye forward across cheek and meeting its fellow on lower jaw; base of pectoral bluish with reddish anterior border.

Color in alcohol (No. 04569) dark brown; a pale creamy band from eye along back, another from corner of mouth, touching eye, back and down across opercle toward base of pectoral; side of head below with convex creamy band running down on side of chest behind ventral; opercle with large creamy blotch, angle of flap narrowly black; 4 pale creamy bands radiate from above base of pectoral along side a short distance; vertical fins dark gray; spinous dorsal with median whitish longitudinal line for short distance giving place posteriorily to dark; soft dorsal with dusky brown blotches and marblings; anal with blotches at base, the marginal portion with narrow oblique blackish lines; caudal with dusky crossbars; pectoral and ventrals plain pale brown.

In our smallest example (No. 404) from Honolulu, there is a black spot at bases of last 2 dorsal rays.

This species is generally common on the coral reefs about Honolulu. It is a well-known fish and was formerly supposed to have medicinal value. It bears much resemblance to *Julis multicolor* of Rüppell, a species of still earlier date.

We have 36 excellent specimens (including the 12 examples obtained by Dr. Jenkins), all from Honolulu but 1, which is from Hilo. The *Albatross* also obtained it at Honolulu.

249. Coris aygula Lacépède. Fig. 134.

Head 3.75 in length; depth 3; eye 7 in head; snout 2.5; interorbital 3.65; depth of caudal peduncle 6; D. ix, 12; A. iii, 12; scales 5–61–24.

Body moderately compressed, dorsal contour ascending rapidly from tip of snout to insertion of dorsal, ventral outline more gently and evenly curved; snout short, bluntly pointed; jaws equal, lower lip thin, divided into 2 lateral pendant lobes; teeth closely opposed or coalesed at base, the points distinct, in a single series; 2 strong blunt canines on tip of each jaw, 2 or 4 smaller teeth in a row behind the canines; no posterior canines present; preopercle entire; opercle with a broad flap, its length 5 in head; interorbital space convex; caudal peduncle deep; gillrakers on first arch 6+11, moderately long, slender, pointed; pseudobranchiæ large; dorsal spines long and slender, not pungent, the longest 2.5 in head; longest dorsal ray 1.8; anal spines similar to those of dorsal, the rays equal to those of dorsal in length, the membranes of both fins thick; outer rays of ventrals lengthened, the fins reaching base of first anal ray; scales moderate, much reduced on nape and on pectoral region; dorsal and anal fins without basal sheath; small scales extending far out on interradial membranes of caudal; head naked; lateral line complete, abruptly bent downward below base of soft dorsal.

Color in life, deep green, the scales edged with brownish; a bluish-green vertical band behind end of depressed pectoral; caudal with a wash of blue on posterior parts; dorsal and anal with golden brown reticulations.

Color in alcohol, uniform blue-black, the scales with a somewhat lighter edge, the fins much darker than the body.

This species, here described from a large example from Wakanoura, Japan, has been once recorded from Hawaii by Mr. Fowler; a record open to doubt, however.

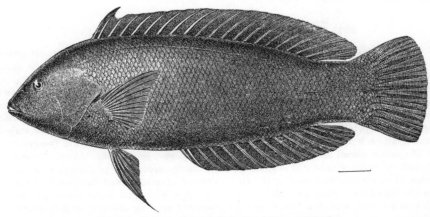

FIG. 134.—*Coris aygula* Lacépède; after Jordan and Snyder.

Genus 159. CHEILIO (Commerson) Lacépède.

Body elongate, compressed, covered with rather small scales, 45 to 50 in the lateral line; lateral line continuous; cheeks scaleless; a few rudimentary scales on the opercle; teeth small, in one series; no posterior canines; dorsal spines flexible; fins not produced; dorsal ix, 13; anal iii, 11. Polynesia to Africa; apparently a single species, varying much in color.

250. Cheilio inermis (Forskål). *"Kupóupóu."* Plate XXXIII.

Head 2.8 in length; depth 4.6; eye 9.6 in head; snout 2.25; maxillary 3; interorbital 5.6; D. ix, 13; A. ii, 12; scales 5–48–10.

Body very elongate, compressed, deepest at pectoral; upper profile of head concave, then convex to occiput; mouth large, upper jaw slightly projecting; snout and jaws produced; maxillary reaching under posterior nostril; lips thick, fleshy; teeth strong, conic, interorbital width broad, convex; nostrils small, close together, posterior a little less than eye diameter from front of eye; margin of preopercle undulate; dorsal spines pungent, tips flexible, longest 3.8 in head; longest dorsal ray 3.7; longest anal ray 3.7; margin of caudal a little convex, 2 in head; pectoral small, 2.5; ventrals 4.25; scales large, thin; lateral line almost straight to base of caudal, tubes very arborescent.

Color in life (No. 03244), olive-green, varying toward rusty red, each scale with a more or less distinct curly blue spot, bluish shades predominating below; head with various streaks and reticulations of olive, brownish and pearly blue; middle of side with a narrow dark streak which breaks up posteriorly into a row of blackish spots; dorsal light orange, the color forming reticulations around pearly spots; anal similar; caudal dirty, olive-gray; with a paler cross shade; pectoral and ventrals colorless.

Three smaller examples (Nos. 03245, 03246, and 03247) have the ground color light olivaceous orange rather than greenish, a dark lateral band much more distinct and traceable across eye to tip of snout; dorsal plain translucent without trace of spots· or reticulations; caudal dull green, the dark lateral band forming a dark mesial shade to its tip; anal and pectoral colorless; vent and anal spine light blue; ventrals light blue, lower ray of pectoral blue; No. 03244 has a· brown spot at axil, the others reddish spots. Another (No. 03348) bright golden; snout orange; lateral stripe black, more or less distinct; fins plain golden; a few pearly blue spots on scales of lower parts.

Example No. 03039 had a large black blotch on each side when fresh, and one taken at Honolulu July 19, 1900, when fresh was bright lemon-yellow over whole of body and fins, with the usual row of black spots.

Color in alcohol, uniform brown above, abdomen whitish; blackish blotch above tip of pectoral, with several white scales; fins pale brown, dorsal and anal with pale oblique crossbars, caudal with brown spots on membrane.

This species is subject to great variation in shade of color. It is common in the markets at Hilo and Honolulu. Our collections contain 62 specimens from Honolulu (12 collected by Dr. Jenkins and 1 by the *Albatross* in 1896) and 4 from Hilo. These are 1.8 to 16.5 inches long. Common at Samoa.

Genus 160. CIRRHILABRUS Schlegel.

Body compressed, oblong, covered with large scales, 20 to 25 in the lateral line; lateral line interrupted; forehead not elevated nor trenchant; cheeks and opercles with imbricated scales; preopercle serrated; teeth in one series, with canines anteriorly; no posterior canine; D. xi, 9; A. iii, 9; ventrals much produced (*Cirrhilabrus*), or short (*Cheilinoides*).

251. Cirrhilabrus jordani Snyder. Plate 42, fig. 1.

Head measured to end of opercular flap 2.8 in length; depth 3.45; depth of caudal peduncle 7; length of snout 3.1 in head; eye 4; interorbital space 4.3; D. xi, 8; A. iii, 8; scales in lateral line 16+8; between lateral line and dorsal 1; between lateral line and anterior part of anal 5.

Snout pointed; cleft of mouth 1.3 in eye; 6 rather widely spaced canines in upper jaw; inner pair projecting forward; the others, of which the outer pair are much the longer, curve outward and backward; 2 small canines in lower jaw; no posterior canines; other teeth very small, sharp, and closely apposed; preopercle with a finely serrated margin. Cheeks and opercles with scales; bases of dorsal and anal, each with a row of long, pointed scales; 3 large scales covering the greater part of basal half of caudal; dorsal and anal fins high; dorsal spines slender, the longest (posterior ones) equal in length to twice diameter of eye, each with a fleshy, spine-like prolongation, a continuation of the thickened membrane surrounding the spine, extending upward and backward and acting as a support for the membrane which extends above spines; first ray equal in height to preceding spine and its thickened attachment, the following rays gradually growing shorter; anal spines with thickened membranous attachments similar to those of dorsal, the rays longer than the spines, their length contained about 1.5 times in head; caudal rounded; ventrals sharply pointed, not greatly elongated, reaching to vent when depressed; upper rays of pectoral longest.

Flesh color in alcohol, probably red in life; a pale purple stripe indistinctly outlined extending along body between base of dorsal and lateral line; a few small white spots scattered along back above lateral line; 3 distinct, narrow, light stripes along side of abdomen. Fins plain, probably yellow in life; anal with a narrow dusky band on margin.

The specimen described is a male, type, No. 50878, U. S. Nat. Mus., from Albatross station 3876, between Maui and Lanai; depth 28 to 43 fathoms.

Other examples, females from the same locality, among them cotypes, No. 7728, Stanford University, have the spinous dorsal lower than the rayed portion of the fin. The thickened portions of the membrane are less developed. The anal has no dusky border.

Genus 161. PSEUDOCHEILINUS Bleeker.

Body compressed, oblong, covered with large scales; lateral line interrupted; cheek with 2 series of large scales; preopercle entire; teeth in a single series; the upper jaw with a pair of very large canine teeth bent outward and backward; no posterior canine tooth; lower jaw not produced backward; 9 dorsal spines, subequal in length; 3 anal spines, the middle one the longest. Eye with the cornea peculiarly modified.

252. Pseudocheilinus evanidus Jordan & Evermann. Plate 43.

Head 3 in length; depth 3.8; eye 4.5 in head; snout 3; preorbital 6.2; interorbital 5.5; D. ix, 11; A. iii, 9; scales 2–25–6.

Body short, deep and compressed; head long, conic; snout long, sharply conic; anterior profile rising in a relatively straight line from tip of snout to nape, thence gently convex to base of caudal peduncle; ventral outline less convex; mouth large, horizontal, below axis of body, gape reaching anterior line of orbit; upper jaw with 3 pairs of anterior canines, outer strongest, curved outward and backward; lower jaw with a single pair at tip, similar to inner above; jaws laterally with a single series of smaller conic teeth; preorbital narrow, oblique; eye high up, its lower border on axis of body; interorbital space rather broad and flat; depth of caudal peduncle about 2 in head; scales large, surfaces finely striate; head, nape, and breast with large scales; lateral line following contour of back until under base of sixth dorsal ray, where it is interrupted, reappearing 2 rows farther down and continuing on 6 or 7 scales to base of caudal fin; fins rather large; dorsal spines somewhat greater than eye in length, spines with a sheath of large scales reaching nearly to their tips; soft dorsal and anal with a lower sheath; soft dorsal elevated, rays equal to snout and eye; anal similar to soft dorsal, second spine strongest, nearly as long as snout; anal rays somewhat longer, equaling those of soft dorsal; caudal rounded, its length 1.3 in head, its base covered with very large, thin scales.

Color in life, according to Mr. Sindo, body dull brick-red; belly and base of anal pale purplish; about 17 thin, thread-like longitudinal yellowish streaks along side anteriorly; dark greenish blotches above eye and on snout; a bluish horizontal bar on cheek, below which is a yellow bar; median line of throat and tip of snout brick-red; edges of opercle and preopercle bright purple; a purple stripe with reddish edges through middle of dorsal fin, below which the color is dull brick-red, like that of body, and above which the spinous dorsal is orange-yellow, the margin of the membranes bright cardinal-red; above the purple streak in the soft dorsal is a bright yellow streak, above which the fin is cardinal-red, fading gradually upward; dorsal rays purplish; tip of soft dorsal somewhat red; caudal rays purple, the membranes immediately next to the rays yellow, middle part dull brick-red; anal same as caudal; ventrals pale purplish; pectoral pale; iris scarlet-red.

The same specimen after having been in spirits more than a year has the body light brownish blue; a pale streak along each row of scales, but no trace of the narrow yellowish streaks above noted; top of head and upper part of cheek dusky blue; opercle and edge of preopercle rich blue; dorsal, anal, and caudal fins bright blue, the soft dorsal pale on the outer two-thirds, dorsal rays bright blue; ventrals and pectoral light blue, latter darker blue at base. The color of this specimen in spirits is wholly different from that which it possessed in life, and it would be difficult to believe that such changes had taken place except that the specimen was carefully tagged when the color note in life was taken.

Since writing the above, we have noticed similar changes in the Samoan species, P. hexatænia. The blue shades are permanent in spirits, while the pink or crimson wash soon vanishes.

The 17 thread-like streaks, mentioned in Mr. Sindo's field notes above, have vanished entirely in the original type. A number of specimens taken at Laysan by the Albatross retain these marks, the streaks being almost white, like white threads, covering most of the side anteriorly. This is a very peculiar color mark, which should well distinguish the species in life.

A single specimen, type No. 50678, U. S. N. M. (field No. 05757), was taken by Mr. Sindo in Henshaw's pool near Hilo, a deep tide pool in the lava rocks.

253. Pseudocheilinus octotænia Jenkins. *"Aleihi lakea."*   Plate XXXVII and Fig. 135.

Head 2.8 in length; depth 3.2; eye 5 in head; snout 2.7; preorbital 6.5; interorbital 5.75; D. ix, 10; A. iii, 9; scales 2–23–6.

Body moderately deep and compressed; head very long and pointed; snout long and pointed; the lower jaw slightly the shorter; anterior profile from tip of snout to origin of dorsal straight, ascending at an angle of about 35°; body deepest at origin of dorsal; mouth rather large, but narrow, nearly horizontal, the gape reaching not quite to vertical of eye; lower jaw with 1 pair and the upper jaw with 3 pairs of enlarged canine-like teeth in front and a series of smaller close-set teeth laterally, the canines sometimes not developed; premaxillaries strongly protractile; skin on lips at sides broad and flap-like; eye rather large, its lower edge on axis of body; scales large, smooth, firm, the surfaces very finely striate; cheek and opercles scaled, 2 rows on cheek; lateral line following curvature of back to scale under base of last dorsal ray, where it is broken, beginning again on scale in same series 2 rows lower, or sometimes in same series 2 scales more anterior; fins rather large; dorsal beginning over base of pectoral, membranes of spines extending beyond their sharp tips, longest dorsal spine about equal to snout, last dorsal ray somewhat produced; anal similar to soft dorsal, the spines and rays about equal to snout; caudal rounded, equal to snout and eye; ventrals short, equal to snout; pectoral rounded equal to snout and pupil.

Color in life, brownish red, the anterior half coppery, the posterior half grayish; side of body with 8 nearly black longitudinal stripes following along the rows of scales, narrower than the interspaces, broadest and most distinct posteriorly, the upper one fading under the dorsal, sometimes traces of a faint ninth line; a faint median streak from nape to front of dorsal preceded by a distinct white streak from vertex to tip of mouth; head vaguely mottled purplish and orange, the opercles largely orange; spinous dorsal dull purplish at base, then dull blue, followed by dull yellow, the fleshy tips crimson; soft dorsal mostly orange yellow, reticulated with bluish, dull purplish at base with a dull bluish streak above it; anal like soft dorsal; caudal bright orange-yellow; pectoral and ventrals dull pink.

The same specimen in alcohol is pale brownish white, the longitudinal stripes black or dark brown; head dusky yellowish; fins bluish and yellowish green; base of caudal most yellowish.

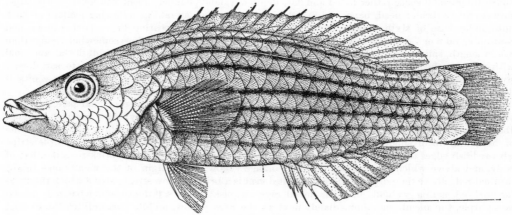

Fig. 135.—*Pseudocheilinus octotænia* Jenkins; from the type.

Another specimen (No. 03498) in life showed the body purple-lake or claret color, with 7 black lines running laterally through the body; the second line from the top runs over the upper lateral line, and the posterior portion of the fourth line over the lower lateral line; head same color as the body, but without the black bars, except the occipital region, which has 4 thin black streaks which are continuous with those of the body; cheek with yellow dots in irregular rows; several (about 5) purple streaks radiate from eye, which may be continuous with the black bars on the body in living examples; interorbital space and top of snout with rose-red streaks running along the median line; lips bright rose-red, a yellowish red streak over eye; spinous dorsal with 3 purple and 2 yellow bars, which are slightly wavy, alternating each other, ending on tip with a purple bar; the yellow preponderates in the soft dorsal, in which the purple bars are reduced to very thin streaks; rays purple; caudal fin bright yellow; anal same as the soft dorsal; pectorals and ventrals plain, pale claret.

The above description is based upon a specimen (No. 03238) obtained at Honolulu, June 11, 1901. The species was found at Honolulu by Wood, Jordan and Snyder, by us, and by the *Albatross*, and by us at Hilo.   The 19 specimens examined are 3.6 to 5.2 inches long.

Genus 162. CHEILINUS Lacépède.

Body oblong, compressed, covered with large scales, 20 to 25 in lateral line; lateral line interrupted; cheek with 2 series of large scales; opercles scaly; preopercle entire; teeth in 1 series, 2 canines in front of each jaw, not bent backward nor outward; no posterior canine; lower jaw not produced backward; lips thick; dorsal spines subequal; D. IX, 10 (rarely x, 9); A. III, 8.

Fishes of Polynesia and the East Indies, usually brightly colored, the shades chiefly red and green.

254. Cheilinus hexagonatus Günther. *"Poou."* Fig. 136.

Head 2.4 in length; depth 2.75; eye 6.5 in head; snout 2.4; maxillary 2.6; interorbital 4; D. IX, 10; A. III, 9; scales 3–24–6.

Body elongate, oblong, compressed, deepest about ventral fin; head elongate, its depth 1.4 in its length; upper profile of head slightly convex to origin of dorsal; snout long pointed, rounded; mouth

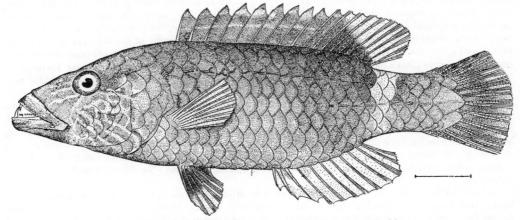

Fig. 136.—*Cheilinus hexagonatus* Günther. Type of *C. zonurus* Jenkins.

large, oblique; jaws large, strong, lower slightly projecting; teeth in jaws forming sharp cutting edge along sides, rather small, sharp pointed, compressed; 2 enlarged sharp canines in front of each jaw, lower fitting in between upper; eye rather small, anterior; margin of preopercle undulate; interorbital space convex; nostril in short tube in front of eye; last dorsal spine 3.75 in head; eighth dorsal ray 3; third anal spine longest 3.4; sixth anal ray 2.6; caudal rounded; pectoral short, rounded, 2.25 in head; ventral short, rounded, 2.5; scales large, thin, cycloid; lateral line straight above, interrupted below last dorsal rays, then beginning low and running straight out on base of caudal. Described from an example (No. 04296) from Honolulu.

Color in life (No. 3506) dull drab above, each scale with a vertical bar of vermilion red; lower surface rosy; markings on head cadmium with a ground-color of dull brownish, neutral tint; dorsal with 3 longitudinal bars of cadmium, interspaces dull-greenish blue; anal venetian red with a faint yellow median longitudinal bar, more distinct anteriorly; caudal rays green, membranes yellow, narrow posterior border red; pectoral yellowish toward base, pink distally; ventrals rosy, with black blotch on proximal half; a light pink zone around anterior portion of caudal peduncle, showing also on posterior end of dorsal.

Color in life of example from Hilo, head livid violet brown, the varied marks orange, posteriorly scarlet; body reddish brown, each scale with a bright red bar, redder in the young than in the adult; caudal peduncle olivaceous, the fin in the adult with blue or olive rays, the tip red; bar across caudal peduncle light pinkish; dorsal dull olive green or brown with orange marks or lines, the last rays pinkish like the crossbar; anal rosy; ventrals rosy, with a red-black blotch on the inner side; pectoral orange, scarlet at base; jaws and throat livid bluish. Smaller examples show no blue on caudal rays. Young are very rosy. Bones and teeth bluish green.

Another example from Hilo had the anterior half of the body dull olive when fresh, posterior becoming more reddish with varied marks of bright orange, those about eye yellow alternately with livid blue; eye blue with yellow streaks; iris red; posterior part of dorsal and anal clear orange pink; dorsal dusky, edged and mottled with reddish; anal with more red, shaded with dusky; caudal light orange, barred and dotted with light olive and with 2 washes of black, 1 basal and terminal; a black spot edged with bright yellow behind eye; another near middle of side not ocellate.

Color in alcohol, dull brown, darker on back; head grayish with narrow pale lines above; below eye oblique pale lines running down across preopercle, suboperde, and interopercle, inclosed above by narrow line beginning behind corner of mouth and running up below eye and across to axil of pectoral; a pale vertical streak across caudal peduncle below basal portion of last dorsal rays, dorsal grayish with 2 narrow pale longitudinal streaks and base of last rays pale; anal pale, rays greenish, posteriorly dusky on outer portion, a median pale longitudinal line; caudal greenish, edged above and below with brownish; pectoral and ventrals pale brownish, latter tinged with dull greenish, basally blackish brown.

This species is very common about Hawaii, coming daily into the markets of Honolulu and Hilo, from which places we have 26 specimens 5.5 to 10.25 inches long. Günther records the species from Yap Island, and the *Albatross* obtained it at Honolulu and off Molokai. Known also from Johnston Island.

255. Cheilinus bimaculatus Cuvier & Valenciennes.   Plate XXXVIII.

Head 3 in length; depth 2.9; eye 5 in head; snout 3.25; preorbital 5.5; interorbital 4.5; D. ix, 10 or 11; A. iii, 8 or 9; scales 2–22–6.

Body short and deep; dorsal profile evenly and gently curved from tip of snout to last dorsal ray; ventral outline somewhat less convex; head conic; snout moderate, bluntly pointed; mouth rather large, slightly oblique; maxillary nearly reaching vertical of eye; each jaw with a pair of strong canines in front and a series of shorter teeth laterally; eye moderate, the lower edge on line of axis of body; interorbital rather broad, moderately convex; fins high; origin of dorsal over gill-opening; first dorsal spine short, the others longer, their length equal to distance from tip of snout to middle of pupil; dorsal rays somewhat higher, their length 1.9 in head; anal similar to soft dorsal, its last rays but one somewhat produced, making the fin pointed; caudal usually with the upper and middle rays greatly produced and filamentous, the produced rays usually consisting of 1 upper and 3 or 4 middle rays; middle rays sometimes little produced; lower caudal rays usually not produced, the tip of the fin forming a sharp angle; ventrals reaching two-thirds of way to origin of anal, their length 1.8 in head; pectoral short, broad and rounded, the upper rays scarcely longer than the lower, 2 in head; scales large, those on nape and breast not reduced; head covered with large scales; lateral line ceasing at base of soft dorsal ray, beginning again 2 scales lower down and 1 to 3 scales anteriorly and continuing to base of caudal. Description based chiefly upon a specimen (No. 03002) 5 inches long, from Honolulu.

Color in life of a nearly fresh specimen, taken at Honolulu June 7, rosy or brick-red, greenish on back, paler below; blackish blotches on caudal peduncle, a small black spot on middle of side below lateral line, below sixth dorsal spine; anterior part of side vermiculated with orange-red on borders of scales, which are yellowish green; head and nape purplish, with narrow reddish orange or yellow lines radiating from eye, those toward snout reddest, those backward more yellow; 2 greenish yellow bars on opercle, which is yellowish green above and bluish below; dorsal pale, specked with olive or brownish, edge of fin red; membrane of anterior ray with a blue spot bounded above by a similar bright red border; last few dorsal rays pale, with rosy specks, yellowish toward tips; caudal mottled greenish and reddish on basal half of rays, elsewhere mottled rosy, yellowish, greenish, and white, the border narrowly blue; anal flesh-color at base, mottled reddish, grayish and greenish on distal parts, the border blue; pectoral and ventrals pale rosy, the latter somewhat mottled with greenish, reddish, and white; iris bluish olive, with radiating orange lines; tip of lower jaw dark bluish, paler on the throat.

This same specimen, after having been in spirits one year, is dusky white, palest below; the lines and markings on the head have changed to pale sulphur-yellow, as likewise the border to the scales on anterior part of body; the dark greenish postocular spot has become dark brown, almost black, and the green of the side pale; the black lateral spot persists; the blue spot on anterior portion of dorsal has become black, and the red above it has faded to pale lemon. In some specimens the black lateral spot is absent on one or both sides, while occasionally in other specimens it is duplicated and appears as a double spot on at least one side. Most specimens show in spirits traces of 4 or 5 broad dark bars, and a dark blotch on basal part of caudal fin.

Another specimen (No. 03350) in life was scarlet, a little olivaceous on back, the color deepest behind opercular flap and produced by a vertical spot on each scale; side of head green, with scarlet line radiating from eye, irregular in position; a brown spot behind eye; a jet black round spot larger than pupil below seventh scale of lateral line; a black ocellus behind middle of first dorsal spine, rest of dorsal with red reticulations around pale spots; caudal and anal similar; soft fins whiter than spinous portion; ventrals whitish, reticulated with red; pectoral pale with a red streak at base. An example (No. 03343) 4.25 inches long, taken at Honolulu, June 14, when nearly fresh had the back and upper parts of side and head brick-red, mottled with dark olive; 2 rows of scales below lateral line with the entire margin orange-red; 3 or 4 faint round dusky spots above lateral line anteriorly; a conspicuous black spot just below lateral line beneath fifth and sixth spines; caudal peduncle dusky underlaid with rosy; snout and interorbital space with irregular greenish white lines; whiter lines radiating forward and coppery ones backward from eye; a large brownish spot back of eye bounded by coppery orange; opercle in front of pectoral greenish, with 2 obscure coppery stripes; under parts paler, the scales with pale orange centers; margin of lower jaw white, rest black; middle line of throat black; dorsal blackish brown, the sheathing scales dusky rosy; first ray blood-red on outer two-thirds, followed by a black spot; margin of fin with a narrow white line, tips of the ray rosy, posterior 6 or 7 rays yellow; caudal with upper half yellow with rosy splotches, median rays with a large blackish blotch on basal half, outer half and lower part of fin greenish yellow; anal greenish olive, posterior margin greenish yellow, with rosy splotches; pectoral pale rosy, yellow on base; ventrals dusky anteriorly, paler on inner rays, crossed by about 4 rows of orange-red spots; iris olive with spots and lines of orange.

This little fish is one of the most beautiful of the many brilliant fishes found among the Hawaiian Islands. The extreme delicacy and beauty of the markings are well shown in the exquisite painting by Mr. Hudson which accompanies this report.

The species was originally described from the Hawaiian Islands, being found among the coral rocks, where it is apparently not uncommon. We have examined 40 specimens from Honolulu, and 1 from Hilo, all of small size, rarely exceeding 5 inches in length. Other specimens were obtained by the *Albatross* at Honolulu.

256. Cheilinus trilobatus Lacépède.

Head 2.6 in length; depth 2.6; eye 6 in head; snout 2.7; maxillary 3; preorbital 3.6; interorbital 3.6; least depth of caudal peduncle 2.2, least width 12; D. ix, 10; A. iii, 8; P. 11; V. i, 5; C. 12; scales 2–20–5.

Body short, deep, and much compressed; back considerably elevated, the anterior profile rising in a bold curve from tip of snout to origin of dorsal fin; a slight depression on snout in front of eyes; interorbital space rather wide and high; head rather small, compressed, its greatest width 2.3 in its length; snout large and heavy; mouth moderate, little oblique, entirely below axis of body, the jaws equal; each jaw with a pair of strong, curved canines in front, and a row of shorter conic teeth on each side, these decreasing in size posteriorly; eye small, entirely above axis of body; preorbital deep; lips thick and fleshy; opercle ending in a broad, short flap; caudal peduncle very deep and thin. Scales large, thin and firm, covering body and entire head except snout, those on head thickest; lateral line beginning at upper end of gill-opening and running in a nearly straight line to scale beneath last dorsal ray, where it ceases but reappears 2 rows farther down and 3 scales farther forward, thence continuing to base of caudal; pores of lateral line not much branched. Dorsal fin beginning over base of pectoral, the spines weak and short, their length not much exceeding half length of snout; soft dorsal pointed, the longest rays 1.5 in head; a sheath of large scales at base of dorsal; caudal trilobate, the outer and middle rays produced, the longest rays about 1.4 in head; anal similar to soft dorsal, pointed, the longest rays 1.3 in head; anal spines graduated, the first very short, less than orbit, the third about 3.5 in head; pectoral broad, truncate, its length 1.9 in head; ventrals very long and pointed, reaching base of first anal ray, their length about 1.25 in head.

Color in life, olive gray; a series of greenish-blue cross-streaks, very numerous and well defined, pale cherry-red cross-shades between them; head with radiating streaks and spots of crimson; chin dull; dorsal light olive with cherry-red edge and intramarginal streak; soft rays mostly colorless; a little dusky spot at base; caudal dusky, edged all around with pale, the tip and edge mostly red; anal olive with green rays and 2 red marginal stripes; ventral with blue rays, an olive blotch and a pink edge; pectoral yellow-olive, dark olive at base.

Color in alcohol, dark brown, blotched irregularly with darker; head with numerous short, narrow pale streaks, some of them more or less wavy, those on opercles breaking up into round spots; dorsal fin greenish olive, with pale border narrowly edged with darker; caudal dark greenish; anal dark greenish, edge pale; pectoral pale; ventrals greenish-blue; iris green. Description of male (No. 04627, 10 inches long) from Pago Pago, Samoa.

A female example 6 inches long (from Pago Pago) differs from the male just described chiefly in the more slender snout, less elevated back, rounded caudal, less pointed dorsal and anal, and much shorter ventrals. The pale markings on the head are less distinct. The female and young with short ventrals correspond to *Cheilinus sinuosus* described from Sandwich Islands by Quoy and Gaimard. We have obtained many specimens of this species from Samoa, but saw none in Honolulu. The only Hawaiian record is that of Quoy and Gaimard.

Genus 163. NOVACULICHTHYS Bleeker.

Labroid fishes with oblong body; postocular region of head scaly; 27 or 28 scales in longitudinal series; each jaw with many series of conspicuous crystalline teeth, the 2 anterior canines curved, no angular teeth; dorsal fin and base of anal scaleless; the 2 anterior dorsal spines flexible, the following 7 pungent; anal spines 3; lateral line interrupted; lower pharyngeals with 4 or 5 series of teeth.

257. Novaculichthys woodi Jenkins. Plate XL and Figs. 137 and 137a.

Head 3.25 in length; depth 3; eye 5.5 in head; snout 2.6; maxillary 3.6; interorbital 4.6; D. ix, 12; A. iii, 12; scales 3–27–7–24 pores; Br. 6.

Body oblong, elliptical, greatly compressed; dorsal outline but slightly more convex than ventral; head longer than deep; snout rather short and pointed; lower jaw slightly the longer; mouth small, slightly oblique, the maxillary not reaching vertical of eye by a distance equal to pupil; each jaw with a pair of large curved canines in front and a series of smaller conic teeth on the sides; anterior profile gently and regularly curved from tip of snout to origin of dorsal; cheek moderately deep, oblique; interorbital high. convex, somewhat trenchant; dorsal fin beginning over middle of opercle, the ante-

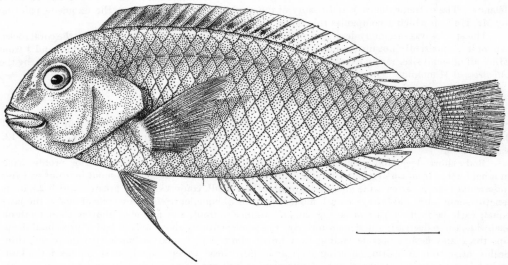

FIG. 137.—*Novaculichthys woodi* Jenkins; from the type.

rior spines not detached nor produced; spines all sharp, about equal in length, 3.6 in head; dorsal rays somewhat longer, about 2.5 in head; anal spine short and sharp; anal rays about equal to those of soft dorsal; caudal slightly rounded, its length 2 in head; ventrals with the spine sharp, a little longer than diameter of eye, the first ray filamentous, reaching somewhat beyond origin of anal, about 1.25 in head; pectoral moderate, barely reaching origin of anal, 1.5 in head; scales thin and firm; lateral line following line of back until under base of fourth dorsal ray from last, where it drops 2 rows of scales and continues to base of caudal; head entirely naked, breast nearly naked, only 2 or 3 small scales apparent. Description based chiefly upon a specimen (No. 03483) 6.6 inches long from Hilo.

Color in life, olivaceous above, rosy on nape, violaceous below, the general effect pale violet; some rosy shades on side; above pectoral yellowish white shaded with rosy; violet on lower side, gold-rosy on side and bright rosy on nape; side of head livid violet; 2 gray streaks across lower jaw, no distinct marks on head, but in fresher male specimens an ill-defined golden area behind head passing off into rosy; spinous dorsal violet-blue, with round ink-like spots of indigo-blue; soft dorsal, anal, and caudal bright salmon-red, unmarked; ventrals violet white; pectoral reddish, the axil scarlet with a violet line; some dark red dots on caudal; pores of lateral line pale orange; iris bright crimson.

Another specimen (No. 03496) obtained at Hilo, showed in life the following colors: Head and caudal peduncle below lateral line pale bluish purple; back along spinous dorsal brownish yellow overlaid with a grayish shade; a pale yellowish patch above axil of pectoral; an orange dot on each scale of lateral line, margin of scale pale brownish; nape brown with slightly reddish tinge; belly with 9 or 10 whitish vertical streaks on the peritoneum, but discernible through the skin; membranes of spinous dorsal purple, with a round, jet-black spot between each 2 spines, purple on edge; soft dorsal delicate orange-red, the base with purplish shade, small black spots similar to those on spinous dorsal on first 2 or 3 membranes of soft dorsal; caudal fin pale orange-red, the distal portion brighter; anal and pectoral same as caudal; ventrals pale purple; iris pinkish red. A nearly fresh specimen (No. 02974) was described as very pale rosy, with bluish and purplish irridescence, somewhat yellowish above pectoral; 2 rows of scales next to dorsal whitish; nape rosy; snout and cheek ashy yellowish; under parts whitish; middle of side with a wedged-shaped paler space ending in a blunt point on caudal peduncle; fins all pale rosy, except spinous dorsal, which has a small bluish-black spot on each membrane; iris pink. Still another specimen (No. 03456) was described as bluish on body with golden tinge; spinous dorsal blue with a white spot on each membrane; soft dorsal and anal rosy; ventrals rosy except produced ray, which is white; pectoral light rosy with slight dusky on upper 2 rays on proximal half; iris rosy. An examination of this same specimen after it had been in alcohol more than 2 years shows the spinous dorsal bluish dusky with one or more rather distinct whiter spots, these continuing on the membrane of 3 or 4 rays, rest of soft dorsal and all the other fins pale yellowish white; axil dusky.

An examination of a large series of specimens, including the types of *N. woodi* and *N. entargyreus*

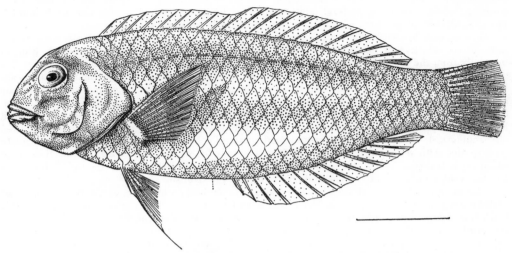

FIG. 137a.—*Novaculichthys woodi* Jenkins. Type of *N. entargyreus* Jenkins.

and a careful study of Mr. Seale's photograph and description of *N. tattoo*, shows that all constitute but one species. The tattoo marks on the belly shown in Mr. Seale's photograph and described by Dr. Jenkins in his account of *N. entargyreus* show plainly in our alcoholic specimens Nos. 05757, 05434, and 05726, and the life color note taken by Mr. Sindo on specimen No. 03496 calls attention to the same markings. In the majority of our specimens, including specimen No. 03496, these "tattoo" marks do not appear externally, as Dr. Jenkins has correctly stated, being upon the peritoneum and not always showing through. Upon dissection, however, we find them present in all of the numerous specimens examined by us. Dissection also shows them to be equally plain upon the cotype of *N. woodi*.

We have examined 19 examples (3 collected by Dr. Jenkins, including the types of *N. woodi* and *N. entargyreus*), 7 from Hilo and 12 from Honolulu; these are 4.6 to 6.75 inches long. The species is rather common about the coral reefs.

258. Novaculichthys tæniourus (Lacépède). Fig. 138.

Head 3.2 in length; depth 3; eye 7.5 in head; snout 2.9; maxillary 3.4; preorbital 4.6; interorbital 5.5; D. ix, 12; A. iii, 12; scales 2–26–9.

Body rather long and greatly compressed; head rather long, longer than deep; snout long, low and bluntly conic; anterior profile oblique, rising in a gently convex line from tip of snout to nape; dorsal and ventral outlines in long, low curves; caudal peduncle very deep, 2 in head; mouth rather large, nearly horizontal, the maxillary reaching anterior edge of pupil; jaws each with a pair of strong curved canines in front, and a series of small, close-set conic teeth laterally, usually a second or third pair of smaller canines toward the front; eye small, anterior, above axis of body; interorbital rather broad, convex but not trenchant; opercles smooth, their edges membranous, the opercle ending in a long broad soft flap; dorsal fin continuous, first 2 spines not detached, the membrane between them and the third not notched, these spines large but soft and flexible, not produced in the female, but markedly produced in the male, their length being more than twice that of third spine; origin of dorsal fin over vertical from upper edge of preopercle, length of second dorsal spine equaling gape; other dorsal spines somewhat stiffer and sharper, their length about equal to second; soft portion of dorsal somewhat elevated, length of longest rays 2 in head; anal similar to soft dorsal, its rays somewhat longer, 1.8 in head; caudal broad, slightly convex, its length 2 in head; ventrals short, not reaching vent by a distance slightly greater than diameter of eye, their length 2.4 in head; pectoral broad, its length slightly greater than half head; scales large, smooth, and thin; lateral line following second row of scales from back, until under base of third dorsal ray from last, where it drops 3 rows of scales and continues to base of caudal, there being 19 pores on the first part and 4 on the other; head entirely naked, except a few very small obscure scales back of orbit.

Color in life, from a specimen (No. 03249) from Honolulu, dull olive brown; each scale, except on belly, with a large vertical oblong spot of olive white; belly light dull red, each scale with a white edge; scales of breast plain dirty olive; head olive, darker above, reddish on lips; 4 dark olive bands radiating from eye, each edged with gray, the second and third confluent at base, the first and second short, the third reaching edge of subopercle and the fourth nearly to edge of preopercle; membranes of first 2 dorsal spines jet-black, with a golden spot below; rest of dorsal fin with alternations of oblique bluish or grayish lines and rows of olive spots, these spots smaller and more reticulate near tip of fin; anal similar, its edge dusky; caudal dark olive, with bluish reticulations, a broad band of dirty white covering its basal two-fifths; pectoral faintly olivaceous, its inner base and a large axillary blotch jet-black; ventrals reddish black, with a black spot in the axil; iris purple.

On specimen No. 03501 there was a bright yellow spot at base of pectoral; axil black, an irregularly curved black spot behind axil, concave anteriorly. Another specimen (No. 03502) differed markedly from the preceding example, having the color in life dull slaty bluish, no orange or reddish on belly; edges of scales on belly not white; no lines radiating from eye; no other markings on head; black and yellow on first 2 dorsal membranes; the black axillary spot large and united with the curved black area at lower edge of pectoral. Another specimen, 8 inches long (No. 03393), taken July 8, was blackish olive, nearly uniform, the scales of side with a pale olive-gray vertical bar; axil jet-black, with a jet-black ocellus above, and bright yellow on base of first pectoral ray; head mottled olive, unmarked; dorsal dingy olive, with a large black ocellus behind second spine; soft dorsal vaguely cross-spotted with dull bluish and dull golden-olive, its edge washed with red; anal mottled olive, edged with blackish; caudal reddish olive, with a dull pink or flesh-colored crossbar, a dusky bar behind; ventrals mottled black; pectoral dusky, its first ray reddish.

The same specimen in alcohol has the scales pale or dusky white, somewhat rosy, with broad dark brown borders; axil of pectoral black, with a large bluish-black blotch above and a narrow blue-black line below; membrane between first and second dorsal spines black, that between second and third spines with a black spot below, which is a light, yellowish area, rest of dorsal fin pale yellowish white, crossed by numerous series of irregular large brownish-purple spots, these coalescing more or less posteriorly; edge of soft dorsal more or less purplish; anal similar to soft

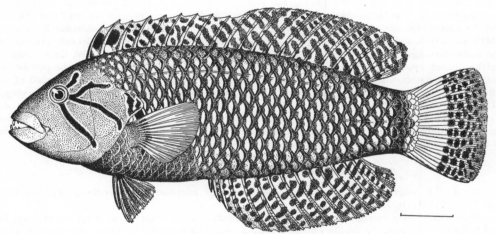

Fig. 138.—*Novaculichthys tæniourus* (Lacépède).

dorsal, markings less distinct, edge darker; caudal with a broad yellowish white bar on its basal two-fifths, the outer portion dusky olivaceous crossed by obscure vertical paler lines; 1 or 2 scales on lateral line beneath first to third dorsal rays, sometimes with a blackish spot; head pale yellowish white, a narrow dark line from eye downward and backward to near edge of preopercle; a similar bar from posterior border of eye downward and backward toward edge of opercle, slightly below upper edge of pectoral; a third much shorter line from posterior border of eye, where it sometimes coalesces with the second, upward and backward toward origin of lateral line; and a fourth, shorter and less distinct, upward and backward from upper edge of orbit toward nape. In some specimens, particularly the males, there are 2 narrow lines across interorbital space from eye to eye, 2 similar ones downward from eye toward end of maxillary, and a fainter one forward from eye under nostril. In some specimens, particularly the larger ones, the general color is darker and the oblong black pectoral ocellus is more distinct.

The above description, except life-color notes, based upon (No. 05611) a specimen 10 inches long from Honolulu. This species appears to be not uncommon at times among the Hawaiian Islands. There was 1 specimen from Honolulu in the collection examined by Steindachner. It was not obtained by Dr. Jenkins, but 2 specimens were obtained by Dr. Wood in 1898, and one male by Jordan and Snyder in 1900. Abundant in Samoa.

The young of this species have the first 2 dorsal spines elongate and more or less detached, as usual in *Novaculichthys*. Our collection contains 21 excellent specimens, only 3 of which are males. Two examples were collected at Honolulu by Dr. Wood and 2 by Jordan and Snyder; of our specimens only 2 are from Hilo. Length, 5.4 to 10.2 inches.

259. Novaculichthys kallosoma (Bleeker). Plate XLI.

Head measured to end of opercular flap 3 in length; depth 3; depth of caudal peduncle 6; snout 3.3 in head; eye 5; dorsal IX, 12; anal III, 12; scales 2–26–9. Color in life green, spotted with white and banded with black.

Width of body 2.7 in head; snout not pointed, the profile convex from tip of snout to occiput; interorbital area acutely rounded or angular, the distance between the eyes equal to their diameter; maxillary extending to a vertical passing through anterior edge of pupil; each jaw with a pair of canine teeth at the symphysis, the lower pair fitting between the upper teeth; head naked, except a small space behind and below orbit, where there are 2 rows of minute scales, which do not extend around the orbit but occupy only a space equal in length to diameter of eye, the center of the scaled area being on a line between pupil and upper edge of base of pectoral; lateral line interrupted on the twentieth scale, beginning again on the third scale below and extending to base of caudal; first and second spines of dorsal greatly lengthened and very flexible, the first equal to the length of head, the second 2.4 in length, these spines connected with each other and with the following ones, the membrane between the first and second about equal in height to the eighth spine, that between the second and third deeply scolloped; each spine with a narrow strip of membrane along the posterior edge of the free part, the fifth longest of the remaining spines, its length 2.2 in head; longest ray 1.6 in head; anal spines slender, graduated in length from first to third, the second 4.5 in head; longest ray 1.7; caudal rounded, its length 1.2 in head; pectoral extending to a point above origin of anal; second ray of ventral elongate; when depressed, reaching anal opening.

Color in alcohol, yellowish white; head with 9 black lines radiating from eye; an elongate white spot on chin extending downward from corner of mouth, another on cheek below eye near angle of preopercle, and a third below the latter in the branchiostegal region; body with 5 narrow dusky bands, the first extending from origin of dorsal downward and backward across edge of opercular flap and base of pectoral to base of ventral; the second passing downward from base of sixth dorsal spine, widening and disappearing in region of pectoral; the third extending between the third dorsal and the third anal rays; the fourth between the eighth dorsal and eighth anal rays; the fifth, shaped like a chevron, the point forward, is on the caudal peduncle; first and second spines with broad, dusky bars, the fin with large dusky clouds, prolongations of the dark body bands; between the large spots are smaller ones corresponding with vertical rows of irregular spots on the body; anal colored like the dorsal; distal half of caudal rays dusky; pectoral white; ventrals dusky, the inner half of fin bordered with white.

Described from a single specimen, 4.5 inches long, obtained by the *Albatross* at Honolulu, which agrees with a specimen, bright green in life, collected by Dr. Jordan at Pago Pago, and with another from the Island of Negros, P. I.

Since the above was written we have received from Mr. Berndt a second specimen, from Honolulu, which is grass-green in color. Our plate is from the Pago Pago specimen, by Dr. Jordan, revised by Kako Morita.

Genus 164. CYMOLUTES Günther.

Body compressed, oblong, covered with small scales; snout rather elevated; head naked; lateral line interrupted; no posterior canine tooth; D. IX, 12–14; A. III, 12–14.

260. Cymolutes lecluse (Quoy & Gaimard).

Head 3.35 in length; depth 3.65; eye 5.65 in head; snout 2; gape 4; interorbital 5.1; D. IX, 13; A. III, 13; scales 7–79–23.

Body fusiform or wedge-shaped, tapering gradually from nape to caudal; head short; snout long but decurved, the anterior profile in a regular bold curve from tip of snout to nape; mouth low, horizontal, the gape not nearly reaching vertical of eye; each jaw with a pair of strong canines in front and a series of smaller conic teeth laterally, inside of which are shorter, bluntly conic teeth; eyes high up, near the dorsal line and close together; cheek very deep; opercles with their edges smooth; opercle with a broad, flexible flap; caudal peduncle moderately deep, 2.8 in head; scales small, densely covering entire body, except a narrow naked area on breast and nape; head naked, but with a small patch of 6 or 8 scales below the eye; lateral line running high, following contour of back until under fifth dorsal spine from last, where it closes, reappearing again 5 scales below and continuing to base of caudal fin, sometimes the last pore of first part bent down and the first of the last part bent upward; dorsal fin beginning over middle of opercle, the spines soft and flexible, their length about 4.4 in head, dorsal rays scarcely longer; anal spine and rays similar to those of dorsal; caudal truncate; outer rays of ventrals slightly produced, their length 2 in head; pectoral rather short and broad, about 1.75 in head.

Color in life of a nearly fresh specimen (No. 03153) pale rosy white, with some yellowish; top of head pale greenish; anterior pectoral region greenish; a small jet-black ocellated spot, with pale blue border on upper part of side under about eighth dorsal spine; dorsal pale greenish, edged with pale orange and blue, a narrow black line near tip of first membrane; caudal pale yellowish white; pectoral and ventrals whitish; anal white; iris yellow surrounded by rosy.

Another specimen (No. 03408) had the belly pale bluish white, the general color of body very pale olive-green; anal colorless; dorsal colorless except for a narrow pale red edge; a yellow ocher spot on opercular flap; a small dark spot on upper posterior part of the caudal peduncle; caudal colorless, the anterior half tinged with pale yellow; other fins colorless; iris bright yellow surrounded by a rim of lake-purple, a stripe along back for entire length, just above lateral line slightly paler and more nearly color of belly. A live example (No. 03458), taken at Honolulu, July 27, had the general color bluish white; edge of gill-opening and posterior part of opercle pale pinkish yellow; a quadrate area from gill-opening to vent and from ventral line of belly to level of lower border of eye pure white; an indistinct irregular band of pale pinkish yellow from below eye backward along upper border of the quadrate white area; posterior half of side with about 13 transverse pale pinkish bars; a small round black spot, with bright greenish blue border on side above tip of pectoral and just below lateral line; anterior part of dorsal fin with a Y-shaped black line with greenish border; posterior part bordered with pale pinkish yellow.

Color in alcohol, very pale yellowish or brownish white; side from above base of pectoral to vertical of origin of anal with a broad yellowish white area, the small black spot on side unchanged, as is likewise the black on first dorsal membrane; black spot on side rarely absent and sometimes double; occasionally an indistinct black spot on each side of upper posterior end of caudal peduncle.

The above general description is based chiefly upon a specimen (No. 03153) obtained at Honolulu. This species reaches a length of 6 or 7 inches and is fairly abundant at Honolulu. We have examined 26 specimens (4.8 to 6.25 inches long), 1 from Hilo, the others from Honolulu.

Genus 165. INIISTIUS Gill.

Body compressed, oblong, covered with large thin scales, about 26 in the lateral line; head scaleless or nearly so; head short and deep, the upper and anterior outline compressed to a sharp edge; profile almost vertical; eye small, placed high; D. ii–vii, 12; A. iii, 12; first 2 dorsal spines detached from the others and inserted on or close behind the occiput; lateral line interrupted, extending on the second row of large scales below the dorsal sheath; canines, 2 in front of each jaw; no posterior canines.

This genus contains some 5 or 6 species, chiefly of the western Pacific. They are similar in most respects to the species of *Xyrichthys*, differing principally in having the 2 anterior spines of the dorsal fin produced, separated from the others, and placed as a separate fin on the nape.

261. Iniistius pavoninus (Cuvier & Valenciennes). Plate XLII and Fig. 139.

Head 3 in length; depth 2.5; eye 6.5 in head; snout 2; maxillary 3.4; preorbital 2.3; interorbital 5; D. ii–vii, 12; A. iii, 12; scales 3–27–9.

Body short, deep, and greatly compressed; head deeper than long; caudal peduncle very short and deep, its length 3 in head, its depth 2.2; snout very short and blunt, the anterior profile almost vertical from tip of jaws to front of eyes, thence in a sharp curve to origin of dorsal, from which line the dorsal and ventral outlines are about equally curved to caudal peduncle; snout and anterior profile very trenchant; mouth small, nearly horizontal, the maxillary reaching vertical of anterior edge of orbit; mandible strong, the lower edge compressed and convex; a pair of strong curved canines on front of each jaw, back of which are smaller teeth; each side of jaw with short conic teeth; preorbital nearly vertical and very deep; interorbital high, very convex and very trenchant; preopercle and opercle smooth, their edges thin and flexible; anterior 2 spines of dorsal detached, placed upon occiput over posterior line of orbit, the first spine produced and filamentous, its length 1.9 in head, both spines very soft and flexible, other dorsal spines rather short and flexible, their length less than gape of mouth; dorsal rays somewhat longer, 3.2 in head; anal similar to soft dorsal, the rays of about equal length, about 2.6 in head; ventrals with outer ray produced, nearly reaching origin of anal, their length 1.6 in head; pectoral short, reaching a vertical at vent, the length 1.7 in head; scales large, smooth, thin, and adherent, those on breast slightly reduced; head naked, except sometimes a few small scales below eye; lateral line ascending for 3 scales, then continuing approximately straight to scale under last anal ray but 2, where it drops 3 rows and continues on 5 scales to base of caudal.

Color in life of a male (No. 03484) 14 inches long, olive green, with 3 dark cross-shades narrower than the interspaces; first band with each scale below level of eye edged with bright blue, a black crescent above, edged in front with light blue; in second band most of the scales below level of eye edged with bright blue, 3 of them with black; in the third band some scales edged with pale blue; first interspace with a quadrate spot of golden white; middle line of forehead, chin, and throat violet, this color varying in shade and edged on each side with light orange; an oblique band on cheek and whole opercular region golden olive, with oblique violet lines and dots; first dorsal dull violet; second dorsal dull olive, with lines and spots of violet blue, greenish blue distally; caudal dull olive, with intramarginal band of sky blue; ventral pale, axil blackish violet; pectoral largely blackish; anal dull olive, with bluish marks and an intramarginal sky-blue band; iris crimson.

Examples from Hilo had the pale lateral spot generally white tinged with golden, sometimes pure white, sometimes pure rosy; some have an additional black spot edged with blue above front of anal. A female has the same cross-bands, the first black spot similar, the white area shaded with both yellowish and violet, the marks in the second band wanting, the least trace of markings on head anteriorly, and on side; fin markings similar, but all faint; iris dull crimson; intramarginal band on caudal distinctly pale blue.

Two other specimens (Nos. 03000 and 03001) were described in life as pale olive gray, whitening on side and belly; side with 4 broad darker bars, the first at base of pectoral, second between anterior end of anal and middle of dorsal, third between posterior ends of dorsal and anal, and the fourth at base of caudal fin, the third darkest; a black spot covering 1 scale under membrane between fourth and fifth dorsal spine; this bordered, except behind, with blue; first and second series of scales below dorsal with narrow blue lines; dorsals grayish, with numerous blue lines extending upward and forward, these separated by broader grayish brown lines; anal white with a narrow blue line near its border, tipped with brown; caudal whitish, dark at tip; pectoral olive gray above, pale yellowish below; ventrals white; iris pink. Another specimen (No. 03025) was described as pale dusky white; opercle with 2 darker bands, one downward from eye to subopercle, the other across opercle, each with some purple; side with a broad vertical dusky bar upward from front of anal, and 2 less distinct ones farther back; edges of some scales pale yellow; a small black spot, bordered anteriorly with blue,

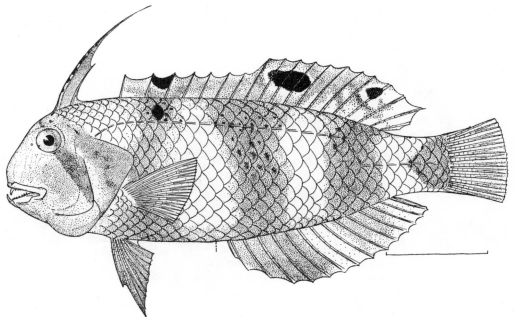

Fig. 139.—*Iniistius pavoninus* (Cuvier & Valenciennes). Type of *I. leucozonus* Jenkins. The first anal ray in figure should be a spine.

on second row of scales below fourth dorsal spine; dorsal pale bluish, crossed by numerous brownish orange bars; caudal white, with 2 or 3 narrow faint yellow cross-bands, the tip black; pectoral white, slightly dusky at base; 2 pale rosy blotches on belly at base of anal; ventrals white; iris purple.

Color in alcohol (No. 03534) pale, somewhat dusky; body crossed by 4 broad brownish vertical bars, the first under proximal half of pectoral, the second upward from anterior anal rays, the third between last dorsal and anal rays, fourth on distal half of caudal peduncle; humeral region, interspaces between dark bars, lower parts of head and belly yellowish white, the space between lower half of first and second dark bars most distinctly white; one scale above lateral line and under base of fourth dorsal spine black, bordered on its base by light blue; dorsals dusky, almost black on edge, the membranes vermiculated with dark and light; caudal smoky, the edge darker; anal dirty yellowish, the edge with a narrow olivaceous border; ventrals pale; pectoral dusky, black within.

A young example from Hilo when fresh was violet olive, without red; 4 dark areas or bands, with pale interspaces, that behind pectoral white; base of each scale light golden, its edge violet; indigo black ocellus, edged before with violet blue; scales all over body showing shades of violet and golden, faint; first dorsal dusky bluish; second dorsal violet and golden in oblique streaks; one blue-black ocellus on dorsal edged with blue; caudal and anal faintly violaceous, the latter with a light violet border and golden edge; pectoral yellowish; ventrals dusky, edged with yellowish and violaceous; eye with faint radiating streaks of violet and golden.

Smaller specimens in alcohol are considerably lighter; ridge of snout and nape bluish, cheek and opercles brownish, with narrow wavy darker brown and bluish lines; dorsal fin paler, with wavy purplish or bluish lines extending upward and forward, the margin somewhat dusky. In many of the smaller examples the black scale on the side is without the bluish anterior border. In some small specimens, one or more scales toward the lower end of the second dark bar are darker, forming a more or less distinct brown blotch; an occasional specimen is found with an extra black spot on side above lateral line.

This species is the largest one of the genus found among the Hawaiian Islands and is one of the most important, being a valued food-fish.

These specimens are certainly *Xyrichthys pavoninus* Cuvier & Valenciennes, as were also the specimens from Honolulu identified by Steindachner with *Xyrichthys pavo* Cuvier & Valenciennes. It is very doubtful whether the latter species is found among the Hawaiian Islands. The color assigned to it by Cuvier and Valenciennes and by Bleeker does not apply to any of the numerous specimens examined by us. The species described from Cape San Lucas by Dr. Gill as *Iniistius mundicorpus* is evidently identical with this species. We have examined a total of 64 specimens, 56 from Honolulu, 7 from Hilo, and 1 from Kailua. The *Albatross* secured some also at Puako Bay.

262. Iniistius niger (Steindachner). Fig. 140.

Head 2.8 in length; depth 2.5; eye 6 in head; snout 2; maxillary 3.3; preorbital 2.65; interorbital 6; D. II–VII, 12; A. III, 12; scales 3–28–10.

Body short, deep and greatly compressed; head as deep as long; snout very blunt, anterior profile rising nearly vertically from tip to front of eye; dorsal and ventral outlines each in a long, low curve;

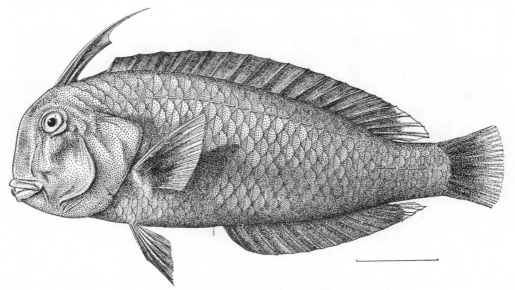

FIG. 140.—*Iniistius niger* (Steindachner). Type of *I. verater* Jenkins.

caudal peduncle compressed very deep, depth 2.3 in head; preorbital very deep, nearly vertical; mouth small, nearly horizontal, the maxillary nearly reaching vertical of anterior edge of orbit, jaws each with a pair of long curved canines anteriorly, and a series of small bluntly conic teeth, laterally; eye small, very high; interorbital space high and strongly cultrate; first 2 dorsal spines remote and entirely detached from remainder of fin, placed upon occiput above posterior half of eye, the spines soft, flexible and much produced, the length of the first equaling distance from tip of snout to edge of preopercle, second shorter by a distance equal to gape of mouth, remaining dorsal spines slender and flexible, their length about 2.7 in head; dorsal rays slightly longer, about 2.5 in head; anal similar to soft dorsal, the rays about equally long; caudal gently rounded, the rays about 2.25 in head; outer rays of ventrals produced, reaching vent 1.7 in head; pectoral broad, its length 2 in head; scales large, thin, smooth, and adherent, those on breast somewhat reduced in size; lateral line rising 3 scales from upper end of gill-opening, thence continued along second row of scales to the scale beneath last dorsal ray but one, where it drops 3 rows to middle of side, continuing on 5 scales to base of caudal; head entirely naked, excepting 1 or 2 small postocular scales.

Color in life (No. 03422) head and body nearly uniform black, underlaid by purplish on belly; caudal black, the outer third white with rosy tinge; pectoral black at base, the outer two-thirds transparent; ventrals black, with some purple; soft dorsal and anal nearly uniform black, the last rays of each usually but not always tipped with white; no humeral spot.

Another specimen (No. 03423) was very dark brown; a black scale with blue border just above lateral line and under fourth dorsal spine; belly showing some reddish purple; soft dorsal and anal with minute spots and reticulations of dark blue, similar spots on caudal; ventrals dusky red, with blue markings, detached dorsal with olive and blue; sides of face with tinges of olive over the dark background; pectoral pale on upper margin; indistinct dark olive area on body under and behind last third of pectoral; tip of soft dorsal, anal and tip of caudal not pale; iris purple.

An example (No. 02940) 2 days in alcohol had the head and body uniform black throughout; dorsal jet-black, narrowly tipped with white, the exposed tips of spines white; caudal with a broad whitish tip. Another specimen (No. 03457) had the body and head and fins quite black without other marking of any kind; the light colored extremity of caudal was rosy toward the posterior border, and the light tips of dorsal and anal showed some rosy tinge with a narrow bit of blue in the dorsal tip.

Color in alcohol, head and body uniform dark brownish black; distal third of caudal, tips of dorsal and anal and most of pectoral plain yellowish white, the pectoral a little dusky, rest of fins rich blue-black.

This species is thus far known only from Honolulu, and does not appear to be very abundant. It was not obtained by Jenkins in 1889, the 2 specimens described by him having been obtained by Wood in 1899.

Through an error, the figure given by Jenkins shows 10 dorsal spines instead of 7, as given in the text. The figure given by Steindachner is also defective, showing only 6 instead of 7 dorsal spines, and having the detached dorsal spines very much too short.

We have 19 specimens, including the type of *I. verater*, ranging from 4.8 to 8 inches long.

Genus 166. HEMIPTERONOTUS Bleeker.

Body compressed, oblong, covered with scales of moderate size; head compressed, more or less elevated and obtuse, with the upper profile generally more or less parabolic; cheek with small scales; lateral line interrupted; no posterior canine tooth; D. II–VII, 12; A. III, 12, the 2 anterior dorsal spines separate from the others.

263. Hemipteronotus copei Fowler.

Head 3.85 in length; depth 3; eye 6.25 in head, equal to interorbital; D. II–VII, 12; A. III, 12; scales 26 in lateral line.

Body elongate, much compressed, deepest in the pectoral region; head elevated, compressed, the anterior profile very parabolic, though slightly convex; snout not produced; eye small, high, 3 in space between its anterior margin and tip of upper jaw; interorbital convex; mouth narrow; teeth strong, the outer lateral teeth larger than the others, except the canines, which are in 2 pairs on the anterior portions of the jaw, those in lower closer together than those of upper jaw and fitting in between the latter when the mouth is closed; gillrakers moderate; pseudobranchiæ developed; head naked except a series of 6 scales, which descends obliquely forward from the postorbital though not to center of eye in the vertical, and 2 scales on upper margin of opercle; origin of dorsal slightly posterior to median vertical keel of preopercle, the first 2 dorsal spines sharp, tip of first ending in a short filament, and about the same height as spines which succeed them, the latter being rather strong, firm, and not sharp; dorsal rays longer than the spines, the last ray, when depressed, reaching base of caudal; caudal rounded; anal similar to dorsal, its origin under the first dorsal ray, third anal spine longest; pectoral 1.75 in head, its origin below center of body and above origin of ventral; innermost ventral ray joined to body by a membrane; tips of fins not reaching origin of anal, but extending beyond tip of pectoral; lateral line concurrent with back, interrupted at the 21st scale.

General color dull brownish, the fins immaculate; a narrow bluish band from lower anterior portion of eye running downward to behind corner of mouth, parallel with this other vertical lines running from eye to upper part of head, the one on preopercle broad; the opercles with narrow lines on their posterior portion.

Oahu Island. This species in known to us only from Mr. Fowler's description.

264. Hemipteronotus umbrilatus Jenkins. Fig. 141.

Head 3.3 in length; depth 2.8; eye 5.1 in head; snout 2; maxillary 3.5; preorbital 2.7; interorbital 5; D. II–VII, 12; A. III, 12; scales 3–27–9.

Body short, deep, greatly compressed; head as deep as long; snout very blunt, the anterior profile rising nearly vertically from tip of snout to front of eye, where it makes a sharp curve to nape; body deepest at base of ventrals, thence tapering gradually to caudal peduncle; mouth horizontal, the jaws equal, maxillary not reaching vertical of anterior edge of orbit; small conic teeth on sides of jaws, a pair of enlarged canines in each in front; preorbital nearly vertical and very deep; eye small, high up; preopercle smooth, opercle ending in a broad soft flap; caudal peduncle deep, its least depth 2 in head; origin of dorsal slightly behind posterior border of orbit; first 2 dorsal spines remote from but connected by low notched membrane with third spine, the detached spines soft and flexible, little produced, their length equaling gape; remaining dorsal spines low, about equaling length of detached portion; dorsal rays subequal, a little longer than spines, 2.75 in head; anal similar to soft dorsal, its origin under base of fourth dorsal ray; caudal short, slightly convex, length 2 in head; outer ray of ventral somewhat produced, not reaching vei. , its length 1.75 in head; pectoral somewhat longer than ventrals, reaching vent, its length 1.4 in head; scales large, thin, and firm, those on breast some-

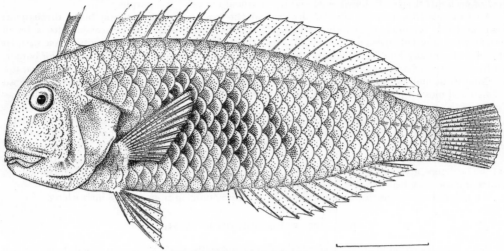

FIG. 141.—*Hemipteronotus umbrilatus* Jenkins; from the type.

what smaller than those on side; cheek with about 6 vertical rows of somewhat smaller scales, 2 scales on upper end of opercle, rest of head naked; lateral line beginning at upper end of gill-opening, curving upward for 4 pores, thence following contour of back, until under base of last dorsal ray, where it drops down for 2 scales and continues to base of caudal.

Color in life, light drab, the posterior portion of each scale white or whitish; a large dark-brown blotch as large as head on middle portion of body, in which the posterior half of each scale is white; first 2 dorsal spines dusky, no distinct markings on fins.

Another specimen (No. 03027) was white, centers of scales anteriorly dusky, a large black blotch on side above tip of pectoral, covering 23 to 25 scales; preocular part of head bluish black; dorsal, anal, and ventrals white; caudal dusky white; pectoral white with slight yellowish shade. One specimen (No. 03447) when fresh dead, was gray with bluish tinge on body and fins; small black spot on tip of anterior dorsal; large black area on side of body 7 scales wide and about 7 scales deep; below this an area of scales bluish with white margins, this extending a little farther backward than the black area.

This species is sometimes very dark, almost black, as is shown by 3 specimens from Hilo, one of which (No. 03478) was in life dirty olive, paler mesially, the head livid dusky, the anterior part of body to tip of pectoral black; fins all mottled blackish, no markings; very faint paler lines below, and a very faint shade of olive in places; no real markings, save the black anterior half of body. A smaller specimen, probably a male, had lower half of black area to front of anal deep violet blue.

Color in alcohol, yellowish white, head, nape, and breast with bluish rosy wash; middle of side with a large brownish-black blotch, about 6 scales in length and 9 in depth, the distal portion of each scale whitish; detached dorsal spines dark, rest of dorsal and anal pale, purplish and orange at base; caudal dirty whitish distally, purplish at base; pectoral and ventrals pale yellowish white; eye with a silvery ring around pupil, surrounded by light brassy, annexed by purplish blue.

This species is known only from the type and 15 other specimens obtained at Hilo and Honolulu; these are 4.75 to 8.75 inches in length.

265. Hemipteronotus baldwini Jordan & Evermann.   Plate XXXIX.

Head 3.25 in length; depth 3; eye 5.75 in head; snout 1.75; maxillary 3; preorbital 2.2; interorbital 4.8; D. ii–viii, 13; A. iii, 13; scales 3–27–9.

Body moderately short and deep, greatly compressed; head slightly deeper than long; anterior profile nearly vertical from mouth to front of eye, sharply cultrate; dorsal outline gently convex, sloping, to the deep caudal peduncle; ventral outline less convex; caudal peduncle very narrow, the depth 2.25 in head; mouth small, horizontal, the maxillary nearly reaching vertical of orbit; the jaws equal, each provided anteriorly with a pair of strong curved canines and laterally with a single row of short close-set conic teeth; lower jaw strong, its outline very convex; preorbital nearly vertical and very deep; preopercle and opercle smooth, with membranous edges, the latter produced somewhat in a broad rounded flap; origin of dorsal but little posterior to orbit, far in advance of base of ventrals; first 2 dorsal spines somewhat removed from third but connected to it by a low membrane, their length scarcely greater than the gape of mouth; remaining dorsal spines short and weak, scarcely equaling gape; soft dorsal low, the rays slightly longer than the spines; anal similar to soft dorsal, rays somewhat longer; caudal slightly convex, rays 2 in head; outer ray of each ventral somewhat produced, not reaching vent, the length about 1.9 in head; pectoral broad, the longest rays 1.7 in head; scales large, thin, smooth, firmly attached, those on breast somewhat reduced; head naked, except about 4 series of small scales extending from eye downward to level of mouth; lateral line curving abruptly upward from upper end of gill-opening, following contour of back to the scale under third dorsal ray from last, where it drops 3 rows and continues to base of caudal, the pores simple, unbranched.

Description based upon the type, No. 50644, U. S. Nat. Mus. (field No. 03414), a male example, 8.5 inches long, obtained at Honolulu.

Color in life (field No. 03123) pale, yellowish white over head and body; a diffuse lemon-yellow blotch under and above pectoral; a large brownish-black blotch on lateral line under seventh to tenth dorsal spines; dorsal fin yellowish-white, tip of detached part with a jet-black crescent (this marking variable in position, sometimes being farther posterior), rest of fin faintly mottled with yellowish and olive, the latter in narrow oblique lines; caudal yellowish white; anal yellowish white, with narrow, wavy, pale-blue lines, and a large jet-black spot bordered with blue on membrane of last 5 rays; iris whitish.

Another specimen, also a male (field No. 03371), was, in life, livid gray, each scale posteriorly with a vertical spot of violet; anterior line of profile bright violet; a violet line downward from eye with a whitish area behind it on cheek; an oblique violet line downward and backward from opercular flap to behind axil; posterior to this a vague yellow area, behind which is an ovate white spot, each scale around which has a vertical bar of bright violet; above this a large black blotch washed with brick-red; dorsal bluish-gray, the rays posteriorly with an increasing amount of orange, where the blue is reduced to oblique crossbands, an intermarginal line of violet, a small black spot on last ray; membranes of second to fourth dorsal spines with a terminal black ocellus; anal pale golden, with oblique bluish stripes, a large jet-black ocellus bordered with blue on last rays; caudal pale orange, crossed by bluish lines; ventrals and pectoral pale.

Still another male example (field No. 03004) was described as follows: General color very pale, smoky white, edges of scales pale bluish, beneath seventh to ninth dorsal spines a large blotch, brick-red above, pale rosy below, all irregularly overlaid with black or brown; median line from tip of snout to base of first dorsal spine bright blue; a narrow bright blue line downward from anterior part of eye to angle of mouth; region above pectoral pale lemon-yellow, a short oblique pale blue line above base of pectoral; dorsal pale flesh-color, with short vertical bluish lines, 3 jet-black spots at tips of first, second, and fourth spines; anal pale yellowish, a black spot on distal half of last 3 rays; caudal pale, with obscure bluish cross-lines; pectoral and ventrals white; iris yellowish, red at lower posterior angle.

A female (field No. 03372), 7.5 inches long, from Honolulu, which is taken as a cotype, differed in life coloration from the male in lacking the black ocellus on the anal and in having more violet on the white lateral spot, also more golden before it; violet lines and spots obscure, but present; 3 to 8 small blackish points above lateral line behind black dorsal blotch; a small black ocellus on second to third dorsal spines and one on seventh, these wanting in some females; fins otherwise colored as in the males, but the blue fainter and the orange of dorsal brighter. Field No. 03005 differed in color from field No. 03004 only in the absence of black on the dorsal and anal fins, the paler blue lines on head, the paler caudal fin, and in having black spots on the back. Another female example (field No. 03271), 7.5 inches long, in life had the head and body smoky white; a large bluish white spot under tip of pectoral; snout bluish around border and surrounded by a broad pale yellow space involving nearly all of anterior half of side below level of eye; a large black spot under fifth to sixth dorsal spines, crossing lateral line and penetrating yellow of side, nearly reaching white spot; back of this a series of about a dozen small black specks, scattered along side above lateral line to near end of dorsal fin; median line of snout and head blue; dorsal pale, with wavy yellow cross-lines, pinkish toward margin; caudal pale; anal pale, with about a dozen pale yellow crossbars; pectoral and ventrals pale; iris yellow and red.

Color in alcohol, creamy yellowish white; head somewhat orange on cheek and opercles; faint rosy lines downward from eye to mouth and on preopercle; median line of anterior profile bluish; middle of back with a large black or brownish black blotch lying on lateral line, beneath which is a large white blotch under and above pectoral fin; anterior part of spinous dorsal blackish at edge, the color ocellated, rest of dorsal yellowish white with narrow purplish cross-lines; anal similar, with a large jet-black spot on last 4 rays; caudal color of soft dorsal; pectoral and ventrals yellowish white. One of the female cotypes (No. 03372) is pale olivaceous, the general color that of the male; dorsal with black spots on membranes of second, third to fourth, and eighth spines, the latter ocellated; a series of about a dozen small black spots back of the dorsal blotch on side above lateral line; no black spot on anal.

The differences in coloration are very marked in the 2 sexes. The male, in all specimens examined, has the jet-black spot upon the last rays of the anal, and this is not present in any of the females examined. The female always has a series of small black specks on the side above lateral line posterior to the large lateral blotch. These markings, the small black spots on the side of the female and the large jet-black spot on the anal of the male, would apparently always serve to distinguish the sexes. The extent of variation in color among individuals of the same sex is indicated in the color descriptions given above. We should have added that occasionally there is a small jet-black spot upon the last rays of the dorsal.

This is one of the most abundant and beautiful fishes found among the Hawaiian Islands. It appears to be related to *H. melanopus* of Bleeker, but differs from it markedly in the presence of the large black lateral blotch and in the absence of the large red lateral blotch shown in Bleeker's figure. The collection contains 42 excellent specimens, 40 from Honolulu and 2 from Hilo, ranging in length from 5.75 to 8.8 inches.

266. Hemipteronotus jenkinsi Snyder. Plate 42, fig. 2.

Head, including opercular flap, 3.5 in length; depth 2.8; depth of caudal peduncle 2.2 in head; eye 6; width of interorbital space 5; length of maxillary 3; D. ix, 12; A. iii, 12; lateral line 22+6.

Eye located 2.66 times its diameter above angle of mouth; mouth nearly horizontal, on a level with upper edge of base of pectoral, the maxillary extending to a vertical through anterior edge of orbit; lower jaw slightly longer than upper; lips with rather thin, fleshy folds; outer row of teeth strong, conical, those on sides of jaws posterior to canines gradually decreasing in size from before backward; canines curving outward and forward, the lower pair, which are slightly the larger, fitting between the upper ones; inner teeth short and blunt, in narrow bands; pseudobranchiæ present; gillrakers on the first arch 6+11, short and sharply pointed; edge of preopercle smooth.

Head naked, except for a narrow, vertical, scaled area extending downward from eye to a horizontal passing along edge of flap of upper lip; first row with 7 scales, curving upward behind eye; second row with 5, the third with 4; scales of breast about half as large as those on sides of body; scales 2–27–9; lateral line curving upward over first 6 scales, then following the dorsal contour, approaching the back near end of dorsal, discontinued after twenty-second scale, beginning again on third scale below and passing along middle of caudal peduncle; first 2 dorsal spines somewhat closer together than others, but not separated from them, the membrane being continuous; height of first spine 2.6 in head, the second shorter; remaining spines 4 in head; height of rays 2.9; end of soft dorsal when depressed just reaching base of caudal fin; anal spines small and slender, the rays equal in height to those of the dorsal; base of anal and also the tips of the rays when depressed extending farther posteriorly than corresponding parts of dorsal; caudal rounded, the basal fourth with scales, the length 1.6 in head; pectoral 1.5; outer rays of ventral filamentous, just reaching vent.

Color in spirits, head plain, without spots, bars, or lines; a conspicuous black spot on back covering 2 scales above sixteenth in lateral line, its distance behind the opercular flap equal to distance between that point and tip of snout; a yellowish white spot on side of body, rather indistinctly outlined, covering an area equal to width of 5 scales and height of 3 or 4, the spot partly covered by pectoral when depressed; scales of body, except on breast, belly, and part covered by the large light spot, each with a vertical pearly bar which grows wider on the ventral scales, covering over half the scale in region above base of anal; soft dorsal and anal with oblique dark bars, those of the anal not so broad as those of dorsal; caudal, pectorals, and ventrals plain.

This species is said to be readily distinguished from closely related Hawaiian forms by the great depth of the body and by the small dark spot, the posterior location of which is notable, but it seems to be a young female of *H. baldwini*.

Known only from the type, a specimen 1 inch long from Puako Bay, Hawaii.

Genus 167. XYRICHTHYS Cuvier & Valenciennes.

Body short, deep, and very greatly compressed; anterior dorsal outline parabolic and very trenchant; cheek scaleless; lateral line interrupted; first 2 dorsal spines removed but not detached from the third, the membrane between the second and third being moderately notched.

267. Xyrichthys niveilatus Jordan & Evermann. Fig. 142.

Head 3.3 in length; depth 2.4; eye 6.2 in head; snout 1.8; preorbital 2; maxillary 3; interorbital 4.7; D. ii–vii, 12; A. iii, 12; scales 3–28–8.

Body short, deep, and very greatly compressed; anterior profile nearly vertical from tip of upper jaw to front of eye, thence in a parabolic curve to dorsal fin; anterior dorsal outline very trenchant; body tapering rather evenly from head to caudal peduncle, which is greatly compressed and very deep, depth at middle equaling preorbital; head short; snout very short and blunt; mouth small, horizontal, the maxillary nearly reaching anterior edge of orbit; jaws equal, each with a pair of strong curved canines in front, and a single series of smaller, conic teeth laterally, the canines of lower jaw most prominent and extending in front of upper jaw; eye small, high up; the interorbital space narrow and trenchant; opercles smooth, without spines or serrations, ending in thin flexible edges; preorbital vertical and very deep; origin of dorsal fin above posterior line of orbit, far in advance of base of ventrals; first 2 dorsal spines somewhat removed but not detached from third, the membrane between second and third spines moderately notched, length of second spine about 2.7 in head, remaining dorsal spines subequal, weak, about equal to gape; dorsal rays low, the last few somewhat produced, their length 3 in head; anal similar to soft dorsal; caudal short, slightly convex, rays about equal to preor-

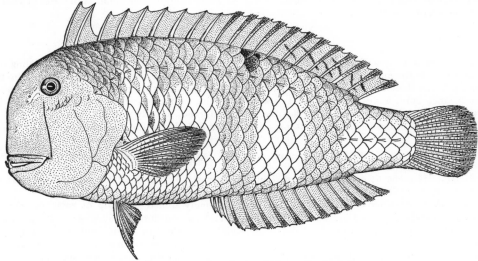

FIG. 142.—*Xyrichthys niveilatus* Jordan & Evermann; from the type.

bital; outer ray of ventral somewhat produced, not reaching vent, its length equaling depth of preorbital; pectoral broad, its tip reaching vent, its length equaling distance from snout to edge of preopercle.

Scales large, thin, and with membranous edges, those on breast somewhat smaller; head entirely naked, except for a few small scales below the eye; lateral line beginning at upper end of gill-opening following closely the curvature of back to the scale under the last dorsal ray but 2, where it drops 3 scales and continues to base of caudal, the pores simple, rarely branched.

Color in life, grayish; each scale of posterior half of body with a large violet spot, more narrow and brighter near middle of body, the edge of each scale broadly golden-olive; a large golden area, anteriorly deep orange, above pectoral and on edge of opercle; behind this a large quadrate pure white area extending to tip of pectoral; a few scales in golden area with bright violet markings; head shaded with violet, a bright violet stripe downward from eye to behind angle of mouth; a lunate black area shaded with red just below front of soft dorsal; spinous dorsal violet-gray; edged with reddish; soft dorsal golden, with violet vermiculations at base, its edge orange; anal golden, with bluish vermiculations; caudal similar, with the bluish markings; pectoral faintly reddish; ventrals dirty white.

One of the cotypes, a male (field No. 03373), agreed in life coloration with the type except that behind the opercle is a golden area with the bright violet stripes across anterior basal part; behind this a large milk-white patch beyond tip of pectoral; a violet border around the white, blackish above the yellow.

Color in alcohol, dirty yellowish white, dusky above; head with some purplish reflections; a thin purplish line downward from anterior edge of orbit to tip of maxillary, a similar but less distinct line, from humeral region downward to subopercle; a yellowish white blotch on side above base of pectoral, in the base of which are 2 or 3 small purplish spots; a large white area on middle of side under and above tip of pectoral, separated from the yellowish blotch by purplish brown on 2 or 3 scales; a black spot covering the larger part of 3 scales on side above lateral line under base of first 3 dorsal rays, back at base of last dorsal rays somewhat dusky; anterior portion of dorsal fin dusky olivaceous, soft dorsal, anal and caudal pale yellowish crossed by narrow, wavy, pale purplish lines; ventrals and pectoral plain yellowish white.

A handsome fish, rather common about Honolulu. The type and 5 cotypes, all from Honolulu, range from 6.5 to 9.75 inches in length.

Family LXX. SCARIDÆ.

Body oblong, moderately compressed, covered with large cycloid scales as in the *Labridæ;* mouth moderate, terminal; teeth in the jaws more or less coalescent, at least at the base; lower pharyngeals much enlarged, united in a concave or spoon-shaped body, their teeth broadest transversely and truncate, arranged in mosaic; dorsal continuous, its formula usually ix, 10; anal ii, 9; 23 to 25 scales in the lateral line; vertebræ about 11+14=25; sexes similarly colored, and the coloration almost always brilliant; fin rays essentially the same throughout the group, and the squamation varying little except on the head.

Herbivorous fishes of the tropical seas, often of large size, especially abundant about coral reefs. Little valued as food in America, the flesh being soft and pasty; but highly prized among the natives of the Hawaiian Islands, especially when eaten raw. The species in the various genera are very closely related, being distinguished chiefly by the coloration and the dentition, both series of characters being highly specialized.

Genus 168. CALOTOMUS Gilbert.

Teeth distinct, equal, imbricated in regular oblique rows in both jaws, wholly concealing the dental plates, to the anterior edge of which they are affixed; cutting edge of each jaw formed by the outer teeth, the dental plate not reaching the edge, and visible only from within; lips double for a short distance only; scales of cheek in 1 row; lateral line continuous; base of dorsal and anal with scaly sheaths; dorsal spines 9, soft and flexible; gill-membranes broadly joined to isthmus.

Large species of the Pacific, allied to *Cryptotomus*, but differing in the arrangement of the teeth.

268. Calotomus irradians Jenkins.   Fig. 143.

Head 3.25 in length; depth 2.5; eye 6.75 in head; snout 2.5; preorbital 3.5; interorbital 4; D. IX, 10; A. III, 9; P. 12; scales 2–25–5.

Body short, deep and compressed; dorsal outline strongly arched from tip of snout to origin of dorsal fin, slightly depressed in front of eyes, thence in a long, low curve to base of caudal peduncle; ventral outline similarly convex; least depth of caudal peduncle 2 in head; head short and deep, a little deeper than long; snout short, preorbital deep, not much oblique; mouth small, the gape not nearly reaching front of orbit, scarcely oblique, lying in axis of body; lower jaw slightly included; upper jaw with 3 series of strong imbricated but distinct teeth in front, the posterior 1 or 2 on each side remote, recurved and canine-like; lower jaw in front with about 4 or 5 series of teeth similar

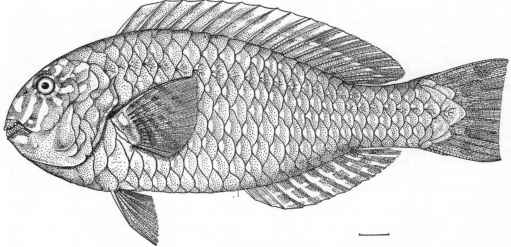

Fig. 143.—*Calotomus irradians* Jenkins; from the type.

to those in upper jaw; upper lip double only on the sides covering about half the teeth, lower lip not double; eye small, high up; interorbital rather narrow, convex.

Dorsal spines soft and flexible, their length about 3.25 in head; soft dorsal somewhat higher, rays about 2.3 in head; anal similar to soft dorsal, the rays equally high; caudal lunate, the lobes produced, the upper one the longer, about 1.3 in head; in some examples the caudal is more nearly truncate; ventrals short, their tips reaching scarcely halfway to origin of anal; pectoral broad, free edge slightly convex, the fin reaching slightly beyond tips of ventrals, length about 1.5 in head.

Scales large, firm, the edges thin and flexible; 4 scales on median line in front of dorsal fin; a sheath of modified scales along base of dorsal, a similar but lower sheath along base of anal; a single row of 5 large scales on cheek, 2 rows of large scales on opercle.

Color in life, body and fins blue; head, chin, and throat bright blue, marked with pink, in about 8 bands radiating from eye and a number of bands and irregular figures on snout, face and occiput, a few small spots on chin; of the pink bands radiating from eye, 2 reach region of angle of mouth, 2 join the irregular markings on face and occiput, and 4 radiate over the region of cheek and behind eye; a vertical bar of pink on each scale, in some regions partly concealed by overlapping scales; vertical fins bright blue with reticulations and spots of pink; ventrals blue; pectorals blue, olive, and pink, sometimes spotted with olive-green and edged with white.

Color in spirits, pale yellowish or bluish-green, the bases of the scales darker, the edges bluish-white; top of head dark, vermiculated with brownish and greenish; side of head light bluish-green, about 8 narrow white lines radiating from eye, one forward and downward toward snout, another to angle of mouth, a third downward across preorbital and just above angle of mouth bending forward and connecting with second, next downward and backward toward edge of preopercle, the next backward from eye and curved slightly upward and the remaining 3 upward and backward from eye; side of nape and downward to opercle with a few small white spots; underparts of head rich bluish-green; dorsal blotched and barred with whitish, green and blue; caudal with irregular crossbars of whitish and bluish green, the outer rays green, the tip of the fin narrowly bordered with white; distal end of caudal peduncle brighter green; anal purplish and greenish, with irregular reticulating white areas near base; ventrals light dusky, scarcely barred; pectoral dusky greenish, darker at base and in axil, paler on distal portion. In some examples the general color is considerably darker brownish and the fins are much darker.

This species is known only from Honolulu, from which place we have examined 6 specimens 14 to 20 inches long.

269. Calotomus cyclurus Jenkins. Fig. 144.

Head 3.1 in length; depth 2.5; eye 5.7 in head; snout 2.2; interorbital 4.2; D. ix, 11; A. i, 11; scales 2–24–5.

Body somewhat elongate, compressed, dorsal outline rising in a gently sloping, nearly straight line to origin of dorsal, from this point descending in nearly a straight line to caudal peduncle; ventral

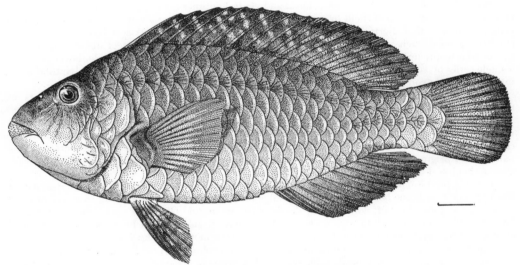

FIG. 144.—*Calotomus cyclurus* Jenkins; from the type.

outline about evenly convex; head a little longer than deep; snout long, bluntly conic; mouth large, horizontal, about in the axis of body; lips thin, double for about two-thirds the side, the lower double only a short distance; lower jaw just included; interorbital slightly convex, considerably broader than eye; least height of caudal peduncle a little less than half head.

Dorsal spines flexible, rather high, nearly half head; soft dorsal 2 in head; anal similar but less high, longest ray 2.3 in head; caudal rounded, no rays produced; ventrals 1.5 in head, reaching halfway to base of third soft anal ray; pectoral broad, its top reaching to or slightly past vertical through tip of ventral, its length 1.4 in head (in the type there are 12 rays on right side and 9 on left, which is doubtless a deformity); distal border convex (on left side); origins of dorsal, pectorals, and ventral about in same vertical.

Scales large, firm,. those on breast not reduced, those at base of dorsal hardly forming sheath, no sheath at base of anal; large scales on upper and posterior portion of the opercle, 1 row of about 7 scales below and behind the edge, remainder of head naked; lateral line complete, portion to the head parallel to the dorsal outline, straight portion beginning below base of fourth from last soft dorsal ray; 2 or 3 supernumerary scales, with tubes, extending from upper portion on the row just above straight portion, tubes much branched, the branching covering well the exposed portion of the scale; teeth in anterior portion of jaws distinct, pointed, imbricated in several series; 2 posterior canines; lateral teeth in upper jaw small, distinct, in a single series; lateral teeth in lower jaw large, in a single series; 2 conical teeth within the outer teeth at symphysis of upper jaw, other small teeth within the outer ones on sides of upper jaw.

Color in alcohol, head and body a uniform brown with some indications of dots of lighter on some of the scales, and a wide margin on the posterior border, each scale showing paler than the base; dorsal fin brown with faint traces of mottlings, no dark spot on anterior portion or darker margin; anal darker brown with less evident mottlings, and no darker margin; caudal much paler than body, upper and distal edges brown; ventral with indications of brown clouding; pectoral pale, without markings except that the base is dark brown; no markings on head except that top of head and isthmus are darker than sides of head.   Description is based on a single specimen 15 inches long to tip of caudal, obtained at Honolulu by the *Albatross*, 1896.

This species appears to be similar to *Scarus spinidens* (*Callyodon waigiensis* Cuvier & Valenciennes, Hist. Nat. Poiss., Vol. XIV), a small species first described, very imperfectly, from the island of Waigiu. A specimen from this island has been identified by Bleeker as Cuvier & Valenciennes's species, which he designates as *Callyodon spinidens* and of which he gives a full description and a figure. The present species differs from Bleeker's description in the dorsal outline, in its greater depth, much smaller eye, longer snout, and much longer ventral, in not having scales on the lower limb of the opercle and in having the base of the anal dark. Dr. Bleeker had many (72) specimens, and found *C. spinidens* of a limited range in distribution.

Honolulu; only the type known.

270. Calotomus sandvicensis (Cuvier & Valenciennes). "*Ponuhunuhu.*"

Head 3.3 in length; depth 2.5; eye 6.4 in head; snout 2.5; preorbital 4; interorbital 4; D. x, 11; A. ii, 9; scales 2–24–5.

Body short, deep and compressed; dorsal and ventral outlines about equally convex, dorsal rising in a gentle curve from tip of snout to origin of dorsal fin, then in a long lower curve to base of caudal peduncle; head rather short; snout short, bluntly conic; mouth small, in axis of body, the lower jaw slightly included, each jaw provided anteriorly with about 3 irregular series of distinct imbricated incisor-like teeth; upper jaw with 2 strong backwardly directed canines on the side, lower jaw with a single series of small close-set teeth on the side; eye small, high up, the preorbital rather wide; interorbital high, convex; caudal peduncle moderately deep, about 2 in head.

Scales very large and thin; lateral line with a slight jog under base of last dorsal ray, the pores numerously branched; a single row of 4 scales on cheek, and 4 scales on anterior portion of opercle.

Dorsal spines soft and flexible, their length scarcely equaling that of snout; last dorsal rays somewhat elevated, their length nearly half that of head; anal similar to soft dorsal, its rays equally long; caudal somewhat lunate, the upper lobe usually the longer, about 1.2 in head; ventrals short, reaching half way to origin of anal; pectoral broad, the free edge convex, the upper rays about 1.4 in head. Description based chiefly upon specimen No. 05646.

Color in life (No. 03368), mottled gray and brown, scarcely reddish below; spinous dorsal with a black spot on membrane between first and second spines, a faint reddish stripe along base, and another along edge of dorsal fin; soft dorsal with pale reticulations around faint dark spots; caudal still more faintly mottled and with white edge, a blackish line before it; anal mottled brown with reddish shade at base and tip; pectoral yellowish, the base dusky; ventrals mottled dusky gray.

Another specimen (No. 03452) had, in life, the general color brown and olive with reddish along ventral portions of body and head; each scale with a group of irregularly-shaped gray dots; dorsal more olive, with reticulations of gray; black dorsal spot faint or obsolete; large dark blotch over distal half of last 5 rays of soft dorsal interrupted by gray spots; caudal reddish olive, crossed by irregular bands of gray; anal with reddish dark mottlings at base, with gray markings; ventrals reddish with gray markings; pectoral membranes transparent, the rays reddish olive; head colored like the body; under surface of pectoral at base black.

Color in alcohol (No. 03368) dull grayish or olivaceous on head and body, somewhat mottled with paler and darker brown, under parts grayish; side without distinct spots or specks; dorsal and anal blackish, with faint marblings of lighter; caudal obscurely barred with light and darker, the edge narrowly white; pectoral blackish at base, distally pale; ventrals dusky.

The numerous examples show considerable variation in color in spirits, chiefly with reference to the marbling of the dorsal and caudal fins. In many examples the mottling of these fins is quite distinct, while in others it is scarcely evident; some examples show all gradations between these two. The sides of body and head also are variously mottled gray. In some examples the body is very dark brown, the vertical fins almost black, and the pectoral black on its basal half.

The originial description of *Callyodon sandvicensis* by Cuvier and Valenciennes, as well as a redescription by Valenciennes, is very incomplete, and except for the agreement in locality we would hesitate to consider ours the same species. This fact, however, makes the identification entirely reasonable.

The species is very common in the market at Honolulu, from which place we have 24 specimens. We have none from Hilo, but have 3 from Kailua. The length ranges from 5 to 14.75 inches.

271. Calotomus snyderi Jenkins. Fig. 145.

Head 3.2 in length; depth 2.6; eye 5.6 in head; snout 2.8; preorbital 4.7; interorbital 4; D. ix, 10; A. iii, 10; P. 12; scales 2–25–6.

Body short, deep, and much compressed; dorsal outline rather straight from tip of snout to nape, from which point it is gently convex to origin of dorsal, thence in a long, low curve to base of caudal

FIG. 145.—*Calotomus snyderi* Jenkins; from the type.

peduncle; ventral outline rather evenly convex; head short, as deep as long; snout bluntly conic, lower jaw slightly included; mouth small, in axis of body; teeth in front of each jaw free, convex, incisor-like, in 2 or 3 rows; upper jaw with 2 moderately strong, recurved canines, inside and posterior to which is a row of close-set smaller teeth; side of lower jaw with overlapping series of rounded incisor-like teeth; preorbital oblique, moderately deep; eye small, high up; interorbital broad, low, convex; caudal peduncle 2 in head.

Scales large, thin, adherent, the free edges membranous; 4 scales on median line in front of dorsal; cheek with a single row of 4 scales; opercle with 2 rows of large scales, 3 scales on the lower limb; lateral line complete, decurved under base of last dorsal ray, where there is usually one or more supernumerary pores; pores of lateral line numerously and widely branched, the branches varying from 4 or 5 to 12 or more.

Dorsal spines soft and flexible, the longest about equaling snout; soft dorsal somewhat elevated, the longest rays equaling distance from tip of snout to pupil; anal similar to soft dorsal; caudal somewhat lunate, the upper lobe the longer, about 1.8 in head; ventral short, reaching barely half way to origin of anal; pectoral broad, reaching past tips of ventrals, its length 1.3 in head.

Color in alcohol, dirty yellowish brown on head and body, marbled with light and darker; side above lateral line with a series of about 5 roundish white spots as large as pupil, and numerous smaller irregular, less distinct white spots; side below lateral line with about 10 or 12 large rounded white spots and numerous small white specks and irregular markings, these especially distinct in pectoral region; head with similar white specks and markings; dorsal fin brown with irregular paler spots; membrane between first and second dorsal spines black; soft dorsal with a large brownish black spot at base of last 5 or 6 rays; anal similar to soft dorsal, blotches not so distinct; a series of black blotches at bases of rays, the one on last ray larger than others, covering base of last membrane; ventrals brownish, dusky at tip, a paler interspace; pectoral dusky, dark at base and in axil, pale on tip.

The only specimen known is the type No. 50850, 10.5 inches long, obtained at Honolulu in 1889.

Genus 169. SCARIDEA Jenkins.

Jaws subequal, the lower barely included; gill-membranes broadly joined to the isthmus, and not forming a fold across it; upper lip double for only about half its length; lateral line continuous; 1 row of scales on the cheek; teeth white, distinct in anterior portion of each jaw, in more than 1 series irregularly imbricated; lateral teeth in upper jaw small, in a single series, the tips free, the bases coalesced; lateral teeth in lower jaw large, distinct, but close-set, in a single series; posterior canines present; dorsal spines pungent.

This genus is related to *Calotomus* in the character of the teeth, but differs from it in having stiff, pungent dorsal spines, in this agreeing with *Sparisoma*. From *Scarichthys* Bleeker it differs in having pungent spines, in having the upper lip double for only a portion of its length, and in the distinct teeth. From *Callyodontichthys* Bleeker it is distinguished by the included lower jaw and the distinct teeth in upper jaw. Two species known.

272. Scaridea zonarcha Jenkins. Fig. 146.

Head 3 in length; depth 2.75; eye 3.7 in head; snout 2.6; mandible 3.7; interorbital 5; preorbital 5.6; D. ix, 9; A. ii, 9; P. 12; scales 2–24–5, 19 tubes before the bend.

Body compressed, the dorsal outline more convex than the ventral, the highest portion at third dorsal spine; head nearly as deep as long; mouth horizontal, in axis of body; lips thin, the upper double for only a part of its length, the lower double for only a short distance; lips covering only bases of teeth; eye moderate, its lower border above axis of body; interorbital somewhat narrower than eye, slightly convex; caudal peduncle 2.6 in head.

Jaws subequal, the lower slightly included; teeth white, distinct on anterior portion of each jaw and in more than 1 series, irregularly imbricated; lateral teeth in upper jaw small, in a single series, outer extremities free, the bases coalesced; lateral teeth in lower jaw large, distinct, in a single series, crowded at base; 2 posterior teeth on one and one on the other side of upper jaw canine-like and turned backward.

Dorsal spines pungent, about 2.1 in head; soft dorsal slightly higher; anal similar to soft dorsal, but lower; caudal truncate or slightly rounded; pectoral 1.6 in head; reaching slightly beyond tips of ventrals; origins of dorsal, pectoral, and ventrals in same vertical line.

Scales large, firm, thin, those on nape and breast not reduced; 3 scales on median line in front of dorsal; 1 row of 3 scales on cheek; large scales on upper and posterior part of opercle, 1 scale showing on lower limb; rest of head naked; a sheath of scales at base of dorsal, none at base of anal; lateral line complete, the tubes much branched.

Color in alcohol, general ground-color of body and fins, except pectoral, light brown, with numerous scattered darker reddish brown spots, of indistinct outline, about size of pupil, these spots

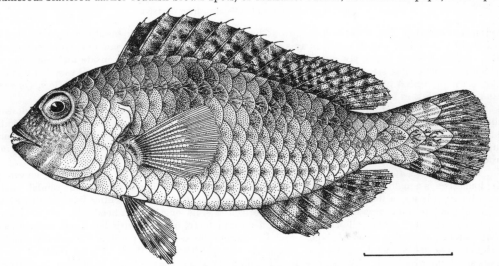

FIG. 146.—*Scaridea zonarcha* Jenkins; from the type.

on body corresponding with the rows of scales, and showing within their area small lighter specks; dorsal light brown with about 2 or 3 cross series of large darker brown spots, edge of fin blackish; anal and caudal similar to dorsal; ventrals mottled but lighter; pectoral pale, dusky at base.

Known only from 3 specimens obtained by Dr. Jenkins at Honolulu, in 1889, the length of these being from 4 to 5.75 inches.

273. Scaridea balia Jenkins. Fig. 147.

Head 3.25 in length; depth 2.4; eye 5 in head; snout 2.9; preorbital 4; interorbital 4.3; scales 2–24–5; D. ix, 10; A. ii, 9; P. 12.

Body short, deep, and compressed; dorsal outline regularly and evenly arched from tip of snout to caudal peduncle, somewhat straighter from tip of snout to origin of dorsal fin, there being no angle at the last-mentioned point; ventral outline evenly convex; head short and deep; snout short; mouth moderate, about horizontal, in line with axis of body, the gape reaching past vertical from nostril; lower jaw included, each jaw with 2 irregular rows of teeth; teeth in anterior portion of each jaw distinct, imbricated in 2 irregular series; upper jaw with 2 posterior canines directed backward, lateral teeth of upper jaw distinct, small, and in a single series; each side of lower jaw with about 5 distinct blunt incisor-like teeth in a single series; no teeth inside of front series of upper jaw; preorbital and interorbital rather narrow, the latter little convex, somewhat concave anteriorly; dorsal spines stiff and pungent, length of longest about equal to snout; soft dorsal somewhat elevated, longest ray 2.1 in head; anal similar to soft dorsal, slightly lower; caudal rounded, 1.6 in head; ventrals short, their tips reaching scarcely half way to origin of anal; pectoral short, free edge rounded, its length a little greater than that of ventrals.

Scales large; lateral line continuous from upper end of gill-opening to posterior end of dorsal fin, where it curves downward 2 rows, continuing to base of caudal fin; tubes of lateral line numerously and widely branched, the branches 4 to 6 or 7 in number, a few additional tubes at the bend of lateral line; one series of about 4 scales on cheek between which and eye are several long tubes; opercle with a series of large scales on basal portion; 4 scales on median line in front of dorsal fin.

Color in spirits, dirty rusty brown, paler below, upper part of side above lateral line with a series of about 6 roundish whitish spots larger than pupil; a similar series of about 4 spots on first row of scales below lateral line; lower part of side with 2 or more similar spots; side of head and body

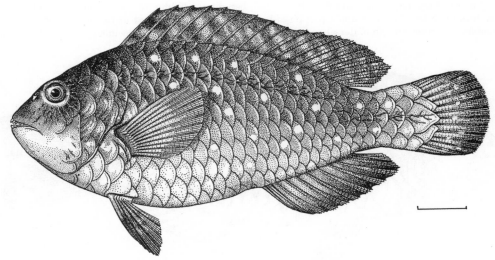

FIG. 147.—*Scaridea balia* Jenkins; from the type.

with a few scattered, smaller, less distinct whitish spots; dorsal fin indistinctly mottled with light and brownish; membrane between first and second spines blackish at the center; anal and caudal rather uniformly plain pale brownish without distinct markings; pectoral and ventrals lighter brownish; base of pectoral darker brown.

This species differs from *Scaridea zonarcha* in the greater depth of body, the much greater distance between tips of ventrals and origin of anal, the greater distinctness of the white spots on body, the less distinct mottling of the dorsal fin, and the entire absence of mottlings on anal and caudal.

The only specimen known is the type, No. 50852, U. S. National Museum (original No. 1985), 10 inches long, obtained by the *Albatross* at Honolulu in 1896.

Genus 170. CALLYODON Gronow.

Lower pharyngeals spoon-shaped, ovate-oblong, transversely concave; teeth in each jaw fully coalescent, appearing as tessellations on the surface; jaws with distinct median suture; edges of jaw even, the teeth whitish, or rosy, in color; upper pharyngeals each with 2 rows of teeth; gill-membranes scarcely united to the narrow isthmus, across which they form a broad fold; dorsal spines flexible, scarcely different from the soft rays; upper lip laterally double, the interior fold becoming very narrow or obsolete mesially; lower jaw included in the closed mouth; lateral line interrupted posteriorly, beginning again on the next series of scales below; tubes of lateral line scarcely branched; scales on cheek in 2 to 4 rows; scales in front of dorsal on median line 6 to 8; dorsal ix, 10; anal iii, 9 in all species; scales $\frac{1}{2}$–24–6; body robust.

Species very numerous, mostly of large size, found in nearly all tropical seas.

274. Callyodon miniatus (Jenkins). " *Uhu.*"   Fig. 148.

Head 2.74 in length; depth 2.6; eye 8 in head; snout 2.2; preorbital 4; interorbital 2.75; D. ix, 10; A. iii, 9; P. 14; scales 2–24–6.

Body deep and compressed; dorsal profile quite evenly convex from tip of snout to base of caudal peduncle; ventral outline scarcely less convex; head large, heavy, and deep; snout very blunt, but long; mouth small, in axis of body; jaws subequal, the lower slightly included; teeth white dusky yellowish at base; posterior tooth scarcely developed, usually not evident; upper lip double only posteriorly, only covering about half the dental plate, lower lip narrow, not covering half the dental plate; cheek with 2 rows of scales, 6 scales in the upper and only 1 or 2 in the lower row, these latter small and sometimes not apparent; in old individuals the cheek scales are embedded and scarcely visible; no scales on lower limb of preopercle; a series of scales on margin of opercle, those on lower limb more or less embedded; 4 scales on median line in front of dorsal; lateral line interrupted under base of last but 1 dorsal ray, reappearing 2 scales below and continuing to caudal; tubes of lateral line much branched.

Dorsal spines soft and flexible, their length about 4 in head; dorsal rays somewhat elevated, the longest 2.7 in head; anal high, similar to soft dorsal; caudal slightly lunate in adult, truncate in the young, the lobes rounded, not produced; ventrals short, about 2 in head; pectorals longer, the free edge oblique, 1.5 in head, the breadth one-third its length, membranes of spinous dorsal, anal, and ventral fleshy.

Color in life, body, head, and fins all dull red, becoming a lighter red on lower parts and darker to a dusky reddish brown on upper portion of body; no distinct markings anywhere except a narrow violet line on outer margin of dorsal and anal fins; iris brown. Another specimen (No. 03365) was in

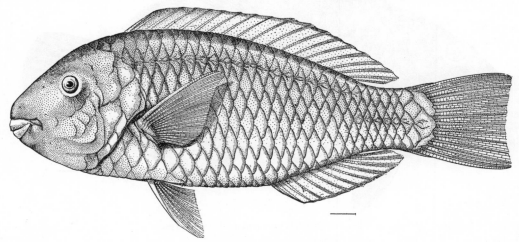

FIG. 148.—*Callyodon miniatus* (Jenkins); from the type.

life brown washed with red; basal half of all the fins brown red, distal half paler, of a bright pink, this especially true of caudal and anal; ventrals pink like the breast.

In alcohol the color fades to a dull dusky or reddish brown, the caudal peduncle paler; the fins all pale dusky yellowish.

This is one of the largest and most important species of this genus in Hawaiian waters. It is not very common and brings an extravagant price in the markets, being eaten raw at native feasts or "luaus." The collection contains a dozen specimens, 5.5 to 19 inches long, all from Honolulu.

275. Callyodon perspicillatus (Steindachner). " *Uhu uli uli.*" Fig. 149.

Head 3.1 in length; depth 2.9; eye 9 in head; snout 2.2; interorbital 2.35; D. ix, 10; A. ii, 10 (9 or 10); scales 2-24-6.

Body short, stout and compressed; dorsal and ventral outlines about evenly arched; head as deep as long, compressed; snout very blunt, its anterior profile perpendicular, as high as long; no canine teeth evident; eye high, median; caudal peduncle deep, 2 in head.

Fins moderate, origin of dorsal over upper base of pectoral, rays higher than spines, last ray but one longest, 2.5 in head; last anal ray slightly the longer, last but one 2.2 in head; caudal very slightly lunate; ventrals not reaching vent by half their length; longest ray 1.8 in head; pectoral broadly falcate, longest ray 1.3 in head.

Scales large and thin; 4 scales before dorsal, a single row of 5 scales on preopercle, a single scale under the last posterior scale in the row, lower edge of preopercle with a single row of large scales; 3 rows of large scales on opercle; last scale of lateral line very broad and large, more than half the width of caudal peduncle and much the largest scale on the fish; 4 scales in front of ventrals; lateral line following curvature of back to the row of scales except one under the last dorsal ray, then dropping down 1 row and continuing on middle of caudal peduncle to base of caudal; pores with 2 tubes generally, sometimes with 3 or more.

Color in life (No. 03367), vitriol green, each scale on sides edged with brown-drab; belly livid lavender drab, the scales with small round blue spots on side as far up as pectoral; a gray drab area behind head reaching nearly to end of pectoral, covered with small blue spots and navy blue streaks; lower part of head violet with elaborate sky-blue markings, opercular flap bright golden green, stripe and ring about eye blue; snout violet, then brown with a light green area bordered by sky blue, then a golden brown area similarly bordered; dorsal with 2 stripes of bluish green, 2 of golden brown, the edge clear blue; caudal clear blue, the rays dusky; anal like dorsal, the stripes broader; pectoral light blue, the upper rays and a stripe across base bright blue; a golden brown shade at base; caudal bright golden brown, the outer and inner rays bright blue.

Color in spirits, body bright greenish, edges of the scales purplish, under parts paler, postocular region, upper half of opercle and region under and above pectoral purplish with numerous small round green spots, those on posterior portion of area modified into irregular green lines; snout purplish; a broad purplish saddle bounded by a narrow blue-green border over middle portion of snout reaching level of mouth on each side; a narrow blue-green line connecting eyes and extending around front of eye and backward upon cheek for an eye's diameter; 2 short postorbital blue-green streaks; 2 or 3 curved green streaks on cheek; lower lip with a broad blue-green border covering entire width

FIG. 149.—*Callyodon perspicillatus* (Steindachner); after Steindachner.

back to bases of branchiostegals, bending upward to angle of snout, and then continuing upward and backward across cheek in a wavy blue-green stripe; a narrow stripe of same color beginning on side of head, under this continuing downward and backward to near edge of subopercle, where it turns backward, inclosing 3 small areas and then extends upward along edge of preopercle to middle of cheek; middle line of branchiostegal membranes blue-green; a few thin green streaks and spots under base of pectoral; dorsal fin with a scallopy blue-green base, a median stripe and a border of same color, the median stripe separating 2 yellowish purple or whitish stripes; anal similar, the basal blue-green streak narrower and broken up into scallopy spots, the median green streak much broader, the green border also broken; caudal bluish green, the edges brightest; ventrals creamy white, the edges pale green, the inner edge narrowly blue-green; pectoral purplish dusky, upper edge bright blue-green.

This is one of the largest and most beautiful species of *Scaridæ* occurring among the Hawaiian Islands. It reaches a length of nearly 2 feet, is fairly common, and is highly esteemed by the natives. We have 6 specimens from Honolulu and the *Albatross* secured it at Puako Bay. It is known also from Johnston Island.

276. Callyodon borborus (Jordan & Evermann). *"Panuhu."* Fig. 150.

Head 3.2 in length; depth 3.2; eye 6.6 in head; snout 2.9; interorbital 2.9; preorbital 4; D. ix, 10; A. iii, 9; P. 14; scales 2-25-6.

Body oblong, not very deep nor greatly compressed; head about as long as deep, conic, compressed; snout short, blunt and rounded; upper jaw produced, its lip double, covering entire dental plate; lower lip covering half of dental plate; no canine teeth; eye anterior, high, its lower border considerably above upper base of pectoral; caudal peduncle short and deep, its depth 2 in head.

Origin of dorsal over upper base of pectoral, spines flexible, short, not quite as long as rays; longest ray 2.1 in head; longest anal ray 2.2 in head; caudal truncate; ventrals 1.9 in head, not reaching vent by half their length; pectoral 1.5 in head. Scales large and thin, very slightly roughened by radiating lines of granulations extending to margins of scales; lateral line interrupted, the pores being on 18 scales, then dropping 2 rows to row of scales under posterior base of dorsal, and continuing to base of caudal on middle of caudal peduncle, 7 pores in the shorter part, which begins

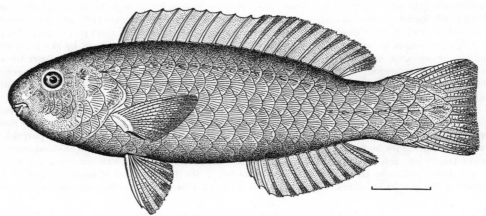

Fig. 150.—*Callyodon borborus* (Jordan & Evermann); from the type.

on the row following the row on which the upper part ends, there not being 2 pores in the same row; scales extending well out on the caudal, the last scale of lateral line very large and thin, being the largest scale on the fish; 4 scales in median line before dorsal; 2 rows of scales on cheek, 5 scales in upper row and 2 to 4 in lower, sometimes only 2 on posterior part; 2 rows on opercle, and 1 on lower margin.

Color in alcohol, grayish leaden brown, lighter below; no markings on fins different from corresponding parts of body.

The above description is based on the type, No. 50649, U. S. N. M. (field No. 04316), a specimen 7.75 inches long, from Honolulu; cotype, No. 27.35, U. S. F. C. (field No. 04354), 7.5 inches long, and cotype, No. 7465, L. S. Jr. Univ. Mus. (field No. 650), 5.5 inches long, both from Honolulu.

277. Callyodon brunneus (Jenkins). ·Fig. 151.

Head 3 in length; depth 3; eye 6.2 in head; snout 3; preorbital 5.2; interorbital 3; D. ix, 10; A. iii, 9; P. 13; V. 6; scales 2–25–6.

Body short, deep and moderately compressed; dorsal and ventral profiles about equally convex; head short and moderately deep; snout bluntly pointed; mouth small, in axis of body, about horizontal, lower jaw slightly included; teeth white, posterior canine in upper jaw occasionally but not usually present; upper lip double for its whole length, almost wholly covering upper dental plate; lower lip covering more than half of dental plate; eye small, the lower edge of orbit on axis of body; interorbital space broad, gently convex.

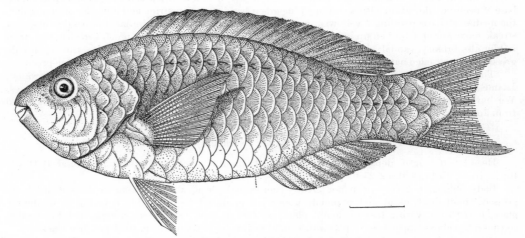

Fig. 151.—*Callyodon brunneus* (Jenkins); from the type.

Scales large, 4 rows in front of origin of dorsal, cheek with 2 rows of scales, 6 in the upper and 4 in the lower, anterior limb of opercle without scales, a row of scales along margin of opercle; lateral line interrupted under base of last dorsal ray, reappearing 2 rows farther down, 18 pores in the first part and 8 in the other, the tubes somewhat branched.

Dorsal spines soft and flexible, low, their length 3.5 in head; dorsal rays not elevated, the edge of the fin gently rounded; anal similar to soft dorsal, the rays shorter than snout; caudal lunate, outer rays somewhat produced, about 1.7 in head; ventrals short, about equaling snout and eye; pectoral longer, reaching past tips of ventrals, its length 1.4 in head.

Color in life, gray mottled, streaked scored and barred with gray and brown; reddish-brown bar on lower jar; some reddish on belly, ventral fins, and front of anal; vent blue; pectoral dull yellowish, a black bar at its base; tip of caudal white; no bright colors; dark behind eye, a dark scale on opercle. Another specimen when fresh was dirty mottled brown, scales with coppery-red below; dorsal like back; caudal and anal more reddish, vaguely mottled; ventral coppery, and pectoral colorless, a dark bar across base.

Color in spirits dark rusty brown mottled and blotched with darker and paler; dorsal and anal dark purplish brown.

This species reaches a length of about 10 or 12 inches, and is not uncommon in the markets of Honolulu.

We have examined 15 specimens, all from Honolulu, 7 collected by Dr. Jenkins, 1 by the *Albatross* in 1896, 1 by Dr. Wood, and 6 by us. The length varies from 4.25 to 9.5 inches.

278. Callyodon dubius (Bennett). Plate 44.[a]

Head 3.1 in length; depth 3.1; eye 6 in head; snout 3; preorbital 5: interorbital 3.2; D. ix, 10; A. iii, 9; P. 14; scales 2–25–6.

Body short, stout, not deep and not greatly compressed; head short and blunt; snout short; anterior profile evenly curved from tip of snout to origin of dorsal; ventral outline less convex; mouth small, horizontal, slightly below axis of body, lower jaw included; upper lip entirely covering upper dental plate, lower lip leaving a portion of lower dental plate exposed; no posterior canine in either jaw; teeth white; eye small, lower edge of orbit in line with axis of body; interorbital space wide, broadly convex.

Scales large, 4 rows on median line in front of dorsal; cheek with 2 rows, 8 scales in the upper and 3 in the lower, subopercle with a single row; opercle with a single row of large scales; lateral line interrupted under last dorsal ray, to reappear again 2 rows farther down, 18 pores in the first part and 7 in the last; tubes of lateral line with very short branches.

Dorsal spines soft and flexible, their length scarcely equaling snout; soft dorsal not elevated, the border of the entire fin uniformly rounded; anal similar to soft dorsal, its rays equaling snout; caudal truncate or very slightly lunate, the outer rays scarcely produced, their length 1.6 in head; pectoral longer, reaching origin of anal, 1.3 in head.

Color of a nearly fresh specimen in formalin, deep lead-color, body and fins uniform, a leaden band across caudal; pectoral light yellowish, yellow at tip; terminal band of caudal pale lead-color; center of each scale darker lead-color; ventral pale; tip of opercle with a large blackish spot.

Color in spirits, dark brownish, the edges of the scales paler; dorsal and anal dark brownish; caudal dusky; ventrals and pectoral pale dusky.

The collection contains but a single example (No. 03405), 6.5 inches long, obtained at Honolulu. This species occurs also in Samoa.

279. Callyodon ahula (Jenkins). "*Ahuula;*" "*Panuhúnuhú.*" Fig. 152.

Head 2.8 in length; depth 2.34; eye 6 in head; snout 2.7; preorbital 5; interorbital 3; D. ix, 10; A. iii, 10; P. 14; V. i, 5; scales 2–24–6.

Body short, deep, strongly compressed; dorsal profile rather strongly arched, slightly depressed in front of eyes; head rather deep; snout prominent, the lower jaw included; mouth small, entirely below axis of body; dental plates white, yellowish at base; no posterior canines; upper lip double its entire length, covering about half the upper dental plate; lower lip short, covering less than half lower dental plate; eye small, lower edge of orbit on body axis; caudal peduncle compressed, its depth 2.2 in head.

Scales large, 4 rows in front of dorsal, a single row of 4 scales on cheek, behind which are 2 scales placed one above the other; posterior limb of opercle with 2 series, the anterior with 1 series of scales; lateral line interrupted under last dorsal ray and continued to base of caudal 2 rows lower down, the tubes somewhat wavy and little branched.

Dorsal fin rather high, the spines soft and flexible, their length about equal to that of snout; soft dorsal scarcely higher; anal similar to soft dorsal; caudal fin slightly convex, the lobes rounded, 1.8 in head; pectoral 1.4 in head; ventrals not reaching vent, 1.8 in head.

Head, body, and fins uniformly brown, with reddish tinges brightest on fins and throat; base of caudal paler; no distinct markings anywhere.

---

[a] *Scarus dubius* on plate.

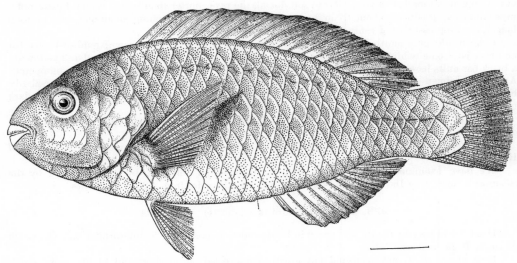

FIG. 152.—*Callyodon ahula* (Jenkins); from the type.

This species reaches a length of about 9 or 10 inches, and is known only from the 5 specimens recorded by Dr. Jenkins and others obtained by the *Albatross* at Honolulu.

280. Callyodon bennetti (Cuvier & Valenciennes). Plate 45. [a]

Head 2.8 in length; depth 3.25; eye 5.2 in head; snout 2.6; preorbital 6; interorbital 3.2; D. ix, 10; A. iii, 9; P. 13; scales 2–24–6.

Body rather short, moderately deep, not greatly compressed; head longer than deep, compressed; snout subconic, lower jaw included; lips covering about half of each jaw; dental plates white; no posterior canine teeth; eve high, entirely above upper base of pectoral, slightly anterior; caudal peduncle 2.5 in head.

Origin of dorsal a little posterior to upper base of pectoral, spines flexible, of about equal length and equal to rays, the longest spine 2.5 in head; longest anal ray 2.75 in head; caudal slightly rounded; ventrals 2 in head, not reaching vent by 0.75 of their length; pectoral broad, 1.6 in head.

Scales large, smooth; scales on cheek in 3 rows, upper with 6 scales, next with 6, lower with 2; 2 rows of scales on opercle, its lower edge with a single row; lateral line interrupted, 17 pores in upper part, which ends on the first row of scales beyond the last dorsal ray, then drops 2 rows and continues along middle of caudal peduncle to base, there being 7 pores in the shorter part.

Color in alcohol, brownish olivaceous, edges of scales darker; 2 rather distinct white stripes from near base of pectoral along lower part of side, disappearing before reaching vertical of anal origin; fins all plain olivaceous, scarcely mottled; tip of caudal not white.

This species was originally described from the Hawaiian Islands. The collection made by Dr. Wood at Honolulu in 1898 contains a single specimen, No. 2081, 5.25 inches long. Also found in Samoa.

281. Callyodon paluca (Jenkins). "*Palúkalúka.*" Fig. 153.

Head 3 in length; depth 2.8; eye 5.5 in head; snout 2.75; interorbital 2.9; D. ix, 10; A. iii, 9; P. 14; scales, 2–24–6.

Body deep, compressed; dorsal and ventral outline evenly arched; head longer than deep, compressed, bluntly conic; lower jaw included; teeth white, no posterior canine; upper lip double, its entire length and covering little more than half the dental plate, lower lip covering half of lower plate; lower edge of eye slightly above upper base of pectoral.

Origin of dorsal over upper base of pectoral, its distance from tip of snout equal to head; dorsal spines flexible, all except first and second of about equal length, longest 2.75 in head, longest ray 2.4 in head; longest anal ray 2.4 in head; caudal truncate, lobes not produced; ventrals 1.85 in head, not reaching vent by two-thirds its own length; pectoral 1.6 in head.

Scales large and thin, very slightly roughened by radiating lines of granulations extending to margin of scales; cheek with 3 rows of scales, 6 scales in upper row, 4 or 5 in middle, 2 in lower,

---

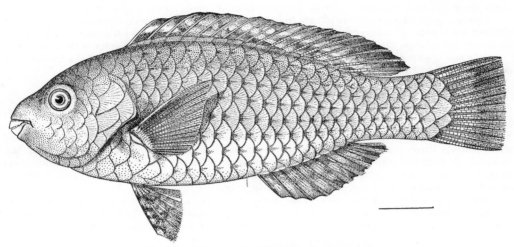

FIG. 153.—*Callyodon paluca* (Jenkins); from the type.

which extends upon anterior limb of preopercle; posterior limb of opercle with 2 rows of large scales; anterior limb with a single series; 6 scales in median series before dorsal; lateral line interrupted at 1 row of scales beyond posterior base of dorsal, pores on 19 scales, lateral line dropping down 1 row and beginning on row in which long part ends, 6 pores being in the shorter part, pores being on the 2 different but adjoining scales in the same upward and backward row; many pores branched, a few single.

Color in life, upper portion reddish-brown, lower parts, including ventrals and anal, a brighter red; vertical fins and ventrals somewhat mottled; body and head without distinct markings.

Color in alcohol, grayish-brown, upper parts darker, edges of scales dark brown; fins all a similar color, the vertical fins and ventrals being mottled with light and brown.

The above description from the type, 7 inches long, obtained by Dr. Jenkins at Honolulu in 1889, the only known specimen until the *Albatross* obtained others in 1902.

282. Callyodon jenkinsi (Jordan & Evermann).

Head 3 in length; depth 2.5; eye 6.5 in head; snout 2.6; preorbital 4.7; interorbital 3; D. ix, 10; A. iii, 9; P. 13; scales 2–24–7.

Body short, very deep and greatly compressed; head short, nearly as deep as long, snout short and blunt; mouth small; each jaw with 1 or 2 blunt canines; dorsal and ventral outlines about equally convex; anterior profile rising rather irregularly from tip of snout to origin of dorsal; caudal peduncle deep, its least depth 2 in head. Scales large, deeper than long; 2 rows of large scales on cheek and 1 row on subopercle; a row of thin modified scales at base of dorsal and anal; a few very large thin scales on base of caudal; lateral line ceasing under last dorsal ray, reappearing 2 rows lower down and continuing to base of caudal, the pores with 2 or 3 irregular branches; dorsal rays soft and flexible, not pungent; dorsal spines somewhat elevated posteriorly, longest a little more than 2 in head; first ventral spine obscure, the others soft and flexible; anal rays somewhat shorter than those of dorsal; caudal shallowly lunate, the outer rays not greatly produced; ventrals moderate, 1.6 in head, not reaching to origin of anal by a distance equal to two-fifths their length; pectoral broad, 1.2 in head.

Color of a nearly fresh specimen, bright blue-green, brightest on posterior half of body, each scale broadly edged with reddish brown; lower anterior part of body reddish brown, with traces of blue-green; top of head brownish red or coppery, a broad deep blue-green band on the upper lip, extending on side of head to below eye; lower lip with a narrow brighter blue-green band connecting at angle of mouth with the one from upper lip; chin with a broad coppery-red bar, followed by a broader bright blue-green one; caudal green, median part pale, banded with green spots; dorsal bright green at base and tip, the middle pale greenish, translucent; anal similar, the distal band broader; pectorals and ventrals deep vitriol-green with whitish markings.

Color in alcohol, dirty greenish, side with about 8 longitudinal series of greenish blotches; head olivaceous above, paler on cheeks; upper lip broadly pea-green at edge, this color continued backward to under eye; edge of lower lip pale green, continued around angle of mouth uniting with the same color from upper lip; chin with a broad, pale crossbar, behind which is a broader, pale-green one which extends up on cheek nearly to orbit; back of this is a still broader, white crossbar interrupted in the middle by greenish; subopercle and lower edge of preopercle with a large, irregular, green patch; a median green line on breast to base of ventrals; dorsal green at base and along edge, the middle portion paler; anal similar to dorsal, the green border broader; caudal bright pea-green on the outer rays, the inner ones pale with 4 or 5 cross series of green spots, tips of rays darker; ventrals pale green, the edges dark pea-green; pectoral pale green, darker green on the upper rays.

This species is related to *Scarus gilberti*, from which it differs in the greater depth and the somewhat different coloration. It is also related to *Callyodon lauia*, but differs in the much greater depth, the less produced caudal lobes, the greater width of the green head markings, and the color of the fins.

Only one specimen was obtained, type No. 50647, U. S. N. M. (field No. 02944), 14 inches long, taken at Honolulu June 6.

283. Callyodon gilberti (Jenkins). *"Panuhúnuhú."* Fig. 154.

Head 2.75 in length; depth 2.44; eye 6.6 in head; snout 2.8; preorbital 5; interorbital 3; D. ix, 10; A. iii, 9; P. 14; scales 2–24–6.

Body moderately deep and compressed; dorsal and ventral outlines about equally convex; head short, scarcely longer than deep; mouth small, horizontal, on axis of body; teeth whitish, lower jaw included; 2 short but strong canines at posterior angle of upper jaw, a similar 1 on lower jaw; upper lip broad, covering whole of dental plate, lower lip covering about half of lower plate; eye small, entirely above axis of body; interorbital space broad, high.

Scales large and thin, a row of modified scales along base of dorsal and anal; scales on base of caudal very large and thin; 2 rows of scales on cheek, the upper with 7, the lower with 4 or 5 scales; a series of scales along margin of opercle and on subopercle. 4 scales along median line in front of

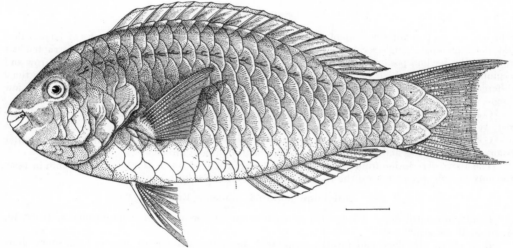

FIG. 154.—*Callyodon gilberti* (Jenkins); from the type.

dorsal; lateral line interrupted under the last dorsal rays, reappearing 2 rows farther down and continuing to caudal fin, the tubes with 1 to 3 or 4 short branches.

Dorsal spines short and flexible, not pungent, their length about 3.5 in head; soft dorsal higher, the last rays longest, about 2.4 in head; first anal spine obscure, the others soft and flexible; soft anal similar to soft dorsal but less high, the last rays 3 in head; caudal moderately lunate, the outer rays moderately produced, about one-half longer than middle rays, ventrals rather long, their length not reaching origin of anal by a distance equal to half distance from tip of snout to middle of pupil; pectorals broad, the free edge oblique, length of upper rays 1.3 in head.

Color in spirits, upper part of head and body greenish or bluish purple; side bluish green on the edges of the scales, underparts paler; upper lip with a broad blue-green line extending on side of head across lower border of orbit to middle of preopercle; 2 short blue-green lines on postocular region; snout above lip with a broad paler band extending back to eye; edge of lower lip bluish green, connecting at angle of mouth with the blue line from upper lip, back of this a broad pale purplish crossbar concolor with the cheek, this bounded posteriorly by a broad, bright-blue crossbar reaching to lower edge of postorbital; middle of lower jaw with a broad white crossbar, behind which is an oblong blue area; median line of throat and breast bright blue, this extending backward between ventrals to origin of anal; dorsal bright greenish blue at base and on border, these 2 lines separated by a much broader dusky whitish band; last ray of dorsal greenish to tip; anal same color as soft dorsal; caudal greenish blue on the outer rays, spotted with blue and green on basal two-thirds, the middle rays narrowly tipped with blue green with a narrow subterminal purplish black line, rest of middle rays whitish; ventrals pale blue on the inner rays, white on middle rays, and bright blue on the outer rays; pectoral bluish on base and anterior part, pale dusky otherwise.

Color description based upon a specimen (No. 05758), 9.5 inches long, which had been in formalin about 2 weeks. Older specimens are of course more faded and the colors correspondingly less distinct.

This is one of the most abundant species of the genus among the Hawaiian Islands. We have examined 13 specimens, all from Honolulu, 2 collected by the *Albatross* in 1891, 7 by Dr. Jenkins, and 4 by us. Length, 8 to 14 inches. It is doubtfully distinct from *C. bataviensis* (Steindachner).

284. Callyodon formosus (Cuvier & Valenciennes).

This species is thus described: Jaws smooth; a small posterior canine; head flat; nape a little elevated; eye placed high; lateral line simple.

The fish in a faded condition shows traces of green streaks under the throat, and near the eyes an area with scattered spots, apparently red. Dorsal and anal green, striped with an undulating band of blue. Caudal green with a violet line above and below which joins a vertical line of the same color at the end of each ray, thus limiting on the base and on the 2 outer rays of the caudal an area probably red in life. Pectorals bordered with blue, the ventrals apparently not.

Two specimens, 7 inches long, obtained at the Sandwich Islands by Eydoux & Souleyet.

To this Guichenot adds, from the same specimens, body rather elongate; posterior canine teeth present or absent; suborbital scales in 2 rows, the lower covering a large part of preopercular limb. Caudal truncate, the angles moderately produced. Color grayish blue, sides yellowish green spotted with reddish. Head with a large yellow spot crossed by a horizontal streak of green and bounded above by a stripe of the same color. Caudal bounded by a red stripe, otherwise green like the dorsal and anal, which are crossed by a blue stripe with wavy edges;. pectorals and ventrals yellow, edged with blue.

This species appear to be close to *Callyodon lauia* and *C. gilberti*. No specimens have been seen by us.

285. Callyodon lauia (Jordan & Evermann). *"Lauia."* Plate XLIII.

Head 2.8 in length; depth 2.7; eye 6.75 in head; snout 2.6; preorbital 4.8; interorbital 2.8; D. IX, 10; A. III, 9; P. 13 on one side, 14 on other; scales 2–25–6.

Body short, stout, and compressed; head heavy; snout rather short, bluntly rounded; dorsal and ventral outlines about equally arched, anterior profile slightly concave before the eyes; nape strongly convex; mouth small, nearly horizontal, in axis of body; upper jaw with 1 or 2 moderately strong backwardly directed canines; a similar but smaller canine sometimes present on lower jaw; cutting edge of upper jaw fitting outside that of lower; teeth white; eye small, entirely above axis of body; opercle with a broad short flap. Scales large, their surface with fine lines and granulations; nape and breast with large scales; cheek with 2 rows of large scales, about 7 in each; subopercle and lower limb of preopercle each with a row of scales; opercle with large scales; lateral line broken under last dorsal ray, reappearing 1 row lower down and continuing to caudal fin, the pores with 2 to 4 branches; a series of these oblong scales along base of dorsal and anal; base of caudal with 3 or 4 very long, thin scales. Dorsal spines soft and flexible, not pungent, the longest about 2.7 in head; soft portion of dorsal somewhat higher, especially posteriorly where the rays are about 2.4 in head; anal spines soft and flexible, the first obscure, the third about 4.3 in head; anal rays higher, the last but one longest, 3 in head; caudal deeply lunate, the 3 or 4 outer rays above and below produced, length of middle rays 2.3 in head, or 2 in outer rays; ventrals moderate, not reaching vent, 1.9 in head; pectoral broad, the free margin oblique, length of longest rays 1.3 in head.

Color in life, head brownish yellow before eyes, the jaws lighter yellow; cheek washed with brownish and blue, throat greenish; nuchal and opercular regions brownish orange; body salmon-color above, the belly lighter yellow, most of the scales with an edging of greenish blue; a deep blue line from nostril before and behind upper part of eye; upper lip deep blue, the streak forming an interrupted line before eye; lower jaw with 2 blue cross lines, 1 marginal; a dark-blue spot behind angle of mouth; deep blue blotches on interopercle; dorsal deep blue with a peculiar jagged stripe of light brownish yellow; anal with blue spots at base, then light yellow, then deep blue, then green with blue edge; caudal brownish yellow, with bright blue edgings and a median area of bright golden green; ventrals golden, trimmed with bright blue; pectoral golden with deep blue above and greenish blue on lower rays, a salmon streak across base with greenish blue behind it.

Another example (No. 03040, 10 inches long) was in life pale coppery rosy, darker on first 3 rows of scales; the center of each scale in the first 5 rows greenish blue; under parts pale rosy, with orange wash; head pale rosy, a small postocular blue spot, a short blue line forward from eye, and a second of same color on upper lip and across cheek to eye, where it has a slight break, then continues under eye as a greenish-blue bar; under lip with narrow blue edge; chin faded salmon, with a double blue crescent; space from chin to isthmus bright blue; an oblong bright blue spot on subopercle, behind which is a smaller irregular one bordered above by a broad greenish-blue space; dorsal greenish blue, with a broad submedian orange band, the lower greenish-blue band made up of large, scarcely connected, bluish spots, the upper half continuous with a narrow bright blue border; a small orange blotch on base of last dorsal ray; caudal pale rosy at base, then with a greenish bar, followed by a broad rosy bar, then by a broad terminal greenish-blue bar, dark blue in front, greenish in middle and pale blue on outer third; upper and lower edges of caudal blue, below which is a broad rosy orange stripe; anal greenish blue at base, then a broad orange stripe, the outer half greenish blue with narrow bright blue edge; pectoral orange anteriorly, pale bluish behind, the anterior border blue; ventrals orange, anterior edge and tip blue; iris pale orange.

Color in spirits, light dirty grayish white, lighter below; a narrow pea-green stripe on edge of upper lip, breaking up into irregular spots from angle of mouth to lower edge of orbit, a similar stripe from nostril to eye and slightly beyond upper posterior border of eye, these lines sometimes continuous and 'unbroken; lower jaw edged with green, a broader pea-green cross-stripe at anterior edge of branchiostegal opening; subopercles each with a broad green stripe; line of union of gill-membranes broadly green; dorsal with a series of large olive-green spots at base and a broad band of similar color on distal half, these separated by a paler band and cut by intrusions from it both above and below; dorsal fin with a very narrow paler border; and with a series of greenish spots at base, then a broad pale yellowish white line, bounded distally by an indefinite, wavy, black line shading off into the greenish of the distal half; last ray of anal dusky on its outer third; caudal greenish-olive at base and on produced outer rays, edges of fin above and below green; middle rays with a broad lunate area of pale green, scalloped proximally by dark green, separated from the lighter green base by a broad whitish interspace, the upper and lower edge also darker green; ventrals creamy white, the outer edge pale greenish; pectoral whitish, the upper edge dusky.

There is some variation in the width of the green markings on the head, sometimes the stripes on the lower part of the head being very broad.

This species is related to *C. gilberti*, from which it differs in the more strongly produced caudal lobes, in the narrower lines on the snout, the broader green lines on the throat, the absence of a green median line on the breast, and in the very different coloration of the fins. It is also near to *Callyodon formosus*, a species we have as yet failed to recognize. Besides the type obtained at Hilo, we have 4 examples from Honolulu collected by us and 1 by Dr. Wood.

286. Callyodon bataviensis (Bleeker). Fig. 155.

Two series of scales on the cheek, the lower preopercular limb being entirely naked; the lower series composed of 6 scales; upper lip broad; jaws rosy, the upper with 1 or 2 conical teeth at the angle, none at the lower; dorsal spines subequal in length; 14 pectoral rays; caudal rounded, with the angles produced.

Color green; lips red, blue anteriorly and green posteriorly; the green band of the upper lip and

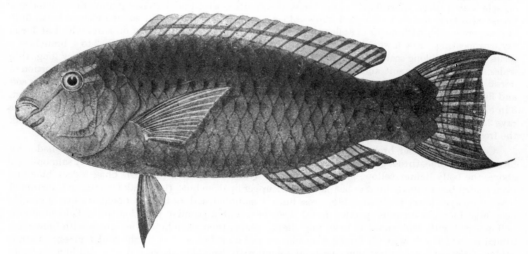

FIG. 155.—*Callyodon bataviensis* (Bleeker); after Bleeker.

the blue band of the lower lip passing behind the angle of the mouth into a green band running to the lower angle of the orbit; 2 short green streaks behind the orbit; dorsal fin red, with a blue margin, and with a green band along the middle; anal similarly colored; caudal rosy, with the upper and lower margins blue, and with 3 or 4 slightly curved blue cross-bands.

Known from the Hawaiian Islands only from Steindachner's record.

287. Callyodon erythrodon (Cuvier & Valenciennes). Fig. 156.

Two series of scales on the cheek, the lower preopercular limb being entirely naked; upper lip broad; jaws rosy, with a conical tooth at the angle (in adult state); dorsal spines subequal in length; 15 pectoral rays; caudal rounded.

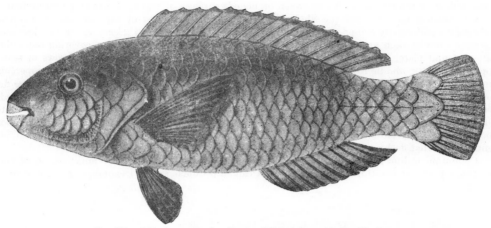

FIG. 156.—*Callyodon erythrodon* (Cuvier & Valenciennes); after Bleeker.

Color, violet-olive, vertical fins darker.

Laysan Island. Known from the Hawaiian Islands only from Steindachner's record. Common in Samoa.

Genus 171. PSEUDOSCARUS Bleeker.

This genus differs from *Scarus*, as here understood, chiefly in the deep green or blue color of its highly modified jaws and teeth. The species are mostly of large size and robust form. This genus is scarcely distinct from *Callyodon*.

288. Pseudoscarus troschelii Bleeker. Fig. 157.

Two series of scales on the cheek, the lower preopercular limb being naked; lips very narrow, covering only the base of the jaws; jaws green, the upper with pointed teeth at the angle; caudal slightly emarginate; 15 pectoral rays.

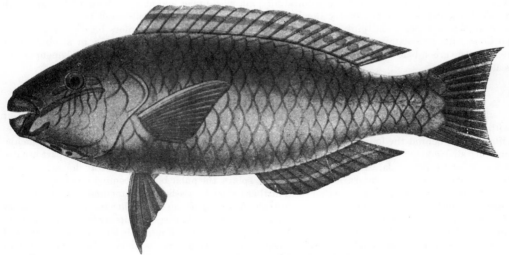

FIG. 157.—*Pseudoscarus troschelii* Bleeker; after Bleeker.

Body green, each scale with reddish margin; lips red; a short red band through the eye, and another from angle of mouth below eye toward the opercle; chin with red transverse and longitudinal streaks; dorsal red, edged with blue, and with a green band along the middle; anal yellowish, with a similar red band; caudal greenish.

289. Pseudoscarus jordani Jenkins. Plate XLIV and Fig. 158.

Head in length to base of caudal 2.7, in total length to middle margin of caudal 3.37; depth in length to base of caudal 2.64, in total length to middle margin of the caudal 3.3; dorsal IX, 10; anal III, 9; pectoral 14; scales 24; lateral line interrupted. In this specimen 2 scales at the interrupted portion out of the series bear tubes. They are located one over each first 2 scales in the series following interruption. Tubes much branched; surfaces of scales, except at posterior margin of each, much roughened over the whole body by striations composed of rows of minute tubercles; body robust and greatly compressed; an adipose lump over snout; teeth green, lower jaw included; a strong tooth at each angle of upper jaw; upper lip double only posteriorly, covering more than half of dental plate; lower lip covering less than half of dental plate; cheek with 3 rows of scales, upper of 7 scales, middle row of 7, the lower row of 2 scales, which extend on lower preopercular limb; a series of scales along entire margin of opercle; a series of 6 scales on median line before first dorsal spine; lobes of caudal fin much produced, being longer than body of the fin; height of caudal peduncle in head 2.54; pectoral 1.5 in head, its breadth being less than half of its own length; ventral 1.75 in head, not reaching vent by one-half its own length, inserted on a vertical from about middle of base of pectoral; dorsal spines flexible; membrane of first few spines of dorsal, anal, and ventral somewhat fleshy on outer margin.

Coloration in life: General color blue, the sides of body and head rosy or pink; region of body just below posterior two-thirds of dorsal and the caudal peduncle green; iris orange; margin of upper

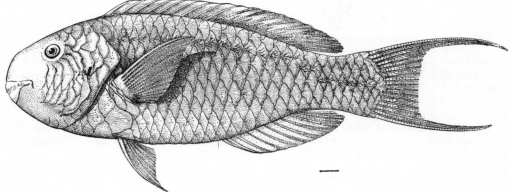

FIG. 158.—*Pseudoscarus jordani* Jenkins; from the type.

lip orange, above which it is bright blue; margin of lower lip blue, below which is an orange area; below this again bright blue which changes to a lighter blue; posterior to this a pink area; a pink wavy line from angle of mouth to eye; dorsal fin pink with upper and anterior border blue, and with a blue bar along each spine; anal yellowish with bright blue anterior outer and posterior margins; ventral blue anteriorly and pink posteriorly; caudal, upper and lower borders bright blue, interior portions with reticulations of pink and blue, colors almost wholly disappearing in alcohol; there remains the green below the posterior two-thirds of dorsal and on caudal peduncle as a pigment on the scales.

Suborder SQUAMIPINNES.—The Scaly-fins.

Body compressed, covered with small or minute ctenoid scales; lateral line unarmed, concurrent with the back; mouth small, with slender or brush-like teeth; opercles armed or not; nostrils double; gills 4, a slit behind the fourth; gill-membranes united to the broad scaly isthmus; pseudobranchiæ present; air-bladder present; dorsal fin long, the spines usually well developed, the soft part usually more or less scaly; caudal usually truncate or double concave; anal similar to soft dorsal; ventrals thoracic, sometimes rudimentary, sometimes with 2 spines, the pubic bone becoming progessively elongate; vertebræ 10+14=24, but sometimes still further reduced. Basis of cranium double, with a double muscular tube; post-temporal trifurcate or bifurcate in *Ephippidæ* and the other transitional forms, as in the scombroids and percoids; in other species firmly united to the skull, its structure showing the usual 3 forks, the space between them filled by bone, so that only a foramen is left; second, third, and fourth upper pharyngeals small, usually reduced to vertical transverse laminæ. Hypercoracoid with median foramen; pectoral with 4 short basal bones. This group comprises a large number of fishes, some of them showing analogies with the *Carangidæ* on the one hand and with certain percoid fishes on the other; the typical forms specialized in directions leading toward the *Plectognathi*. The limits of the group are uncertain, although there is no doubt about the relationship of any of the genera here treated. Perhaps several of the families currently recognized as scombroid belong here. The *Plectognathi* are certainly descended from the *Squamipinnes*. The close relation of *Balistes* to *Hepatus* admits of no doubt. This relationship is shown in the osteology, in the reduced post-temporal and coalesced bones of jaws, in the great development of the public bone, in the restriction of the gill-openings, and in the character of the scales, especially the armature of the tail. In a natural system the *Balistidæ* would follow the *Teuthididæ* and *Siganidæ*. The *Teuthididæ* and the *Balistidæ* are as nearly related to each other as the *Ephippidæ* are to the *Chætodontidæ*.

Family LXXI. ANTIGONIDÆ.—Boar-fishes.

Body compressed and elevated, covered with small, ctenoid scales; sides of head scaly; preorbital and preopercle more or less serrate or armed; opercle small; gills normal; gill-membranes separate, free from isthmus; top of head bony; premaxillaries very protractile, the posterior process very long; mouth moderate, lower jaw projecting; teeth very small; lateral line not extending on caudal; dorsal fin long, the stout spines separated from the soft rays by a deep notch; dorsal spines not graduated; anal fin with 3 spines separated by a notch from the soft rays, the first spine longest; soft part of anal as long as soft dorsal; ventrals i, 5, the spine strong, inserted below pectorals; caudal fin rounded, on a moderate peduncle; upper limb of post-temporal widened at its distal end, which affords a very firm attachment; lower limb short and thick; supraclavicle long and slender, its posterior edge sharply serrate, the serrations standing out above the surface of the skin; vertebræ in normal number, 10+13=23 (in Capros). Species few, arranged in 2 genera, living in rather deep water. Capros aper, the boarfish, superficially resembles the John Dory, Zeus faber, and is common on the coasts of southern Europe. This family, like the preceding, is of doubtful affinities. It is only remotely allied to the Zeidæ, and it has no relationship to the Carangidæ or other scomboroid forms. Antigonia bears much superficial resemblance to the Ephippidæ, a resemblance doubtless arising from real affinity, as is shown by the form and attachment of the post-temporal. An extinct genus, Proantigonia, is said to connect Antigonia with Capros.

Genus 172. ANTIGONIA Lowe.

Body very deep, the depth much greater than the length of body, which is excessively compressed and covered with moderate-sized, firm, rough ctenoid scales; profile from nape to dorsal very steep and nearly straight; surface of head above with rough bony striæ; preopercle and suborbital bones armed with slender antrorse spines; mouth small, its cleft nearly verticle; premaxillary with a very long process, extremely protractile, perhaps less so than in Capros; lower jaw projecting; upper jaw somewhat protractile; maxillary broad, scaly; small, very slender teeth on jaws in 1 row, none on palate; chin rough; preopercle with rough striæ, becoming antrorse spines below; cheek deep, covered with rough scales, opercle short, scaly; branchiostegals 6; gill-membranes separate, free from the isthmus; lateral line concurrent with the back; fin spines stiff and strong; dorsals united, the third spine stout and elevated, the sixth or last spine shortest, lower than the soft rays, the fin thus distinctly notched; soft dorsal and anal similar, long and low, none of the rays produced; anal spines 3, joined to the fin, the first longest; base of dorsal and anal with a sheath of small rough scales extending on the fin spines and slightly on the rays, not on the membranes; caudal peduncle short and deep, deeper than long; caudal short, squarely truncate; ventrals strong, of moderate length, at lowest point of ventral outline, well behind pectorals and directly below spinous dorsal, which is at highest point of dorsal outline; ventral spine large, roughened anteriorly; pectoral moderate, not falcate. Species few, in waters of moderate depth.

290. Antigonia steindachneri Jordan & Evermann. Plate XLV.

Head 3.35 in length; depth equal to length; eye 3 in head; snout 3.2; maxillary 4.2; interorbital 3.3; D. viii, 36; A. iii, 33; scales 16–71–40.

Body very deep, compressed; back elevated, trenchant; abdomen deep, trenchant; upper profile concave in front of eye above to occipital process, then convave to spinous dorsal; snout short, blunt, rounded; mouth small, nearly vertical; jaws small, lower protruding; teeth small, pointed, uniserial; eye large, superior, nearly in middle of length of head; preorbital and interopercle spiny along margins; anterior nostril with valve, the posterior larger, circular; gill-opening large, gillrakers small; pseudobranchiæ and gill-laminæ large; dorsal spines sharp, third longest, 1.5 in head, others graduated to last, which is about 2 in snout; anterior dorsal rays longest, 3.5 in head; first anal spine longest, 2.8, others graduated to last; caudal small, truncate, 1.7; pectoral 1.2, upper rays longest, and posterior margin straight; ventrals 1.6, spine very large, strong, front margin asperous, and nearly as long as fin; caudal peduncle compressed, its depth 2.7; scales small, roughly ctenoid; head roughened, especially above; basal scales of soft dorsal and anal rough; lateral line arched, nearly conforming with upper profile, running along middle of side of caudal peduncle.

Color in life (No. 03492) bright light salmon-pink, nape, back of head, and down to ventrals deeper red, behind the bar from dorsal to ventral a pale shade; fins pale crimson, caudal paler with darker red tip; iris red.

Color in alcohol very pale brown, almost uniform.

Described from an example (No. 03701), 7.6 inches long, from Kailua. We have 2 other examples (Nos. 03492 and 03702), each about 6.8 inches long, taken by us at Hilo. The species is taken with hook and line occasionally in rather deep water off Hawaii; otherwise known from Japan only.

Family LXXII. ZEIDÆ.—The John Dories.

Body short, deep, much compressed and elevated, naked or covered with minute smooth scales, or with bony protuberances. Mouth large, terminal, the upper jaw protractile. Teeth small, in narrow bands or single series on the jaws and vomer and sometimes on the palatines. Eyes lateral, placed high; opercle much reduced; some of the bones of head usually with spines; preopercle not serrate; post-temporal very firmly attached to the skull; lower limb adnate for its whole length, the distal end only of upper limb attached. The supra-clavicle short and triangular, bearing a short spine near its anterior angle, its posterior edge divided into 3 spines, 2 or 3 of which stand out above the surface of the skin. Ventral edge often serrate, with strong bony plates; lateral line well developed, concurrent with the back; branchiostegals 7 or 8; gill-openings wide, the membranes little united, free from the isthmus; pseudobranchiæ large; air bladder large; gillrakers usually short; gills 4, a slit behind the fourth; dorsal fin emarginate or divided, the anterior part with spines, which are often strong, the posterior part longer, its highest rays behind the middle; soft anal entirely similar to soft dorsal, usually preceded by 1 to 4 spines, which are not graduated and which often form a separate fin; ventral fins thoracic, well developed, their rays usually I, 6 to I, 8; pectorals small; caudal fin rounded, on a moderate peduncle. Lateral line obscure, unarmed. Pyloric cæca exceedingly numerous. Vertebræ about 32 (*Zeus*). Genera 8; species about 15; fishes of singular appearance, inhabiting warm seas, often at considerable depth. The species undergo great changes in the course of development.

The single Hawaiian genus and species is fully described in Section II.

Family LXXIII. CHÆTODONTIDÆ.—Butterfly-Fishes.

Body strongly compressed, elevated, suborbicular in outline, covered with moderate-sized or small scales, which are finely ciliated or nearly smooth; lateral line present, concurrent with the back, not extending on the caudal fin; mouth small, protractile, terminal; maxillary very short, irregular in form, divided in 2 by a longitudinal suture; upper part of skull solid, occipital crest strong; post-temporal firmly joined to the skull, its form really trifurcate, though appearing simple, the spaces between the forks filled in by bone so that only a foramen is left; last bone of the suborbital ring firmly joined to the preopercle; teeth brush-like or setiform, often extremely long, in narrow bands on the jaws; no teeth on vomer or palatines; no canines, molars or incisors; eyes lateral, of moderate size; branchiostegals 6 or 7; pseudobranchiæ very large; air-bladder present; gill-membranes more or less attached to the isthmus; gillrakers very small; dorsal fin single, continuous, its rays sometimes filamentous, its soft part as well as the soft part of anal densely covered with small scales; anal similar to soft dorsal with 3 or 4 spines; ventrals thoracic, I, 5; caudal usually truncate; vertebræ 10+14=24, the anterior abbreviated; insertion of ribs inferior; post-temporal usually reduced, and not bifurcate.

Carnivorous fishes of the tropical seas, noted for their bright colors and great activity. Their excessive quickness of sense and motion enables them to maintain themselves in the struggle for existence in the close competition of the coral reefs, notwithstanding their bright colors. The young are very different from the adult and pass through a stage termed *Tholichthys*, in which the membranes are greatly developed, forming collars and sheaths about the head and neck.

Genus 173. FORCIPIGER Jordan & McGregor.

This genus differs from *Prognathodes* Gill in having smaller scales, about 75 in a lateral series instead of 40. *Chelmo* Cuvier is also closely related, having the same forceps-like mouth; but in the latter genus the spinous dorsal is much less developed, containing about 9 spines.

291. Forcipiger longirostris (Broussonet). Plate XLVI.

Head with beak 2.2, without beak 2.8; depth 2.2 with beak, 1.75 without beak; beak 1.6 in rest of head; eye 3.75; mouth 7; interorbital 4.75; D. XII, 25; A. III, 18; scales 12–78–30.

Body very deep, compressed, back trenchant; head low, upper profile concave; snout nearly horizontal, jaws produced in a long pointed beak, mouth small, at extremity; teeth minute, in villiform bands in jaws; eye nearly in middle of length of head without beak; anterior nostril in short fleshy tube, posterior a short oblique slit before eye; fourth spine 1.5 in head without beak; anal spines graduated to last, which is longest, strong, 1.35; caudal small, slightly emarginate, its upper ray slightly produced; pectoral long, pointed, upper rays much longer than others; ventrals long, sharply pointed, spine 1.6; caudal peduncle small, compressed, its least depth 3.7; scales ctenoid; lateral line strongly arched, not concurrent with profile of back. Described from an example (No. 04537) 7 inches long from Honolulu.

Color in life of a specimen (field No. 327) collected by Jordan & Kellogg at Apia in 1902, brilliant yellow, deeper and orange-shaded behind, a black triangle on head, livid white below; ventrals and pectorals yellow; caudal colorless: a large jet-black spot on anal.

Color in alcohol, pale brown or whitish; head above, back in front of spinous dorsal, interorbital space, and opercles above, deep brown; snout, beak above, and band on each side to front of eye, blackish-brown; posterior margin of soft dorsal and anal with narrow grayish line; anal with a squarish black spot on distal part of last rays; last half of soft dorsal and anal with a narrow submarginal black line; caudal grayish, the pectoral orange; under parts of head and breast whitish.

We have 9 specimens from Honolulu, (4 collected by Doctor Jenkins, 1 by the *Albatross* in 1896, and 4 by us), ranging in length from 5.2 to 6.75 inches. The *Albatross* also obtained specimens at Honolulu in 1902.

This is the first species of fish ever described from the Hawaiian Islands.

Genus 174. CHÆTODON (Artedi) Linnæus.

Body short, deep, very strongly compressed, especially above and behind; head small, compressed, almost everywhere scaly; mouth very small, terminal, the jaws provided with long, slender, flexible, bristle-like teeth; vomer sometimes with teeth; preopercle entire or nearly so, without spine; dorsal fin single, continuous, not notched, the spinous part longer than the soft part, of 12 or 13 spines, the spines not graduated, some of the middle ones being longer than the last; last rays of soft dorsal usually rapidly shortened, some of them occasionally filamentous; caudal peduncle short, the caudal fin fan-shaped; anal similar to soft dorsal, with 3 strong spines; body covered with rather large ctenoid scales, somewhat irregular in their arrangement; lateral line curved, high, parallel with the back; gill-openings rather narrow, the membranes narrowly joined to the isthmus; branchiostegals 6. A very large genus of singular and beautiful fishes, abounding in the tropical seas, especially about volcanic rocks and coral reefs; body usually crossed by transverse black bars; all very active fishes, feeding on small animals.

292. Chætodon setifer Bloch. Plate XLVII.

Head 3.1 in length; depth 1.75; eye 4 in head; snout 2.5; mouth 7.25; maxillary 3.9; interorbital 4; D. xiii, 24; A. iii, 21; scales 7–40–11.

Body very deep, compressed; back elevated, very trenchant; head deep; snout short, nearly horizontal; mouth very small; jaws produced, rather pointed, equal; lips thin, fleshy; teeth broad, brush-like in bands in jaws; eye superior, midway in head; interorbital width broad, convex, nostrils close together, with raised fleshy edge, posterior an oblique slit in front of eye; dorsal spines graduated to last, which is longest, 2 in head; fifth and sixth dorsal rays longest, produced in a point; third anal spine longest, 1.5; median anal rays longest, ninth, 1.25; caudal small, truncate; pectoral small, 1.3; ventral pointed, 1.3; spine strong, 1.9; caudal peduncle compressed, its least depth 2.9; scales very large on middle of side; thin, finely ctenoid; scales on vertical fins, head, and belly, small, very small on outer portions of vertical fins; series of scales on side disposed in very oblique series; lateral line very strongly arched, not continued behind base of last dorsal rays.

Color in life (field No. 03435), general color in front and below, including paired fins, light violet, lighter on snout and below; dorsal, excepting first 2 spines and membranes, which are violet, caudal, anal, and upper posterior part of side, chrome yellow; lips pinkish; a broad black ocular bar becoming narrower above, narrowly edged on each side with white, extending from interopercle almost to origin of dorsal; about 6 narrow yellow lines across interorbital area; a series of 8 narrow dark bars running forward and downward from base of dorsal, the first 5 extending down to humeral region, the last 3 meeting at right angles, the last 3 bars of a similar series of 12 bars on lower part of body, the first 9 bars of which meet the fifth bar of upper series about at right angles; soft dorsal edged with black, an oval black spot on its center; lower edge of anal with a narrow black stripe outside of which the edge is light yellow; caudal broadly tipped with light violet, two narrow brownish bars across its center.

Color in alcohol, very pale or whitish, greater portion of side pale olive gray; about 8 dark-gray lines running obliquely up from head to dorsal, and others posteriorly above lateral line; side with about 11 oblique dark-gray lines running to anal; a broad dark-brown band beginning on nape before dorsal and running down to eye, continued below wider and blackish, with narrow whitish border in front; margin of dorsal to angle on soft fin, narrowly blackish; longest dorsal rays with black spot on distal portion; margin of soft anal with narrow black line running parallel with lower margin; margin of caudal grayish with a narrow dark-gray submarginal line; pectoral and ventrals grayish.

Described from an example (No. 04562) 6.25 inches long, from Honolulu.

We have 28 specimens, 4 to 8.2 inches long, from Honolulu, where the fish is common. Others were secured at that place by the *Albatross*. The species occurs also at Johnston Island and Samoa.

293. Chætodon lineolatus Cuvier & Valenciennes. Fig. 159.

Head 3.25 in length; depth 1.5; eye 4.5 in head; snout 2.25; maxillary 3.5; interorbital 3.25; D. xii, 26; A. iii, 22; scales 7–36–14.

Body deep, compressed, back elevated; head very deep, upper profile very concave, so that occiput is obliquely vertical; snout rather long, nearly horizontal; jaws produced, equal; mouth small, nearly horizontal; thirteenth anal ray longest, 1.5; caudal broad, margin slightly rounded; caudal peduncle compressed, its least depth 2.8; pectoral 1.3; ventrals pointed, 1.5; scales very large on side, smaller on head, breast, at bases of soft dorsal and anal, and on side of caudal peduncle; scales on vertical fins very small; series of scales very oblique above lateral line in front, becoming slightly oblique on sides; teeth in rather broad brush-like bands in jaws; eye small, posterior; edge of preopercle rough below; interorbital space broad, convex; nostrils small, close together, anterior with elevated fleshy rim and flap, posterior a nearly horizontal slit; dorsal spines graduated to last, which is longest, 1.8 in head; dorsal rays longest just behind middle, twelfth 1.35; third anal spine longest; lateral line running up high toward soft dorsal but not continued behind spinous dorsal.

Color in alcohol very pale brown, upper surface tinged with very pale olive; side above with narrow blackish vertical lines, one along the margin of each series of scales; head with a broad black band down from occiput over side of head above, below eye, including preopercle, and across interopercle; a round brown spot on forehead; base of soft dorsal with broad blackish band running down across caudal peduncle in front, and on basal portion of anal posteriorly; soft dorsal with a median brown line longitudinally; caudal with gray margin bounded in front with narrow blackish submarginal line; pectoral and ventral whitish.

Described from an example (No. 04535) taken at Honolulu.

We have examined only 3 Hawaiian specimens, 4.75 to 9.2 inches long, all from Honolulu, where the species is not very common, and many specimens from Samoa. The species is of wide distribution in the Pacific and Indian oceans.

Fig. 159.—*Chætodon lineolatus* Cuvier & Valenciennes; after Günther.

294. Chætodon lunula (Lacépède). "*Kikakápu.*" Plate LIV and Fig. 160.

Head 3 in length; depth 1.6; eye 4 in head; snout 3.25; maxillary 3.9; interorbital 3.4; D. xii, 24; A. iii, 19; scales 9–36–18.

Body very deep, compressed, back elevated; head deep; upper profile from interorbital space obliquely straight; jaws produced, subequal; mouth small; teeth fine, brushlike in jaws; eye median in length of head; margin of preopercle very finely serrate; interorbital space broad, convex; anterior nostril with thin fleshy rim and flap; posterior nostril a short oblique slit; anterior dorsal spines strong, enlarged, posterior slender, equal from middle posteriorly, last 1.8 in head; tenth dorsal ray 1.4; third anal spine longest, 1.7; eleventh dorsal ray 1.5; pectoral 1.2, rather broad; ventral pointed, 1.25; ventral spine 1.65; scales large on middle of side, those on vertical fins becoming very small; scales in slightly oblique series on side; ventrals with scaly flap at base; caudal broad, deep, margin slightly rounded; least depth of caudal peduncle 3 in head; lateral line arched, not continued beyond base of soft dorsal.

Described from an example (No. 04540) taken at Honolulu.

Color in life (No. 03036) yellowish olive, crossed by a series of brownish-orange lines from pectoral region backward and upward; snout pale orange; a broad black saddle over nape and downward over eye to upper edge of subopercle, narrowing at lower end, and bordered anteriorly by a narrow white line; following this is a broad white saddle extending down over humeral region, opercle and edge of shoulder-girdle to lower part of opercular openings; a black blotch at origin of dorsal separated from the white saddle by orange yellow; beneath this a light brown or olive space bounded below by a broad yellow line extending from humeral region upward and backward to base of seventh dorsal spine; below this a broad triangular black space with its base at shoulder-girdle and extending backward and upward to base of sixth to eighth dorsal spine, bounded below or behind by a narrow yellow line; a curved yellow line beginning on dorsal at base of seventh spine, following base of dorsal to caudal peduncle, which it crosses, then widening out upon base of anal; dorsal dusky olive, a broad black band parallel with the yellow, widening on soft portion and connecting with black caudal peduncle; above this a broad pale orange stripe, bounded on soft dorsal by white; edge of dorsal

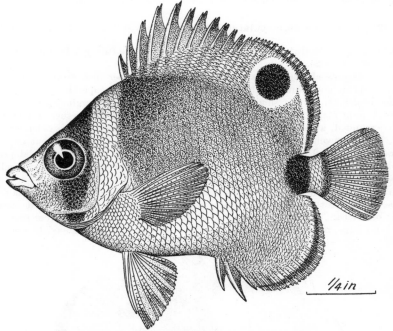

FIG. 160.—*Chætodon lunula* (Lacépède); from the young.

membranes black, forming a broad black border on soft dorsal; caudal yellow at base, a narrow black bar at middle, beyond which the fin is white; anal yellowish orange, bordered by brownish, and with a narrow dark orange band near margin; pectoral pale; ventrals pale orange, slightly dusky at tips; iris pale bluish.

Another example (No. 03313) has upper part of side rich greenish olive, crossed by about 9 or 10 reddish-brown bars; lower part of side rich lemon-yellow crossed by about 5 reddish-orange bars, the 2 under pectoral breaking up into reddish-orange spots; tip of snout pale rosy, rest of snout pale yellow; a broad black saddle over head and through eye to upper edge of subopercle, about one-half broader than orbit; back of this a broad white saddle of about same width extending to near lower part of opercle and enveloping part of shoulder-girdle; back of this a yellowish-green space, then a black saddle at anterior base of dorsal extending along base of dorsal to near fifth spine; a large oblong black spot beginning on humeral region and curving upward and backward to base of sixth and seventh spines, this bounded by rather broad yellow borders; belly pale yellow; a jet-black spot on caudal peduncle; dorsal pale yellow at base, tips of spines and enveloping membranes black; soft dorsal with a pale orange band at base, next a narrow greenish olive one, then a broader yellow one, a very broad orange one broadening behind, a narrow yellow one, and finally a narrow black border; basal half of anal fin pale yellow, a median bar of reddish-orange spots, next a broad yellow bar, a narrow black bar, then tip broadly white; pectoral and ventrals pale yellow; iris black.

Color in life of a specimen (field No. 261) obtained by Jordan and Kellogg at Apia in 1902, deep golden, a little orange tinged and more dusky on back; chin gray; patch behind ocular stripe clear gray; oblique black band bordered before and behind by clear golden brown, a blackish blotch at first dorsal spine with golden brown behind it; spot on caudal peduncle and stripe on dorsal golden, a brown shade across dorsal and anal, besides black tips and dark-brown bands; ventral golden with some dusky; pectoral and edge of caudal colorless.

Color in alcohol, very pale brown, back above with a very pale olivaceous tinge; a blackish brown band across interorbital space, including eye, running behind down on preopercle, not continued below, narrowly bordered in front below eye with white; adjoining interorbital band, continued on side of head and down on opercle, a broad white band; a broad blackish-brown band from opercle up to middle of spinous dorsal broadly edged with white; a blackish-brown blotch on back at base of first 5 dorsal spines, bordered below with whitish; side with oblique golden olive bands following courses of scales; marginal portion of spinous and soft dorsal broadly blackish, not continued on posterior rays; a dusky streak running along basal portion of soft dorsal broadens out on posterior rays and forms a blackish blotch at front of caudal peduncle, bordered in front and behind with whitish; margin of caudal whitish, bordered in front with a broad blackish bar; pectoral grayish.

We have examined 29 examples from Honolulu (9 collected by Jenkins), where the species is common in the markets, 4 from Kailua, 5 from Hilo, and 10 from Cocoanut Island at Hilo. They are from less than an inch to 7.2 inches long. Specimens were obtained by the *Albatross* at Honolulu and Waialua Bay, Oahu; Hilo and Puako Bay, Hawaii; common at Samoa.

295. Chætodon unimaculatus Bloch. "*Kikakápu.*" Plate L and Fig. 161

Head 3.4 in length; depth 1.7; eye 3.35 in head; snout 3; maxillary 3.35; interorbital 3; D. XIII, 23; A. III, 20; scales 9–45–25.

Body deep, compressed, back elevated; head very short, upper profile obliquely concave; snout short, blunt, rounded; jaws equal, slightly produced; mouth small, gape short; teeth coarse, brush-like, in rather broad bands; eye small, midway in length of head; marginal portion of preopercle finely serrate; interorbital space broad, slightly convex; nostrils close together, anterior with fleshy flap, posterior rounded; anterior dorsal spines strong, enlarged, posterior spines slender, longest, and about equal, last 1.5; seventh dorsal ray 1.3; second and third anal spines about equal, third 1.7; sixth anal ray 1.4; pectoral 1.1, pointed; ventral pointed, 1.2, spine sharp 1.6; caudal peduncle compressed, its least depth 2.8; scales large on front of side above, otherwise small, very small on ventral fins, arranged in nearly horizontal series.

Color in life of a specimen (field No. 388) obtained by Jordan and Kellogg at Apia in 1902, light golden above, gray beneath, shoulders and front of sides with angled (>>>-shaped) vertical bars of deep yellow; ocular band very broad from front of dorsal, meeting its fellow across breast; snout and forehead gray; a large, round black spot on middle of side of back surrounded by gray; dorsal and

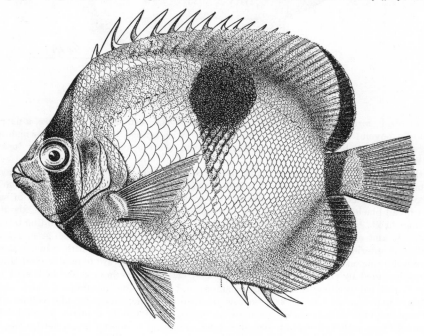

Fig. 161.—*Chætodon unimaculatus* Bloch. Type of *C. sphenospilus* Jenkins.

anal clear light yellow, each with a narrow subterminal black bar posteriorly, the edge whitish; caudal peduncle with a similar black bar at base, followed by a white or whitish bar; a pale yellowish bar at base of caudal rays; caudal fin whitish with dusky dots; ventral yellow.

Color in alcohol, pale brown; a blackish band from occiput down through eye across side of breast; posterior margin of soft dorsal and anal broadly blackish above, edge very narrowly grayish; back above with large blackish blotch fading above and below in grayish; a dark or blackish band on front of caudal peduncle; 7 or 8 oblique dusky streaks along margin of large scales on front of side above; snout grayish above.

The above general description is based chiefly upon a specimen from Honolulu, from which place we have 17 examples, the species being rather common about the reefs. The younger examples show the wedge-shaped form of the lateral spot which suggested the name *sphenospilus*, but these intergrade fully with the ordinary form both in Hawaii and Samoa.

296. Chætodon punctatofasciatus Cuvier & Valenciennes. Fig. 162.

Head 3.5 in length; depth 1.5; eye 3.25 in head; snout 3; maxillary 5; interorbital 3.6; D. XIII, 25; A. III, 18; scales 7–50–18.

Body oblong, deep, compressed, back elevated; head deep, compressed, bluntly pointed; upper profile oblique undulate from snout to origin of dorsal; jaws small, bluntly produced, snout a little longer than eye, blunt, rounded above; mouth small; teeth thin, in rather narrow brush-like bands in jaws; eye small, high, anterior; nostrils close together, circular, anterior with elevated fleshy rim, posterior larger; interorbital space rather narrow, convex; dorsal spines enlarged at first, strong,

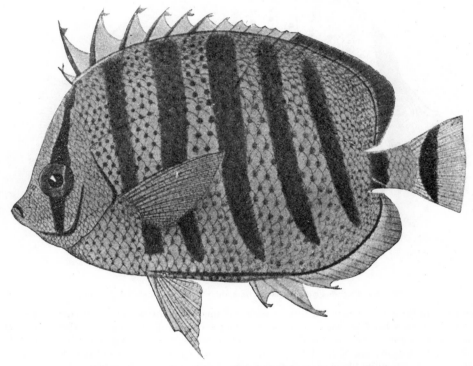

FIG. 162.—*Chætodon punctatofasciatus* Cuvier & Valenciennes; after Günther.

posterior slender; eighteenth dorsal ray 1.7 in head; second and third anal spines longest, of about equal length, 1.6; pectoral rather long, a little longer than head; ventrals equal to pectorals; depth of caudal peduncle about 3; scales moderately large on middle of side, small on head and caudal peduncle, becoming very small on vertical fins; lateral line arched, running down to below base of last dorsal ray.

Color in alcohol, very pale brown tinged with dull brassy olivaceous; a dark brown spot above occiput before spinous dorsal; below this a brown band running down through eye to edge of preopercle; side with 7 nearly vertical olivaceous bands, last 2 rather indistinct; each scale with a dusky spot, becoming smaller as the scales become smaller toward the soft dorsal and anal, those of these fins being small and crowded; outer portion of dorsal with 2 submarginal longitudinal lines, the outer very pale, the 2 close together; anal with a blackish brown submarginal longitudinal line; caudal peduncle with a deep brown band; base of caudal dull orange-brown; a median black lunate cross bar on caudal; pectoral and ventrals pale.

Described from an example 3.9 inches long taken at Honolulu by the Fur Seal Commission. Another example 3.75 inches long was collected by Dr. Jenkins, and others, by the *Albatross* in 1902. The species was described by Garrett from the Hawaiian Islands.

297. Chætodon miliaris Quoy & Gaimard. Plate XLVIII and Fig. 163.

Head 3.6 in length; depth 1.8; eye 3.4 in head; snout 2.8; maxillary 4.5; interorbital 3.8; D. XIII, 23; A. III, 20; scales 6–50–20.

Body deep, compressed, back elevated; head deep, upper profile very slightly convex above eye to origin of dorsal; mouth small, maxillary reaching below anterior nostril; interorbital space broad, convex; teeth in broad bands, brush-like; eye midway in head, rather high; margin of preopercle entire; nostrils close together, first round, rim elevated and with fleshy flap; posterior nostril elongate; anterior dorsal spines strong, enlarged, sixth 1.5 in head; eleventh dorsal ray 1.6; third anal spine 1.6; third anal ray 1.2, elongate; caudal broad, margin obliquely straight, upper rays longer; pectoral 1.2; ventral 1.2, pointed; ventral spine 1.6; depth of caudal peduncle 3; scales rather large on middle of side, those on vertical fins, head and breast, small; lateral line running to below base of posterior dorsal rays.

Color in life (No. 03035), pale cadmium-yellow, richest posteriorly, and on soft dorsal and anal about a dozen series of small round pale blue spots extending upward and a little backward across

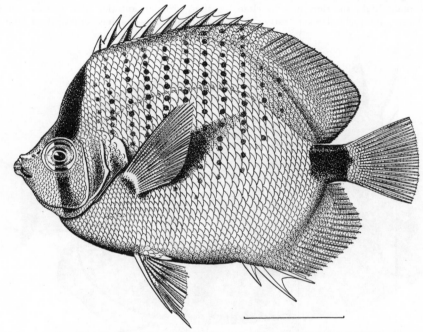

FIG. 163.—*Chætodon miliaris* Quoy & Gaimard. Type of *C. mantelliger* Jenkins.

upper two-thirds of body; between these a series of smaller yellow spots a little darker than body color; a broad black bar from edge of subopercle under eye vertically through eye, thence broadening upward and backward to near origin of dorsal, where it meets its fellow, a pale bluish border behind; interocular area yellow; rest of head bluish gray; a jet-black ring covering entire caudal peduncle; 3 or 4 irregular bluish-white blotches on posterior part of side; sheathing membrane of dorsal and anal cadmium-yellow, the spines white; soft dorsal and anal yellow, then white, narrowly edged with black; caudal pale yellow, outer part white; pectoral pale; ventrals pale yellow, outer parts white; iris dull silvery, crossed by a vertical black line.

Color in alcohol, pale brown or whitish; a deep brown broad band from before spinous dorsal to eye, margined posteriorly with whitish, continued below eye down on interopercle, but much narrower; caudal peduncle blackish brown, last rays of dorsal broadly blackish-brown; margin of soft dorsal and anal narrowly brownish; side with 10 nearly vertical series of large deep brown round spots a little smaller than pupil of eye and with many smaller spots of more or less equal size distributed in oblique rows above, becoming straight on side below; fins all pale.

Described chiefly from example No. 04556, from Honolulu.

Our collection contains 37 excellent specimens from Honolulu, where it is common about the coral reefs, and 4 from Hilo, ranging in length from 1.5 to 6.25 inches. Of those from Honolulu 1 was collected by Jordan and Snyder in 1900 and 8 by Doctor Jenkins.

298. Chætodon trifasciatus Mungo Park. Plate LII.

Head 3.75 in length; depth 1.75; eye 3.5 in head; snout 3.25; maxillary 4; interorbital 3; D. XIII, 22; A. III, 20; scales 7–40–14.

Body deep, rather elongate, compressed; back trenchant; head very deep, profile steep above; snout short, blunt, rounded; mouth small, horizontal; teeth brush-like, in rather narrow bands; eye high, anterior; interorbital space broad, convex; nostrils close together in front of eye; sixth and seventh dorsal spines longest, former 1.6 in head; fourteenth dorsal ray longest, 1.75; third anal spine longest, 1.6; anal rays long, thirteenth ray 1.7; caudal small, margin rounded; pectoral a trifle less than length of head; ventral 1.2; caudal peduncle compressed, its least depth 2.8.

Color in life of a specimen (field No. 260), taken by Jordan and Kellogg at Apia in 1902, creamy orange, grayer above, with many streaks of violet-blue; head and jaws blackish, forehead brown, a golden streak, then the ocular band, then a whitish streak, yellow below, then brownish, whitish, and purplish black; spinous dorsal light yellow, with a purplish line below; soft dorsal yellow, black, yellow, violet, gray, purplish, violet-gray, the outside creamy brown; caudal peduncle slaty, then whitish, golden, black, golden, and transparent; anal with a golden stripe at base, then black, becoming rich brown on spines, then golden, then dark brown, then golden; breast golden, with a black blotch; ventrals golden; pectoral pale yellow.

Color in alcohol, pale brown above, lower surface whitish; side with longitudinal narrow brown bands extending up on spinous dorsal, where they are very narrow and close together; snout and lower jaw blackish brown, fading to a lighter brown on interorbital space; a blackish-brown band from occiput to eye, bordered narrowly with white continued through eye and below to front of throat; a white vertical band from below nostrils separating brown of snout and band below eye; broad white vertical band behind dark band below eye; a narrow dark line from below anterior dorsal spine obliquely down and close behind eye; soft dorsal with a black band beginning on upper part of first dorsal rays, continued down along base of soft dorsal and upper part of caudal peduncle, at first narrow then widening below; two narrow dusky lines close together on upper part of soft dorsal running down farther apart and at equal distance; soft dorsal, anal, and caudal grayish, a median vertical blackish band on caudal; anal with a long blackish longitudinal band edged with pale yellow broadening posteriorly, running along basal portion at first, then extending out on median part of soft anal posteriorly; margin of anal narrowly light gray below, above this a broad area of dark gray, edges above and below deeper; pectoral and ventrals pale or whitish. Described chiefly from example No. 04549, taken at Honolulu.

The collection contains but 5 specimens, 4.75 to 6 inches long, all from Honolulu. Of these, 1 was obtained by the *Albatross* in 1896, and 2 were collected by Doctor Jenkins. The species is widely distributed throughout Polynesia, but is rare about the coral reefs at Honolulu.

299. Chætodon ornatissimus Solander. "*Kikakápu.*" Plate LIII.

Head 3.3 in length; depth 1.4; eye 4 in head; snout 3; maxillary 3.5; interorbital 3.1; D. xxii, 28; A. iii, 23; scales 12–58–25.

Body very deep, compressed; head deep, upper profile from snout to origin of dorsal almost straight; snout very short, bluntly rounded; mouth small; terminal jaws a little produced; lips rather thin, broad; teeth in broad brush-like bands; eye high, a little anterior; preopercle very finely serrate; interorbital space broad, convex; nostrils close together, anterior with rim elevated, with fleshy flap, posterior circular; dorsal spines graduated to last, which is 1.6 in head; seventeenth dorsal ray 1.2; fourteenth anal ray 1.3, longest; caudal with slightly rounded margin, 1.2; pectoral short, 1.1; ventrals inserted a little before pectoral, 1.2; ventral spine 1.35 in length of fin; depth of caudal peduncle 2.4; scales ctenoid, in nearly horizontal series becoming very small on vertical fins; lateral line strongly arched, not continuous beyond base of last dorsal rays.

Described from example No. 04560, from Honolulu.

Color in life of a specimen (field No. 383), obtained by Jordan and Kellogg at Apia in 1902, gray; head and belly golden; 6 black stripes across head, the interspaces yellow; 3 orange bars before pectoral; 6 rich orange-brown oblique stripes upward and backward; a seventh stripe on anal dark brown, this edged with a narrow black streak, then clear yellow; dorsal black, with a yellow and 2 black stripes; caudal with 2 black stripes and a dull yellowish one, its base gray; ventral golden; pectoral dull orange; breast anteriorly black.

Color of a nearly fresh example white; head and belly light yellow; side with 7 oblique bands of orange-brown; 6 bands and blotches on head black; dorsal white with 2 black stripes and a yellowish one; anal with 2 black stripes and a yellow one; caudal white with 2 black stripes; pectorals yellowish; ventrals golden.

Color in alcohol, pale brown ground-color tinged with yellow; side with 6 rather broad oblique creamy brown bands with gray edges; head with blackish vertical bands, 2 of which are broad, 1 running from snout down on side of lower jaw, the other from above occiput down to eye, continued below and down to breast; lower lip broadly blackish; 2 narrow blackish vertical lines behind eye, first continued from behind eye up along margin of dorsal to last dorsal rays; a broad band of gray-brown between eyes; spaces between black bands and lines on head yellowish; margins of soft dorsal and anal narrowly blackish; anal with a broad black marginal band parallel with margin of fin; caudal with margin white, a blackish terminal band; a black median cross band; pectoral and ventrals pale, former with white bar across base.

The collection contains 6 specimens obtained by ourselves, 2 by the Fur Seal Commission and 2 by Doctor Jenkins, all from Honolulu, where the species is frequently taken among the coral reefs. The length varies from 4.5 to 7.25 inches. Other specimens were obtained at Honolulu by the *Albatross*.

300. Chætodon quadrimaculatus Gray. Plate XLIX.

Head 3.5 in length; depth 1.6; eye 3.5 in head; snout 2.9; maxillary 4.4; interorbital 3.4; D. xiv, 24; A. iii, 18; scales 8–42–20.

Body deep, compressed, back elevated; head very deep, upper profile oblique; snout long, oblique; jaws produced, blunt, equal; mouth small, nearly horizontal; teeth brush-like, in broad bands in jaws; eye small, anterior; marginal portion of preopercle crenulate below; interorbital space broad, convex; nostrils small, close together, circular, anterior with small fleshy flap; anterior dorsal spines strong, somewhat enlarged, fourth longest, 1.5 in head; second anal spine longest, 1.4; thirteenth anal ray longest, 1.5; caudal broad, slightly rounded; pectoral pointed, a little longer than head; ventrals sharply pointed, 1.1; spine 1.6; scales large on side, small on head, caudal peduncle, and chest, and becoming very small on vertical fins; scales in oblique series at first above lateral line, in horizontal series below, lateral line running to caudal peduncle above at base of last dorsal rays. Described from example No. 04544, taken at Honolulu.

Color in life (field No. 03406): Ground-color of lower half of body, head, spinous dorsal and pectoral, citron-yellow; of caudal, anal, and ventrals chrome-yellow; interorbital orange; a chrome-yellow ocular bar deepening into orange above, edged on each side by a narrow black line, outside of which is a narrow light blue line extending from lower margin of interopercle to origin of dorsal; upper half of body, scaly sheath of dorsal, and caudal peduncle sooty gray, excepting 2 elongate white spots on lateral line, one below center of spinous dorsal, the other below origin of soft dorsal, the latter spot connected with the general yellow below by a short, broad yellow stripe; a narrow light blue band edged outwardly with a narrow black line along edge of dorsal and anal sheath; upper edge of soft dorsal and lower edge of soft anal black; caudal edged with light blue; base of each scale on anterior of side with a round reddish brown spot.

Color in alcohol, upper surface deep blackish-brown; a brown band from occiput to eye edged with darker, which is continued below eye on interopercle as 2 dark brown lines; white band from first 2 dorsal spines separating dark band above eye and blackish-brown of back; a large white blotch on middle of side above and another below base of soft dorsal on back; a dusky band across caudal peduncle; basal portion of dorsal fin blackish-brown; margin of soft dorsal above with a narrow black line, another submarginal black line beginning on last half of spinous dorsal and running to posterior rays; below this and closer to it than it is to edge of fin, a gray line; caudal with a submarginal gray line; anal with a black line along edge of lower rays; edge of soft anal below narrowly blackish; a narrow black line from origin of spinous anal running out submarginally to posterior rays; above this a narrow gray line; middle of side, just below dark color of back, yellowish; each scale on side below with a dusky spot in middle; lower surface of body, head (except dark band), margin of dorsal, anal, caudal, pectoral and ventral, whitish.

We have examined 19 examples obtained by Doctor Jenkins and 10 collected by us, all from Honolulu; length 3 to 5.5 inches. The *Albatross* also obtained examples at Honolulu, where the species is moderately common about the coral reefs.

301. Chætodon corallicola Snyder. Plate 46, fig. 1.

Head, measured to edge of opercle 3 in length to base of caudal fin; depth 1.7; depth of caudal peduncle 3 in head; eye 2.4; snout 2.3; interorbital space 3. D. xiii, 21; A. iii, 18; scales 4–30–12. Anterior profile between snout and dorsal almost straight, with a slight convexity over eye; snout short, its length somewhat less than diameter of eye; jaws equal; teeth fine and brush-like; pseudobranchiæ very large; gillrakers on first arch 5+14, short and pointed; scales on top of head and on snout very minute, those on cheeks, opercles, and breast larger; width of scales near middle of body about equal to diameter of pupil, those on caudal peduncle greatly reduced in size; rayed portions of dorsal and anal closely scaled, the scaled area extending forward on spinous portion of dorsal fin, decreasing in height from near tip of eighth spine to base of first, leaving the membranes of the anterior spines largely naked; lateral line curved upward and constantly approaching the back until it disappears near end of dorsal fin, not extending on caudal peduncle, with 36 pores, scales very small. Except the first the dorsal spines are high anteriorly; height of second to sixth equal to distance between tip of snout and center of eye; height of first spine about equal to diameter of pupil; length of longest rays about equal to that of longest spines; membrane deeply notched between anterior spines, the notches growing shallow posteriorly as the scales approach edge of fin; second anal spine longest, about equal to highest dorsal spine; membrane deeply notched between first and third spines, the latter closely connected with rayed portion of fin; border of anal fin extending a little farther posteriorly than that of dorsal; caudal truncate, upper rays slightly longer than lower, 1.27 in head; pectoral 1.17 in head; ventrals not quite reaching vent

Color in alcohol, dull silvery, brownish along the back, the dark color extending downward in region of pectoral fin; scales on greater part of body with darker centers and lighter edges; posterior part of body with many dark spots about half as large as pupil; head with a vertical brownish-black band, the posterior border of which passes from insertion of dorsal through posterior border of eye, thence curving backward to origin of ventrals; width of band somewhat less than diameter of eye; interorbital area, snout, and upper lip dark brown; dorsal and anal narrowly bordered with dusky, rays tipped with white; scaled portion of dorsal with large irregular dusky spots separated by narrow light spaces, which take the form of a network; caudal light, broadly bordered with dusky; pectoral plain; ventrals blackish toward the free margins.

Described from the type, No. 50880, U. S. Nat. Mus., 2.3 inches long, from station 4032. Other specimens, among which are cotypes, No. 7732, Stanford Univ. Mus., differ little from the type. Specimens were taken off the southern coast of Oahu at station 4032, depth 27 to 29 fathoms; station 4031, depth 27 to 28 fathoms; station 4034, depth 28 fathoms.

302. Chætodon fremblii Bennett. Plate LI.

Head 3.4 in length; depth 1.8; eye 3.5 in head; snout 3; maxillary 4.4; interorbital 3.5; D. xiv, 21; A. iii, 18; scales 10–50–27.

Body deep, compressed, back elevated; head deep, upper profile oblique; snout long, blunt, rounded; mouth small, jaws produced, equal; teeth small, in brush-like bands in jaws; eye small, superior, midway in length of head; margin of preopercle very finely serrate; interorbital space broad, convex; nostrils circular, close together, anterior elevated rim with fleshy flap; anterior dorsal spines enlarged, strong, sixth 1.6 in head, longer than posterior spines; eighth dorsal ray 1.6; eighth anal ray 1.6; caudal with upper rays longest, margin obliquely straight; pectoral 1.1; ventral pointed, nearly reaching anal, 1.2; scales small, very small on vertical fins and head; scales forming slightly oblique series.

Color in life, pale yellow, lighter below, edges of scales darker; no ocular bar; a black saddle, narrowly edged with blue, in front of dorsal; a large black spot edged with blue extending over the posterior half of soft dorsal, the caudal peduncle and the last 2 rays of soft anal; side with 8 longitudinal (slightly oblique) narrow blue lines edged with black, 3 of which converge to the eye and 1 passes to the angle of the mouth; above these an interrupted blue line on the dorsal, and below them a continuous blue line on the anal; pectoral translucent white, ventrals yellow; dorsal and anal yellow; soft dorsal narrowly edged with a submarginal line of black below and above white; lower edge of soft anal edged with black; caudal white, in its center a broad bar of yellow with its hind edge crescentic, narrowly edged above, below, and behind with black.

Color in alcohol, very pale brown, light on lower surface; posterior half of soft dorsal, caudal peduncle and outer portion of posterior rays blackish; soft dorsal and anal with blackish submarginal lines; spinous dorsal with median dusky line; side with pale slaty slightly oblique longitudinal stripes (clear blue in life) margined narrowly with dusky; caudal with pale submarginal gray line, with basal gray cross band; pectoral and ventrals gray.

Described from an example (No. 04531) 5.8 inches long, taken at Honolulu, where the species is not rare. Doctor Jenkins collected 8 specimens at Honolulu and we have 5 from the same place, as well as 1 from Hilo. Length 3.25 to 6.25 inches. The *Albatross* also secured specimens at Honolulu.

Genus 175. MICROCANTHUS Swainson.

This genus differs from *Chætodon* chiefly in the small scales, their being about 60 in the lateral line; the soft dorsal and anal are shorter than is usual in *Chætodon*, the fin formula of the typical species being D. xi, 17; A. iii, 14; it is in fact doubtful whether the genus contains a second species, as the other species with small scales have the soft fins many-rayed and constitute Bleeker's genus *Hemiiaurichthys* (type, *polylepis*), which is apparently valid; in any case it has no close relation to *Microcanthus strigatus*.

303. Microcanthus strigatus (Cuvier & Valenciennes).

Head 3 in length; depth 1.75; eye 2.8 in head; snout 3.5; maxillary 4; interorbital 3.25; D. i, xi, 16; A. iii, 14; scales 10–50?–27.

Body deep, rather short, compressed, back elevated; head rather small, compressed, pointed. upper profile straight from tip of snout to eye, then slightly convex to dorsal fin; teeth sharp, pointed, pungent, in rather broad bands in jaws; jaws rather small, blunt, slightly produced; snout short, pointed; mouth small, terminal, small maxillary expanded distally to below anterior nostril; lips rather fleshy; eye large, anterior to middle of length of head, superior; nostrils close together, anterior with a small flap, posterior a short slit; interorbital space broad, flattened and slightly convex; preorbital broad, 2 in eye; dorsal spines longest anteriorly, fourth 1.75 in head, last 2.3; anterior dorsal rays longest, 1.9; second anal spine largest, enlarged, 1.8; anterior anal rays longest, second 2; caudal rather small, emarginate, about equal to head; caudal peduncle compressed, its depth 2.3; pectoral small, 3.8 in body; ventral 1.25 in head; ventral spine 2.25; scales rather weakly ctenoid, small; soft dorsal and anal covered with very small scales, caudal with small scales only at base; pectoral and ventrals with small scales basally; lateral line evenly arched to caudal peduncle, then straight to base of caudal.

Color in alcohol, ground-color creamy white, side with 6 dark olive-brown nearly horizontal broad bands; first along middle of spinous dorsal across anterior rays, second along base of spinous dorsal across middle of soft dorsal, third below this along back and over posterior rays, fourth from occiput to middle of base of caudal, fifth from above eye across last third of anal, and sixth from snout, behind eye to base of pectoral then down to anal spine, running up along anterior soft rays; pectoral and caudal pale brown; ventrals pale brown basally, outer portions grayish.

Described from an example taken by Jordan and Snyder at Honolulu, where the species is scarce. We have 4 specimens from Honolulu, 1 collected by Jordan and Snyder and 3 by Jenkins. Length 3.3 to 4.3 inches. Other specimens were obtained by the *Albatross* at Honolulu. Compared with examples from Nagasaki we find no difference.

Genus 176. HENIOCHUS Cuvier & Valenciennes.

Body much compressed and elevated; forehead in adult often with bony projections; dorsal spines 11 to 13, the fourth greatly elevated and filiform; muzzle rather short; no teeth on palate; no spine on preopercle; scales moderate.

Allied to *Chætodon*, but well distinguished by the prolongation of the fourth dorsal spine.

304. Heniochus acuminatus (Linnæus). Plate LV.

Head 3 in length; depth 1.5; eye 3 in head; snout 3.2; maxillary 5; interorbital 3.75; D. xii, 24; A. iii, 18; scales 7–50–22.

Body very deep, compressed, back very trenchant; head small, deep, upper profile undulate; snout pointed, rounded above; jaws produced, pointed, equal; mouth small, very oblique, maxillary small; teeth rather firm, forming a narrow brush-like series in each jaw; eye large, round, anterior; interorbital broad, convex; nostrils large, close together in front of eye, anterior circular; dorsal spines strong, sharp pointed, fourth very long, produced in a slender filament, longer than entire length of fish; fifth dorsal spine longer than others; middle dorsal rays longest; second anal spine very large, equal to third, which is rather slender, 1.7 in head; fourth anal ray longest, 1.35; caudal small, probably truncate; pectoral pointed, upper rays longest, equal to head; ventral pointed, spine large, strong, long, length of fin equal to head; caudal peduncle small, compressed, its least depth nearly 3 in head; scales long, ctenoid, those on head above and basal portions of vertical fins very small; rows of scales curved up above lateral line in front, those on middle of side nearly horizontal; lateral line strongly arched, then running down on middle of side of caudal peduncle to caudal. Described from an example (No. 03531) taken at Honolulu.

Color in alcohol (No. 03531) 6.5 inches long, ground-color white, head and snout above brownish; a broad blackish-brown vertical band from before and including first 4 dorsal spines, down over side, including also posterior margin of opercle, base of pectoral, belly, and ventrals, then extending on each side of vent out along spinous anal to second anal ray; another broad blackish-brown band beginning at tip of fifth, including next 3 spines, extending down on side obliquely backward till it includes last half of soft anal.

We have examined 4 examples, all from Honolulu, 1 of them collected by Doctor Jenkins. These are 4.5 to 7.25 inches long. Also obtained by the *Albatross* at Honolulu, where the species is rather rare.

Genus 177. HOLACANTHUS Lacépède.

Body oblong or elevated, rather robust; scales rather small, roughish, often mixed with smaller ones; vertical limb of preopercle with serræ, large or small; a strong spine at angle of preopercle, this usually grooved; dorsal fin with 12 to 15 strong spines, which are usually graduated, increasing in height to the last; soft dorsal moderate, with 17 to 20 rays, usually not ending in streamers; coloration usually brilliant and well defined. Species numerous in all tropical seas, abounding about the coral reefs.

305. Holacanthus arcuatus Gray. Fig. 164.

D. xiii, 18; A. iii, 18; scales 8–48–26; preopercular spine reaching posterior margin of opercle; dorsal and anal fins nearly equal in height; a broad, dark-brown band, slightly arched, extending from eye to posterior border of dorsal fin; tips of the caudal and a broad border of the anal fin brown; the brown marking with a bright border, known from the original type only, which came from the Hawaiian Islands; not seen by us.

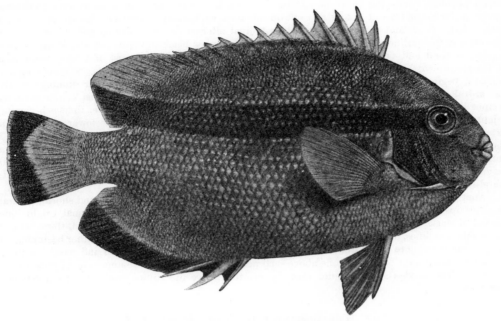

FIG. 164.—*Holacanthus arcuatus* Gray; after Günther.

306. Holacanthus bispinosus Günther.   Plate LVI.

Total length 8.5 inches; head 3.83 in length; depth 2; eye 4.5 in head; snout 2.5; interorbital 3.6; scales about 5–50–18 or 20, the longitudinal scales counted just below lateral line; D. XIII, 19; A. III, 19.

Body elliptical, compressed, moderately arched from nape to base of first rays of soft dorsal, then more abruptly descending to the straight caudal peduncle; ventral outline more evenly but somewhat more deeply arched; caudal peduncle short, about 3 in head, its depth about 2 in head; scales above lateral line variable in size and shape, smaller and more rounded than those on the sides below, which are mostly much deeper than long; dorsal spines graduated, the last one the longest, about 1.7 in head, soft dorsal and anal with rounded angles, the middle rays of dorsal extending to middle of upper caudal ray, and of anal to end of first third of lower caudal ray; pectoral shorter than head; ventral longer than pectoral about equaling head, its upper rays filamentous, reaching beyond vent nearly to first anal spine, the spine about 1.6 in head; fins all densely scaled with small scales.   Head short and deep, deeper than long, closely scaled; profile steep at its junction with preorbital, concave from the protrusion of the muzzle; snout short and bluntly rounded from outward projection of teeth; nostrils small, close together in front of eye, the anterior with a small tube prolonged into a small triangular flap behind; posterior nostril with a slightly raised ridge in front; opercle unarmed; suborbital with few nearly concealed sharp teeth, or none; interopercle without teeth, preopercle along its nearly vertical posterior margin with a series of wide-set small sharp teeth, the lowest the longest; and at its angle a long, stout, somewhat curved spine, reaching nearly to under base of pectoral, at base or in front of which are 1 or 2 short spines or cusps.

Body ground-color in alcohol, yellowish white, crossed by 8 pairs of narrow brown bars, separated by a distance about equal to the interspace between the pairs of bars, the widest bar about 2 in eye, extending on spinous dorsal and anal, the anterior pair beginning immediately in front of spinous dorsal, running downward and forward about halfway to the lateral line, then abruptly bending and running straight to upper end of gill-opening, the anterior brown bar there terminating, or continuing as a bluish brown margin to opercle, the posterior of the pair passing under the membranous prolongation of the opercle to top of base of pectoral, beginning again at lower base of pectoral or axil, and running downward and backward to side of belly, ending before reaching tip of ventral spine, the interspace being bluish white rather than yellowish like the others; the next 5 pairs, beginning as a single bar upon the spinous dorsal, running thereon very obliquely downward and forward, separating and bending abruptly at the base of the fin; second pair extending downward and forward to lateral line, thence nearly vertically to upper pectoral ray, from there curving backward to front of first anal spine; the third pair in a similar manner ending at front of soft anal, the bars coalescing just before reaching the fin; the fourth pair with less forward curve on body, the others almost straight with somewhat backward and downward direction, ending at base of soft anal, the interspace of the seventh beginning on front of soft dorsal as a pale blue bar running downward and backward, the brown bars on anal coalescing and curving forward almost parallel with the body outline; the eighth pair crossing caudal peduncle coalescing above and below; the ninth hardly distinguishable as a pair crossing caudal peduncle at base of caudal fin; soft dorsal black with many small pale blue spots; soft anal with 5 dirty bluish and 6 yellowish olive longitudinal alternating bars, curving and following in a general way the outline of the fins, the fin with a very narrow blackish border; caudal abruptly pale yellow; pectoral and ventral pale, outer ray of latter slightly dusky; breast and belly plain pale yellowish brown; head in front and above eyes black, dark brown on sides, becoming lighter beneath; beginning immediately in front of spinous dorsal a narrow pale blue bar running directly forward along ridge of back, bordered by narrow dusky margins, on one side just before reaching occiput bending somewhat abruptly downward to upper posterior margin of eye, thence becoming brighter with still narrower borders passing around edge of orbit to about the lower middle, then extending a short distance on suborbital; on the other side of head a similar bar beginning with 2 short branches on occiput following the other eye in the same manner; these bars connected by a narrow light blue bar following upper edge of orbit to about its middle, thence arching over frontal region; a single light blue bar between eyes in front extending straight to upper lip on top of snout; margin of preopercle light blue.

Another specimen 8 inches long differs in having a longer preopercular spine and shorter ventral fins, the tips reaching only to vent, and also slightly in the markings; margin of anal bright blue instead of black, and the olive bars on that fin darker; postorbital bars not connected, there being 2 wavy pale blue lines, one beginning on nape and running to upper front of eye, the other beginning on occiput and running to upper front of other eye; besides the median interocular and nasal bar there are several small light blue spots, one above each nostril, and one just above upper end of blue line.

Hawaiian Islands (Günther); not seen by us; the above description and plate from Samoan specimens.

307. Holacanthus fisheri Snyder.   Plate 46, fig 2.

Head, measured to end of opercle, 3.4 in length (to base of caudal fin); depth 2.1; depth of caudal peduncle 8.3; eye 3 in head; snout 2.5; interorbital space 3.1; D. xiv, 15; A.17; scales 28,–21. Suborbital with 3 prominent spines which curve downward and backward; lower or anterior one very small, in some specimens preceded by a fourth minute spine; the upper or posterior 2 about equal in length to diameter of pupil; preopercle with a strong, slightly curved spine at its angle, which extends to a vertical through posterior border of opercle, excluding the flap; length of spine 3 in head; margin of preopercle above spine with sharp denticulations; lower spine with 2 small spines, the upper of which is the larger; opercular spines not grooved; interopercle with denticulations; teeth fine, brushlike trilobed, the lateral lobes much shorter than the median, all being sharply pointed; pseudobranchiæ large; gillrakers 5+15, slender, pointed.

Scales large, regular, strongly ctenoid, those on snout, chin, and interorbital space minute; dorsal, anal, and caudal densely scaled; lateral line arched over the pectoral, extending along back near base of dorsal, disappearing near end of soft dorsal fin; dorsal spines growing gradually longer from the second to the last, the first half as long as the second, the last equal in length to distance between tip of snout and posterior border of eye; membranes of first 5 spines notched, membrane between first and second spines nearly cleft to base, the notches growing successively more shallow between the following spines; membranes between first and third spines without scales, the scaled area beginning behind third spine; fin rounded posteriorly, its edge reaching a vertical through base of caudal; third anal spine longest; membranes between spines deeply cleft, without scales except on a narrow area along the base; third spine closely attached to rayed portion of fin; posterior edge of fin pointed, extending nearly to a vertical through middle of caudal; edge of caudal truncate or slightly convex; tips of rays without scales; ventrals sharply pointed, the first ray being filamentous at tip, extending to origin of anal; pectoral when depressed extending to a vertical through vent.

Color in alcohol, light brown with a yellowish tinge; lips, interorbital area, chin, and throat somewhat dusky; membranes covering suborbital and opercular spines dark; scales of body with rather indistinct dusky edgings; a round, brownish black spot somewhat larger than eye, just above base of pectoral; dorsal narrowly edged with black, the border widening on posterior edge to form a well-marked spot; anal narrowly bordered with pearly white, posterior part of fin blackish; spine and first ray of ventral pearly white; caudal with upper and lower borders dusky, the lower part much the darker, the central area yellowish; pectorals immaculate.

Color in life, bright reddish orange, posterior two-thirds suffused with dusky; spot above pectoral brownish black; preopercular spine dark blue; dorsal and anal colored like body, the dorsal narrowly edged with black, the black spot on posterior part with an indistinct boundary; anal with a broad blackish margin narrowly edged with blue on the outside; middle of caudal lemon-yellow; pectorals orange; ventrals orange suffused with dusky near margins, spine and first ray pearly blue.

Different examples vary somewhat in intensity of color. Small specimens have a broad lemon band on the anal edged above and below with blue, the outer blue line narrowly edged with black.

Type, No. 50881, U. S. Nat. Mus., a specimen measuring 3.25 inches; cotype, No. 7738, Stanford

Univ. Mus., from station 4032 off Diamond Head, Oahu, depth 27 to 29 fathoms.   Other specimens are from station 3847, southern coast of Molokai; stations 3872 and 3876, between Maui and Lanai; stations 4031, 4033, and 4034, southern coast of Oahu, in 14 to 43 fathoms.

308. Holacanthus bicolor (Bloch).   Fig. 165.

Head 4 in length without caudal; depth 2; eye about 4 in head; snout 3; interorbital 3; D. xvi, 15; A. iii, 17; scales about 3–45–19, the longitudinal series counted below lateral line.

Body ovoid, deep, compressed, dorsal and ventral outlines evenly arched; dorsal spines graduated, the last longest, about 1.5 in head; third ventral spine long, about 1.2 in head; middle rays of soft dorsal and anal produced, the tips very sharply angulated, the dorsal almost filamentous; caudal rounded; pectorals somewhat rounded; outer rays of ventrals filamentous, reaching first anal spine; ventral spine long, about 1.33 in head; depth of head about equaling its length; profile steep, slightly depressed or concave at junction of nape and occiput; snout not projecting, concurrent with profile; opercle unarmed; the nearly vertical margin of preopercle finely toothed, the spine at angle long, quite reaching lower base of pectoral, one or more short, sharp spines at its base below; suborbital finely toothed; an anterior scaled lobe of interopercle with several conspicuous teeth or spinules.

Color in alcohol, body sharply divided into 2 colors at a line running irregularly from sixth dorsal spine to ventral region; posteriorly black, with bluish reflections, including dorsal and anal fins, nearly to end of caudal peduncle; tips of middle rays of soft dorsal straw-yellow, extending a short distance on the upper part of the fin as a narrow margin; caudal abruptly straw-yellow; anterior part of body and spinous dorsal, including fifth spine, pectoral, and ventrals, pale yellow or straw; entire head with an irregular tint of purplish brown composed of fine punctulations on background of pale yellow; a broad black band, somewhat V-shaped, the apex up, from upper margin of eye over occiput and nape.   The above description from an example 5.62 inches long obtained in Samoa by Dr. Jordan.

Fig. 165.—*Holacanthus bicolor* (Bloch); after Günther.

Numerous other smaller specimens vary slightly.   The dorsal spines run xiv–xv, mostly xv.   The ventral fins are not always so long; the preopercular spine in all cases is not quite so long, and there are finer teeth on interopercle and at the base of preopercular spine below.   The color does not vary much.

Hawaiian Islands and Polynesia.   Not obtained by us, the only Hawaiian reference being that of Günther.

Family LXXIV. ZANCLIDÆ.—Moorish Idols.

Body oblong, much compressed and elevated, covered with minute, rough scales; mouth small, with long, slender, brush-like teeth; no teeth on palate; bones of top of head thick and solid, developing with age a conspicuous median horn on the forehead, wanting in the young; preopercle unarmed; dorsal single, with 7 spines, the third and succeeding spines prolonged into long filaments; interspinal bone projecting before dorsal; anal similar to soft dorsal, long, with its anterior rays produced; a small antrorse spine before anal; caudal peduncle unarmed, the fin lunate; pectoral short; ventrals pointed; intestine long; coracoid bones largely developed; vertebræ reduced in number, 9+13=22; air-bladder large; branchiostegals 4; pyloric cœca 14.

One species, widely distributed about the rocky islands of the Pacific.

Genus 178. ZANCLUS Cuvier & Valenciennes.

Characters of the genus included above. The generic name *Pomacanthus* Lacépède belongs properly to this genus, as the first species placed in that composite group by its author is the *Chætodon canescens* of Linnæus. The name *Zanclus* occurs still earlier in Lacépède's work, though not formally accepted. It is, however, by reason of priority, properly adopted by Bleeker.

309. Zanclus canescens (Linnæus). "*Kihikihi.*" [a]   Plate LVII.

Head 2.6 in length; depth 1.25; eye 4.25 in head; snout 1.5; maxillary 5; interorbital 4.2; D. II, 47; A. III, 35.

Body very deep, rather short, compressed, back elevated; head deep, compressed, pointed; upper profile steep, oblique; jaws long, conic, produced, equal; mouth small, terminal; teeth slender, pointed, pungent in outer series, those inside jaws very fine; eye small, high, above posterior third of head; nostrils small, anterior, with small flap; margin of preopercle finely serrate; interorbital space moderately broad, with short spine in front of each eye above nostrils; dorsal spines very short, strong, second longest; anterior dorsal rays elongate, first very long, enlarged, filamentous, much longer than entire fish; first and second anal spines short, third elongate, 1.30 in head; pectoral 1.25; ventral 1.2, pointed; ventral spine sharp, 2; depth of caudal peduncle 3; caudal rather small, broad, margin nearly straight; scales very small, ctenoid, crowded, extending out on basal portions of dorsal and anal; ventrals roughened on spine and basal portion of rays; lateral line high, arched, running down on middle of side of caudal peduncle to base of caudal.

Color in alcohol, creamy white, a broad black band including space to interorbital, down below eye, side of chest, base of pectoral, ventrals, and anus; a black band beginning on upper dorsal ray, running down on posterior part of side, broadening out below, on longest anterior anal rays; caudal black except for a lunate white margin; a black band from interorbital space to tip of snout, extending down on side of snout inclosing a triangular pale area; lower lip and chin black; a narrow white triangle on forehead, its lower base running across interobital space; a creamy white band from front of eye to throat narrowly margined with white extending down to middle of breast more than half way to ventrals; a curved gray line from below gill-opening bending down and out, nearly to base of ventral; second black transverse band with posterior submarginal white line; black of caudal bordered in front with white; anterior part of soft dorsal grayish, outer portion behind second black band white, narrowly margined with black; anal similar to dorsal; pectoral grayish; ventrals black.

Described from an example 6 inches long taken at Hilo (No. 04548). In smaller examples the anterior line on breast is continued up behind eye forming an angle before spinous dorsal on side of back in front. From below base of pectoral a whitish line down to anus.

This species is very common about the coral reefs, and is often brought into the market. It has been frequently recorded from the Hawaiian Islands, and specimens have recently been obtained by Jenkins, by the Fur Seal Commission, by us, and by the *Albatross* at Honolulu, Puako Bay, and Laysan Island. Our very complete series of 63 specimens contains but 1 from Hilo, all the others being from Honolulu. Length 3 to 7 inches.

Family LXXV. ACANTHURIDÆ.—Surgeon-fishes.

Body oblong, compressed and usually elevated, covered with very small scales; lateral line continuous; tail armed with one or more spines or bony plates; eye lateral, high up; preorbital very narrow and deep; nostrils double; mouth small, low; each jaw with a single series of narrow incisor-like teeth; vomer and palatines toothless; premaxillaries somewhat movable but not protractile; maxillary short, closely united with the premaxillary; gillrakers obsolete; pseudobranchiæ large; gills 4, a slit behind the fourth; gill-membranes attached to the isthmus, the openings thus restricted to the sides. A single dorsal fin, with strong spines, the spinous part of the fin shorter than the soft part; anal fin similar to soft dorsal; pectorals moderate; ventral fins present, thoracic, I, 5. Pelvic bones long, narrow, curved, closely connected, evident through the skin, as in *Balistidæ*. Pyloric cœca rather few; air-bladder large; intestinal canal long. Vertebræ 9 + 13=22. Posterior suborbital bones in close contact with the preopercle; post-temporal immovably united with the skull, apparently simple, but really trifurcate with the interspaces filled in with bone, the foramen not passing through it; interneural bones with transversely expanded buckler-like subcutaneous plates, which intervene

---

[a] The name "Kihikihi" is from "kihi," angle, applied to the horns of the crescent moon.

between the spines and limit their motion forward; epipleurals developed from the ribs. Herbivorous fishes of the tropical seas, which undergo great changes with age, as do the *Chætodontidæ*, the young having often been described as distinct genera.

Genus 179. HEPATUS Gronow.

This genus includes those *Acanthuridæ* which have the tail armed with a sharp, antrorse, lancet-like, movable spine; strong, fixed, incisor teeth; ventral rays I, 5, and about 9 spines in the dorsal fin. The numerous species are found in all tropical seas. Herbivorous fishes, living about coral reefs; the adult protected by the murderous caudal spine, which grows larger with age.

310. Hepatus achilles (Shaw). *"Pa kui kui."* Plate LVIII.

Head 3.5 in length; depth 1.8; snout 1.35 in head; eye 4; interorbital 2.65; D. IX, 32; A. III, 27.

Body rather deeply ovoid, greatest depth at middle of pectoral; head deep, compressed, upper profile rather strongly and evenly convex; jaws slightly produced, lower inferior; mouth small; teeth broad, forming sharp, cutting crenulate edge; margin of preopercle very oblique, angle falling below anterior margin of eye; interorbital space moderately elevated, somewhat broad, roundly convex; nostrils round, close together in front of eye, anterior with small fleshy flap; dorsal spines graduated to last, which is longest, 1.8 in head; dorsal rays of uniform height except last few, sixth ray 1.5; third anal spine longest, 2.25 in head; seventh anal ray 1.5; pectoral 3.25 in body; ventral pointed, 1.1 in head; ventral spine small, sharp pointed, 2.8; least depth of caudal peduncle 2.35 in head; caudal broad, upper and lower rays produced in a point, margin of fin straight in middle; scales very small, crowded, ctenoid; lateral line concurrent with dorsal profile of trunk; caudal spine depressible in groove, 3 in head.

Color in life (field No. 03511) dark brown, nearly black, a light blue ring around chin, and spot of same color on opercle at angle of gill-opening; large patch on side including caudal spine rich orange; a narrow line on body, below base of dorsal, and another above base of anal, light blue; dorsal dark brown, nearly black, with an orange tinge, base narrowly scarlet at first, the color widening posteriorly; anal similar to dorsal, base narrowly scarlet for nearly whole length; caudal black on basal portion, upper and lower edge white, margin broadly white posteriorly, a narrow black submarginal crescent, before this a broad scarlet patch; pectoral black; ventrals dusky orange at base, anterior edge and upper portion light blue, posterior lower half dark brown, nearly black; iris blue with yellow inner border.

Color in life of a specimen (field No. 392) collected by Jordan and Kellogg at Apia in 1902, brownish black, paler below; the lateral spot of a vivid scarlet; a bluish white band across lower jaw; front profile bright bluish gray, the preorbital and cheeks clear brown; dorsal brownish, becoming orange behind, the base of soft dorsal scarlet with a whitish line below, the upper parts blackish and suffused with red, the edge narrowly whitish; anal similar, with more black and a much broader edge; caudal dusky at base, with concentric crescents of orange, black, and white; ventrals dusky, edged with bluish white; a black, vertical line across preopercle; opercle black with a whitish edge.

Color in alcohol, blackish brown; gill-flap below, large ovoid patch including caudal spine, bases of soft dorsal and anal with narrow band broadening out to last rays, and median band on middle of caudal creamy yellow; close along bases of soft dorsal and anal a narrow gray white line, deepest behind; caudal with narrow blackish submarginal line following outline of fin and inclosing creamy white band; a narrow pale blue or slaty band from corner of mouth across chin; pectoral pale slaty; ventral with broad slaty blue margin, axil creamy yellow.

Described chiefly from an example (field No. 05387) taken at Honolulu.

This species is abundant at Honolulu, where it was obtained by Jenkins, the *Albatross*, and by us. Steindachner and also Fowler had specimens from Honolulu, and the *Albatross* obtained it at Puako Bay, Hawaii. We have examined 28 specimens, all from Honolulu, ranging in length from 4 to more than 10 inches. Also found in Samoa.

311. Hepatus olivaceus (Bloch & Schneider). *"Nae-nae."* Fig. 166.

Head 3.75 in length; depth 2; eye 4 in head; snout 1.25; interorbital 3.25; D. IX, 24; A. 23.

Body rather deeply ovoid, greatest depth at middle of pectoral; head deep, compressed, upper profile steep, convex; jaws slightly produced, lower inferior; mouth small, oblique; teeth broad, forming sharp cutting crenulate edge; margin of preopercle very oblique, angle below anterior margin of eye; interorbital space moderately elevated, broad, roundly convex; nostrils round, close together in front of eye, anterior a little below posterior, with small fleshy flap; last dorsal spines longest, about equal, eleventh 1.65 in head, seventeenth dorsal ray 1.5; third anal spine 2.1; seventeenth anal ray 1.75; pectoral equal to head, pointed; ventral pointed, 1.2; ventral spine 1.8; depth of caudal peduncle 2.5; caudal deep, broad, upper rays long, produced, pointed; caudal spine depressible in a groove, 3.25 in head; scales very small, crowded, ctenoid; lateral line arched, nearly concurrent with dorsal profile of back.

Color in life (field No. 03384), general color olivaceous, breast slightly bluish, a white stripe edged with black running straight back from upper angle of opercle to a point below sixth dorsal spine; dorsal nearly black, membranes slightly bluish; caudal nearly black, same as dorsal, posterior one-third white, edged with black, this white band extending from fourth ray at top to fourth ray at base, forward edge of band crescent-shaped; anal same as dorsal; ventrals edged with black, membranes mottled with blue; pectoral same as ventrals, except posterior third, which is dirty white; iris black, with inside edge of bright yellow.

Another example (field No. 03009) orange olivaceous, a brownish blotch on humeral region inclosing an oblong area of body-color; caudal peduncle more orange, the spine dusky; lips dark; dorsal greenish-olive at base, the margin black; anal similar but colors brighter; caudal yellow at base, a lunate white border on middle rays, tips of lobes dusky; pectoral yellow, dusky at base and on anterior rays; ventrals blackish brown; iris yellow, with black on upper and lower parts.

Field No. 03512 had body, head, and caudal dark brown in life; caudal with pale orange tinge along edge of upper and lower lobes in front, and a large white crescent along the emarginated portion narrowly edged with black.

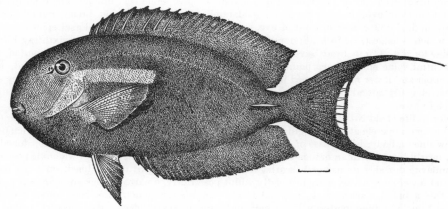

FIG. 166.—*Hepatus olivaceus* (Bloch & Schneider). From a Formosan specimen.

Still another specimen (field No. 03473) was dusky olive; a scarlet stripe behind upper angle of gill-opening as long as head and very bright, its wide border black, not blending with ground color; a white crescent on caudal; posterior half of pectoral obscurely whitish.

Color in alcohol, blackish brown; a horizontal band of buff equal to length of snout from behind upper margin of opercle bordered with deeper brown; median caudal rays broadly margined with dull buff, edge with narrow blackish marginal line; pectoral with blackish basal portion, outer portion grayish.

Described chiefly from an example (No. 03512) taken at Honolulu.

The species appears to be fairly abundant at Honolulu. Doctor Jenkins obtained 11 examples, Jordan and Snyder 1, and we preserved 9. The *Albatross* obtained it at Honolulu and at Puako Bay, Hawaii. The 21 specimens examined are 6 to 10.6 inches long.

312. Hepatus leucopareius (Jenkins). "*Maikoiko.*" Fig. 167.

Head 4 in length; depth 1.75; eye 3.25 in head; snout 1.25; interorbital 2.7; D. ix, 26; A. iii, 24.

Body deep, compressed, upper profile stongly convex, lower shallowly convex; head deep, compressed, upper profile steep to dorsal, lower profile nearly straight from chin to root of ventrals; jaws large, lower slightly produced; snout long, slightly concave in profile; mouth small, low; teeth broad, edges crenulate, compressed, forming a sharp cutting edge; margin of preopercle very oblique (blunt angle of which would form below middle of eye); eye rather large, high, in posterior third of length of head; nostrils small, close together, anterior with small thin flap, circular, posterior a small slit; interorbital space broad, convex; dorsal spines strong, graduated to posterior, last 1.3 in head; first anal ray 1.25; anal spines graduated to third, longest 1.65; fourth anal ray 1.25; caudal broad, emarginate; pectoral pointed, 2.8 in body; ventral sharp-pointed, 4 in body; ventral spine, 2 in head; caudal peduncle compressed, its depth 2; caudal spine moderately long, depressible in a groove, 4 in body.

Color in life of the type (No. 50712, U.S.N.M.), a whitish band from base of first 2 dorsal spines downward behind eye, including opercle to its lower margin; also a transverse whitish band at base of caudal.

Color in alcohol deep brown, vertical fins and ventrals darker; top of head and space in front of spinous dorsal pale brown, running down as an oblique band along gill-opening over opercle and margin of preopercle; base of last dorsal rays blackish; base of caudal pale brown.

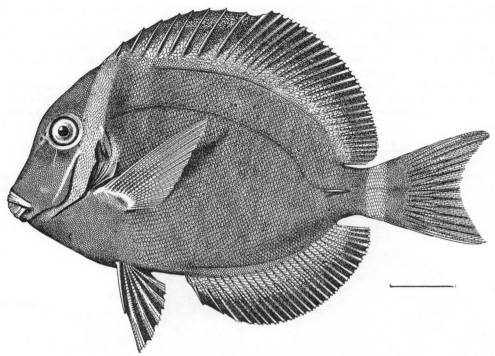

FIG. 167.—*Hepatus leucopareius* (Jenkins); from the type.

Described from the type taken at Honolulu by Doctor Jenkins. The species is thus far known only from Honolulu, whence we have 9 specimens, and from Hilo, from which we have 1. These specimens vary in length from 3.7 to 8.75 inches. Seen alive in aquarium at Waikiki.

313. Hepatus umbra (Jenkins). Plate 47.

Head 3.8 in length; depth 1.7; eye 3.75 in head; snout 1.2; interorbital 2.65; D. ix, 27; A. iii, 25.

Body deeply ovoid, greatest depth at pectoral region; head deep; upper profile nearly straight from tip of snout to interorbital space, then convex to origin of dorsal; jaws low, lower inferior; mouth small; interorbital broad, convex; nostrils small, round, close together, anterior larger, with small thin fleshy flap; last dorsal spine 1.7 in head, anterior spines graduated to posterior; fifth dorsal ray 1.25; third anal spine longest, 2; eighth anal ray 1.5; caudal rather broad, emarginate; pectoral broad, a trifle longer than head; ventrals sharply pointed, a trifle shorter than pectoral, or about equal to head; caudal peduncle compressed, 2 in head; caudal spine small, sharp, about 5 in head, depressible in a groove; scales small, finely ctenoid, very small on top of head, breast, and basal portions of vertical fins; lateral line irregular, arched at first, then sloping down to caudal spine, more or less straight from below anterior portion of spinous dorsal to below middle of soft dorsal.

Color in alcohol more or less uniform dark chocolate brown, outer portions of the fins blackish; pectoral pale olivaceous brown; ventrals blackish on outer portion.

The above description is from the type (field No. 05363), a specimen 7.5 inches long, taken at Honolulu by us, where we obtained 1 other example. A single small specimen was obtained by Doctor Jenkins, and the *Albatross* secured others at Puako Bay, Hawaii.

314. Hepatus matoides (Cuvier & Valenciennes). "*Maiii.*"

Head 3.8 in length; depth 1.9 in length; snout 1.4 in head; eye 5.4; interorbital 2.5; D. ix, 26; A. iii, 24.

Body deeply ovoid, greatest depth at origin of anal; head deep, compressed, oblique; snout long, compressed, upper profile convex; eye small, high, in last third of head; nostrils small, close together, anterior larger, with small thin flap; mouth small, inferior; jaws not much produced, lower inferior; interorbital space broad, elevated, convex; margin of preopercle forming an angle below anterior nostril; nostrils small, round, close together, anterior larger, with small fleshy flap; dorsal spines rather thin, last 2 in head; dorsal and anal rays produced in short points posteriorly; sixth dorsal ray 1.4 in head; anal spines graduated to third, which is 2.5; thirteenth anal ray 1.5; caudal long, deeply emarginate; pectoral equal to head; ventral sharply pointed, 1.25; ventral spine 2.25; caudal peduncle rather deep, compressed, 2.35; caudal spine small, 5.5 in head; scales small, finely ctenoid, very small on basal portions of vertical fins; lateral line partly concurrent with dorsal profile of back, nearly straight from below anterior dorsal spines to below posterior rays, then running down on caudal peduncle along upper edge of groove of caudal spine to base of caudal.

Color in alcohol, deep brown, dorsal and anal fins blackish; caudal dusky along middle of margin; side without blue or pale lines; margin of gill-opening dusky; pectoral dark brownish, margin broadly pale yellowish-white; ventrals blackish on outer portion, brownish on basal portions of rays, the membranes whitish; lips brown.

Described from an example (No. 05662) taken at Honolulu. This species has been recorded from Oualan, Isle of France, and the Hawaiian Islands. It does not appear to be common, as only 1 small specimen was secured by Jenkins and 3 by us, all from Honolulu. Our examples are 6 to 14.5 inches long.

315. Hepatus guntheri (Jenkins). *"Pualu."* Fig. 168.

Head 4 in length; depth 1.8; eye 3.5 in head; snout 1.4; interorbital 2.7; D. ix, 26; A. iii, 24.

Body deeply ovoid, greatest depth at origin of anal; head deep, compressed, upper profile obliquely convex from tip of snout to spinous dorsal; eye rather large, high, in last third of head; nostrils small,

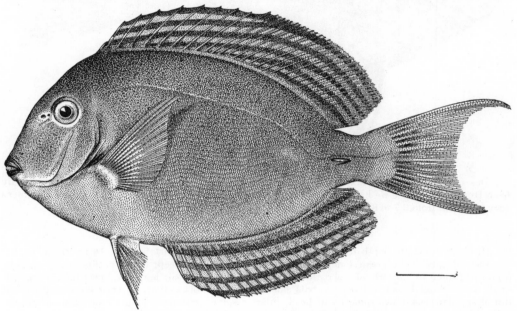

FIG. 168.—*Hepatus guntheri* (Jenkins); from the type.

close together, anterior the larger, rounded, with thin fleshy flap; mouth small, low, inferior; jaws blunt, slightly produced, lower inferior; interorbital space broad, elevated, convex; margin of preopercle forming an angle below anterior rim of orbit; dorsal spines slender, graduated to last, which is 1.25 in head; soft dorsal and anal not pointed behind; eighth dorsal ray 1.2 in head; third anal spine longest, 1.9; eighth anal ray 1.25; caudal long, emarginate; pectoral longer than head, 3.5 in body; ventrals sharp-pointed, 1.2 in head; ventral spine 1.9; caudal peduncle compressed, its least depth 2.2; caudal spine short, 1.5 in eye; scales small, crowded, ctenoid; very minute scales on basal portions of vertical fins; lateral line nearly concurrent with dorsal profile of back, straight from anterior dorsal spines to below middle of soft dorsal, then running down above edge of caudal spine to base of caudal.

Color in life (field No. 199, O. P. J.), general color brown; an orange-yellow band along back just below base of dorsal, just above yellow band a blue line; 4 golden longitudinal bands on dorsal fin, with an intercalary band which in some examples makes 5 bands; anal with 4 similar ones; pectoral yellow; yellow area through eye; yellow line over snout.

Color in alcohol, dark brown, vertical fins darker; side plain or uniform brown, without any lines; soft dorsal and anal grayish posteriorly; both dorsals and anal with 4 broad deep brown longitudinal bands; caudal deep brown, apparently without spots, base of fin pale; pectoral brown on basal portion, marginal portion broadly yellowish-white.

Described from the type taken by Doctor Jenkins at Honolulu.

This species is of rather wide distribution among the islands of the tropical Pacific, having been recorded by Günther from the Caroline, Society, Navigator, Pelew, and Kingsmill islands, and identified with *Acanthurus blochi* of Cuvier and Valenciennes.

Twelve specimens were obtained at Honolulu by Doctor Jenkins and 2 by us. We also have 3 examples from Hilo. Our specimens are 1.5 to 8.6 inches long. Perhaps identical with *H. matoides*.

316. Hepatus elongatus (Lacépède). *"Maii'i."*

Head 4 in length; depth 2.8; snout 1.3; eye 3.75 in head; interorbital 2.5; D. ix, 26; A. iii, 24.

Body elongate, ovate, greatest depth at middle of pectoral; head deep, upper profile straight from tip of snout to interorbital space, then convex from interorbital space to origin of dorsal; jaws low, lower inferior; mouth small; teeth compressed, crenulate; nostrils close together, anterior larger, with small fleshy flap; last dorsal spine longest, 1.5 in head; twentieth dorsal ray 1.5; third anal spine longest, 3; first anal ray 1.3; caudal long, very deeply emarginate in a crescent, upper and lower rays produced in sharp points, upper the longer; caudal peduncle compressed, its least depth 2.4; pectoral 3.25 in body; ventrals long, pointed, 3 in body; spine a little less than half length of fin; caudal peduncle compressed, its depth 2.25 in head; caudal spine long, depressible in a groove, 2.7 in head; scales very small, cycloid, crowded, finely ctenoid; lateral line arched in front to fifth dorsal spine, then straight to below middle of dorsal, dropping down and running along middle of side of caudal peduncle.

Color in alcohol, uniform dark chocolate brown; lips blackish; vertical fins brown like body-color, margin of caudal narrowly white; axils and bases of posterior dorsal and anal rays black; pectorals brownish; ventrals blackish on outer portion; margin of groove of caudal spine very narrowly blackish.

Description from an example (No. 05354) 7.75 inches long, taken by us at Honolulu. The species is of wide distribution and has been recorded from Fiji Islands, China, Kotosho (Formosa), Miyoko Island, Riukiu, New Hebrides, Pelew and Tahiti islands, as well as from the Hawaiian Islands. It was obtained by Doctor Jenkins at Honolulu and by us at Honolulu and Hookena, Kona; also by the *Albatross* at Puako Bay, Hawaii, and at station 3834, on the southern coast of Molokai, in 8 fathoms. We have examined 28 specimens, which range in length from 4.4 to 8.4 inches.

317. Hepatus xanthopterus (Cuvier & Valenciennes). *"Wálu."*

Head 4 in length; depth 2; snout 1.35 in head; eye 4; interorbital 2.65; D. ix, 25; A. iii, 24.

Body deep, rather long, greatest depth at middle of ventral; head deep, compressed, upper profile rather strongly and evenly convex; jaws low, strong, lower inferior; mouth inferior, low; teeth compressed, broad, edges crenulate; margin of preopercle very oblique, the angle below anterior margin of eye; interorbital space broad, convex, elevated; nostrils close together, anterior large, circular, with small fleshy flap; dorsal spines graduated to last, posterior 1.35 in head; dorsal and anal rays rather high, rounded, posterior not produced; eighth dorsal ray 1.25 in head, anal spines graduated to third, which is 1.8 in head; ninth anal ray 1.2; caudal long, deeply emarginate, the upper and lower lobes produced in long sharp points; pectoral 3.5 in body; ventrals sharp pointed, 2 in head; caudal peduncle compressed, depth 2.25; caudal spine moderately large, 4 in head, depressible in a groove.

Color in alcohol, deep blackish-brown, side with many dusky brown longitudinal vermiculating lines; dorsal and anal blackish at base, paler on terminal portion, with 4 rather broad brown longitudinal bands; caudal blackish-brown; pectoral blackish-brown, margin broadly dull buff; ventrals blackish on greater portion, innermost basal portion slaty.

Described from an example (No. 05666) taken at Honolulu.

The species is known only from Seychelles (the type locality) and the Hawaiian Islands. One specimen 7.25 inches long was secured by Jenkins and 2 others (13 and 17 inches long) by us at Honolulu. This species may not be distinct from *H. guntheri* or *H. matoides*.

318. Hepatus dussumieri (Cuvier & Valenciennes). *"Puálu;" "Palaui.* Fig. 169.

Head 3.35 in length; depth 1.9; snout 1.4 in head; eye 4.5; interorbital 3.2; D. ix, 27; A. iii, 26.

Body deep, upper and lower profiles nearly evenly convex, greatest depth about middle of length of trunk; head deep, compressed, upper profile evenly and obliquely convex from tip of snout to origin of dorsal; jaws large, inferior, very slightly produced; mouth small, inferior; teeth broad, compressed, edges crenulate; margin of preopercle very oblique, angle in front of anterior rim of orbit; eye small, high, in posterior third of head; nostrils small, close together, anterior with small fleshy flap, posterior a short oblique slit; interorbital space broad, convex; dorsal spines graduated to posterior, last 1.75 in head; seventh dorsal ray 1.5; posterior dorsal and anal rays rounded, not produced in points; anal spines graduated to last, which is 2.4; seventh anal ray 1.5; pectoral 3.5; ventral sharply pointed, 1.25 in head; spine 2.8; caudal large, emarginate, upper rays produced in a point beyond lower; caudal peduncle compressed, its depth 2.5 in head; caudal spine rather large, depressible in a groove, 3.5 in head; scales very small, ctenoid, crowded, few on soft dorsal, anal, and caudal, minute; lateral line concurrent with the profile of back, more or less running down to caudal spine in front.

Color in life (Field No. 02990) dull bluish olive, upper part more brassy, wavy brassy lines separated by narrower blue one most distinct on upper third of side; head marbled with blue-black and pale yellowish; a broad brassy interocular band; a narrow brassy line extending forward and curving upward from anterior part of eye, this continued around under eye and on to upper end of opercle; a brassy band behind eye and faint lines of same above eye; lips mottled with black and bluish; lower jaw and throat pale bluish; a narrow brassy line along back at base of dorsal fin, and a similar bluish one along base of anal; dorsal fin yellow, somewhat mottled with olivaceous along base anteriorly, and with bluish on last few rays; a narrow blue line along base; caudal bluish, with numerous small blackish olive spots, yellow at base, brightest above; tips of fins black; anal olivaceous with narrow stripes of blue and yellowish, distal portion of fin blackish, narrowly bordered with blue; pectoral smoky below, yellowish above, the anterior edge bluish; ventrals blue-black, paler at base; lance white, surrounded by black; iris brassy, bluish above.   (Caudal spots wanting in young.)

Another example (Field No. 03369) olive brown, streaked with faint blue; a yellow area about eye; cheek with light blue lines; edge of opercle black; no shoulder spot; dorsal golden brown with a pale blue and a golden line at base, the margin blackish, last rays with bluish shadings and lines; anal dark brown with very faint bluish streaks, a faint blue and a fainter golden line at base, and a black and a blue line at tip; caudal with blue gray reticulations around golden brown spots, well defined; a golden ring at base of fin, lobes dusky; ventrals with bluish rays, yellowish membranes and blackish edges; pectoral yellowish-brown, upper ray black; no black spot in axil of dorsal and anal.

Field No. 03500, body with numerous narrow wavy longitudinal golden-yellow alternating bluish-gray lines in life; dorsal bright yellow, narrow blue line along base of fin, immediately below this a narrow golden yellow line across base of caudal between spine and base of rays; anal dusky yellowish, with 4 distinguishable and traces of perhaps 2 or 3 other bars of yellow running parallel with outline

FIG. 169.—*Hepatus dussumieri* (Cuvier & Valenciennes); after Günther.

of body; caudal bluish-gray with many indistinct dusky spots; pectoral golden yellow; ventrals bluish-gray with yellowish tinges; yellow about eyes; yellow bar from eye to eye; front and sides of head covered with yellow wavy lines alternating with blue; chin and breast bluish.

Field No. 03383, in life, general color brownish-ocher, bluish toward belly and lower jaw; lower jaw dirty ultramarine; snout and gill-cover striped with blue and cadmium; a broad yellow stripe running from upper part of gill-opening at opercle through eye, but not joined over frontal region, this stripe outlined with blue; anterior portion of dorsal deep cadmium, 8 to 10 rays of posterior part blue, blending into the cadmium; narrow blue streak running entire length of dorsal at base; caudal deep blue; peduncle cadmium; anal olivaceous, cadmium at anterior 6 or 7 rays, blue posteriorly; narrow blue stripe running entire length of anal, and narrow line of light blue on outside edge; ventral cadmium with stripes of light blue running lengthwise, edged with neutral tint; first pectoral ray blue, next 3 cadmium, others blue, all rays cadmium at base; eye yellow, iris black.

Color in alcohol, dark chocolate brown; side with 35 or more wavy bluish longitudinal lines, those on head also horizontal; front of eye above pale brown; dorsal grayish on spiny portion, becoming dark slaty on soft portion; anal dark slaty; soft dorsal and anal each with 7 or 8 blackish longitudinal lines; caudal dark slaty, marked with many small blackish spots; base of caudal yellowish white; caudal spine with a rather broad blackish margin; pectoral deep olive brown, terminal portion broadly pale brown; margin of gill-opening blackish; margin of the anal narrowly bluish.

This species is very common about Honolulu.   We have also a number of larval examples less than an inch long, from Hilo, which correspond perfectly with Quoy and Gaimard's account of *Acanthurus argenteus*, but no specific characters, except the number of fin rays, can be determined.   The latter species, from Guam, can never be certainly identified, and the name *argenteus* should not be used, although it was very likely intended for the young of *H. dussumieri* or *H. matoides*. The species is represented in our collection by 59 specimens from Honolulu and 2 from Hilo. Of the specimens from Honolulu 7 were obtained by Doctor Jenkins, 5 by the *Albatross* in 1896, 4 by Doctor Wood, 2 by Jordan and Snyder, and the others by us. Specimens were also secured by the *Albatross* in 1902.

319. Hepatus guttatus (Bloch & Schneider). Fig. 170.

Head 3.6 in length; depth 1.4; eye 4.5 in head; snout 1.2; interorbital 2.25; D. VIII, 27; A. III, 24.

Body deep, compressed; back elevated, high at spinous dorsal; abdomen and lower part of trunk expanded below, lowest point at origin of anal; head deep, rather small, compressed, upper profile oblique from tip of snout to origin of dorsal; profile of snout nearly straight, jaws large, blunt, slightly produced; mouth low, inferior; mandible inferior, lips rather broad and thin; teeth broad,

FIG. 170.—*Hepatus guttatus* (Bloch & Schneider); after Günther.

compressed, forming sharp cutting edge, each one with 7 crenulations, the 3 median large, their edges level; nostrils large, close together, anterior larger, with small, fleshy flap; interorbital space broad, convex, not much elevated; dorsal spines graduated to posterior, stiff, last 1.5 in head; anterior dorsal rays longest, others gradually decreasing to last, first 1.5, last 4; fifth anal ray 6.5 in head, last 4.75; caudal broad, margin straight when expanded; caudal peduncle deep, compressed, depth 2 in head; pectoral pointed, 3 in body; ventral 4.25; caudal spine small, short, depressible in a groove, 1.35 in eye; scales small, ctenoid, deeply imbricated on sides, scales on vertical fins very small; lateral line arched, nearly concurrent with profile of back; anus directly behind bases of ventrals, well before anal spines.

Color in alcohol, uniform brown on greater portion, chest and belly somewhat pale; a pale brown band from before spinous dorsal down behind eye, another narrow pale band from base of fourth dorsal spine to belly, and last indistinct from fourth dorsal ray down to third anal ray; basal portion of caudal pale brown, the outer half deep brown; posterior half of trunk with many small white spots, also extending on soft dorsal and anal fins and over third pale bar on side; pectorals and ventrals pale brown, latter edged with brownish.

Described from an example (No. 646) taken at Honolulu by Doctor Jenkins. The species is rather scarce about Honolulu, living on the outer edge of the reefs. We have examined 5 specimens, 3 collected by us and 2 by Jenkins, all at Honolulu. They range in length from 8 to 11.5 inches. The species was also found by the *Albatross* at Puako Bay; common at Samoa.

320. Hepatus atramentatus (Jordan & Evermann). "*Maikoiko;*" "*Maiko.*" Fig. 171.

Head 3.8 in length; depth 1.9; eye 4.2 in head; snout 1.2; interorbital 3; D. IX, 27; A. III, 25.

Body deep, compressed, ovoid, the upper profile steeper than lower, evenly convex; jaws low, not produced, lower inferior; mouth small, inferior; teeth broad, compressed, edges crenulate; nostrils close together, anterior larger, with small fleshy flap; anterior dorsal spines graduated to posterior, the longest 1.5 in head; fourth dorsal ray 1.4; third anal spine longest 1.9; first anal ray 1.5; caudal large, emarginate, upper and lower rays produced in sharp angular points, upper much longer than lower; pectoral about 3.5 in body; ventrals sharp-pointed, 3.6 in body, spine half the length of fin; caudal peduncle compressed, 2 in head; caudal spine large, depressible in a groove, 3.1 in head; scales very small, ctenoid, few, and very minute on vertical fins; lateral line high, arched, at first descending under fifth dorsal spine, then straight to below middle of soft dorsal, finally falling down and running along side of caudle peduncle to tail.

Color in life (No. 02996), coppery brown, crossed by numerous very narrow, pale blue lines, those above axis of body running somewhat upward and backward, and with short broken lines of same interspersed, those below more regular but less distinct; cheek brassy, with about 5 narrow pale blue

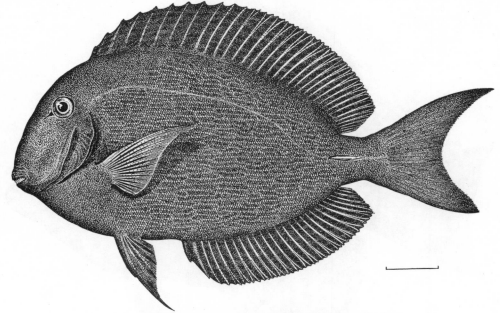

Fig. 171.—*Hepatus atramentatus* (Jordan & Evermann); from the type.

lines from eye to snout, each of these extending slightly upon pale rusty, and each with 5 or 6 narrow brassy lines parallel with margin, edge of each blackish; last rays of dorsal and anal more brassy; a conspicuous jet-black spot on caudal peduncle at base of last dorsal ray; caudal dark, blackest on outer part of middle rays; pectoral pale lemon; ventrals dusky, blacker toward tips; iris brownish, white on posterior part. Another example (No. 03474) was dull olive-gray, unmarked, save a faint whitish band across nape and back part of head; fins plain dusky gray.

Color in alcohol, very dark chocolate brown; side with about 40 narrow irregular or incomplete series of indistinct dark slaty longitudinal lines; cheek with similarly colored lines running obliquely downward; fins, except pectoral, all more or less blackish or dusky; dorsal with about 5 blackish longitudinal bands; anal with several similar indistinct blackish bands; base and axils of last dorsal and anal rays blackish; pectoral brown.

This common species is well distinguished from *Hepatus dussumieri* and other streaked species by the black ink-like spot in the axil of the dorsal and anal fins. It has several times been recorded under the erroneous name of *Acanthurus lineolatus*, but the species originally called by that name must be something else, probably *H. dussumieri*. Numerous specimens were obtained by us at Honolulu, where it was also secured by Doctor Jenkins and Doctor Wood. Other examples were collected by the *Albatross* at Laysan Island. Our specimens are 3 to 9.5 inches long.

321. Hepatus sandvicensis (Streets). "*Manini.*" Fig. 172.

Head 3.75 in length; depth 1.9; snout 1.4 in head; eye 3.5; interorbital 3; D. ix, 25; A. iii, 22.

Body deep, compressed, ovoid, the lower profile from mandible to anus very weakly convex; head deep, the upper profile concave from tip of snout to interorbital space, then straight to origin of dorsal; jaws low, produced, the lower inferior; mouth small; teeth compressed, crenulate; nostrils close together in front of eye, anterior larger, with small fleshy flap; last dorsal spine 1.5 in head, anterior spines graduated to last; fourth dorsal ray 1.5; caudal rather deep, emarginate, upper rays longer; pectoral a little longer than head; ventral sharp-pointed, 1.2; caudal peduncle compressed, its least depth 2.5; caudal spine very small, short, strong, 3 in head; scales very small, ctenoid, very few on vertical fins; lateral line high, arched at first below first dorsal spines, then very slightly convex to below middle of soft dorsal and along middle of side of caudal peduncle.

Color in alcohol, dull purplish gray, darker on back above; chin, breast, belly and lower surface of caudal peduncle creamy white; side with 5 narrow blackish vertical lines; first from occiput to eye, passing down below to anterior lower edge of preopercle; second from first dorsal spine to pectoral, continued down and back toward spinous anal; third beginning at sixth dorsal spine, running down to a little in front of spinous anal; fourth beginning at base of first dorsal rays and running down to first anal rays; fifth beginning at first third of soft dorsal, running down to first third of soft anal; upper portion of caudal peduncle with a short narrow blackish saddle; brown longitudinal line separating creamy area of lower surface from dark color above, running along side of throat and abdomen backwards; vertical fins dusky brown; pectoral brownish; ventrals grayish on outer portion, basally white. Described from an example (No. 03347) taken at Honolulu.

A series of specimens showing all stages of growth from the larval to the adult form was secured. In the young measuring about 20 mm. the body is perfectly transparent except a broad, vertical silvery band extending across the head and visceral region. Anterior edge of band passes obliquely downward and backward, just in front of orbit, to a point a little in advance of insertion of anal fins. The posterior boundary extends from nape, behind axil of pectoral, to insertion of anal. Between the

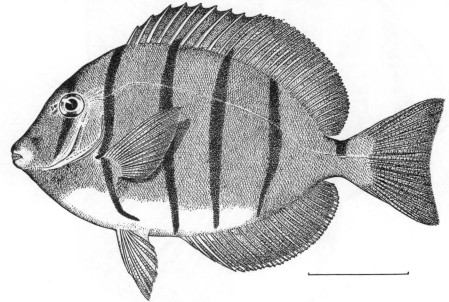

FIG. 172.—*Hepatus sandvicensis* (Streets).

lateral line and the pectoral is a posterior prolongation of the silvery band, about as large as eye. Nape, interorbital space, and a narrow band at base of caudal dusky; a row of dark dots along base of anal and a dusky spot on tip of caudal. The dusky, vertical bands of adult are first seen faintly outlined in the young of 31 mm. length; in others, no larger, the color pattern of the adult is perfectly developed. In the young the snout is shorter, anterior profile more rounded, and body deeper than in adult; head and body covered with long, narrow, vertically placed, scale-like plates; first dorsal spine serrated on anterior edge. Shortly after assuming the adult color, the length being about 32 mm., the serrations of the spine disappear and the plates are replaced by minute scales.

Teuthis elegans Garman is the young of this species. Living examples of the larval form are almost perfectly transparent except the silvery area and dusky spots, there being no blue or red tints.

This species is excessively abundant among the Hawaiian Islands about the reefs and in rocky pools. On comparison with examples of *Hepatus triostegus* from Okinawa, Japan, and from Samoa, it differs in all the salient characters pointed out by Streets. To the Hawaiian species, *Hepatus sandvicensis*, belong the specimens recorded by Jordan and Evermann from Clarion and Socorro islands. Those of Samoa and Polynesia generally are *Hepatus triostegus*.

Our very large series of specimens contains 88 from Honolulu, 82 from Hilo, 109 from Kailua, and 4 from Waianae. Specimens were obtained by the *Albatross* at Honolulu; Waialua Bay, Oahu; Hanalei Bay, Kauai; Puako Bay, Hawaii; Hilo; Necker Island; and Laysan Island.

Genus 180. ZEBRASOMA Swainson.

This genus differs from *Hepatus* in the short spinous dorsal of 4 or 5 graduated spines; soft dorsal high; snout short, projecting at an angle.

322. **Zebrasoma veliferum** (Bloch). *"Kihikihi."* Fig. 173.

Head 3.35 in length; depth 1.7; snout 1.5 in head; eye 3.35; interorbital 3.25; D. IV, 32; A. III, 24.

Body deep, rather elongate, upper profile of back slightly convex from occiput to caudal peduncle, lower profile evenly and rather strongly convex from throat to caudal peduncle; head deep, com-

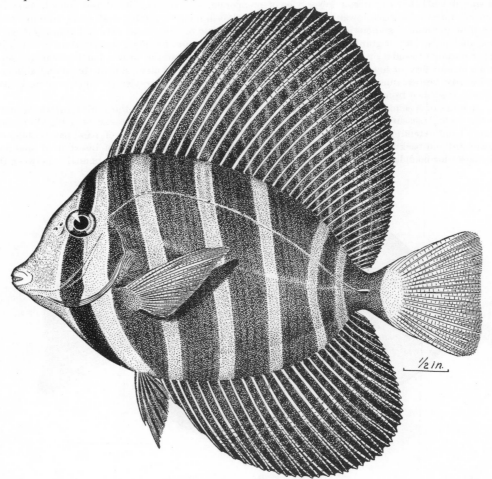

FIG. 173.—*Zebrasoma veliferum* (Bloch).

pressed, upper profile steep, undulate, that of snout concave; jaws produced, low, the lower inferior; lips rather thin, fleshy; teeth broad, compressed, the edges crenulate; mouth small, inferior; nostrils close together, anterior rounded with small flap, posterior a short oblique slit; interorbital space convex; dorsal fin very high; spines thin, slender, graduated to the last, 2.5 in body; anterior dorsal rays very high, the others gradually decreasing to last, fifth 1.8 in body; anal spines graduated to last, second 1.5 in head, third 1.25; median anal rays elongate, eighth 2.7 in body; caudal rather broad, its margin straight; pectoral pointed 3.35 in body; ventral 1.25 in head; caudal peduncle small, compressed, its least depth 3.25; caudal spine short, stout, 2 in interorbital space, depressible, not in a groove, the space about somewhat concave: scales exceedingly small, ctenoid, those about pectoral region more or less smooth; lateral line nearly concurrent with dorsal profile below base of soft dorsal.

Color in life (No. 03389), nearly black, with 6 bands of dirty white, first band beginning on lower jaw and continuing back to anterior edge of opercle and down as far as ventrals; a stripe of general body-color as wide as chin, beginning at chin and growing narrower until it ends on a line at anterior edge of gill-opening; second band including posterior portion of eye and just behind base of ventral; third band containing 2 small yellow bands; fourth, fifth, and sixth each with 1 yellow band, each of the 6 darker bands between the lighter bands also banded with yellow ones; the third and fourth with 4 bands, the fifth 3, and the sixth 2; dorsal nearly black, first 3 white bands continuing up on the dorsal; caudal same as dorsal, but slightly olivaceous toward base; other fins same as dorsal; snout and front of head with small whitish spots, the dark color forming a network around them; iris yellow; tail growing darker with age

Another example (No. 03416), dark brown in life; transverse bands of bright lemon-yellow bordered on each side by a narrow violet band, which is more distinct on forward part of body, the sixth anal ray yellow; dorsal and anal dark, nearly black; dorsal with narrow transverse bands of violet; pectoral with yellow toward base; ventrals dark.

Color in alcohol, blackish brown, anterior half of head, throat and chest, and 6 narrow pale vertical bands on side, whitish, one behind eye silvery; first band running from just before first dorsal spine down side of head and chest including posterior margin of eye, to root of ventral, second beginning at last dorsal spine and first 2 dorsal rays, and running to spinous anal; the others run from the sixth and seventh, eleventh and twelfth, nineteenth and twentieth, and twenty-fifth and twenty-sixth dorsal rays, to the base of anal; last lateral vertical bar ill defined; dorsal and anal blackish brown, with about 12 vertical narrow gray lines on posterior half of dorsal, the second and third vertical bands extending a very short distance on basal part of dorsal parallel with spines and rays; anal with a few indistinct gray lines similar to those on posterior part of dorsal; caudal whitish; pectorals grayish; ventrals blackish.

In adult examples the side has 4 or 5 blackish vertical lines running down each dark band; anterior part of head with dark brown reticulations, the anterior pale bars with dark brown vertical lines on reticulations; caudal dark brown; dorsal and anal blackish. Described chiefly from an example (No. 03416) taken at Honolulu.

This species is fairly common at Honolulu, where specimens were obtained by Jenkins, by the *Albatross*, and by us. The 16 examples which we have examined range from 3.1 to 11.5 inches in length. This species, common at Samoa, is doubtless Bloch's *A. velifer*.

323. Zebrasoma flavescens (Bennett). "*Laipala.*" Plate LIX.

Head 3.75 in length; depth 1.75; eye 4 in head; snout 1; interorbital 3.25; D. v, 24; A. iii, 19.

Body deep, compressed; head deep, compressed, pointed, the upper profile very concave in front of eye; snout long, produced, pointed; jaws produced, the lower inferior; lips rather thin; mouth small, inferior; teeth compressed, rather broad, edges crenulate; nostrils close together, anterior a little lower and larger, with a small fleshy flap; dorsal spines graduated to the last, which is longest, 1.25 in head, anterior dorsal rays longest, the fourth 1.1; third anal spine longest, 1.75; caudal rather broad, its margin straight; pectoral equal to head; ventral sharply pointed, 1.2; ventral spine sharp pointed; caudal peduncle compressed, its least depth 2.5; side of caudal peduncle in front and posterior portion of side with a large tract of hooked villiform prickles; caudal spine strong, depressible in a furrow between prickles, 4 in head; scales small, forming a finely roughened surface; lateral line nearly concurrent with profile of back at first, running closer to it posteriorly and disappearing at patch of villiform bristles below posterior dorsal rays. Description based on an example (No. 05034) 7.3 inches long from Honolulu.

Color in life (No. 03504), body and fins everywhere uniformly chrome-yellow; iris same color; pectoral sometimes with a tinge of golden over the yellow and the middle of side of body sometimes lighter yellow; spine on caudal peduncle white. Another example (No. 03537) had edge of spinous dorsal and anterior part of anal fin with a line of bright cadmium. Color in alcohol very pale yellowish white. This species is often dark olive in color, but from Hawaii we have yellow examples only.

We have 3 examples from Kailua and 8 from Honolulu, 1 of which is from the collection of Doctor Jenkins. These examples are 3.2 to 7.3 inches long.

The young (*Zebrasoma virgatum*), is thus described:

Depth 2.33; D. iv, 31, its height 1.25 in depth; A. iii, 24; 14 teeth in upper jaw, 16 in lower; edges of upper teeth conspicuously lobed; lower teeth each with a strong median point, on each side of which are 2 conspicuous notches; eye situated well back.

Coloration of body brownish yellow crossed by about 25 straight bands of deeper color reaching the ventral region; head speckled with little blue spots, the end of snout being of a deeper color than rest of head; a more deeply colored band extending from nape across eye; 4 moderate bands extending to lower part of body and touching posterior edge of eye, continuing to base of ventrals, the second band reaching to base of anal; dorsal and anal deeply colored with clearer portions and yellowish bands obliquely parallel posteriorly; caudal brownish yellow, with the posterior part more deeply colored. Hawaii.

Genus 181. CTENOCHÆTUS Gill.

Teeth movable, strongly serrate; otherwise essentially as in *Hepatus*. Herbivorous species of dull coloration; 8 dorsal spines.

325. Ctenochætus striatus (Quoy & Gaimard). "*Kale.*" Fig. 174.

Head 3.5 in length; depth 1.8; snout 1.8 in head; eye 4; interorbital 2.75; D. viii, 27; A. iii, 25.

Body deep, short, compressed; upper and lower profiles evenly convex; head deep, compressed, upper profile evenly convex from tip of snout to occiput; snout long, jaws low, very slightly produced; lips thin, teeth slender, dilated, compressed at end, the outer side crenulate; margin of preopercle very oblique, angle below anterior margin of eye; interorbital space broad, elevated, convex; nostrils small, close together, anterior circular, with small, thin, fleshy flap, posterior short, slit-like; dorsal spines graduated to last, which is 1.65 in head; soft dorsal with rays of last third produced in a sharp point, sixteenth ray 1.25; anal spines graduated to last, which is 2; posterior anal rays produced in a point, thirteenth 1.2; caudal rather large, broad, deeply emarginate, upper and lower rays produced in points; pectoral broad, 3.25 in body; ventrals long, sharply pointed, 3.2 in body; ventral spine sharply pointed, 2 in head; caudal peduncle compressed, its depth 2.35; caudal spine long, depressible in a groove, 3; scales very small, ctenoid; lateral line nearly concurrent with dorsal profile, running down behind to caudal spine; very minute scales on basal portions of vertical fins.

Color in life (No. 03300), side coppery red with about 30 narrow pale blue, somewhat wavy, irregular longitudinal lines; head dark brown; dorsal much like side; anal solid bluish-black; cauda

FIG. 174.—*Ctenochætus striatus* (Quoy & Gaimard); after Günther.

coppery black; ventrals rosy, black at tips; pectoral orange, paler below; iris blue surrounded by orange.

Color of an example from Hilo when fresh, darkish black, faintly streaked with dark reddish.

Color in alcohol, deep chocolate brown; snout, jaws, ridge of the head, ventrals and vertical fins, blackish; side with about 40 narrow grayish horizontal lines, those above running up vertically on dorsal, those below running down vertically on anal; pectorals dilute grayish-green. Described chiefly from an example (No. 03728) from Honolulu.

This species, described originally from Guam, is rather common at Honolulu, from which place we have 11 specimens, 7 collected by Doctor Jenkins. It was also obtained at Honolulu by the *Albatross*, and we have 3 examples from Kailua, 1 from Hilo, and 5 from Napoopoo, Hawaii. Our specimens are 4.4 to 7.6 inches long.

The original description of this species was doubtless based on very young examples. *Acanthurus strigosus*, described by Bennett, from Honolulu, is the adult of the same species.

Genus 182. ACANTHURUS Forskål.

Body oblong, compressed, covered with small roughish scales; tail with 2 large immovable, bony, keeled plates, these entirely wanting in very young individuals; head in the adult with the forehead prominent, developing a very long horn above the eyes, this wanting in the young; teeth small, in one series, slightly compressed incisors, usually with serrate edges; ventral fins incomplete, the rays I, 3; dorsal with 5 or 6 spines; anal with 2 spines; intestinal canal elongate.

Herbivorous fishes of the East Indian and Polynesian seas, some of them remarkable for the bony frontal projection and for the large ornate caudal spines.

326. Acanthurus incipiens Jenkins. Fig. 175.

Head 2.75 in length; depth 2.2; eye 3.4 in head; snout 1.4; interorbital space 3; D. v, 28; A. ii, 27; P. 18.

Body oblong-ovate, compressed, the greatest depth under third dorsal spine; head short; anterior profile from tip of snout to front of eye concave, a distinct prominence in front of eye at level of its lower border, from which the profile is nearly straight to origin of dorsal; ventral outline strongly convex from tip of snout to base of ventrals; dorsal and ventral outlines from origin of dorsal and ventral fins to base of caudal peduncle each in a long low curve, most convex anteriorly; head short; snout blunt; mouth small, horizontal, below axis of body; jaws each with a single series of fine, sharp, close-set, finely serrulate canine teeth; a short-curved groove in front of eye below nostrils, its length 2 in eye; gill-opening long and oblique, extending far anteriorly, the upper end at vertical of first dorsal spine; interorbital space not strongly convex, the median ridge low. Body rough velvety; each side of caudal peduncle with 2 very low weak horny plates, without spines, the distance between them 1.5 to 2 in eye; first dorsal spine rather strong, moderately rough, its length 1.7 in head; other dorsal spines smoother and more slender, the fifth 2 in head; soft dorsal not high, the rays of about uniform length, the longest about 2.5 in head; anal spines rather short and slender, the second equal to diameter of orbit, soft anal similar to dorsal, equally high; caudal deeply emarginate, the free edge of the 2 lobes forming a broad angle; upper lobe of the caudal somewhat the longer, its length nearly equaling head; ventral spines moderate, reaching base of first anal spine, their length 2 in head; pectoral short, its length a little less than snout.

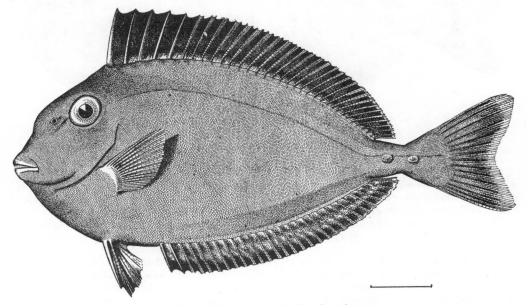

Fig. 175.—*Acanthurus incipiens* Jenkins; from the type.

Color in alcohol, pale dusky olivaceous, lower parts palest; dorsal and anal with pale purplish brown, mottled with lighter; edge of dorsal and anal each with a narrow blackish border, edged posteriorly with whitish; caudal dirty brownish, narrowly edged with white, ventrals whitish, dusky at tips; pectoral dusky at base, lighter at tip.

The only known examples of this species are the type obtained by Doctor Jenkins at Honolulu in 1889, a single cotype secured by the *Albatross* at Honolulu in 1896, and 2 specimens which we have from Samoa. Length, 12 inches or less.

327. Acanthurus brevirostris (Cuvier & Valenciennes). "*Kalalolo.*" Fig. 176.

Head 4 in length; depth 2.5 ; eye 4 in head; snout 1.6; interorbital 2.9; D. vi, 27; A. ii, 28; P. 16.

Body oblong-ovate, the dorsal and ventral profiles equally curved from vertical at base of pectoral to caudal peduncle; a long pointed horn extending forward and very slightly downward from upper margin of eye, its direction nearly parallel with axis of body, its length equal to distance from tip of snout to anterior edge of pupil, its inferior edge about one-fifth greater than diameter of orbit and projecting beyond snout a distance nearly equal to diameter of eye; mouth very small, horizontal, slightly below axis of body; each jaw with a single series of very short close-set bluntly pointed canines, their edges faintly serrulate; a short, curved groove below nostrils in front of eye, its length 1.4 in eye; gill-opening long and much curved, the anterior arm extending forward to vertical of nostrils, length of slit equal to distance from tip of snout to posterior edge of pupil; a short groove extending upward and forward just back of angle of mouth, its length 1.4 in eye; interorbital space rather broad, convex, the median ridge scarcely appearing until on occiput.

Body and head smooth and velvety when stroked from head backward, but very rough in opposite direction; each side of caudal peduncle with 2 moderate bony plates, each plate with a rather high median keel, highest anteriorly, not hooked in any of our specimens; lateral line complete, appearing as a slight ridge or raised tube, arched somewhat above the pectoral, thence following curvature of the back to caudal peduncle.

First dorsal spine strong, rough laterally, slightly broadened toward base, inserted in front of upper end of gill-opening, its length 2.2 in head; second and third dorsal spines a little longer, fourth to sixth a little shorter, the spines alternately stronger and weaker; dorsal rays weak, their length about equal to that of the spines; anal spines slender, the second the longer, about 1.4 in first

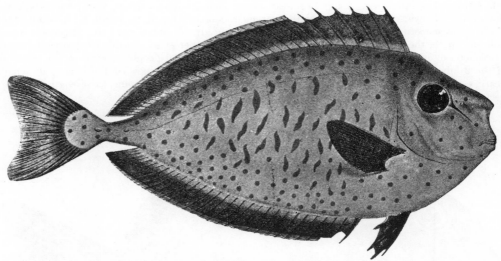

Fig. 176.—*Acanthurus brevirostris* (Cuvier & Valenciennes); after Günther.

dorsal spine; caudal emarginate, the distal edges of the lobes forming a shallow reentrant angle, the lobes not produced, their length about 1.2 in head; ventral spines slender, their tips reaching base of second anal spine, their length 1.9 in head; pectoral moderate, 1.4 in head.

Color of nearly fresh example (No. 03354), blackish olive; side of head and body covered profusely with small black specks; fins all brownish black; caudal palest, a black blotch on its base, the edge dark; iris pale yellow.

Another example 7 inches long (No. 03398), when fresh, was dark drab, almost dove-color above, paler below; a pale horizontal streak below eye, which shows faintly as a pale lateral streak; caudal peduncle and spines of same color, dorsal and anal unmarked, the spines drab, the membranes darker; caudal dusky at base, then broadly creamy, the posterior edge blackish drab; pectoral and ventrals also drab, the edge paler; no yellow, blue, or red markings or shades anywhere; posterior edge of caudal black.

Still another example (No. 03538) has the general color dark brown with bluish showing through, the blue being evident on lower parts of body, over the head, breast and belly, and on region along edge of opercle; fins with a distinctly bluish tinge; side of body with many transverse rows of dots and short bars of darker brown.

The species shows considerable variation in form and color, the former varying much with age. In our smallest individuals the depth is greater (2.25 in length), the back is somewhat more arched, and the horn is shorter, not projecting beyond the snout. Not until in examples about 8 inches long does it project beyond the snout, and in some individuals 9 inches long it scarcely projects. In the young (7 inches) the caudal spines are very small and weak. They usually, but not always, grow stronger with age. The distance between them varies somewhat. In one example (No. 05668) they are much closer together than in others of the same size.

The color seems to vary without reference to size. Most of our examples in alcohol show few or no dark spots or vertical bars, while one 11-inch example (No. 03354) is profusely covered on head and body with small round black spots which on posterior half of side tend to arrange themselves in vertical bars. Another example 8 inches long (No. 02968) is almost without spots, but has about 25 rather distinct dark-brown vertical lines.

One example (No. 02968), which has been in alcohol a year, still shows tip of tail sulphur-yellow, pale within; side with vertical darker lines. These variations are all within the species.

Description based chiefly on a specimen (No. 05668) 11 inches long.

This fish is of wide distribution, having been recorded from Ceylon, the Malay Archipelago, Macassar, Amboyna, Port Resolution, Aneityum, Kingsmill Island, Tahiti, and the Hawaiian Islands, in which latter region it is not rare, though previously recorded only by Doctor Jenkins. Our collection contains 12 examples (4 obtained by Jenkins), all from Honolulu. Specimens were also obtained by the *Albatross* at Honolulu.

328. Acanthurus unicornis (Forskål).　"*Kala.*"

Head 3.9 in length; depth 2; eye 4 in head; snout 1.2; interorbital 3.4; D. vi, 30; A. ii, 28; P. iv; V. i, 3.

Body short, deep, and compressed, elevated anteriorly, highest at beginning of dorsal; snout pointed, usually projecting behind the frontal horn; profile of snout straight from tip to the long bluntly pointed or conic horn which projects forward and downward from preocular region, this horn varying greatly with age, most prominent in the adult, scarcely developed in the young, in which it appears merely as a blunt projection, the upper profile of the snout being concave; teeth small, bluntly pointed canines, not serrated, close-set and slightly recurved; a short, nearly vertical shallow groove in front of eye under nostrils, its length equal to half diameter of eye; gill-opening long, oblique, strongly curved, its length nearly equaling that of head; origin of dorsal fin over upper end of gill-opening; dorsal spines strong, rough, the first 2 in head, the others successively shorter; dorsal rays slender, weak, the longest about equal to first spine; origin of anal fin under base of sixth dorsal spine; anal spines short, about 2 in first dorsal spine; anal rays short, 1.25 in first dorsal spine; caudal deeply lunate, the lobes pointed; ventral spine rough, sharp pointed, 2 in head; pectoral short, 1.4 in head. Skin uniform, rough velvety; caudal peduncle with 2 low, spiniferous plates on each side, distance between them about two-thirds diameter of eye.

Color in life of a specimen (No. 02980) 12.5 inches long, dirty olive, paler below; top of head and horn dark olivaceous; caudal spines pale blue; dorsal fin pale blue, crossed by about 6 narrow pale yellow lines, curving upward and backward, edge of fin narrowly blue; anal similarly marked, the blue border broader; caudal dirty olive, darkest in the center and on the upper and lower margins, posterior part pale olive; pectoral pale, brownish underneath; axil pale, with 2 or 3 small blue spots; ventrals pale. An example (No. 02997) 7 inches long, did not differ particularly from larger examples; general color pale olive, yellowish anteriorly; snout and top of head back to dorsal blackish; dorsal fin pale orange, crossed by narrow pale blue lines, the fin edged with blue; anal pale orange, with 2 broad pale blue bands, a narrower darker blue band at edge, with a narrow whitish border; caudal dusky; pectoral pale; ventrals whitish, darkish at tips; iris silvery, whitish yellow, a dark spot above and another below. Another example (No. 03449), had the upper part of the body gray, the lower part yellow forward, with golden tinge along region of anal; dorsal fin dirty yellow, with very narrow blue border; anal golden, with 2 narrow bands of bluish white parallel with outline of body, outer border same as dorsal, with narrow blue line; caudal grayish; ventrals yellowish; pectoral colorless. An example from Hilo when fresh was dirty olive, spines violet blue.

Color in alcohol, dusky brownish above, paler below; caudal spines black; dorsal fin dark brown along base, the membranes above lighter brown crossed by pale bluish stripes extending upward and backward; anal similar to soft dorsal; ventrals pale, dusky at tip; pectoral dusky.

This curious and interesting fish is abundant among the Hawaiian Islands, and is widely distributed in the tropical Pacific and the East Indies to the Red Sea. Jenkins obtained 9 examples at Honolulu, and we have 10 from the same place; also 3 specimens from Hilo. The *Albatross* found it at Honolulu and at Puako Bay, Hawaii.

Our specimens are 4.5 to 14 inches long.

Genus 183. CALLICANTHUS Swainson.

This genus differs from *Acanthurus* in having no horn upon forehead. Tail with 2 bony plates, with or without spines; dorsal spines 5 or 6; teeth not serrulate. Not very distinct from *Acanthurus*.

329. Callicanthus lituratus (Forster).　Plate LX[a] and Fig. 177.

Head 3.8 in length; depth 2.2; eye 5 in head; snout 1.2; interorbital 3.4; D. vi, 29; A. ii, 30; P. 16.

Body oblong-ovate, the greatest depth at base of third dorsal spine; dorsal outline nearly straight from tip of snout to origin of dorsal fin, thence in a long low curve to caudal peduncle; no horn or prominence on forehead; ventral outline strongly convex from posterior part of chin to origin of anal, thence curved uniformly with the back; chin strongly concave, the snout projecting; mouth small, horizontal, in line with axis of body; jaws each with a single series of close-set, bluntly pointed canines of moderate size, the edges not serrulate; groove in front of eye short, not half length of orbit; gill-opening long and oblique, equaling snout, its upper end in line between upper base of pectoral and base of second dorsal spine; interorbital evenly convex, the preocular edge of orbit somewhat prominent. Body velvety; each side of caudal peduncle with 2 strong horny plates each with a strong, broad flat spine curved forward, these little developed in the young; in the example upon which this description is chiefly based (No. 03493, 12.25 inches long), these spines are nearly as wide at base as high, the chord of the posterior edge being longer than orbit; distance between tips 3 in head; first dorsal strong, broad at base, rugose, its length about 2.1 in head; dorsal spines heteracanthous, alternately strong and weak on opposite sides; dorsal rays somewhat longer than the spines, especially anteriorly; anal spines shorter, of about equal length, about 3.6 in head; ventral spines strong, reaching midway between bases of first and second anal spines, their length 2 in head, pectoral longer, 1.2 in head; caudal evenly lunate, the lobes greatly produced and filamentous in the adult male the filaments in an example 12.25 inches long (No. 03493) being 3.5 times length of middle rays; in specimens Nos. 05379 and 05381, which are nearly of equal size, the former has the lobes more than 3 times the middle rays, while in the latter they are not at all filamentous, the fin being simply lunate.

Color in life (No. 03386), nearly uniform black, slightly olivaceous below, a lemon-yellow stripe in front of eye forward on snout and curving downward just back of angle of mouth; another yellow stripe beginning behind eye extending downward as a narrow line along edge of preopercle, then curving forward and joining the other near angle of mouth; lips orange; breast and belly to anal with a lemon-yellow stripe blending into the general color; base of anal burnt umber, then changing to yellowish, then very black, the edge tipped with light blue; spines on caudal peduncle set in a deep orange-yellow blotch, the spines themselves blackish; caudal blackish, the produced rays entirely

Fig. 177.—*Callicanthus lituratus* (Forster); after Günther.

blackish, but the rest of the crescent with a band of yellowish-green about as wide as pupil, the edge tipped with white; dorsal black, with white stripe on distal portion extending from first ray to end of fin, outside of which is a very narrow black stripe, the edge narrowly tipped with white; dorsal spines black, the membranes black except edge of last 3 membranes which is whitish.   An example (No. 03505), taken at Honolulu July 27, had the body dark brown; an orange-yellow line from eye to angle of mouth; lips orange; line on breast and belly orange; postocular region and between eyes somewhat yellowish, anal plates orange, the interspace white, the spines brownish; dorsal fin black, a bright blue line on body at base, a narrow white line near margin, the edge black; caudal dirt brown, a subterminal yellowish-green crescent; anal orange on outer half, shading to yellow on inner third; ventrals orange; pectoral dirt brown.

Another example (No. 03493) had color in life olivaceous, blackish above, a golden patch about and behind eye, a golden line thence forward and down to angle of mouth, joining the white edge of opercle and the orange jaws, a pale blue stripe at base of dorsal, fin black with broad white upper part and some yellowish streaks on the white, edge blackish; caudal spines deep orange; caudal blackish-olive, edged with olive within and then white; anal yellowish-olive, then bright orange, its edge black, tipped with white; ventrals dirty orange; pectoral olive and black.

The colored plate in Günther's Fische der Südsee belongs to *Callicanthus garretti* (Seale). We have both *garretti* and *lituratus* from Samoa, but can not decide whether they are really distinct species. The blue line at base of dorsal is characteristic of *lituratus*. It is wanting in *garretti*. If *garretti* is valid we have specimens from Hawaii.

This appears to be one of the most common fishes of this family among the Hawaiian Islands, though it has been previously recorded only by Günther, Steindachner, and Jenkins. It is a species of wide distribution, ranging from the Red Sea throughout Polynesia. Günther recorded it from Tahiti, Aneityum, Malayan Archipelago, Red Sea, and the Hawaiian Islands, and Quoy and Gaimard from Guam.

It is represented in our collections by 26 specimens from Honolulu (7 obtained by Jenkins, 1 by

Wood, and 3 by the *Albatross* in 1896), 1 from Honuapo, Kona, and 3 from Hilo. Others are in the *Albatross* collections from Honolulu and Puako Bay. Our 30 examples are 5 to 12.25 inches long. Known also from Johnston Island.

330. Callicanthus metoposophron Jenkins. Fig. 178.

Head 4 in length; depth 2.5; eye 3.5 in head; snout 1.9; interorbital 3; D. VI, 29; A. II, 30.

Body rather oblong, greatly compressed, the greatest depth under last dorsal spine; anterior dorsal profile strongly and evenly convex from tip of snout to about fourth dorsal ray, entirely without horn or protuberance of any kind, thence less convex to caudal peduncle; ventral outline similar, but less convex; snout rather short; mouth small, horizontal, slightly below axis of body; teeth small, slender, close-set, and pointed, not serrulate, in a single series in each jaw; a short lunate groove in front of eye, its length equaling that of maxillary; gill-opening long and oblique, the lower arm extending far forward, the upper end on a level with lower edge of orbit and directly above upper base of pectoral; interorbital space moderately broad, the 2 sides meeting at a broad, rounded angle. Entire body and head finely granulated or velvety; each side of caudal peduncle with 2 weak, keeled horny plates, the

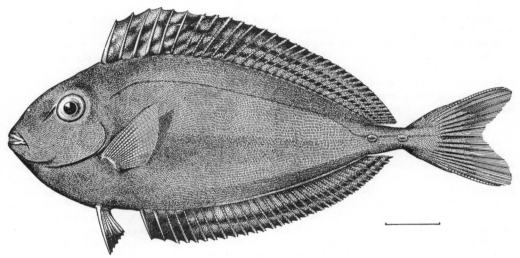

FIG. 178.—*Callicanthus metoposophron* Jenkins; from the type.

distance between them 1.4 in eye. First dorsal spine strong, roughened laterally, inserted above gill-opening; other dorsal spines slender, nearly smooth, pointed, the third longest, its length about equaling that of snout; dorsal rays slender and weak; shorter than the spines, the longest about 2.8 in head; anal spines slender and pointed, the second a little the longer, its length equaling diameter of eye; anal similar to soft dorsal but somewhat lower; caudal deeply lunate, the lobes not greatly produced, the upper slightly the longer; ventral spines long, rather strong, reaching base of second anal spine, their length equaling that of longest dorsal spine; pectoral of moderate length, 4 in head.

Color in alcohol, nearly uniform olivaceous brown, paler below; dorsal fin darker brown, crossed by 3 broad longitudinal lighter bands; on the spinous portion the lighter and darker markings are broken up into more or less vertical bars; membrane between first and second dorsal spines with a pale or transparent area on distal portion, the edge of fin narrowly black; anal similar to dorsal, but with less distinct bands; caudal uniform dusky; pectoral dusky, paler at tip; ventrals dusky.

This species was not obtained by us. The only known examples are the type and one cotype secured by Jenkins at Honolulu in 1889, length 9 and 10 inches, and another example 11.2 inches long, recently obtained by Mr. Berndt at Honolulu.

Group PLECTOGNATHI.—The Plectognathous Fishes.

One of the most important offshoots of the *Acanthopteri* is the group or order *Plectognathi*, including the 3 suborders of *Sclerodermi*, *Ostracodermi*, and *Gymnodontes*. The extremes of this group show a remarkable divergence from the usual type of spiny-rayed fishes. The more generalized forms are, however, very close to the group called *Squamipinnes*, and especially to the family of *Teuthididæ*. There can be no doubt of the common origin of *Balistidæ* and *Acanthuridæ* and that the divergence is comparatively recent. The close connection of these groups leads us to subordinate the *Plectognathi* to the *Acanthopteri* and to place its 3 suborders in their natural position as an offshoot from the *Squamipinnes*. The Plectognathi may be thus defined:

Scapula suspended to the cranium by a post-temporal which is short, undivided, and ankylosed to the epiotic. Premaxillaries usually coossified with the maxillaries behind and the dentary bones with the articular; interopercle a slender rod; lower pharyngeal bones distinct; upper pharyngeals laminar, usually vertical and transverse; skin usually with rough shields or scales or bony plates; skeleton imperfectly ossified, the number of vertebræ usually small, typically fewer than 24 (usually 14 to 20), rarely considerably increased. Gill-openings restricted to the sides; ventral fins reduced or wanting, the pelvic bones usually elongate; spinous dorsal small or wanting; air-bladder without duct. Fishes chiefly of the Tropics, mostly inactive and depending on their tough skin or bony or spinous armature for their protection.

Suborder SCLERODERMI.

The Sclerodermi may be defined as Plectognathous fishes with a spinous dors.. composed of one or more spines inserted just behind the cranium; body of the normal fish-like shape; scales rough, or spinigerous, of regular form; jaws with distinct teeth, conical or incisor-like.

Family LXXVI. BALISTIDÆ.—Trigger-fishes.

Body oblong or ovate, moderately compressed, covered with rather large, rough scales or scutes of various forms, not forming an immovable carapace; lateral line obscure or wanting; mouth small, terminal, and low; jaws short, each with about 1 series of separate, incisor-like teeth; eye near occiput; preorbital very deep; no barbels; gill-openings small, slit-like, above or in front of pectoral fins, not before eyes; dorsal fins 2, the anterior of 2 or 3 spines, the first highest and very strong, the second locking it in erection; second dorsal remote from the first, of many soft rays. Shore fishes of the tropical seas, of rather large size, carnivorous or partly herbivorous, very rarely used as food, many of them reputed to be poisonous.

Genus 184. BALISTES (Artedi) Linnæus. Trigger-fishes.

Body compressed, covered with thick, rough scales or plates of moderate size, 50 to 80 in a lengthwise series; a naked groove before eye below nostrils; lateral line more or less developed, very slender, undulate, conspicuous only when the scales are dry, extending on the cheeks; pelvic flap large, movable, supported by a series of slender, pungent spines; caudal peduncle compressed, its scales armed or unarmed, with or without spines or differentiated tubercles similar to those on rest of body; gill-opening with enlarged bony scutes behind it; cheeks entirely scaly, without naked patches or grooves; each jaw with irregular, incisor-like teeth, usually 4 on each side in each jaw; first dorsal of 3 spines, the anterior of which is much the largest, the second acting as a trigger, locking the first when erected; the third nearly as large as second and remote from it; second dorsal and anal long, similar to each other; caudal fin rounded, with the outer rays much produced in the adult; branchiostegals 6; vertebræ 7+10. Species rather few, chiefly American; some of them straying to the old world.

331. Balistes nycteris (Jordan & Evermann). Fig. 179.

Head 3.5 in length; depth 1.9; eye 5 in head; snout 1.25; interorbital 2.6; preorbital 1.5; D. iii–33; A. 29; scales about 80.

Body short, stout, deep and greatly compressed; head short, the dorsal and ventral profiles about equally curved; caudal peduncle short, compressed, its least depth about twice diameter of eye, its

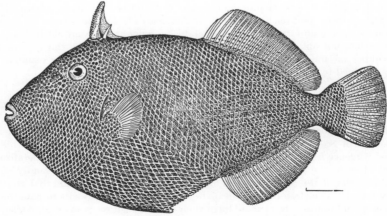

Fig. 179.—*Balistes nycteris* (Jordan & Evermann); from the type.

least width about equal to diameter of eye; a short horizontal groove in front of eye below nostrils; nostrils small, close together, in front of upper part of eye; teeth broad, close set, forming a continuous plate, teeth not united, however; lips thin; mouth small, horizontal, in axis of body, lower jaw very slightly the longer; gill-opening short, nearly vertical; a group of bony scutes under pectoral back of gill-opening, one of these considerably enlarged; scales regularly arranged in rows, their surfaces granular; lateral line beginning at posterior edge of eye, ascending to within 7 scales of spinous dorsal and continuing to near origin of soft dorsal, where it disappears; scales on posterior portion of body and on caudal peduncle each with a slightly raised crest at center, these forming series of ridges along the side. First dorsal spine strong, blunt and rough, its length about 2 in head; second dorsal spine shorter and much weaker, its length scarcely more than one-third that of first; third dorsal spine remote from the second and very short, not extending above the dorsal groove; soft dorsal gently rounded, its rays of approximately equal length, the longest equaling distance from tip of snout to posterior edge of eye; base of soft dorsal slightly greater than distance from tip of snout to posterior base of first dorsal spine, or equaling distance from tip of snout to lower base of pectoral axil; anal similar to soft dorsal, the rays somewhat longer, the base somewhat shorter; caudal short and rounded, the rays about 1.75 in head; pectoral short, the upper rays longest, about 3 in head.

Color in alcohol, rich brownish or velvety black; spinous dorsal black; soft dorsal pale yellowish or whitish, margined with black, the lower half crossed by 4 narrow parallel black lines; anal similar to soft dorsal, but with only 2 narrow black lines on its basal half; caudal dusky, yellowish at tip; pectoral yellowish.

Only one specimen obtained, type, No. 50821, U.S.N.M. (field No. 05089), 6.25 inches long, Honolulu.

332. Balistes fuscolineatus Seale.

Head 3.5 in length; depth 2; eye 4.5 in head; snout 1.65; interorbital 2.3; D. III–33; A. 30; scales 54, 30 from vent to spinous dorsal; first dorsal spine 1.65 in head, equal to snout; longest dorsal ray 2.2; longest anal ray 2.2; longest pectoral 2.25.

Body oblong, compressed, blunter anteriorly; head short, deep, compressed, upper and lower outlines evenly arched; eye small, high, posterior; snout blunt; mouth small, terminal; jaws equal; lips thick; teeth incisor-like, with sharp notches, giving some of them a canine-like appearance; origin of spinous dorsal midway between eye and gill-opening, first spine strong, blunt, with 4 rows of decurved short spines, 2 rows on anterior face and 1 on each side; second dorsal spine 3 in first; dorsal and anal low, outlines slightly rounded, last rays 2 in longest rays; dorsal base equal to distance from anterior base of spinous dorsal to lower edge of lower lip; anal base equal to distance from origin of spinous dorsal to origin of soft dorsal; caudal rounded, its middle ray about 2 in head, slightly shorter than first dorsal spine; ventral spine short, broad, and movable only at tip; pectoral short, broad, and rounded; body and head entirely covered with scales, those of anterior portion of body and head slightly enlarged; 6 or 7 enlarged osseous plates, each with straight lines from center to edge, behind gill-opening; 6 or 7 rows of small spines or raised tubercles on the center of each scale on posterior portion of body.

Color in life, silvery, with more or less opalescent reflections; 3 narrow dusky lines extending from anterior margin of orbit horizontally forward over snout; another dusky line over snout just above upper lip; 2 dusky lines over interorbital space; 2 rather indistinct dusky lines along base of dorsal fins, the lower of these lines beginning at orbit; also a narrow indistinct dusky line extending from posterior margin of orbit obliquely back and down to slightly above anal fin; another short dark line from upper posterior edge of orbit to axis of pectoral; 2 narrow dusky lines extending along bases of ventral and anal fins; spinous dorsal black; soft dorsal, pectoral, ventral spine, and anal fin white; caudal dusky. (Seale.)

Color in alcohol, grayish olivaceous above, lighter below; the narrow stripes across snout and interorbital dark; soft dorsal and anal pale, with indications of dark mottling; spinous dorsal dark brown; caudal color of upper part of body; pectoral pale.

One specimen, No. 03559, 5.65 inches long, from Honolulu. This and the type are the only known specimens.

333. Balistes vidua Solander. "Humuhumu hiukole;" "Humuhumu uli." Plate LXI.

Head 3.5 in length; depth 2; eye 5.4 in head; snout 1.5; interorbital 2.5; D. III, 34; A. 30; scales 60, 38 from vent to origin of spinous dorsal; first dorsal spine 2 in head; longest dorsal ray 1.3; longest anal ray equal to snout; pectoral 2.25 in head.

Body oblong, compressed, more blunt anteriorly; head short, deep, compressed; eye small, high, posterior; snout thick and blunt; mouth small, terminal; jaws equal; teeth notched, incisor-like, the 2 anterior teeth of lower jaw not notched, but broad and sharp, the next 2 teeth with the anterior portion produced and hooked backward, their inner side with a grinding process; origin of spinous dorsal over gill-opening; soft dorsal and anal slightly concave, the anterior rays being produced; caudal truncate; ventral spine very short and blunt; pectoral short, slightly rounded; scales covering entire body and head, those on median portion of body largest; a distinct groove in front of eye (inadvertently omitted by the artist in the drawing); a series of osseous plates behind gill-opening; a slight evidence of rows of small spines on median rows of scales on posterior part of body. Young examples have spines on side of caudal peduncle.

Color in life, uniformly dark brown with tinge of olive; membranes of spinous dorsal olive; soft dorsal and anal white, with a narrow black border along anterior and distal margins; distal portion of caudal peduncle white, fin light red, the upper and lower margins each with a narrow black line; pectoral rays bright yellow; faint violet at angles of mouth; iris yellow.

A specimen from Hilo showed in life, body blackish olive with obsolete traces of rows of yellowish spots below, which fade at death; first dorsal and pectoral dull olive; caudal broadly white at base, the rest of fin bright flesh color, its upper and lower edge narrowly blackish; second dorsal and anal pure translucent white with broad black edge.

Color in alcohol, dark brown; spinous dorsal dark brown; dorsal and anal white, edged with black; caudal white, upper and lower edges black; pectoral white.

The above description based chiefly upon No. 03140, a specimen 9.5 inches long, from Honolulu.

334. Balistes bursa Lacépède. "Humuhumu lei." Fig. 180.

Head 3 in length; depth 2.1; eye 5 in head; snout 1.35; interorbital 3.3; D. III, 27 (27–29); A. 24 (24–27); scales 50, 29 from vent to first dorsal spine; length of first dorsal 1.75 in head, equal to outer caudal rays; longest dorsal ray equal to longest anal or pectoral, 2.5 in head.

FIG. 180.—*Balistes bursa* Lacépède; after Bleeker.

Body oblong, compressed; head short, deep, compressed; eye small, high, posterior; snout thick, blunt; mouth small, terminal; lips thick; jaws equal; sharp, uneven, incisor-like teeth, those of upper jaw more distinctly notched, in the 2 anterior ones the inner notch is produced to a point, giving the teeth a canine appearance; origin of spinous dorsal slightly posterior to base of pectoral; first spine short, thick, blunt, and rugose; soft dorsal low, ends slightly rounded, rest of outline nearly straight; anal similar to dorsal; caudal subtruncate, slightly convex; ventral spine short, broad, movable; scales covering the entire body and head; a patch of osseous plates behind gill-opening; the median part of each scale on posterior part of body with spinous tubercles, these forming stout, short, sharp spines posteriorly, weakening anteriorly, the tubercles and spines forming elevated lines along each series of scales, extending anteriorly to pectoral region.

Color in life, light drab, with darker cloudings; a narrow distinct white line from near angle of mouth to near origin of soft anal, which returns along base of ventral to base of ventral spine; an olivaceous dash extending in a curve from upper part of base of pectoral upward and backward toward middle of, but not quite reaching, the first dorsal fin; another from above and through the eye downward and backward to lower part of base of pectoral; throat and belly, below white line, light; first dorsal olivaceous with white; second dorsal and anal transparent; caudal dusky; inside of mouth black. (Jenkins.)

A color note taken from No. 03503 when alive, gives the general color light olive; the markings about eye dark olive; eye blue; line from mouth to anal bright white, area within this line white; membrane of anterior part of spinous dorsal dark olive, membrane and posterior part white; soft dorsal and anal transparent, their bases with a dark olive line; caudal dusky.

Another example, No. 03518, showed in life, in addition to the above markings, a bright yellow area along back in region under spine back as far as under posterior portion of soft dorsal. This color soon disappeared.

A specimen from Hilo showed body blackish drab; a curved blackish bar below eye, and another meeting it at an acute angle from eye across gill-opening; a blackish bar across base of pectoral; a bluish white line across mouth; a curved line from mouth to above vent then turned forward across pelvic flap, bounding the pale drab color of belly; first dorsal blackish, edge of pelvic flap black; dorsal and anal grayish white with a blackish line at base; pectoral and caudal drab, blackish at base.

Color in alcohol, brownish olivaceous, lighter below; a fine grayish white line from angle of mouth to vent, where it forms an edge to a black spot covering the vent and anal region to base of anal spine; rest of region within this line grayish white; a vertical crescent-shaped black band across posterior portion of eye, backward to below base of first dorsal and downward to lower base of pectoral; another similar band through upper base of pectoral, behind gill-opening and upward toward second dorsal spine, reaching a line on upper edge of orbit; first and second dorsal spines and membrane brown, upper part of rest of fin and edge of membrane between first and second spines white; soft dorsal and anal pale; caudal dusky. Description based chiefly upon No. 03518, a specimen 7.75 inches long, from Honolulu.

We have 16 specimens 4.75 to 8 inches long, all from Honolulu, where the species is common about the reefs.

335. Balistes capistratus Shaw. *"Humuhumu mimi."* Fig. 181.

Head 3 in length; depth 2.1; eye 7 in head, —5.5 in smaller examples; snout 1.4; interorbital 3.4; D. iii, 30; A. 27; scales 56, 33 from vent to first dorsal spine; longest dorsal spine 2 in head, equal to depth of caudal at root of rays; longest dorsal ray equal to longest anal ray, 3 in head; pectoral 3 in head.

Body oblong, compressed; head blunt, compressed; eye small, high, posterior; snout blunt, thick; mouth small; lips thick; jaws equal; teeth incisor-like, with a sharp projection on the anterior side; this more marked in upper jaw, giving the teeth a somewhat hooked canine appearance. Origin of first dorsal slightly posterior to upper base of pectoral (this base being midway between eye and dorsal); first spine strong, blunt, and rugose; dorsal and anal low, outline slightly rounded; caudal truncate, subtruncate, or slightly doubly convex in smaller examples; ventral spine short, broad, and blunt.

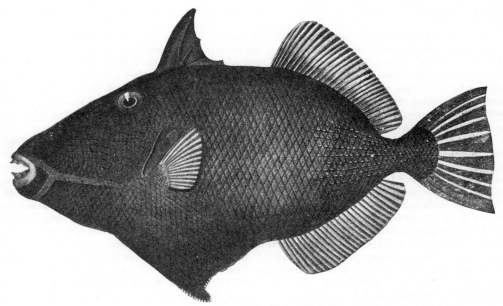

FIG. 181.—*Balistes capistratus* Shaw; after Bleeker.

Scales cover entire head and body; osseous scutes behind gill-opening; a tubercle on the anterior median portion of scales on the posterior median part of body and caudal peduncle, forming 7 or 8 rows of tubercles.

Color in life, body uniform light brown, fins same color, plain; rosy line beginning slightly behind and below angle of mouth, extending backward and slightly downward to vertical from eye, here joined by another of same color extending under chin. Another specimen showed membrane of first dorsal olivaceous, with a black blotch; scaled skin pushed back from the chin shows bright orange-yellow; outer margins of soft dorsal and anal light.

A specimen from Hilo showed body dirty olive-brown; fins dirty olive-brown, dorsal and anal somewhat paler along the edge; a golden half ring along lower jaw, a faint whitish half ring behind it, then another on chin still fainter, this prolonged backward a little at the angle, sometimes forming a distinct stripe back to breast.

Color in alcohol, brown; dorsals, caudal and anal a slightly darker brown than body with tips of fins lighter; a black blotch on upper part of first membrane of spinous dorsal; pectoral dusky at base, tips pale dusky whitish; a yellowish white ring around lower jaw a short distance from the lip; a straight yellowish white stripe from angle of mouth through upper edge of ring and toward lower base of pectoral, not quite reaching the pectoral; this ring and stripe not very evident on some examples, and easily overlooked. Description based chiefly on No. 03139, from Honolulu. This species is common about Honolulu, from which place we have 4 other specimens. They are 8.5 to 11.75 inches long.

Genus 185. BALISTAPUS Tilesius.

This genus has the head and body closely scaled, the scales of the posterior parts more or less spinous; enlarged scales behind the gill-opening, the lateral line obsolete and no groove before the eye. Species numerous in the Indian and tropical seas, small and rather brightly colored.

336. Balistapus rectangulus (Bloch & Schneider). *"Humuhumu nukunuku apua'a."* Plate LXIII.

Head 2.6 in length; depth 2; snout 1.25 in head; eye 5.3; interorbital 3.75; D. III, 26 (24 to 26); A. 20; first dorsal spine 2.3 in head, equal to length of pectoral; longest dorsal ray 2.8; base of soft dorsal equal to snout; longest anal ray 3, base of anal 1.65 in head; scales 40, 28 from anterior base of spinous dorsal to vent; interorbital space prominent, equal to cleft of mouth.

Body oblong, compressed, dorsal and anal outlines similarly and evenly arched; head large; snout long, thick and blunt; mouth small, with thick lips; a single row of 8 sharp-notched, incisor-like teeth in each jaw; eye small, high, posterior; first dorsal commencing above the gill-opening, the first spine blunt and strong, its anterior edge rugose; soft dorsal and anal moderate, with rounded profile; caudal slightly rounded; ventral spine movable, supported by a series of slender sharp spines; pectorals broad, rounded; entire body and head scaled, some osseous plates behind the gill-opening; three and a half rows of sharp recurved spines on side of caudal peduncle. In a smaller example, 5 inches long, the upper row is the short row, in the larger examples, 8 inches long, the rows are irregular and sometimes as many as 6 are present; the number of rows does not seem to be uniform.

Color in life, upper part of body and head light brown, becoming lighter toward snout; 3 narrow black bands reaching from one eye to the other, the borders and spaces, wider than the bands, green; the posterior band on head passing downward, and after an abrupt bend backward just above gill-opening, becoming a violet line running along middle of body to a vertical from tip of third dorsal spine, where it forms an acute-angled fork, each prong a brilliant yellow line, the upper ending at about base of third from last dorsal ray, the lower ending at a corresponding position on base of anal; within the fork are 2 other bright yellow lines parallel with the prongs of the fork, forming anteriorly an acute angle on a vertical through the first third of dorsal.

Color in life of another example (No. 03358, Honolulu), top of head, back, and upper half of side dusky light orange-brown, interocular region dusky greenish-blue, brighter blue on anterior and posterior edges, crossed by 3 narrow black lines, one ending at middle of orbit above and one each at anterior and posterior border; below eye a black area at first as broad as eye, then widening, inclosing pectoral and extending downward and backward to vent and as broad as to fourth from last anal ray, this bounded anteriorly by 2 pale blue bars separated by a narrow dull orange one; a similar blue border along upper margin to near middle of side, where it changes to a bright greenish-yellow band extending to base of last anal ray but 2; at point where this line changes from blue to yellow, a similar line leaves it and passes across side to third dorsal ray from the last; caudal peduncle jet black, extending forward in a sharp point and bounded in front and behind by narrow greenish-yellow lines; snout brownish-white, a rather broad pale blue band over snout and down to angle of mouth on each side; soft dorsal, anal, and caudal pale, the latter with a broad light brown bar on basal part; spinous dorsal dusky, brownish, or black; vent black; pectoral jet black at base, then a rich red crescent, outer part of fin blackish-white; iris dull brown; belly white.

Color in alcohol, grayish brown above, becoming lighter below; a very dark blackish brown band passing through and downward from eye, widening below eye to lower base of pectoral, continuing backward to vent, its width on body being from vent to posterior third of anal; a small, narrow, similarly colored line extending from anterior part of eye to upper anterior base of pectoral, curving slightly forward; a light narrow violet band extending over snout from cleft to cleft of mouth; the 3 narrow bands between eyes almost black, the lines edging the broad band on side and the acute-angled dark brown spot on caudal grayish blue; spinous dorsal brown; soft dorsal, anal, and pectoral light; caudal dusky; base of pectoral black. Description based chiefly on No. 03714, a specimen 8 inches long, from Honolulu.

We have 9 examples, 4.85 to 9 inches long, all from Honolulu, where the species is common.

337. Balistapus aculeatus (Linnæus). *"Humuhumu nukunuku apua'a."* Plate LXII.

Head 2.75 in length; depth 2.2; snout 1.15 in head; eye 7; interorbital 3.75, equal to cleft of mouth; D. III, 24; A. 22; first dorsal spine 2.3 in head, equal to length of pectoral; longest dorsal ray 3 in head, base of soft dorsal 1.3 in head; longest anal ray 3.5 in head, base of anal 1.5 in head; scales 38, 24 from anterior base of spinous dorsal to vent.

Body oblong, compressed; dorsal and anal outlines similarly and evenly arched; head large; snout thick and blunt; mouth small, with thick lips; teeth rather long, incisor-like, notched, those in lower jaw the longer, those of upper jaw more notched; eye small, high, posterior; origin of first dorsal slightly posterior to gill-opening, the first spine blunt and strong, its anterior edge rugose; soft dorsal and anal moderate, with rounded profile; caudal slightly rounded; ventral spine movable, supported by a series of slender sharp spines; pectorals broad, rounded; scales covering entire head and body, those under soft dorsal slightly enlarged; some osseous plates behind gill-opening; usually 2½ rows of sharp recurved spines on caudal peduncle, in some examples 2 full rows and from 1 to 3 shorter broken rows.

General color in life (taken from No. 03455) yellowish green above, whitish below; lips pale yellow; a narrow blue stripe extending from back of angle of mouth over snout to opposite side; snout and side of head pale greenish yellow, becoming paler below; 4 bright blue lines across top of head between eyes, these separated by greenish lines of similar width; three narrow blue lines extending from eye downward to lower anterior base of pectoral, the first and last somewhat convex, the middle one nearly straight, the space between first and second yellowish white, that between second and third greenish; an irregular club-shaped band of orange-yellow from base of pectoral to snout, the posterior end somewhat expanded and more reddish, the anterior end gradually broadening and passing on each side into the blue band across nose; side below spinous dorsal pale yellow, somewhat dusky at base of spines; back of this an oblique broad, brick-red bar, then a shorter greenish-yellow one which is followed by a broader bluish-green bar, these all encroaching upon the soft dorsal and extending downward and forward, merging into an irregular broad longitudinal dusky area on middle of side, from which extend downward and backward 5 narrow curved greenish-yellow projections, separated by whitish spaces of similar width which are encroachments from the general color of the ventral surface; side of caudal peduncle with a broad longitudinal pale bluish band in which are set the 4 series of small spines; base of caudal fin and tip of peduncle pale rosy; soft fins all dirty whitish, somewhat washed with rosy and yellowish; first dorsal spine dusky in front, bluish on side; membranes connecting spines pale, with slight bluish wash; base of pectoral with a narrow black vertical line.

Color in alcohol, grayish with a large ragged-edged dark spot on side of body, one of the long edges extending to anal, broadening around anal region; 4 dark bluish black bands, divided by 3 narrower brown ones, between eyes; 3 narrow bluish gray lines from eye to base of pectoral, the anterior one curved forward and extending from front part of eye to lower part of pectoral base, the other 2 are separated by a darkish brown band as wide as eye and extending to base of pectoral; a bluish gray band over front of snout, ending just posterior to cleft of mouth; the edges of dark spot on side edged with violet gray, these nearly filling the spaces and giving the appearance of 4 or 5 bands extending from the axis downward to anal fin; a large grayish spot under spinous dorsal, another under anterior half of soft dorsal, these separated by an arm of the dark spot on side; violet gray on the anterior region covered by spines of caudal peduncle; spinous dorsal brown; other fins pale. Description chiefly from No. 03456, a specimen 8.5 inches long, from Honolulu.

We have 6 examples, 8 to 9.25 inches long, all from Honolulu, where the species is rather common, though less so than in Samoa. Known also from Johnston Island.

Genus 186. CANTHIDERMIS Swainson.

This genus differs from *Balistes* chiefly in having the gill-openings surrounded by ordinary scales, there being no developed bony scutes behind them. Body much more elongate than in *Balistes;* dorsal spines 3; dorsal and anal elevated in front; caudal with its angles acute; scales moderate, not very rough; scales of caudal peduncle unarmed, or with a median spine; cheek completely scaled; a naked groove before eye. Species inhabiting both Indies.

338. Canthidermis angulosus (Quoy & Gaimard).

D. III, 26; A. 24; scales 55 or 56.

Tail without spines or tubercles; scales very conspicuously granulated and provided with a larger prickle at the base, which is prominent in young examples, but disappears more or less with age. From 31 to 39 scales in a transverse series running from the origin of the dorsal fin to the vent; no enlarged scales behind the gill-opening; anterior parts of the dorsal and anal fins much elevated, more so in the adult than in young examples; caudal subtruncate; ventral spine short, somewhat ankylosed with the pelvic bone.

Color brown, with round or ovate whitish spots, in young examples these spots more indistinct and mixed with darker spots of the same size, and pure white dots; sometimes uniform brown or uniform deep black (Günther). (Description of *Canthidermis rotundatus*, called "*Balistes maculatus*").

The only record of *Canthidermis* from the Hawaiian Islands is that of Quoy and Gaimard, who described as a new species, *Balistes angulosus*. The following is a translation of their description:

"Balistes, with black body; blunt snout; short sharp antrorse dorsal spine; dorsal and anal fins triangular; caudal short, rounded.

"2ᶜ D. 23; p. 15; A. 20; C. 12.

"The form of this balistes is subovoid; its forehead is broad, with a small keel in the middle; its snout rounded; its teeth are incisor-like and pointed; the mouth and the eye are small. It is somewhat behind the latter that the short and strong spine of the first dorsal rises, which presents in front three lines of spines.

"The dorsal and anal fins are elevated, triangular, obtuse, directed backward, and one is nearly as large as the other; however, the first has twenty-three rays and the second has only twenty; the lobe of the tail is quadrilateral and the fin rounded; the pectorals very small, directed upward, are composed of fifteen rays. The body is black and covered with small scattered prickles, with a triangular base and bent backward.

"The length of this fish is 3 inches; its depth 20 lines, and its thickness 6. It inhabits the waters of the Sandwich Islands." It is perhaps different from *C. rotundatus* of the East Indies and *C. maculatus* of the West Indes.

339. Canthidermis aureolus (Richardson).

Dorsal III, 28; anal 25; lateral line 44; tail without spines or tubercles, but with indistinct raised lines along the series of scales; no enlarged scales behind the gill-opening; dorsal and anal fins not elevated, caudal truncated; ventral spine not movable, short. Uniform brownish above, sides shining golden; fins without color. Dorsal spine of young examples (1 inch) with recurved spinelets.

The only record of the occurrence of this species within our limits is that given by Steindachner. Its relation to other nominal species of the genus is somewhat uncertain.

Genus 187. XANTHICHTHYS Kaup.

Body oblong, covered with moderate-sized smoothish scales, those on posterior part of body usually with blunt keels; no enlarged scutes behind gill-opening; no lateral line, or only a trace at the shoulder; a groove before the eye; 3 to 5 narrow grooves on the cheek; caudal peduncle deeper than broad; dorsal spines 2, comparatively small; soft dorsal and anal moderately elevated, the tips acute; caudal lunate; mouth small, placed high, the teeth as in *Balistes;* lower jaw much projecting; ventral flaps undeveloped, immovable, and scaled over. Chiefly American; allied to *Canthidermis*, but differing in several respects, especially in the grooved cheeks, projecting chin, and fewer dorsal spines.

340. Xanthichthys lineopunctatus (Hollard). Fig. 182.

Head 3.5 in length; depth 2.5; eye 4.75 in head; snout 2; interorbital 3; D. II-I, 29; A. I, 27, scales 37, 23 from anal to origin of spinous dorsal; first dorsal spine 2 in head, equal to snout; third dorsal ray longest, 1.6 in head, equal to longest caudal ray, last caudal ray shortest, 4.5 in longest; third anal ray 1.9 in head, 2 in soft dorsal base; last anal ray shortest, 4.5 in longest; pectoral 2.3 in head.

Body oblong, compressed, blunter anteriorly; dorsal and ventral outline similarly curved; head compressed, deep, blunt; eye small, high, posterior; snout blunt, deep, about half of head; mouth small, terminal, high, its width equal to eye; jaws unequal, the lower, below the lip, produced, making the chin prominent; teeth pale brownish, notched, incisor-like; the 2 front lower teeth not so greatly notched as the next 2, the anterior edge of the latter being produced, making this part canine-like; upper teeth not so greatly notched, smaller, and shutting outside lower teeth; groove in front of eye about equal to eye; the 5 grooves on cheek are below eye, extending from near angle of mouth and below, backward to gill-opening and base of pectoral; scales comparatively large, largest on middle portion of body, those from pectoral region running downward and backward and not as those on body; a slight tubercle on center of scales on posterior portion of side, forming low lines or ridges on median part of scales; gill-opening surrounded by small scales, no large plates; origin of spinous dorsal over gill-opening, first spine short, stout, wedge-shaped, roughly rugose anteriorly, top incisor-like, sometimes saw-like; second spine about half first; soft dorsal and anal concave, the rays shortening posteriorly evenly and gradually from about the tenth; caudal lunate; pectoral short, broad, slightly falcate, almost rounded; ventral spine short, blunt, slightly movable.

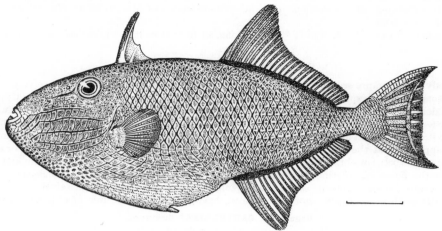

FIG. 182.—*Xanthichthys lineopunctatus* (Hollard).

Color in alcohol, grayish olivaceous, lighter below, head darker, the center of each scale darker, making weak brownish gray lines on sides; the edges of the scales are also brown, making narrow oblique lines, upward and forward and upward and backward over body; grooves on head brown; spinous dorsal brown, its membrane lighter; soft dorsal, anal, and pectoral pale; caudal dusky yellowish, its margin, for about width of pupil, white; scaly base of soft dorsal, anal, and belly to ventral spine, dark brown.

The above description from No. 05411, a specimen 8.25 inches long. We have other examples, No. 05412, 5 inches long, No. 05413, 7.75 inches long, No. 03557, 7.5 inches long, from Honolulu, and No. 03723, 8 inches long, from Hilo.

The species is rare. We can not distinguish our specimens from others taken off the coast of Mexico.

Genus 188. MELICHTHYS Swainson.

This genus differs from *Balistes* chiefly in the presence of a series of even, white, incisor-like teeth, instead of the irregular incisors of *Balistes*. The tail is unarmed or the scales only slightly keeled; a groove is present before the eye below the nostrils, and the cheeks are wholly scaled. The vertical fins are angulated, but not produced in filaments; ventral flap small, immovable, and covered with rough scales. Tropical seas.

341. Melichthys radula (Solander). *"Humuhumu eleele."* Plate LXIV.

Head 3.75 in length; depth 2; eye 5.25 in head; snout 1.65; D. III, 33; A. 29; interorbital 2.5; first dorsal spine 1.75; longest dorsal ray 1.3; longest anal ray 1.5; depth caudal peduncle 3; pectoral 2; scales 53, 33 from vent to anterior base of spinous dorsal.

Body oblong, more bluntly shaped anteriorly than posteriorly; head short, deep; eye small, posterior, high; snout blunt; mouth small; lower jaw slightly produced; 8 teeth in each jaw, the 2 anterior ones of each jaw broad truncate, incisors without notch, the other teeth in lower jaw notched; posterior tooth of upper jaw truncate; other 2 lateral teeth but slightly notched; anterior teeth even, not notched; teeth of lower jaw with a strong horizontal backward process; origin of spinous dorsal over gill-opening; first dorsal spine strong, blunt, and heavy, its front rugose; second spine very slender, about two-thirds of first; last spine very short and blunt, its tip just even with edge of groove, easily overlooked; in the small examples it is quite evident, in large examples it is blunt and not so evident (Doctor Gilbert evidently had a large example and thought there were but 2 spines, hence called it *bispinosus*, a new species); the fourth dorsal and anal rays the longest, then uniformly shortening posteriorly, the last one-third length of longest; caudal fin slightly convex, almost truncate, the tips produced for a distance equal to orbit; in the young the caudal is convex, no tips evident; ventral spine short, slightly movable; pectoral short, broad, and rounded; body nearly uniformly scaled, scales around mouth, eye, pectoral and ventral regions, and caudal peduncle smaller; osseous plates behind gill-opening; rough median spinous crests on 8 or 9 rows of scales on posterior portion of body.

Color in life, uniformly black, with slight show of bluish; a very distinct, conspicuous, narrow line of light blue running longitudinally on bases of dorsal and anal. Another specimen, when taken alive, was light green, with golden longitudinal narrow bands along spines of scales; stripe along base of dorsal and anal light blue; the whole fish turning black when dead.

Color in alcohol, bluish black, the fins darker; a narrow white longitudinal stripe at base of dorsal and anal; a narrow white line within arch of caudal about half diameter of eye from its edge, this line not evident in the young.

The above description based chiefly upon No. 03325, a specimen 9 inches long, from Honolulu, where it is common. The specimens from the offshore islands of Mexico, called *Melichthys bispinosus,* seem to be the same.

We have 11 examples, 4.75 to 11.75 inches long, all from Honolulu. Recorded also from Johnston Island.

Family LXXVII. MONACANTHIDÆ.

Body much compressed, covered with very small rough scales, forming a rough or velvety covering; males sometimes with spines on the caudal peduncle, these either robust or needle-like. Upper jaw with a double series of incisor-like teeth, 6 in the outer and 4 in the inner series; lower jaw with 6 similar teeth in a single series; first dorsal with a single strong spine and generally a rudimentary one behind it; second dorsal long, similar to anal; ventral fins reduced to a single osseous, fixed or movable, small appendage at the end of the long pelvic bone, this appendage often rudimentary or entirely absent; no barbel; vertebræ 7+11 to 14=18 to 21. Herbivorous shore fishes of the warm seas closely allied to the *Balistidæ,* differing chiefly in having the first dorsal represented by a single spine, behind which is sometimes a rudiment; scales small, spinigerous, the skin mostly rough velvety. The species are mostly small in size and are not used for food, having little flesh and that of a bitterish taste.

Genus 189. CANTHERINES Swainson.

This genus differs from *Monacanthus* chiefly in having the vental spine immovably ankylosed to the pelvis. The barbs on the dorsal spine, if distinct, are usually in 4 series; vertebræ 19 or 20. In the genus *Cantherines* the gradation is perfect from those species without barbs (*Cantherines*) to those with 4 equidistant series of strong barbs (*Pseudomonacanthus*).

342. Cantherines sandwichiensis (Quoy & Gaimard).   *"O'ililepa;" "Ohua."*   Fig. 183.

Head 3.3; depth 1.9; eye 4.4; snout 1.1; interorbital 3.65; D. I-36; A. 30; P. 14.

Body oblong, moderately elevated; snout long; mouth low, below axis of body; anterior profile rising in a slightly concave line to dorsal spine, a little convex in front of eye; from dorsal spine to caudal peduncle the dorsal outline is in a long low curve; ventral outline slightly convex from tip of snout to pelvic plate, thence in a straight line to origin of anal fin; base of anal gently and evenly rounded; upper jaw with an outer series of 8 strong close-set incisors, the 6 anterior ones rather pointed, the lateral one on each side much broader, lower jaw with a single series of 6 similar teeth fitting inside the upper in the closed mouth; teeth white, the tips brownish; lips thin; eye high up,

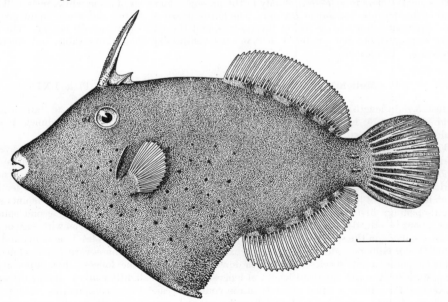

FIG. 183.—*Cantherines sandwichiensis* (Quoy & Gaimard).

the interorbital space strongly convex; nostrils in a rounded shallow pit; gill-slit slightly oblique upward and backward, its lower end in front of upper base of pectoral, its length 1.5 times diameter of orbit.

Body uniformly rough sandpapery, 2 rows each of 2 short, recurved spines on caudal peduncle in males, none in females. Dorsal spine long, slender and somewhat roughened, its insertion slightly anterior to middle of orbit, its length 1.2 in head; dorsal groove deep anteriorly or shallow posteriorly, not quite reaching soft dorsal; distance between origin of soft dorsal and posterior base of dorsal spine slightly greater than snout to eye; anterior dorsal rays somewhat elevated, their length a little more than half head; anal similar to soft dorsal, the rays about equally long; caudal when spread slightly convex; pectoral short, its edges nearly parallel, its length 2.3 in head; pelvic spine short, stiff, not movable.

Color in life, but somewhat faded (No. 03352), uniform rich brownish black; jaws whitish; dorsal spine olive-brown; soft dorsal with the rays rich orange, the membranes pale; caudal with membranes pale, flesh color, the rays brownish black, tipped with reddish orange; anal like soft dorsal; pectoral with the membranes colorless, the rays rich orange; iris dirty greenish.

Color in spirits variable, but usually a dull satiny brown, uniform over head and body; dorsal spine dusky; the series of scales sheathing the bases of dorsal and anal abruptly brownish black; the fins yellowish white; caudal dusky brown; pectoral yellowish white, the base dark brown; side of body and head sometimes with scattered small round black spots, these showing on only one (No. 05418) of our specimens.

This species is represented in our collection by 14 specimens, 1 from Hilo, the others from Honolulu; of the latter 5 were collected by Doctor Jenkins and 4 by Doctor Wood. Other examples were obtained by the *Albatross* at Honolulu and at Puako Bay, Hawaii. Also recorded from Socorro Island

347. Cantherines albopunctatus (Seale).

Head 3 in length; D. 11–38; A. 33; P. 15; eye 5 in head; snout 1.2, its profile concave.

First dorsal spine long and strong, about equal to snout, with 4 rows of small barbs directed down, insertion of spine directly over anterior half of eye; uneven cutting incisors in each jaw; a single row of 3 on each side of lower jaw; an additional row of small inner teeth in upper jaw; caudal peduncle with 4 short round spines on each side; skin without distinct scales, but everywhere rough with a velvety feeling to the touch; caudal rounded, its longest ray 1.75 in head; ventral spine coalesced to the pelvic bone, the membrane rather well developed, extending slightly beyond the spine; dorsal and anal rays of about equal length; base of the anal 1.2 in base of dorsal; pectorals short, 2.5 in head.

Color light gray, with slight silvery gloss, everywhere covered with scattered round, white spots about size of pupil; on lower half of body a small number of scattered black dots, smaller than the white dots; dorsal and anal with the basal fourth black, the remaining yellowish white; caudal dusky; iris white. Honolulu (Seale); also recorded from Tahiti.

Genus 190. STEPHANOLEPIS Gill.

This genus differs from *Monacanthus* in having the ventral flap, even in the adult, only moderately developed, not reaching beyond pelvic spine, and in having no recurved spines on caudal peduncle.

345. Stephanolepis spilosomus (Lay & Bennett). "*Oili uwiwi.*" Plate LXV.

Head 3.4 in length; depth 2.1; eye 3.7 in head; snout 1.3; interorbital 3.3; height of spine over eye equal to snout; D. 38; A. 34.

Body oblong, deep, strongly compressed, covered with minute scales, the posterior edge of each scale with 1 to 3 little spines, the center one the largest, these spines larger posteriorly over the peduncle, forming a cardiform patch, all hooked forward; mouth very small, teeth incisor-like, broadest in the sides of the jaws; outline of head, from snout to dorsal spine, slightly concave; dorsal spine rough anteriorly, its posterior edges each armed with a row of rather long retrorse barbs or spines; ventral spine small, movable, armed similarly to dorsal; caudal rounded.

Color in life (No. 03499, taken at Hilo), ground-color of body yellow; black spots of various sizes and shapes closely set in irregular rows on tail and back, those on belly being more sparse; nape and base of dorsal dark brown; a pale patch about size of suborbital space over the abdominal cavity, the black spots in this patch being paler than those on the yellow ground, this white patch probably absent in most living examples; interorbital and suborbital regions dark yellowish-brown, with black streaks running obliquely from ridge to pectoral region; armed dorsal spine orange-yellow, purplish-black spots on the membrane; ridge of snout very dark, obscuring all marks if there were any; lips flesh or pale pinkish color; a yellow streak with bright purple spots running along the median line of throat to ventral spine; from the ventral spine to vent a bright yellow line on the edge of keel, and 2 bright bluish-purple lines running along with the yellow one; space between 2 latter lines pale black; ventral spine yellow with purple spots; soft dorsal yellow, with 10 or 11 pale purple bars of equal width running longitudinally throughout entire length of fin; caudal fin bright yellow, the proximal half with black spots in rows, these spots becoming oblong as they spread toward the end, and forming more distinct rows, gradually fading into bright orange, and filling up the yellow ground color, imparting to the entire fin a bright orange aspect; rays yellow at base, merging into orange near the end; a black bar near tip of fin, a thin purple streak running through the black bar near its outer margin; a bright yellow streak along tip of fin; anal same as soft dorsal.

Another specimen had the following coloration in life: Head and belly pearly blue, shading into light brassy, the color of other parts of the body; head and body with lines and spots of brownish black; membrane of dorsal deep orange with brownish black spots, the spine bluish; dorsal and anal banded with lemon and pearly blue; caudal deep orange, narrowly bordered with lemon; a subterminal band of black; fin spotted with black; iris brassy; teeth orange.

An example from Hilo, when fresh, was mottled olive-green with traces of lighter horizontal light olive streaks, about 5 in number; fins soiled olive; caudal with 2 blackish bars; iris golden yellow; jaws flesh-color.

General color in alcohol, brownish olivaceous, darker above; body covered with small spots as large as pupil and smaller, arranged in about 14 or 15 irregular lengthwise series; over the cheek these spots formed into lines making 6 or 7 small narrow lines running upward and forward; dorsal spine with small dark spots on its anterior portion, pale posteriorly; soft dorsal pale, with about 10 narrow dusky stripes; caudal white, a dark band, width of pupil, on its edge, this band tipped with white, about 10 rows of small dark spots arranged in bars; anal similar to soft dorsal; pectorals pale.

Description chiefly from a specimen (No. 2557) 5.25 inches long, from Honolulu.

According to Mr. Johann Hering, of Hilo, this fish comes occasionally in great numbers, but otherwise is very rare. The natives believe its appearance to prophesy the demise of some great personage, such as a king or chief. There is another red fish, which seems, according to Mr. Hering's description, to be a species of *Holocentrus*, whose appearance is viewed with the same belief.

Our collection contains 26 specimens from Honolulu and 1 from Hilo, ranging from 2.14 to 5.4 inches in length. The *Albatross* obtained specimens at Honolulu; at station 4180, near Niihau, from the stomach of a Coryphaena; at Necker Island, carried in by a bird; at station 4147, near Bird Island, in 26 fathoms; at station 4167, near Bird Island, in 18 to 20 fathoms, and at station 4148, near Bird Island, in 26 to 33 fathoms.

346. Stephanolepis pricei Snyder. Plate 48.

Head 3 in length measured to base of caudal fin; depth between insertion of dorsal and anal 2.6; eye 3.3 in head; interorbital space 3.3; snout 1.4; depth of caudal peduncle 2.4; D. 39; A. 36.

Snout rather pointed, upper and lower contours concave; gill-slit small and narrow, its height equal to width of base of pectoral, two-thirds diameter of eye; ventral flap notably narrow, its width equal to half diameter of eye; dorsal spine inserted above pupil, its length equal to distance between angle of mouth and upper edge of gill-opening, reaching the insertion of dorsal fin when depressed; 6 lateral spines which project downward and slightly backward; 3 or 4 small granules in a row below the spine; anterior part of spine with prickles which point upward; length of base of dorsal about equal to length of head; height of fin equal to diameter of eye; length of base of anal equal to distance between tip of snout and posterior edge of orbit; height equal to that of dorsal; rays of dorsal and anal rough on basal halves; caudal round, the alternate rays with strong prickles; length of fin equal to length of snout; length of pectoral equal to twice the length of gill-slit; ventral spine large, length of movable part about equal to length of gill-opening, the sides with large spikes which project backward; body and head evenly covered with prickles, those of the dorsal part slightly coarser than the others; no enlarged spines on caudal peduncle.

Color silvery, dusky along top of head and back; membrane of dorsal spine blue-black; 3 small, round, dark spots in a line extending upward from base of pectoral; dark clouds somewhat larger than the eye extending downward at insertion of dorsal, from posterior half of dorsal, and on the caudal peduncle; a similar cloud extending upward from posterior half of base of anal.

One specimen 2.56 inches long, station 4021, vicinity of Kauai, depth 286 to 399 fathoms. Type, No. 50882, U. S. Nat. Mus. Only the type known.

Genus 191. OSBECKIA Jordan & Evermann.

This genus differs from *Alutera* in having the caudal fin elongate and with rounded angles; coloration not uniform, the head and body with irregular blue spots and lines, besides small round black spots; upper profile of snout concave.

346. Osbeckia scripta (Osbeck). *"O'ililepa;" "Ohua."* Fig. 184.

Head 3.7 in length; depth 2.9; eye 6.5 in head; snout 1; D. I–47; A. 49; C. 12; P. 14.

Body oblong, compressed, tapering, the greatest depth, which is over vent, greater than eye and snout by an eye's diameter; snout produced, the anterior profile concave; dorsal profile convex from in front of spine to caudal peduncle, a broad angle at beginning of soft dorsal which is midway between

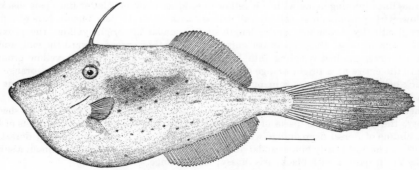

FIG. 184.—*Osbeckia scripta* (Osbeck); after Jordan and Evermann.

tip of snout and base of caudal fin; ventral outline evenly and less convex; caudal peduncle compressed, its least width 3.2 in its least depth, which is 2 in snout; chin prominent; teeth white, broad incisors, strongly emarginate in lower jaw, more pointed in the upper; gill-opening oblique, 1.6 times diameter of orbit; interorbital high, the sides forming an acute angle. Dorsal spine short, slender, shorter than eye, granular, inserted over middle of orbit; soft dorsal with the margin rounded, none of the rays produced, length of middle ones 4 in snout; anal similar to soft dorsal, the rays somewhat shorter; caudal fin rounded, longer than head, about 2.6 in body; pectoral short, 3.6 in snout; no ventral spine.

Color in life (No. 03006, a specimen 23 inches long, taken June 8), olivaceous; head and body with numerous irregular lines and spots of sky blue, the lines most numerous on head and near bases of dorsal and anal fins, the round spots most numerous on middle of side and on head; scattered smaller brown spots on the interspaces; lips black; dorsal and anal pale yellow; caudal dusky, paler at tip; iris yellowish silvery, dark above.

Color in alcohol, dusky olivaceous, the blue spots and lines faded to pale blue or brownish. In some examples the color is much darker, almost dark velvety brown, the spots black.

This species inhabits all tropical seas, and is common in the West Indies. It has been taken on the Atlantic coast as far north as the Carolinas, and occasionally among the islands of the Pacific coast of Mexico. It does not appear to be very common among the Hawaiian Islands, however, and was not obtained by Doctor Jenkins in 1889, though Jordan and Snyder secured one example in 1900.

We have 5 specimens, 17.5 to 25.25 inches long, all from Honolulu.

Genus 192. ALUTERA Cuvier.

Body elongate, strongly compressed, covered with minute scales; snout short, the anterior profile convex; mouth and teeth essentially as in *Monacanthus*, but the lower jaw more projecting, so that the lower teeth are directed obliquely upward and backward. Gill-opening an oblique slit, longer than eye, situated below and in advance of eye, its posterior end behind base of pectorals; pelvic bone long, falcate, movable under the skin, without spine at its extremity; dorsal spine small, inserted over the eye, rough, but without barbs; soft dorsal long and anal long, each of 45 to 50 rays; caudal fin short, shorter than head, almost truncate, the middle rays little produced; pectorals small. Size large.

347. Alutera monoceros (Osbeck).

"*Loulu.*" Fig. 185.

Head 3.6; depth 2.4; D. i, 49; A. 51.

Body oblong, much compressed, and skin with a fine velvety touch. Head very deep, convex both above and below; snout slightly produced upward; eye small, not much above the mouth, 5 in snout, 5.67 in head, 1.67 in space between its upper margin and origin of spinous dorsal, and 1 in space between its lower margin and upper margin of gill-opening; teeth broad, emarginate, the middle mandibular pair pointed; lips thin and narrow, smooth; nostrils small, in front of upper part of eye; gill-opening rather long, oblique forward until a little anterior to the nostrils, 2.67 in snout and equal to pectoral; origin of spinous dorsal over anterior edge of eye, and midway between tip of snout and origin of soft dorsal; soft dorsal and anal with the anterior rays the longer, the longest in both fins equal; caudal damaged; pectoral inserted below mouth and a little behind middle of eye; caudal peduncle compressed, equal to one-third the distance from posterior margin of eye to tip of snout.

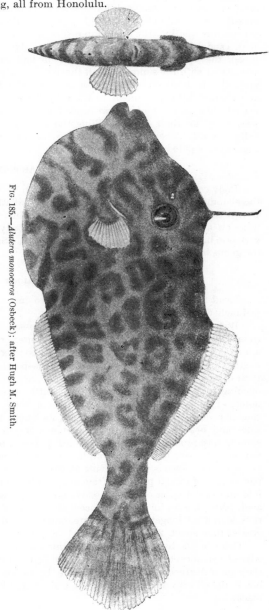

Fig. 185.—*Alutera monoceros* (Osbeck); after Hugh M. Smith.

Color in alcohol, uniform brown, mottled with darker, the fins all plain-colored and pale. Not seen by us.

A painting in the collection of Mrs. Dillingham made in Honolulu represents this widely diffused East Indian species. It bears the native name of Loulu.

Suborder GYMNODONTES.

Plectognaths without a spinous dorsal, with the body short and with the belly inflatable; the scales typically spiniform, with root-like insertions, and with the jaws enveloped in an enamel-like covering, without distinct teeth. This group contains degraded Plectognaths, which have lost the scales, spinous dorsal, and distinct teeth. In the extreme forms the pelvis, ribs, and caudal vertebræ are also lost, the species depending on their dermal armature, leathery skin, or inflatable belly for protection from enemies, while little power of active movement remains.

Family LXXVIII. TETRAODONTIDÆ.—The Puffers.

Body oblong or elongate, usually little compressed, sometimes very broad; head and snout broad; belly capable of great inflation; skin scaleless, usually more or less prickly, the spines or prickles usually weak and movable, not rooted; rarely the skin is armed with bony scutes forming a sort of carapace; each jaw confluent, forming a sort of beak, which in each jaw is divided by a median suture; maxillaries curved outward behind the premaxillaries; lips full; nostrils various. Spinous dorsal and ventral fins wanting, the fins composed of soft rays only; dorsal fin posterior, opposite and similar to anal; caudal fin distinct; no ventral fins, the pelvic bone undeveloped; no ribs; pectoral fins short and broad, the upper rays longest; caudal fin and caudal vertebræ normally developed; medifrontals articulated with the supraoccipital, the postfrontals confined to the sides, the ethmoid more or less projecting in front of frontals; post frontals extending outward as far as frontals; proethmoid short and narrow, little prominent to the view above; vertebræ few, 7 or 8+9 to 13; gill-openings small, placed close in front of pectorals; air-bladder present. Fishes of sluggish habits, inhabiting warm seas, noted for their habit of filling the belly with air. When disturbed they float on the surface, belly upward. They are not much used as food, even in Hawaii, the flesh being ill-flavored and sometimes reputed poisonous.

Genus 193. LAGOCEPHALUS Swainson.

Body comparatively elongate; skin smooth or variously prickly, the prickles most developed on the abdomen; abdomen capable of very great inflation; dorsal and anal rather long, falcate, of 12 to 15 rays each; caudal lunate; nostril without distinct papilla, each one with 2 distinct openings; mucous tubes on upper part of head and on sides of body very conspicuous; lower side of tail with a fold; vertebræ in increased number (about 8+13=21). Species reaching a rather large size, chiefly tropical, the genus intergrading fully with *Spheroides*.

348. Lagocephalus oceanicus Jordan & Evermann. Plate 49.

Head 2.8 in length; depth 3.6; eye 4.5 in head; snout 2.4; interorbital 3.2; depth of caudal peduncle 6; D. 12; A. 12; C. 10; P. 14.

Body rather elongate, moderately compressed, greatest depth at vertical of pectoral; head long; snout long, blunt at tip; the sides flattened; anterior profile from tip of snout to vertical of pectoral in a long, low, even curve; ventral outline little convex when not inflated; mouth small; teeth pointed at median line, the cutting edge sharp; nostrils separate; not in tubes, the anterior somewhat the larger, their distance from eye about half their distance from snout or about half the interorbital space; gill-opening vertical, 1.2 in eye, extending a little above base of pectoral, inner flap entirely hidden by outer; eye rather large, wholly above axis of body; interorbital space very little convex; cheek long; caudal peduncle nearly round, tapering, its length from anal fin equaling snout; back, upper parts of sides and head entirely smooth, no spines or prickles evident; belly covered with small 4-rooted spines, most prominent when belly is inflated, spiniferous area not extending on throat anterior to eye, nor on side above base of pectoral, but in front of anal extending upward to level of lateral fold; a line of very small mucous pores curving above eye on interorbital space; a strong cutaneous fold on lower part of side of caudal peduncle from above anterior base of anal to lower base of caudal fin; no dermal fold on head or anterior part of body; mucous pores inconspicuous; dorsal fin somewhat anterior to anal, pointed, anterior rays produced, their length equal to that of snout; anal similar to dorsal, its rays somewhat longer; caudal lunate, outer rays about 2 in head; pectoral broad, its length a little greater than snout, 2.3 in head.

Color in life, back blackish, fading into deep steel-blue on side; side and below from level of upper edge of eye abruptly silvery-blue; sides of belly white, with round black spots about as large as pupil, these most distinct about pectoral, before, below, and behind the fin; upper fins dusky; caudal mottled black, tipped with white; pectoral black above and behind, pale below; anal pale, broadly tipped with blackish.

Color in alcohol, bluish black above; side from upper level of eye abruptly bluish silvery; back crossed by 7 or 8 narrow darker cross-streaks; belly white, with a series of about 9 to 12 small roundish black spots, chiefly below the pectoral; cheek dusky; pectoral, dorsal, and caudal dusky, tips of the latter paler; anal whitish, a little dusky at tip. A somewhat smaller example (4.5 inches long) has larger dark spots along middle of side above level of pectoral.

This species is known to us from 2 small examples obtained in the market of Honolulu. It is related to *Lagocephalus stellatus* (Donovan) of Europe (*Tetrodon lagocephalus* of Günther, not of Linnæus), but differs in the much shorter pectoral, more conspicuous spots, and rather greater extension of the prickly region of the breast. The types of *Tetrodon lagocephalus* Linnæus are reputed to have come from India. According to Linnæus this species had 10 dorsal and 8 anal rays. It may have been based on *Lagocephalus sceleratus* or some other East Indian species, but there seems to be no evidence that it was identical with the European *Lagocephalus stellatus*. In any event the Hawaiian form seems different from any other yet known.

Type, No. 50820, U. S. N. M. (field No. 03379), 5 inches long, obtained at Honolulu; cotype, No. 7784, L. S. Jr. Univ. Mus. (field No. 534, paper tag), 4.5 inches long, also from Honolulu.

Genus 194. SPHEROIDES Lacépède.—The Swell-fishes.

Body oblong or elongate; skin variously prickly or smooth, sometimes with cirri; a single, short, simple, nasal tube on each side, with 2 rather large openings near its tip, the tube sometimes reduced to a mere rim; dorsal and anal fins of 6 to 15 rays each; caudal truncate, rounded or concave; vertebræ 18 to 21; frontal bones expanded sidewise and forming the lateral roof of the orbit, the postfrontals limited to the posterior portions. Species very numerous in warm seas. The group contains 2 or 3 strongly marked subgenera which would be regarded as distinct genera if only extremes were considered; but the transition is very gradual from *Lagocephalus*, with elongate body, silvery skin, prominent lateral fold, long falcate dorsal and anal, with forked caudal, to typical *Spheroides*, with short fins and the form of *Tetraodon*.

349. Spheroides florealis (Cope).

D. 8; A. 7; eye 4.25 times in head, 2.75 in muzzle; head 3.66 in total length; anal fin behind dorsal, both subfalcate, narrow; caudal long, truncate or slightly concave; interorbital region concave, profile regularly descending; belly to vent and anterior part of sides with strong distant bristles, back to end of pectoral fin and head above to nares, with distant weaker bristles; no dermal appendages; a groove from the orbit to the tail on each side of the back, which is nearly connected by a medially interrupted cross groove at the occipital crest; a groove concentric with and within the superciliary margin extending to the preocular region and returning, but sending also a curved branch round the front of each nostril.

Color, below immaculate white, a yellowish band on the side; above reddish brown, ground reduced to narrow lines by the innumerable small light (? white) spots with a ring of smaller spots around each, over the upper regions of the head and body. Caudal fin delicately cross-barred; other fins unicolored. Length 5 inches.

Two specimens from the Sandwich Islands, obtained by Dr. J. K. Townsend 20 years ago. This species is allied to *S. alboplumbeus* Richn., but differs in the fewer fin rays as well as the color (Cope).

In our collection from Hilo are 8 young puffers, from three-quarters to an inch in length, which we identify with this species of Cope's. In so far as can be determined from such small examples they agree perfectly with Cope's description and with the figure of his type, given by Fowler, having the few fin rays, slender body, and coloration of *S. florealis*, and we have no doubt they are the young of that species.

Genus 195. TETRAODON Linnæus.

Body rather robust, skin usually more or less prickly; nostril on each side with a tentacle, bifid to the base, its tips without opening, the branches of the large olfactory nerve ending in cup-like depressions along the inner edges of the 2 flattish lobes; dorsal and anal fins rounded, each of 7 to 14 rays; dorsal more or less in front of anal; caudal rounded; vertebræ usually 8+10=18; a ring muscle about the eye forming eyelids; distinguished from *Spheroides* by the solid nasal tentacle.

350. Tetraodon hispidus Linnæus. "*Oópuhúe;*" "*Maki-maki;*" "*Keke.*" Plate LXVI.

Head 2.9; depth 3; eye 5.75; snout 2; preorbital 2.9; interorbital 2.4; D. 9; A. 10; P. 17; C. 8.

Body rather short and stout, heavy forward, tapering evenly when not inflated, to the caudal fin; head broad, its width at gill-openings about 1.3 in its length; snout moderate, broad, the anterior profile somewhat concave; interorbital space concave, the orbital rims prominent; nostril a short, bifid tentacle in front of eye; lips tubercular, in about 3 rows, scarcely covering teeth; teeth white, strong, strongly convex anteriorly, the lower jaw slightly included; gill-opening short, about as long as eye;

body covered more or less uniformly with small, slender, bristle-like prickles, generally but not always present in the young, usually disappearing more or less with age. The variations in this character are entirely too great to leave it any morphological value. Some young examples not exceeding 3 inches in total length have the entire body profusely covered with slender, weak spines, usually longest and strongest on the belly, and weakest on the caudal peduncle, middle of back and top of snout. Examples similarly spiny are found among individuals of all sizes up to 7.5 or 8 inches in length. Other examples of similar range in size are almost wholly without prickles; if any at all are present they will be found in a scattered patch on each side of the vent and a few on lower jaw. In an example 13 inches long prickles are present on most of the body, the naked areas being the sides of caudal peduncle, the cheeks, snout, interorbital, and prepectoral region. In another example of the same size nearly smooth, only a few scattered prickles are evident. Dorsal fin rounded, 2.5 in head, distance of its posterior base from caudal fin 1.6 in head; anal with its anterior rays longest, the free edge oblique, the longest rays 2.6 in head; caudal rounded, 1.75 in head; pectoral broad, 2.9 in head.

Color in life of one specimen, light olive-green, with spots of pearly or bluish white which are smallest on tail; gill-openings black, with bright yellow curved streaks; belly with parallel stripes of light olive, growing fainter below; belly sometimes plain white, sometimes with yellow stripes covering it completely; prickles all white; yellow and black lines under pectoral; fins bright olive-yellow without spots except on caudal which has a few on basal portion; axil black, with a yellowish white border; posterior part of side sometimes 6 or 8 vertical white bars; no spines on snout, tail, lower jaw, or on region about vent and anal fin.

Another example in life was light olive-green with pearly white spots, smallest on tail; region about gill-opening black with bright yellow curved streaks; belly with parallel stripes of faint olive growing fainter below; belly sometimes plain white; prickles all white; fins bright olive-yellow without spots except on caudal, which has a few on basal portion; snout with a small dark edged bluish spot; no spines on snout, tail, lower jaw, or on region about vent and anal fin.

Another example in life was light olive-green with pearly white spots, smallest on tail; region about gill-opening black with bright yellow curved streaks; belly with parallel stripes of light olive, growing fainter below; spines all white; belly white, often without stripes in the young; fins bright olive-yellow without spots except base of caudal; nose with a small dark edged bluish spot; no spines on snout or tail or region about vent, anal fin or lower jaw.

Still another example was described in life by Doctor Jenkins as golden olive above, white below; bluish-white spots about as large as pupil over top of head and back, becoming smaller on caudal peduncle and caudal fin; 2 white concentric rings around eye; one distinct and one or two other less distinct rings of white around base of pectoral including opercular opening; about 5 white longitudinal bands on side of belly below head and pectoral fin, alternating with a like number of olive bands; base of pectoral and region below black, and some black blotches anterior to the lower of these; dorsal dusky yellow; pectoral bright yellow; anal orange yellow; caudal dusky, the membranes yellowish with bluish-white spots.

Color in spirits, head, top of body, caudal peduncle on top and sides, and most of the side, dull olivaceous, covered quite uniformly with small round bluish-white spots, these sometimes oblong, the largest much smaller than pupil, those on side somewhat larger; base of pectoral black, surrounded by a narrow bluish-white line forming a nearly complete circle, interrupted only below the fin; a white bar across base of pectoral between which and the white ring are 2 shorter ones; a broad curved black band behind the white circle, continuing forward under the fin, some of the spines on its anterior surface white; 2 or 3 broad but short, horizontal black bars on breast under cheek and the same number on belly just back of pectoral, these sometimes continuous; belly chiefly white; posterior part of side mottled black, brown and paler; base of caudal fin with a few blue-white spots; spines usually pale or whitish. The colors in alcohol are as variable as they are in life. The yellowish or blackish lines on the belly become blackish or dark brown. In some examples the dark lines continue over entire belly, in others they are limited to the sides, the middle portion being plain white.

These differences are noticeable even in the very young, many of which we have ranging in total length from six-tenths of an inch to 2.75 inches. Some very small examples (5) from Cocoanut Island at Hilo are uniform rich brownish black above, and all but the smallest have each about 18 distinct horizontal lines of same color on belly from chin to anal fin, the lateral ones ceasing sooner. The spaces between these lines are dull or dusky white and equally narrow. The smallest example (six-tenths of an inch in total length) is uniform dark brownish black on belly as well as on back and sides; fins all pale, caudal somewhat dusky. Other equally small examples from Hilo have the belly striped with brownish black and the pale interspaces broken up into spots anteriorly. Somewhat larger examples (1 inch to 1.75 inches long) from a pond at the Moana Hotel at Waikiki are usually striped underneath, the interspaces white, and the back and sides olivaceous. Some, however, are rich brown, agreeing perfectly with those from Hilo. In some cases the body is strongly papillose below and on sides, presenting the appearance of plush. In one example 1.6 inches long, from Hilo, the stripes on the belly are much broader and consequently fewer in number, there being only 12 of the dark stripes.

Although there is much variation among our numerous specimens both in color and in the development of the prickles, they all evidently belong to the same species. This is an abundant fish in all suitable places about Honolulu, it frequenting the mullet ponds and more or less inclosed brackish water areas, and even the fresh-water ponds near the coast. Nearly all our numerous specimens were obtained from one of the smaller ponds at Moanalua, Mr. S. M. Damon's country place. At a single haul with a 25-foot seine more than 2 bushels of these fishes were taken. As they were being hauled out upon the bank many of them became greatly inflated, in which condition they usually remained indefinitely or until returned to the water, where they would float about for some moments helplessly on their backs, their distended bellies above the water. Finally they would collapse, right themselves and swim away. Those placed in formalin or alcohol often remained inflated for some time, some permanently.

This puffer reaches a large size, our biggest examples having a total length of more than a foot. The 100 specimens in the collection from Honolulu are 1.8 to 14 inches long. In addition we have 9 small examples (1 to 1.75 inches long) from a pond at the Moana Hotel at Waikiki, and 11 examples (0.6 to 2.75 inches long), from Cocoanut Island at Hilo. The fish is thought to be poisonous, a belief expressed in one of its native names, Maki Maki, meaning deadly death. The species is of wide distribution, having been recorded from various places in the Red Sea, the East Indies, Japan, and Australia, as well as from Panama and the islands off the Pacific coast of Mexico. It has been recorded from the Hawaiian Islands only by Streets, Jenkins, and Quoy and Gaimard previous to our explorations.

351. Tetraodon lacrymatus (Cuvier). Fig. 186.

Head 2.7; depth 2.6; eye 6.5; snout 2; preorbital 2.8; interorbital 2.3 in head, 6.5 in body; D. 10; A. 12; P. 19.

Body short and stout; head short and broad; snout short; teeth in each jaw in 2 strong convex plates, produced and beak-like at line of union; lips thin, not covering teeth completely; interorbital space broad and flat, the profile from tip of snout to occiput slightly concave; orbital rim prominent; gill-opening nearly vertical, its length half the distance from tip of snout to middle of pupil; nostril a short closed bifid tube. Fins broad; dorsal posterior, distance of base of anterior ray from base of caudal 1.5 in head, or 4 in body, length of base of fin 1.6 in length of fin, whose free edge is evenly rounded; caudal rounded, its length 2 in head; anal similar to dorsal, posterior to it, its base longer,

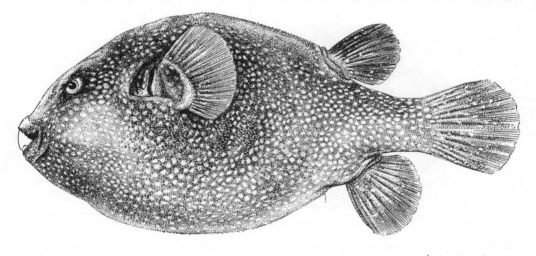

FIG. 186.—*Tetraodon lacrymatus* (Cuvier). Type of *Ovoides latifrons.*

its height about the same; pectoral broad, evenly rounded, its length 2.6 in head, its depth 1.2 in its length. Body more or less covered with small, simple, setæ-like spines, mostly embedded in the skin, only the tips projecting, most of them inclined backward; snout, cheeks, caudal peduncle, base of dorsal, caudal and anal fins, chin, and a broad stripe along middle of side, and region about pectoral naked.

Color in life (No. 03409, 13 inches long, obtained at Honolulu, July 7), raw umber, streaked with mottling in black, covered everywhere with small white spots; belly covered also with small white prominences, the general tone grayish white; edge of dorsal, anal, and pectoral grayish white, yellowish behind pectoral.

Color of same specimen in alcohol, rich brownish black, profusely and quite uniformly covered with small roundish blue-white spots, varying in size from very small, mere specks, to nearly as large as pupil, those in axil, caudal peduncle, and caudal largest, the large ones on caudal being in the second and fourth fifths of the depth; setæ white, especially on belly; all the fins with numerous roundish white spots, all except the caudal narrowly edged with white.

This species is close to *T. setosus* Smith, from the Pacific coast of Mexico, from which it differs chiefly in the smaller size of the spots. It is known to us from the type of the nominal species *Ovoides latifrons*, a specimen about 8 inches long, and 2 examples (No. 03409, 12 inches long, and No. 05574, 9.5 inches long) obtained by us at Honolulu.

Family LXXIX. CANTHIGASTERIDÆ.—The Sharp-nosed Puffers.

This family includes small puffers, similar in external appearance to the Tetraodontidæ, but with the snout sharp and the back more or less compressed or ridge-like. The skeletal characters by which the group is defined are thus given by Doctor Gill: Medifrontals separated from the supraoccipital by the intervention of the sphenotics, which are connected and laterally expanded, but short; the prosethmoid prominent above, enlarged and narrowed forward. Vertebræ about 8 + 10. Head compressed, with a projecting, attenuated snout; dorsal and anal short, few-rayed. Nostrils wanting or little developed. Tropical seas; small species; none of them reaching a length of more than 6 inches.

Genus 196. CANTHIGASTER Swainson.

Body short, deep and compressed, the back more or less sharply ridged; nostrils very small and inconspicuous, apparently sometimes imperforate.

352. Canthigaster jactator (Jenkins). Fig. 187.

Head 2.66 in length of body; depth of body from back to lower edge of base of pectoral 3.33 in length. Eye equal to interorbital space, 2 in snout; D. 9; A. 10; P. 16; C. 7. Profile rising from tip of snout to middle of back where the median dorsal crest forms a prominent point; dorsal profile of head concave from tip of snout to eyes, straight from eyes to dorsal prominence. Interorbital space very slightly concave; profile descending to a straight line from apex of back to dorsal fin, from dorsal fin to caudal fin descending with gentle concavity; caudal peduncle deep anteriorly, depth just back of dorsal and anal fins equal to snout; much less deep posteriorly, depth just before bases of caudal rays 2.33 in head; ventral parts of body much dilated, depth below pectoral 1:25 in depth above pectoral; dorsal and anal fins very short, dorsal above anal; rays equal, about 3 in head; caudal slightly

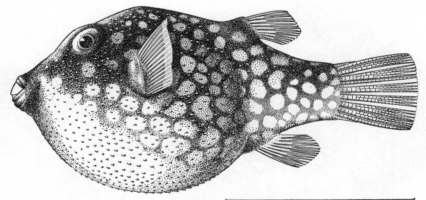

Fig. 187.—*Canthigaster jactator* (Jenkins); from the type.

rounded, median rays equal to snout; pectoral wide, distal edge slightly concave; upper rays longest, 2.66 in head. Body and head everywhere except on caudal peduncle covered with small asperities consisting of small, erectile, two-rooted spines directed backward; spines largest on belly.

Color in alcohol, dark brown above and on sides, belly pale yellowish; dark parts with numerous, regularly distributed, pale (apparently bluish in life), round or polygonal spots; spots largest on sides where the brown ground-color appears as a network between them, obsolete on fore part of head in one specimen, extending distinct to tip of snout in a smaller one, none smaller than pupil, those on sides three-fourths of eye in diameter; dusky ring about eye, most conspicuous above; fins colorless.

As was stated by Doctor Jenkins, this species is very similar to *C. punctatissimus* (Günther). Its distinction rests on a difference in the color pattern, the spots being fewer and generally more widely separated than those of *C. punctatissimus*. The distended belly, an alleged distinctive character seen in the type specimen of *C. jactator*, is merely the result of the specimen having been preserved while distended with air. In 3 specimens from Laysan Island, measuring 2.56, 3.07, and 3.66 inches, respectively, the spots on the sides of the head are nearly as large as those on the body; those on the upper part of the snout are about half as large; there are 7 or 8 on a line between upper part of eye and tip of snout. Those on the snout and upper part of head and nape are narrowly bordered with dark brown. On the body there are about 13 spots in a line between the dorsal and anal fins, and 6 in a vertical line near the middle of caudal peduncle. The largest example has an indefinite dark spot below the base of dorsal fin. In life the spots are light blue. Most of them are as large as the pupil, and so close together that the brown ground color appears as a network.

Three examples from the reef at Honolulu measure 1.46 inches each. The spots on the upper part of the snout and head are very small, 5 in a line between upper part of eye and tip of snout. They are ocellated, as are also the spots along the back to the base of dorsal. There are 7 or 8 spots in a line between anal and dorsal fins, and 4 in a vertical line near middle of caudal peduncle. The cotype collected by Doctor Jenkins in Honolulu also has large spots on the snout.

C. punctatissimus, represented by 8 specimens from Panama, has from 7 to 10 small ocellated spots in a line on upper part of snout. The spots on the back from nape to base of caudal are small and have dark margins. There are from 11 to 23 spots between anal and dorsal, and from 8 to 15 on the caudal peduncle. One example has 4 short lines extending backward from the eye. A specimen from the Galapagos Islands referable to *C. punctatissimus* has the spots on the sides of the snout fused, forming vertical bands. There are 3 short bands or elongate spots radiating backward from the eye.

The species was not obtained by us, the only specimens known being the 2 examples, 1.5 and 2.5 inches long, respectively, obtained by Dr. Jenkins at Honolulu, and 6 examples collected by the *Albatross*, 3 at Honolulu and 3 at Laysan Island.

353. Canthigaster oahuensis (Jenkins). Fig. 188.

Head 3 in length; depth 2; eye 4 in head; snout 1.5; interorbital 3; D. 11; A. 10; C. 9; P. 16.

Body short, deep, and compressed, the back narrow and strongly elevated; anterior profile rising pretty evenly to a point slightly posterior to vertical of gill-opening; interorbital nearly flat; snout long, flattened laterally; teeth strong, convex, the edge sharp; eye small, high up, the supraorbital prominent; gill-opening short, slightly oblique, less than diameter of eye; nostril small and inconspicuous, but evident and perforate; caudal peduncle compressed, its least depth about 2 in head.

Body covered more or less uniformly with small, short prickles, most prominent on snout, back, chin, cheek, belly, and under pectoral fin; caudal peduncle and posterior part of side naked; base of pectoral and other fins naked.

Color of a nearly fresh example (No. 03528), 2.8 inches long, bluish gray, upper parts of head and body dusky; region from axil of pectoral fin to dorsal fin and backward to base of caudal and below for some distance below level of chin covered with small, bright blue spots; dark brown spots below and behind pectoral, mingled with the blue ones; 5 or 6 narrow brown lines running obliquely downward and forward on side of head, underneath which are brown spots and lines; radiating blue lines

FIG. 188.—*Canthigaster oahuensis* (Jenkins); from the type.

from eye; 2 blue lines extending from upper posterior border of eye, diverging and then coming together at an eminence back of occiput in such a way as to include an irregular oval area about as large as eye; caudal dusky, with some small blue spots like those on body; dorsal and anal transparent, with dusky bases; blue spots on base of dorsal, and some on base of anal. Color in alcohol of same specimen, dark olivaceous; body from gill-opening to caudal fin with numerous small, round, pale bluish spots, among the lower of which are interspersed brownish spots; cheek with 4 or 5 narrow bluish lines separated by dark brown ones running upward and backward from chin to region in front of gill-opening; beneath and back of these are numerous brown spots and short wavy lines; short blue lines radiating forward and downward from eye; 2 similar blue lines running backward and upward from eye, coming together on nape and inclosing an oblong area about as large as eye; fins all dusky; dorsal black at base and with a few blue spots on base; basal third of anal blackish; base of pectoral black.

This species is known only from the type (original No. 326), a specimen 4.5 inches long, obtained by Doctor Jenkins at Honolulu in 1889, and one example (No. 03528) 2.5 inches long, obtained by us at Honolulu, August 4, 1901.

354. Canthigaster cinctus (Solander). Fig. 189.

Head and body, except front of snout, covered with spinules; profile of snout very steep, slightly concave; interocular space concave, equaling eye; D. 10, no ocellus at its base, but a large black blotch extending under it upon the flank; a broad black band, between these blotches on the flanks, connecting the pectorals; a band of the same color between the eyes, bordered in front with bluish spots;

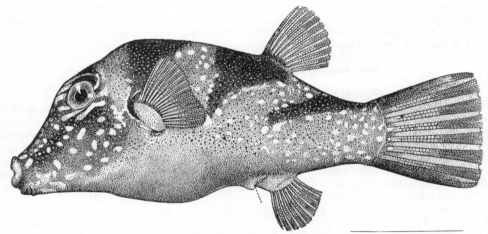

FIG. 189.—*Canthigaster cinctus* (Solander); from an Hawaiian example taken by the *Albatross* in 1902.

snout, side and caudal peduncle covered with smaller spots of same color, these spots equaling diameter of pupil, the spots of lower part of snout having a tendency to unite in the form of slightly curved horizontal lines; caudal bordered with black. Polynesia.

355. Canthigaster psegma (Jordan & Evermann). Plate 50.[a]

Head 3 in length; depth 2; eye 4.5 in head; snout 1.5; interorbital 2.3; D. 11 or 12; A. 11; C. 8; P. 16.

Body short, stout, moderately compressed; snout long, conic; anterior dorsal profile rising evenly to region above gill-opening, at which point the body is deepest; interorbital flat; gill-opening nearly vertical, short, its length less than diameter of eye; mouth low, below axis of body; teeth strong, convex, cutting edge sharp; eye small, supraorbital rim not prominent; caudal peduncle deep, its least depth about 2 in head, its least width 4 in its least depth; length of caudal peduncle from dorsal fin to base of caudal fin 1.3 in head; from base of anal fin 2 in head; dorsal prominence equally distant between tip of snout and posterior base of caudal; base of dorsal 1.5 in height of fin, which latter is 2 in head; anal similar to dorsal, its edge rounded; caudal truncate, or very slightly convex, 1.2 in head; pectoral broad, its base 2.6 in head, free edge oblique, posterior rays 1.5 in anterior ones; body mostly smooth; interorbital space and snout above and on side with small prickles; belly with a few prickles; a scattered patch also on side above pectoral.

Color in alcohol, dark brown above, paler below; 3 or 4 short black lines running forward from orbit, and same number backward; lower part of side, especially posteriorly, and lower part of caudal peduncle, with small roundish black spots; snout and interorbital space crossed by about 12 narrow black lines, these extending down on side of snout; side of snout with 3 or 4 narrow black lines from chin toward eye, separated by paler lines; posterior to these, small irregular black spots covering entire cheek, dotted over with fine white specks; ends of spines, pectoral, dorsal, and anal pale whitish, their bases largely brownish black; caudal dark brownish or black.

This species is known from the type, No. 50885, U. S. N. M. (field No. 2561), 3.75 inches long, obtained by us at Honolulu in 1901, a second specimen recently received from Mr. Berndt at Honolulu, and from numerous specimens obtained by Doctor Jordan at Samoa.

---

a Tropidichthys psegma on plate.

356. Canthigaster janthinus (Vaillant & Sauvage)

Dorsal with 13 rays; head without nasal tentacles; snout 2.5 in head; back rounded; profile not steep, convex, gradually merging into the dorsal outline; body without spines, except the ventral pouch, which is furnished with short, strong spines; caudal fin as long as caudal peduncle.

Body slate color, some black blotches between pectoral and eye; a few large rounded black blotches at intervals along the upper part of ventral pouch; upper part of pectoral black; caudal and dorsal stronger in color; anal transparent.

Hawaiian Islands; not seen by us. Known only from the record by Vaillant and Sauvage.

357. Canthigaster epilamprus (Jenkins). "Puu olai." Fig. 190.

Head 2.8 in length; depth 2.7; eye 3.6 in head; snout 1.6; interorbital 3.5; D. 10; C. 10; P. 17.

Body oblong, compressed; head long, snout pointed, its sides flattened; mouth small, the teeth strong, convex, meeting in a produced point at the center; eye high up, the supraobital rim prominent; interorbital space concave; anterior profile from tip of snout to occiput nearly straight; caudal

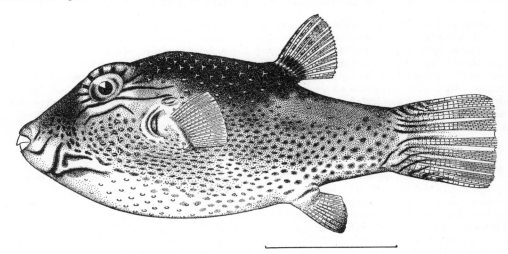

FIG. 190.—*Canthigaster epilamprus* (Jenkins); from the type.

peduncle compressed and deep, its depth 2.25 in head; gill-opening vertical, its length less than diameter of eye; nostril small, perforate, not in a projecting tube.

Body chiefly smooth on sides and caudal peduncle; dorsal region between eyes and dorsal fin with small, sharp prickles; a similar patch on lower part of cheek and belly; snout and interorbital region naked; lower jaw naked; posterior part of body and caudal peduncle naked; fins moderate; dorsal with the anterior rays longest, the free edge oblique, nearly straight, height of fin 2 in head; anal pointed, its length about 2.8 in head; caudal truncate, its length 1.3 in head; pectoral broad, little oblique, its length 2.6 in head.

Color in alcohol, pale brownish above, paler on sides and belly; a large blackish area on side below base of dorsal; cheek and entire body covered with small roundish brown spots; 2 dark-brown lines on cheek under eye; 2 or 3 similar lines radiating backward from eye and 2 others running forward from eye; 5 narrow, dark lines across head between eyes; a dark median line from tip of lower jaw to vent; side of snout with 2 vertical and 2 horizontal brown lines; fins all pale, the caudal with converging light-brown lines on base.

This species is known only from the type, a specimen 3.5 inches long, collected near Kihei, Maui, by Mr. Richard C. McGregor.

358. Canthigaster bitæniatus (Jenkins). Fig. 191.

Head 2.66 in length of body; depth a little greater than head. Back compressed, culminating in a very obtuse point above middle of pectoral fin. Profile from tip of snout to before eyes somewhat concave, straight from interorbital to top of dorsal prominence, descending in a straight line from here to base of caudal fin, being interrupted, however, at middle by elevation bearing dorsal fin. Ventral outline evenly curved, no more convex than the dorsal; eye 3.33 in head; snout 1.75 in head; interorbital concave, slightly greater than eye, 3 in head; one nostril in each side, each a simple opening with slightly raised margin, but scarcely tubular; distance from eye to nostril 2 in distance from nostril to tip of snout; front of dorsal fin midway between dorsal prominence and base of caudal fin, outline rounded; rays 10, longest 1.5 in snout; caudal slightly rounded, median rays equal distance from tip of snout to center of pupil; anal similar to dorsal, front of its base below posterior end of base

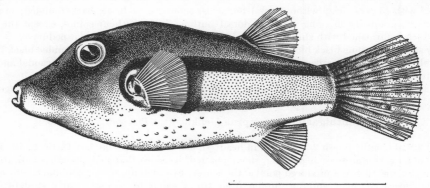

FIG. 191.—*Canthigaster bitæniatus* (Jenkins); from the type.

of dorsal; pectoral broad (in specimen median and lower rays on both sides broken), upper rays 2.5 in head; a few minute spines on lower surface of body; surface otherwise smooth.

Color in alcohol, general color brown or dusky above, paler brownish below; a wide dusky band from base of upper rays of the caudal running forward along side of body, above base of pectoral, to upper end of gill-slit, here becoming narrow and curving downward around anterior edge of gill-slit, then backward again below it as a narrow band below base of pectoral and along side of body, parallel with the upper band, to a little below middle of caudal fin, a black spot on outer side of base of pectoral; bases of upper and lower caudal rays black. One specimen, 2.04 inches long, secured by Dr. Wood at Honolulu. It is apparently not distinct from the Japanese species, *C. rivulatus* (Schlegel).

Family LXXX. DIODONTIDÆ.—The Porcupine Fishes.

Body short, broad, depressed above; belly moderately inflatable, covered everywhere except on the lips and caudal peduncle with spines, which are usually 2-rooted or 3-rooted at their bony base; caudal peduncle short and slender; mouth moderate, terminal, each jaw covered with a bony plate like the beak of a bird, these not divided by a median suture; nostrils on each side forming a small tentacle, usually with 2 openings; eye rather large, gill-opening moderate, immediately in front of the pectoral, which is short, broad, and rounded; dorsal and anal fins short, similar to each other, rounded in form and placed posteriorly. Genera about 6; species 15. Sluggish fishes, living on the bottom among weeds and corals in tropical seas. When disturbed they swallow air and float belly upward on the water. Their capacity of inflation is very much less than that of the *Tetraodontidæ*, from which family they differ chiefly, however, in the stronger armature and in having no division in the bony plate of either jaw. They are rarely used as food, being generally regarded as poisonous. The species are mostly well known in collections, the singular form having attracted the attention of travelers in the earliest times.

Genus 197. DIODON Linnæus.

Body robust, the belly moderately inflatable; dermal spines strong, stiff, most of them 2-rooted and erectile, a few 3-rooted and therefore immovable; both jaws entire; nasal tube simple, with 2 lateral openings; pectoral broad, the margin undulate, the upper lobe longest; vertical fins rounded, the dorsal and anal short, posteriorly inserted, similar to each other. Tropical seas; the few species very widely distributed.

359. Diodon holacanthus Linnaeus.

D. 12; A. 12. Very similar to *Diodon hystrix*, but with the frontal spines usually longer than the spines behind the pectorals, about twice as long as eye; predorsal spines not shortened, 2-rooted; erectile; about 14 to 17 spines in a series between snout and dorsal; post-pectoral spines not especially elongate, but movable; pectoral broader than long, upper lobe pointed, lower lobe rounded. Coloration much as in *Diodon hystrix*, but more variable, the spots fewer and larger; usually a broad black bar from eye to eye, continued below eye as a narrow bar; a broad bar across occiput; a black blotch above each pectoral; a short bar in front of dorsal, another in which the dorsal is inserted; a blotch behind the pectoral, and many small spots and blotches on the upper parts; fins with few spots, mostly immaculate in the young. Found in all warm seas, north to the Florida Keys, Lower California, and the Hawaiian Islands, its range coinciding with that of *Diodon hystrix*, from which it may prove to be not distinct. The differences are generally evident in the adult, but young individuals apparently intermediate are often found. Possibly they are the 2 sexes of the same species. Jordan and Snyder had this species from Japan and Doctor Steindachner records it from Laysan, whence he had one specimen. It was not seen by us among the Hawaiian Islands, but the *Albatross* obtained at Laysan Island, a single specimen, 9.25 inches long, upon which Professor Snyder has the following note:

"The fins are immaculate; 10 or 12 small dusky spots scattered over the body; a broad, dark bar, interrupted in the middle, extending between the eyes; a similar bar on nape, a spot as large as eye above and behind pectoral, a median brown bar on back anterior to dorsal, and a blotch surrounding base of dorsal."

360. Diodon hystrix Linnæus. Fig. 192.

Head 2.9; depth 4; eye 4.5; snout 2.5; preorbital 4; interorbital 1.4; width of head 1.1; width of body at base of pectorals 1.1; D. 12; A. 12; C. 10; P. 23.

Body stout and heavy forward, tapering posteriorly; anterior profile from tip of snout to interorbital region concave; interorbital very broad and nearly flat, scarcely convex; eyes large, oblique, farther apart posteriorly; mouth broad, its width 3 in head; dental plates strong, the edge blunt and rough, not much convex at middle; gill-opening vertical, short, with a broad anterior flap; nostril in a short, simple tube with 2 openings, one smaller and more lateral than the other. Body covered with strong, sharp, erectile spines, longest in the post-pectoral region, where they equal distance from eye to gill-opening; those on nape about 2 in eye; those on belly usually short but more slender than those on back; those on posterior part of back and on tail short and 3-rooted, and therefore not erectile; snout naked; sides of caudal peduncle naked; about 6 spines on dorsal side of caudal peduncle back of dorsal fin and 2 on ventral surface posterior to anal fin.

Color in alcohol, light brown, pale or yellowish-white below; entire upper part of head and body

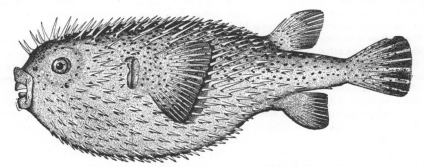

FIG. 192.—*Diodon hystrix* Linnæus; after Jordan and Evermann.

and also sides covered thickly with small round or roundish black spots, smallest and most numerous on snout, fewest on caudal peduncle; belly with a few small dark spots on belly; a broad dark band across under side of head, convex forward; fins all profusely marked with small dark spots.

Occasionally taken among the Hawaiian Islands. We have examined a specimen 20 inches long taken by the *Albatross* at Honolulu in 1896, one 25 inches long, and another of 10 inches obtained in 1889 by Doctor Jenkins; and 2 examples 20 and 21 inches long, respectively, secured by us at Honolulu, where other examples were collected by the *Albatross* in 1902. Smith and Swain record it also from Johnston Island.

361. Diodon nudifrons Jenkins. *"Oopu kawa."* Fig. 193.

D. 15; A. 12; forehead sloping upward from snout at angle of about 45°; interorbital 1.3 in head;

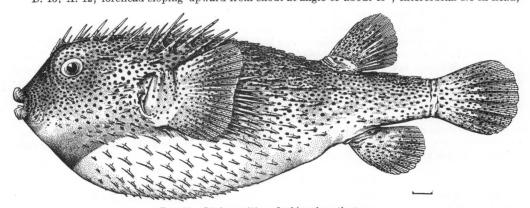

FIG. 193.—*Diodon nudifrons* Jenkins; from the type.

spines mostly short, not longer than eye, except those back of pectoral, the longest of which are equal to length of pectoral and about 2 in head; no spines on forehead below level of upper margins of eyes; foremost spines of head few and short; head, back, sides, all the fins and the membranous sheaths of the spines closely covered with small. roundish, black spots, much smaller than pupil; below pale; a brown band from below gill-opening forward along lower angle of head to below eye, then across throat continuous with corresponding band of opposite side. Known only from one specimen, 21 inches long, obtained by Doctor Jenkins at Honolulu, and from several examples recently seen in the Waikiki aquarium.

Genus 198. CHILOMYCTERUS Bibron.—The Burr-fishes.

Body broad, depressed, moderately inflatable; dermal spines short, stout, immovable, triangular, each with 3 roots; nasal tube simple, with 2 lateral openings; the tube sometimes rounded, sometimes flattened, and with the partition feeble and easily torn, so that the tentacle appears divided; caudal peduncle short; fins small, formed as in *Diodon;* jaws without median suture.

Species numerous, of smaller size than those of *Diodon*, the spines broader and lower, their bases forming a coat of mail.   Only one species known from the Hawaiian Islands.

362. Chilomycterus affinis Günther. *"Oópuhúe."*

Head 2.7; depth 3.5; snout 2.5; eye 4; preorbital 4.6; interorbital 1.6; depth of caudal peduncle 5.2; length of gill-opening equals eye; D. 12; A. 10; C. 14; P. 20.

Body short, stout and broad, its width at pectorals equal to length of head; anterior profile from tip of snout to interorbital concave; interorbital broad, concave, the supraocular rim not prominent; eye large, placed obliquely, the anterior margins being closer together than the posterior; mouth rather large, its width 1.6 in interorbital width; teeth strong, in a broad, flat, rough plate, the cutting edge low and concave, the upper with a strong blunt point at middle; nasal tentacle flattened, somewhat bilobed, the surface with small, roundish cup-shaped cavities; gill-opening vertical, a little wider than base of pectoral; spines all short and blunt, increasing in length posteriorly except above and below, 3-rooted, the anterior very long; a very low 4-rooted spine on posterior part of interobital space; 3 low supraocular spines followed by a row of 3 somewhat higher spines, the first of which is 4-rooted, the next 3-rooted, and the last with a very long anterior root and 2 very short lateral roots; no spines on cheek; middle of belly with very low spines having long and strong anterior roots; caudal peduncle crossed by 2 bony plates, the anterior formed by the inner roots of the spine on each side of dorsal fin, the posterior being the bifid bony base of a single median short spine, which disappears with age; a small, slender, supraocular cirrus near base of middle supraocular spine, this sometimes obscure; spines of back each often with broad but short dermal flap posteriorly, these sometimes obscure or wanting. Fins all rounded; dorsal high, its height about 2 in head; caudal long, its rays about 1.8 in head; anal similar to dorsal, a little lower; pectoral verv broad, its edge nearly truncate, its depth 1.2 in distance between eye and gill-opening.

Color in alcohol, dark brownish or olivaceous above, yellowish white below, the color on back distributed in indistinct clouds; side with 4 broad dark brown bars extending downward from the dark upper parts, the first under eye, the second in front of pectoral, the third under posterior half of pectoral, and the fourth in front of vertical of dorsal fin; entire back and upper parts of sides with numerous small round black spots, less than half diameter of pupil; 2 or 3 spots in front of gill-opening, and 1 or 2 sometimes on cheek; under parts immaculate; caudal peduncle sparsely spotted; fins all very closely covered with small, round brownish black spots, much smaller than those on body.

The collection contains 3 excellent specimens of this fish, which agree so perfectly with Günther's description of *C. affinis* that we have no hesitancy in identifying them with that species.   Günther's specimen was a stuffed skin 15 inches long, from an unknown locality.

We have compared our examples with a specimen from Tokyo, Japan (Coll. K. Otaki), and one from the Galapagos Islands (Coll. Snodgrass and Heller), both of which were thought by Jordan and Snyder and by Snodgrass and Heller to be identical with *C. californiensis* Eigenmann, from San Pedro, California.   We have not been able to examine the type of *C. californiensis*, but this identification is probably correct, although Doctor Eigenmann states that his specimen had no cirri or tentacles anywhere and the color appears to be somewhat different.   In any case all our specimens are certainly referable to Günther's *C. affinis*, which is the oldest available name.

This species reaches a large size, our longest example exceeding 20 inches in length.   It does not appear to be common among the Hawaiian Islands, and was not obtained by Jenkins, Streets, nor any previous collector.   Snyder records it as having been obtained at Honolulu by the *Albatross*, but fails, curiously, to give any further information.

Family LXXXI. MOLIDÆ.—Head Fishes.

Body oblong or more or less short and deep, compressed, truncate behind, so that there is no caudal peduncle. Skin rough, naked, spinous, or tessellated. Mouth very small, terminal; teeth completely united in each jaw, forming a bony beak without median suture, as in the *Diodontidæ*. Dorsal and anal fins similar, falcate in front, the posterior parts more or less perfectly confluent with the caudal; no spinous dorsal; no ventral fins; pelvic bone undeveloped; pectorals present. Belly not inflatable; gill-openings small, in front of pectorals; an accessory opercular gill; no air-bladder.

Fishes of the open seas, apparently composed of a huge head to which small fins are attached; found in most warm seas, pelagic in habit, and reaching a very large size. The very young are variously shortened in form and armed with spines. The flesh of these fishes is coarse and tough and not used for food.

Genus 199. RANZANIA Nardo.

Body oblong, the depth about one-half height; skin smooth, tessellated, divided into small hexagonal scutella; caudal truncate. Otherwise essentially as in *Mola*. The larval forms are unknown. Pelagic.

363. Ranzania makua Jenkins. *"Apahu;" "Makua."* Fig. 194.

D. 17; A. 18; C. 19; P. 3; depth 2.12 in length; head 2.8; eye 6 in head, 2.33 in snout.

Body much compressed, the ventral margin a sharp, evenly curved keel; eye much above axis of body, a little nearer snout than base of pectoral; teeth forming a turtle-like beak completely hidden by projecting folds of skin, which form a truncated opening to the mouth; gill-opening just in front of upper base of pectoral, covered by a 2-lobed valve; body covered by an armor of small plates, more or less hexagonal and concealed; pectoral about 1.5 in head, above axis of body; height of dorsal about equal to head; anal slightly lower; dorsal and anal each separated from the caudal by a notch. Color, bright silvery on sides, upper parts dark; sides with brighter silvery bands, the first 3 with

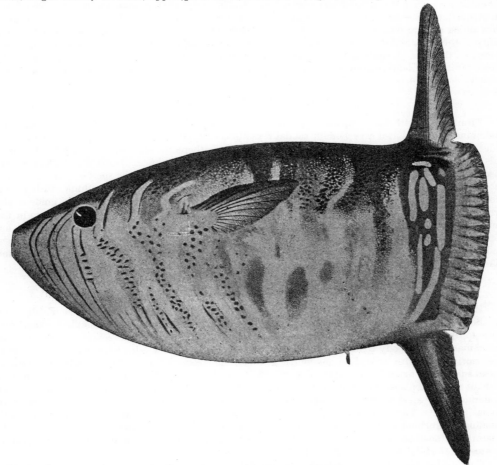

FIG. 194.—*Ranzania makua* Jenkins; from the type.

distinct black borders, the next 4 with numerous black spots, the black margins appearing only on lower parts.

Differing from *Ranzania truncata* chiefly in the smaller eye, placed well above the mouth and above the axis of the body, in the high position of the pectoral fin, in the higher dorsal and anal, and in the coloration. Originally known from one specimen, 20 inches long, taken at the mouth of Pearl Harbor, Oahu, by Mr. Hiel Kapu, and sent to Stanford University by Mr. Charles B. Wilson. A second example about 4 inches long was secured by us at Honolulu in the summer of 1901.

Suborder OSTRACODERMI.—The Trunk Fishes.

This group includes those Plectognaths which are without spinous dorsal and which have the body inclosed in a 3-angled, 4-angled, or 5-angled box or carapace, formed by polygonal, bony scutes, firmly joined at their edges, and with distinct teeth in the jaws. There is but one family, the *Ostraciidæ*, a singular offshoot from the *Sclerodermi*.

Family LXXXII. OSTRACIIDÆ.—The Trunk Fishes.

Body short, cuboid, triquetrous or pentagonal, covered by a carapace formed of firmly united polygonal bony patches, the jaws, bases of the fins, and caudal peduncle free and covered by smooth skin. Mouth small; each jaw with a single series of long, narrow teeth; maxillaries and premaxillaries firmly united; gill-opening a nearly vertical slit, below and behind the eye; dorsal fin single, short, without spine; anal short, similar to dorsal; caudal rounded; no ventral fins; vertebræ 14, the anterior 9 elongate, the last 5 extremely short; no ribs. Genera 3; species about 20, all of the tropical seas, living near the bottom in shallow waters. The species of this group are so singular in appearance and so easily preserved that they have been common in collections ever since the collecting of tropical curiosities began. The 4 American species were well known to Artedi and Linnæus. "The locomotion of the trunk fishes is very peculiar. The propelling force is exerted by the dorsal and anal fins, which have a half rotary, sculling motion, resembling that of a screw propeller; the caudal fin acts as a rudder, save when it is needed for unusually rapid swimming, when it is used as in other fishes; the chief function of the broad pectorals seems to be that of forming a current of water through the gills, thus aiding respiration, which would otherwise be difficult on account of the narrowness and inflexibility of the branchial apertures. When taken from the water, one of these fishes will live for 2 or 3 hours, all the time solemnly fanning its gills, and when restored to its native element seems none the worse for its experience, except that, on account of the air absorbed, it can not at once sink to the bottom." (Goode.)

Genus 200. OSTRACION Linnæus.

Trunk-fishes with the carapace closed behind the anal fin; carapace with or without frontal and abdominal spines; dorsal rays 9 or 10; caudal rays always 10; lateral ridges developed; median dorsal ridge undeveloped, or else raised in a sharp spine, the body therefore 4-angled or 5-angled. Although this character is a striking one it is not one of high structural importance. Hollard and Bleeker have discarded it as being of no real systematic value. All writers agree that the species of the group are most closely related, and that the relations are closer than they appear. We think, with Doctor Goode, and Jordan and Fowler, that the shape of the carapace affords the most reliable guide to the arrangement of the species of the genus, and we find it difficult to define more than 2 genera in the family, unless we assign generic rank to each of the leading sections. In Japan 3 of these sections are represented, *Tetrosomus*, *Lactoria*, and *Ostracion*. The remaining 4, *Rhinesomus*, *Chapinus*, *Lactophrys*, and *Acanthostracion* are all based on 3-angled species, a type confined to the West Indian region and taken as a distinct genus, *Lactophrys*, by us in our Fishes of North and Middle America.

364. Ostracion sebæ Bleeker. "*Móa.*" Fig. 195.

Head 3.75 in length; depth 3; eye 2.6 in head; snout 1.2; interorbital 1.2; D. 9; A. 9; P. 10; C. 10.

Body 4-sided; back slightly rounded; interorbital flat; profile before eyes strongly convex, from there to tip of snout straight or slightly concave in small examples, forming a reentrant angle in larger individuals; side of body concave; ventral surface slightly convex, its sides uniformly curved, less so posteriorly, the width at middle one-fourth greater than head, its length 2.6 times head; width of dorsal surface 1.2 times head; depth of side 1.25 in head; preorbital 1.6 in head; carapace entirely without spines; 2 plates posterior to dorsal fin and 1 behind anal fin; anterior opening of carapace moderate, its greatest width 1.8 in interorbital; greatest width of posterior opening 1.6 in interorbital; caudal peduncle, measured along middle of side, equal to snout; pectoral short, broad, its length equaling interorbital width; dorsal shorter, the distal edge somewhat oblique, length of rays 1.2 in interorbital; anal fin shorter, the rays 1.3 in interorbital; caudal long, rounded, its length equaling greatest interorbital width or length of head.

Color in life, dark blue or black on back, belly dark blue; a lighter patch below eye; an irregular golden band, nearly as broad as eye, across top of head between the eyes; back covered with many small round white spots, uniform in size and uniformly distributed; side with golden spots; caudal peduncle black, with one or more rows of golden spots on each side and white dots on dorsal surface; axil blue; fins dusky, posterior half of caudal lighter; iris white, with orange spots. Different specimens show considerable variation in color, some being decidedly dark blue, others black.

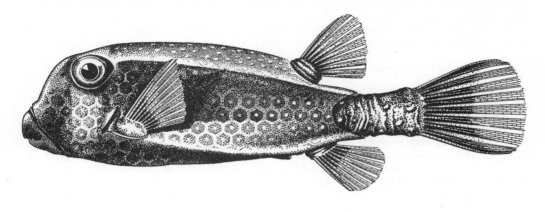

FIG. 195.—*Ostracion sebæ* Bleeker. Type of *O. camurum*.

In alcohol the general color becomes dirty brownish, the spots bluish white; the basal portion of caudal black, the distal part yellowish white; anal and pectoral pale yellowish white, each crossed by 1 or 2 darker bars; base of pectoral dark brown; the orange stripe across interorbital pale dusky.

The Bureau has recently received from Mr. Berndt 5 specimens of this species, 3.3 to 4.7 inches long. These differ in no way from specimens collected by Doctor Jordan in Samoa. Two examples have the ventral surface without spots, while 2 others have the same area spotted like the back. In 1 specimen the spots extend inward along the edges of the ventral surface of the carapace. Some have the caudal peduncle with spots only, while others have elongate white bands of irregular shape, no two being alike in this respect. The largest individual has a transverse white band between the eyes.

This is the most abundant species among the Hawaiin Islands, although not represented in our collections by many specimens. Doctor Wood obtained 1 example, the *Albatross* 2 in 1896, Doctor Jenkins 1 (the type), and 1 was secured by us, all at Honolulu. The *Albatross* found it at Puako Bay, Hawaii. There are 2 specimens from Honolulu in the California Academy, and we have examined a specimen collected by Snodgrass and Heller at Clipperton Island. The species was also found by Doctor Jordan at Apia where it is known as Moamoa Samasama.

365. Ostracion oahuensis Jordan & Evermann. *"Moamoa waa."* Plate 51.

Head 3.9 in length; depth 2.9; eye 2.9 in head; snout 1.2; preorbital 1.6; interorbital 1; D. 9; A. 9; P. 10; C. 10.

Body 4-sided; dorsal side of carapace evenly convex, its greatest width one-fourth greater than head; lateral dorsal angles not trenchant, slightly convex anteriorly, then evenly convex; snout blunt, the anterior profile ascending abruptly then strongly convex in front of eyes; interorbital space nearly flat; cheek flat; side of body concave, its width about equal to head; ventral keel prominent, evenly convex; ventral surface nearly flat posteriorly, but little convex anteriorly, its greatest width 1.4 times length of head, its length just twice its width; gill-opening short, not exceeding two-thirds diameter of eye; least width of anterior opening of carapace 1.75 in interorbital, or 1.5 times diameter of orbit, the depth nearly twice orbit; mouth small; teeth rich brown; least depth of posterior opening of carapace much less than width of anterior opening, equaling distance from lower edge of preorbital to pupil; length of caudal peduncle less than that of head, its depth 2.2 in its length; no spines anywhere. Dorsal fin high, its edge obliquely rounded, its length 1.3 in head; anal similar to dorsal, the edge rounded, its length 1.2 in dorsal; caudal slightly rounded, its rays nearly equal to head; pectoral with its free edge oblique, the rays successively shorter, length of fin equal to height of dorsal.

Color in life, dark brown with blue tinges; interorbital space showing more or less golden; small whitish spots profusely covering entire dorsal surface; no spots on side of body or on face; no spots on ventral surface, except a faint one of a slightly darker color than general gray color of surface; one longitudinal row of golden spots on each side of upper part of caudal peduncle from carapace to base of caudal fin; pectoral, anal, and dorsal fins with transverse rows of faint spots; caudal bluish black at base, white on posterior half; a broad light or yellowish area below eye; iris golden.

Color in alcohol, rich brown above, the sides darker, and the ventral surface paler, brownish about margins, dusky yellowish within; entire back with numerous small, roundish, bluish-white spots; upper half of caudal peduncle with similar but larger spots; forehead and snout dark brown; lips brownish black; cheek dirty yellowish; sides and ventral surface wholly unspotted; base of caudal blackish, paler distally, the dark extending farthest on outer rays; other fins dusky, with some obscure brownish spots.

This species is related to *O. sebæ* Bleeker, from which it differs in the smaller, more numerous spots on back, the entire absence of spots on side, the smaller size of the spots on the caudal peduncle, and the brighter yellow of the suborbital region.

The type and 1 cotype were obtained by us at Honolulu where other specimens were later collected by the *Albatross*. One example was obtained by Doctor Wood. Our specimens are 5 to 6 inches long.

366. Ostracion lentiginosum Bloch & Schneider. *"Oopakaku."*

Head 4 in length; depth 3; eye 2.8 in head; snout 1.25; preorbital 1.9; interorbital 1.2; D. 9, sometimes 7; A. 9; C. 10; P. 10.

Body 4-sided; dorsal surface moderately rounded, the lateral dorsal angles not sharp, uniformly convex, except at extreme anterior and posterior ends, where each is slightly concave; greatest width of dorsal surface one-fourth greater than length of head, there being 10 hexagonal plates in a transverse series; 3 plates posterior to dorsal fin; side concave, its greatest depth about 1.2 in head; ventral surface evenly convex, its sides uniformly curved, its greatest width 1.6 times length of head, its length 3 times head, about 10 plates in a transverse series, one plate behind anal fin; anterior opening of carapace narrow, its greatest width less than orbit; mouth small; the teeth brown; anterior dorsal profile concave to front of eyes, then strongly convex; interorbital nearly flat; least depth of posterior opening of carapace equal to width of anterior opening, its greatest width a trifle greater than depth of preorbital; length of caudal peduncle equaling head, its depth 2 in its length; dorsal fin high, its rays 1.6 in head; anal similar, equally high, its distal edge rounded; caudal broad, rounded, its length nearly equaling that of head; pectoral with its distal edge oblique, the longest rays about as long as caudal.

Color in life of an example (No. 035z7), 3.25 inches long, gray, covered all over carapace on all sides, including head, with small white spots; similar spots all over caudal peduncle and on basal half of caudal fin; posteriorly the spots have a tinge of blue; spots on head very small, those posteriorly larger, but none nearly so large as pupil; dorsal, ventral and pectoral fins transparent.

Color in alcohol dark brownish black; back and sides profusely covered with small, round, or stellate bluish white spots, uniformly disposed; ventral surface paler, the lighter spots and markings disposed to run together, forming reticulations; cheek with few or no spots; caudal peduncle brown, with somewhat larger, round, or oblong bluish white spots; base of dorsal black, the fin dusky; base of anal pale brownish, with a few small white spots, the base of the rays with a brown line, the fin dusky; caudal dark at base with a few white spots, the distal portion paler; ventrals dusky.

This is a species of wide distribution, having been recorded from the Indian Ocean and Archipelago and from various places in the tropical Pacific. Steindachner had 1 example from Honolulu, Jenkins has 2, and we have 5, all from the same place. Others were obtained by the *Albatross*. Jenkins also had 1 from Hilo and there is 1 from Hilo in the California Academy.

Genus 201. LACTORIA Jordan & Fowler.

This genus agrees with *Ostracion* in having the carapace 4-angled, but differs in having strong spines in front of the eyes and a pair terminating the ventral keels; a median dorsal spine is sometimes present.

367. Lactoria schlemmeri Jordan & Snyder. Plates 52 and 53.[a]

Head measured to gill-opening, 3.7 in length to base of caudal; depth 2.3; eye 2.7 in head; snout 4.6; D. 9; A. 9.

Anterior profile of head very steep, interrupted by a constriction one-third of distance between tip of snout and middle of interorbital space; interorbital space V-shaped, when viewed from before, the depression extending almost to a level with upper edge of pupil; carapace with 5 ridges, the dorsal ridge scarcely evident, with a large spine located midway between tip of snout and base of caudal fin; dorso-lateral crest with 3 spines, the anterior projecting upward and forward from the orbit; the posterior located slightly behind middle of dorsal spine, midway between anterior edge of orbit and posterior end of carapace; the median, which is small and weak, located somewhat nearer to the orbital than the posterior spine; ventro-lateral ridge with 4 spines, the first very small, the second larger, located below dorsal spine, the posterior one projecting backward, the distance between it and the one of the opposite side equal to distance between center of pupil and dorsal spine; ventral surface of carapace convex, a slight median depression extending from breast to anal fin; plates granular, except 10 or 12 in the region posterior to pectoral fin, each with a central granule usually larger than the others.

Dorsal fin located midway between dorsal spine and end of carapace; base of anal fin occupying most of the space between vent and end of carapace; pectoral just behind vertical through posterior edge of orbit.

Dorsal portion of body dusky with small dark spots scattered over snout and back; ventral half of carapace translucent with zigzag dusky bars along the region of crest, the color following the

---

a Ostracion schlemmeri on plate.

vertical sutures between the plates; throat and breast with scattered dusky spots somewhat smaller than pupil.

This species is closely related to *L. diaphanum* (Bloch & Schneider), of Japan and the East Indies. Compared with Japanese examples it differs in having the spines better developed, and in greater number, there being 2 on the dorso-lateral ridge, 1 of which is opposite the large median spine, the other between the former and the orbital spine; also in having the carapace deeper in the region of the ventro-lateral ridge and broader near the anal fin, and the plates posterior to the pectoral less granular. The only Hawaiian form with which it might be confused is *L. galeodon* Jenkins. In this species the ventral portion of the carapace is not translucent, the orbital spines are longer and project in a more horizontal direction, and there are no spines on the dorso-lateral crest posterior to the orbit.

One specimen, 4.13 inches long, from Laysan Island, collected by Mr. Max Schlemmer, for whom the species is named. Type No. 8440, Stanford Univ. Mus.

368. Lactoria galeodon Jenkins. "*Makukana.*" Fig. 196.

D. 9; P. 11; A. 8; head 2.8; depth 2; eye 2; snout 4.5; interorbital 1.2.

Carapace 4-sided; a pair of long, slender, slightly divergent spines in front of eyes, their direction slightly upward; a similar pair terminating the lateral ventral angles, horizontal and not divergent; middle of back with a strong, compressed, triangular spine, notched on posterior border, slightly

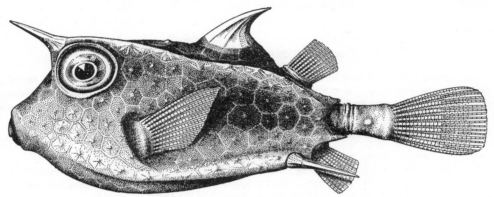

FIG. 196.—*Lactoria galeodon* Jenkins; from the type.

projecting backward, and resembling a sharp tooth; snout short, the anterior profile concave; dorsal lateral angles little convex, the ventral angles more convex, 12 plates along its edge from snout to spine; 8 plates in lateral dorsal angle, no spine at its middle; ventral surface with 11 or 12 plates in longitudinal median series, 7 in transverse series.

Color in alcohol, dirty yellowish or olivaceous above; middle of side with a large oblong dark or blackish area; ventral surface yellowish.

This species is closely related to the East Indian species, *L. diaphanum* (Bloch & Schneider), from which it is readily distinguished by the entire absence of median spines on the lateral ventral keel, by the longer and straighter frontal and ventral spines, the character of the dorsal spine, and the opaque carapace.

A single example was obtained at Honolulu in 1889 by Doctor Jenkins, and our collection contains three small specimens 1 to 1.3 inches long, all from Hilo. We have also examined a painting made by Andrew Garrett, preserved in Hilo, the specimen having been taken at Kailua; also a colored drawing made at Kailua by Miss Louise Kimball, of Los Angeles.

The *Albatross* obtained several specimens at Honolulu from the stomach of a *Coryphæna*.

Genus 202. ARACANA Gray.

This genus differs from *Ostracion* in having the carapace 6-angled and open behind the anal fin. The species vary in form almost as much as do those of *Ostracion*. In *Aracana* proper there are spines over the eye, and the abdomen is crested, while in *Apoplocapros* the back and belly are crested, but no spines are present anywhere.

The single Hawaiian species of this genus is fully described in Section II.

Group CIRRHITOIDEI.—The Cirrhitoid Fishes.

This group agrees with the *Percoidea* in most respects, the chief external difference being in the form of the pectorals, which have broad, procurrent bases, as in the *Scorpænidæ*, the lower rays being unbranched and more or less thickened. Its relations doubtless lie with both *Percidæ* and *Scorpænidæ*. One family is represented in Hawaiian waters.

Family LXXXIII. CIRRHITIDÆ.

Body compressed, oblong, covered with moderate scales, which are cycloid or ctenoid; lateral line continuous, concurrent with the back, not extending on caudal; mouth low, terminal, with lateral cleft; eye lateral, of moderate size; premaxillaries protractile; maxillary narrow, not sheathed by preorbital; teeth small, pointed, occasionally with canines, sometimes present on vomer or palatines; cheek without bony suborbital stay; branchiostegals 3 to 6, usually 6; gill-membranes separate, free from the isthmus; preopercle serrate or entire; opercle unarmed; no spines or serrations on bones of cranium; dorsal fin continuous, long, the spinous and soft parts subequal, the spines not depressible in a groove; soft dorsal low; spines rather low and strong; pectoral fin short and broad as in the *Cottidæ;* lower half of fin with its rays simple and generally stout; the membranes deeply incised; ventral fins thoracic, but considerably behind root of pectorals, the rays I, 5; air-bladder large and complicated or wanting; pyloric cæca few; vertebræ $10 + 16 = 26$; skull very compact and solid. Carnivorous fishes of the warm seas; genera 10; species 40; apparently really allied on the one hand to the *Serranidæ*, with which group Dr. Boulenger finds that the skeleton has much in common; on the other hand they show affinities with the *Scorpænidæ*. Through such forms as these the great group of *Loricati* or mail-cheek fishes may be connected with their perch-like ancestors. This family is represented in American waters·by one genus (*Cirrhitus*) with 2 species, and in the Hawaiian Islands by 4 genera and about 7 species.

Genus 203. CHEILODACTYLUS Lacépède.

Body greatly elevated anteriorly, the anterior profile rising abruptly from occiput to origin of dorsal fin; nape trenchant, back very greatly compressed, the body tapering rapidly posteriorly; anterior dorsal spines long and strong. Several species, only one known from the Hawaiian Islands.

369. Cheilodactylus vittatus Garrett. "*Kikakapu.*" Plate 54.

Head 3 in. length; depth 2.6; eye 3.2 in head; D. xviii, 29; A. iii, 7; scales 11–63–12.

Body greatly compressed, anteriorly greatly elevated, the profile rising nearly vertically from posterior line of orbit to origin of dorsal fin, from which point it descends in a long low curve but slightly convex; nape trenchant; head moderate; snout not produced; mouth small, little oblique; maxillary scarcely reaching orbit; lower jaw short, included; preopercle entire; eye moderate or large, entering anterior profile; nostrils round, close to eye, the anterior with a small, branched filament; fins well developed; origin of dorsal over posterior edge of orbit, its base covering nearly entire length of body; first dorsal spine very short, second somewhat longer, third very long, nearly equaling head; fourth and fifth dorsal spines both a little shorter than third, about 1.4 in head, the other spines progressively shorter; edge of soft dorsal nearly straight, the rays about equal in length, a little greater than snout or about equal to last dorsal spine; caudal deeply forked, the lobes pointed; anal spines short, the anterior spines produced somewhat, equal to snout and eye; ventrals reaching past vent, their length 1.6 in head; pectoral long, the lower rays produced, nearly equaling head; scales rather small, firm and smooth; head densely covered with much smaller scales; scales of breast very small.

Color in life, according to Garrett, grayish silvery, ornamented with 5 oblique blackish brown bands disclosed as follows: one from snout to margin of preopercle; the second from eye across cheek to base of pectoral fin, which it involves; the third, which passes over the occipital region, extending downward and backward to axil of pectoral; the fourth and broadest from origin of dorsal downward and backward, widening in its descent and passing beneath the abdomen under the ventral fins; a fifth beginning at the tip of fourth dorsal spine, passing downward and backward, reaching back at base of seventh spine, and continuing chiefly on side to caudal peduncle, partly crossing lateral line under about twelfth dorsal ray; within this dorsal band are 3 irregular pale or whitish spots; caudal peduncle with a large blackish spot near the middle and 2 smaller ones at base of caudal fin; opercular flap and snout tinged with orange red; interorbital with 2 transverse brownish red bands; dorsal fin anterior to fifth black band, white; soft portion of dorsal, caudal and anal light yellowish, the caudal lobes tipped with blackish brown; pectoral orange-red; ventrals deep blackish brown; iris yellowish silvery. In alcohol the general pattern of coloration holds.

The above description is based upon a specimen about 6 inches long, taken at Honolulu some years ago by Doctor Rosenstern, of San Francisco, and now in the California Academy of Sciences.

The species is an extremely rare one. It was described originally from Honolulu, by Garrett, his type being a specimen 7 inches long, the present location of which is unknown. It is probably not in existence. The description and colored plate in Günther's Fische der Südsee were based upon Garrett's description and sketch. A second example, 8 inches long, was obtained by Professor Schauinsland at Honolulu in 1896, and described by Doctor Steindachner. Recently we have received from

Mr. Berndt, at Honolulu, 2 other examples much larger than either of those previously known. They measure 6.9 and 9.7 inches, and with the specimen in the California Academy of Sciences and the one in the Museum at Vienna seem, therefore, to be the only known examples, and are probably the only representatives of the species extant.

Genus 204. CIRRHITOIDEA Jenkins.

No palatine teeth; teeth on vomer; jaws with narrow band of small canine-like teeth; intermaxillary denticulate; preopercle finely toothed; dorsal single, of 10 spines and 12 rays; 5 rays of pectoral simple, lower rays of pectoral elongate, 1.8 in head; snout sharp, pointed, 3 in head. This genus is allied to *Oxycirrhites* Bleeker, from which it differs chiefly in the shorter snout.

370. Cirrhitoidea bimacula Jenkins. Fig. 197.

Head 2.6 in length; depth 3; eye 4.6 in head; snout 3.8; maxillary 2.7; D. x, 12; A. iii, 6; scales 3–37–7.

Body short, deep, and compressed, the dorsal profile strongly arched from tip of snout to base of first dorsal spines; back very narrow, trenchant; ventral outline nearly straight, head rather long, pointed; snout long and pointed; mouth moderate, slightly oblique, the jaws equal; maxillary reaching pupil; jaws with small, close-set canine-like teeth, small teeth on vomer, none on palatines; preopercle serrate; opercle ending in a long flap; fins rather large; dorsal spines slender, weak, their length equal to distance from tip of snout to middle of pupil; dorsal rays somewhat shorter; second anal spine longest, about equal to longest dorsal spine; anal spines similar to those of soft dorsal; caudal slightly rounded; ventrals rather long, reaching past vent; pectoral moderate, the middle rays longest, about 1.2 in head; scales rather large, lateral line complete, beginning at upper end of gill-opening and running a little nearer dorsal outline posteriorly; scales on nape, breast, cheek, and opercle.

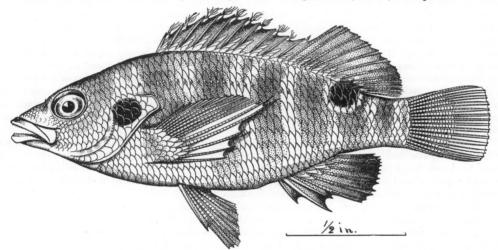

½ in.

FIG. 197.—*Cirrhitoidea bimacula* Jenkins; from the type.

Color in alcohol, dusky; body crossed by about 7 rather broad darker vertical bars, the first at origin of dorsal, second under middle or spinous dorsal, third under beginning of soft dorsal, last 2 on caudal peduncle; head dusky yellowish; a large brownish black spot on opercle, and another large round brownish black spot on side above lateral line and under posterior third of soft dorsal; fins somewhat dusky, the anal darkest.

The above description is based chiefly upon the type, No. 50702, U. S. N. M. (original No. 275), a specimen 2 inches long, obtained by Jenkins at Honolulu. One other specimen, which was taken as a cotype, is of the same length and was obtained at the same time.

Genus 205. PARACIRRHITES Bleeker.

Premaxillaries not produced; some of the teeth on jaws canine-like; teeth on vomer but none on palatines; head obtuse, convex; body and head covered with large scales.

This genus is close to *Cirrhitus*, from which it differs chiefly in the absence of palatine teeth and in having large scales on cheek. Most of the species of *Cirrhitidæ* of Polynesia belong to this genus.

371. Paracirrhites cinctus (Günther). *"Pilikoa;" "Oopuka-hai-hai;" Póopá 'a."*
Plate LXVIII.

Head 3 in length; depth 2.8; eye 4.5 in head; snout 3.4; maxillary 2.4; interorbital 5.3; D. x, 14; A. iii, 6; scales 5–48–10; Br. 5; gillrakers 12 + 5, finely ciliated.

Body oblong, compressed, deepest through base of pectoral; dorsal outline from tip of snout to origin of dorsal rather steep, straight, thence to end of fin evenly slanted; ventral outline slightly curved; head longer than deep, compressed, subconic; snout bluntly pointed; mouth rather large, nearly horizontal, lips thick, lower jaw slightly included; maxillary reaching about to anterior edge of pupil; a single row of small conic teeth in each jaw, behind these anteriorly a patch of small villiform teeth; bands of villiform teeth on vomer and palatines; posterior edge of preopercle roughly serrate; eye high up, the supraorbital above line of anterior profile; interorbital narrow, concave; anterior nostril with a short branched filament about as long as pupil; fins rather large, origin of dorsal slightly in advance of base of pectoral, the latter much in front of ventral, distance from origin of dorsal to tip of snout equal to head; dorsal spines not as high as rays, the fifth or sixth longest, 2.1 in head; base of spinous dorsal slightly longer than that of soft dorsal, the anterior dorsal rays slightly the longer, longest 1.75 in head; caudal truncate; anal short, its base equal to snout and eye, second spine stout and longest, equal to base of fin, front rays slightly the longer, equal to second spine; ventrals rather short, scarcely reaching anal, 1.75 in head; pectoral long, the 6 lowermost rays thick and not united beyond the tips of the shorter rays, longest ray, reaching base of third anal spine, 1.3 in head; scales firm, moderate, cycloid, none on top of head and snout; lateral line concurrent with dorsal outline.

Color in life, head olive brown, finely vermiculated and spotted with bluish and greenish white, the vermiculations on lower part of cheek and lower jaw red and white; opercle blackish, with bluish white spots; nape with a narrow lighter area, behind which are delicate bluish white and red points on a dark ground; side with broad, white crossbars, alternating with broader red bars; first white crossbar extending from base of third or fourth dorsal spines to just posterior to base of pectoral, this bar narrowest and somewhat brownish at upper end; then less red just above lateral line, followed by blood red, ending under middle of pectoral; second, third, and fourth white bars each with purplish shade and each with an obscure orange blotch near lower end; second and third red bars brightest, the second extending from bases of last 3 dorsal spines to base of third anal spine, broadest at top, narrowing gradually downward; third red bar beginning under fourth to ninth dorsal rays and ending at base of last anal rays; fourth red bar crossing base of caudal peduncle, its center splotched with blackish; rest of caudal peduncle pale rosy or purplish; under parts bluish white, with reddish or orange spots and lines, the latter confined chiefly to the breast; membranes of dorsal fin red, blotched and dotted with irregular bluish or greenish white markings; edge of membranes narrowly white, tip of dorsal spines red, a small black speck on base of first spine; soft dorsal greenish with bluish and purplish wash, indistinct orange or brassy spots through the center; caudal rays purplish or rosy, the membranes greenish, anal bluish, the rays brassy green, 3 or 4 small brassy spots near the base; ventrals similar to anal; pectoral pale rosy; iris golden.

Color in alcohol, head brownish above, paler below, with numerous fine bluish-white spots, larger and more irregular and most distinct on lower jaw and gill-membranes; opercle dark; side with 4 broad brownish black crossbars, separated by narrower yellowish white bars, the crossbar on caudal peduncle blackest and most distinct, under parts rosy white; dorsal, pectoral, and ventrals uniform yellowish white, little dusky; caudal and anal somewhat dusky.

This beautiful species is very abundant among the Hawaiian Islands and is one of the most interesting and attractive fishes seen in the Honolulu market. It reaches a length of 4 to 5 inches. The collections contain 71 specimens, 8 from Hilo, the others from Honolulu, ranging in length 2.8 to 4.4 inches. Specimens were obtained by Jenkins, Jordan, and Snyder, the *Albatross*, and by us.

372. Paracirrhites forsteri (Bloch & Schneider). "*Hilupilikoa;*" "*Piliko'a.*" Plate LXVII.

Head 3 in length; depth 2.75; eye 6.2 in head; snout 3.2; maxillary 2.25; interorbital 5.4; D. x, 11; A. III, 6; scales 6–48–10.

Body oblong, deepest at base of pectoral; head longer than deep, the upper profile a little concave over eyes; snout long, blunt; jaws large, powerful, the lower slightly projecting; lips fleshy; maxillary large, reaching middle of eye; teeth strong, 2 large canines in front of upper jaw; teeth on sides of mandible enlarged, conic; eye small, high, in anterior part of head; preopercular margin finely serrate; interorbital space nearly flat, the supraocular ridges little elevated; anterior nostrils with large ciliated flap; spinous dorsal beginning a little behind base of pectoral, fifth spine longest, 2.5 in head; first dorsal ray longest, 1.65 in head; second anal spine enlarged, longest; first anal ray longest, 1.8 in head; lower pectoral rays longest, 1.5 in head, and free for only small portion distally; ventrals 1.75 in head, inserted well behind pectorals and not reaching anus; scales large, cycloid, in even series, those on top of head, snout, and mandible very minute; small scales on basal portions of soft dorsal, caudal, anal, pectoral, and ventrals; lateral line straight.

Color in life, upper parts of head and back pale yellowish olivaceous; a broad paler or whitish line along base of dorsal fin, below this yellowish brown posteriorly with a long broad black blotch extending from about middle of side under last 3 dorsal spines, along upper edges of caudal peduncle and upon bases of middle and 1 or 2 upper caudal rays; beneath this, along axis of body, a broad whitish band, bordered above and below by yellowish brown, the anterior end with few reddish or brown spots, the posterior half somewhat bluish; lower half of side with about 7 narrow longitudinal orange yellow stripes separated by nearly equally wide bluish silvery lines; lips and face with very bright red spots; red and black spots on opercle, preopercle and body above the pectoral; chin and throat with red spots; under parts of head and breast with red and black spots; iris red; dorsal fin red, the spinous portion dusky on outer margin, the soft rays with the membranes somewhat dusky; caudal chiefly red or rosy; rays of anal yellow, the membranes dusky; rays of pectoral red, red spots on base and in axil.

Color in alcohol, dull brown, deepest anteriorly; head and anterior part of trunk with small round black spots, very much smaller on snout and mandible; iris dull yellow with a few deep brown spots; back along base of dorsal fin dusky orange; upper half of body posteriorly with a broad black band from middle of back to middle of caudal; broad, whitish band out on caudal; spinous dorsal dusky brown, soft dorsal with outer half whitish, the basal portion blackish; anal, pectoral, and ventrals dusky, the last slightly tinted with olivaceous; caudal more or less dusky, outer or marginal portion broadly whitish.

Described from No. 04574, 6.8 inches long, from Honolulu. The collections contain 25 examples, all from Honolulu but one, which is from Hilo. Length 4.4 to 8.25 inches.

373. Paracirrhites arcatus (Cuvier & Valenciennes). "*Pilikó'a.*"   Plate LXIX.

Head 2.9 in length; depth 2.33; eye 5.5 in head; snout 3.2; maxillary 2.2; interorbital 5; D. x, 11; A. iii, 6; scales 6–50–11.

Body oblong, deepest about pectoral region; head deep; snout long, obtuse; jaws large, equal, powerful; lips fleshy, broad; mouth large, oblique; maxillary broad, reaching posterior margin of pupil; 2 large canines in front of upper jaw, and enlarged teeth on sides of mandible; eye small, anterior, and superior; margin of preopercle convex, finely serrate; interorbital space concave; anterior nostrils with ciliated fleshy flap; third and fourth dorsal spines longest, 2.75 in head; anterior dorsal ray longest, 1.6 in head; second anal spine longest, 2.6 in head; first anal ray longest, 1.65 in head; margin of caudal convex; pectoral short, 1.5 in head, lower rays little free at tips; ventrals pointed, reaching vent, spine 1.6 in longest ray; scales moderately large, cycloid; small scales on bases of soft dorsal, soft anal, caudal, and of pectoral; no scales on snout above or on lips; lateral line nearly straight, not concurrent with dorsal profile.

Color in life (from No. 03401) olivaceous, with narrow longitudinal lines of cardinal-red on back, becoming deep brown on lower surface; a broad white band on back posterior to base of caudal, where it becomes purple; head purplish-red, more or less deep red along margin of maxillary above, preorbital region, and side of mandible posteriorly; an orange spot with scarlet edge on lower margin of preopercle; below and posterior to margin of preopercle, blue with 3 orange bands with scarlet margins, the median with a blotch of green; interorbital width, snout above and tip of upper jaw deep olivaceous, the lower lip, groove between nasals and maxillaries, and anterior nostrils, orange; patch behind and above eye olivaceous, bordered narrowly with light blue, cardinal-red, and orange; margin of orbit blue-green; iris cardinal-red; chest purple; rudimentary caudal rays greenish yellow; fins clear blue-green; basal portion of caudal membranes paler blue; row of scales at base of soft dorsal bluish.

A fresh specimen 4 inches long (No. 03194) from Honolulu had sides faded red; an oblong olive-brown spot back of eye bordered by an orange line, which, in turn, was bounded by an orange-red line; upper lip rosy; tip of lower jaw and maxillary yellow; subopercle rosy white with 3 crossbars of orange red; chin rosy; throat black; spinous dorsal red, black at tips; soft dorsal rusty rosy at base, a middle blackish line, yellowish on outer half; caudal rosy; upper lobe yellowish at tip, the lower blackish; anal pale rosy at base, smoky black at tip; pectoral pale rosy; ventrals dull rosy, blackish edged; iris rosy with some yellow.

Color in alcohol, faded dull or pale brown, dark on back above; a white band on posterior part of back to caudal very distinct in all examples; deep brown blotch behind and above eye with narrow white brown border; 3 white streaks below preopercle with dark borders; branchiostegal region dusky; margin of spinous dorsal faintly blackish, the same color continued as a narrow blackish band across soft dorsal; margins of ventrals and anal below dusky; fins otherwise pale.

There seem to be 2 patterns of coloration, the white streak on back posteriorly and the generally paler coloration distinguishing typical individuals at all ages and in alcohol as well as in life, while in the other pattern the white stripe is never present, the general coloration is more rosy in life, and in alcohol the body is uniformly darker. Some specimens have a broad wash or band of pink on each side of back, covering most of the length of trunk.

This beautiful species is abundant at Honolulu, from which place we have 62 specimens. We have also 8 examples from Hilo and 2 from Kailua, ranging from 2.75 to 5.4 inches in length. Specimens were collected by Jenkins, Jordan and Snyder, the *Albatross*, and by us.

Genus 206. CIRRHITUS Lacépède.

Body oblong, compressed, formed much as in *Sciæna*, covered with large cycloid scales; head rather obtuse; scales on cheek very small; premaxillaries not produced; teeth on vomer and palatines;

jaws with small canine teeth; anterior nostrils fringed; preopercle evenly curved, its edge finely serrate; soft parts of vertical fins scaled at base; dorsal rays 11 or 12; caudal truncate.

This genus contains several species, only one of which is known from the Hawaiian Islands.

374. Cirrhitus marmoratus (Lacépède). *"Pô'opáa;" "Oópukái."* Plate LXX.

Head 2.75 in length; depth 2.75; eye 5.75 in head; snout 3; maxillary 2.4; mandible 2.1; preorbital 4.8; interorbital 5.75; D. x, 11; A. iii, 6; scales 6–40–8; Br. 5.

Body short and stout, moderately compressed; head heavy, longer than deep; snout bluntly conic; mouth large, slightly oblique, the jaws subequal; maxillary rather long, reaching middle of pupil; patches of villiform teeth on vomer and palatines; tongue naked; jaws with bands of villiform teeth, 2 or more enlarged canines in front of upper jaw and about 4 somewhat longer canines on each side of lower jaw; dorsal profile moderately arched, the curves strongest between nape and origin of dorsal; eye moderate, high, the supraorbital rim projecting strongly above the profile; interorbital concave; nostrils moderate, nearly circular, close together, the anterior with a bushy filament about as long as diameter of pupil; origin of dorsal over base of pectoral, its distance from snout equaling its base; dorsal spines rather strong, fourth or fifth longest, about equaling snout; dorsal rays about equal to length of spines, a little greater than longest spine; caudal truncate or slightly rounded when expanded; anal spines stout, second and third about equal in length, a little shorter than snout; anal rays moderately long, longest ray 2 in head; the 7 lowermost rays of pectoral thick and free at the posterior ends, the sixth from bottom longest, 1.8 in head or, measured from base of fin, 1.4 in head; scales large, smooth, arranged somewhat irregularly; nape, opercle, and breast with large scales; cheeks with very small scales, rest of head naked; preopercle finely serrate; opercle ending in a soft flap, projecting beyond a flat obscure spine; gill-membranes broadly connected across the isthmus.

Color in life, body marbled and blotched with bluish olivaceous brownish and white, with numerous red spots of varying sizes, the white appearing as 5 ill-defined vertical bases; head bluish white with irregular lines of yellowish or orange brown, these palest on cheek; lower jaw pale blue with cross-markings of darker blue; base of pectoral pale with yellowish-brown blotches; posterior portion of back with 4 large reddish-brown blotches, the first under the last 2 dorsal spines, the second under sixth and seventh dorsal rays, the third under last dorsal rays, fourth on upper edge of caudal peduncle; spinous dorsal pale-yellowish blue, crossed by 3 series of large orange-red spots on the membranes, the uppermost series least complete; tips of membrane of spinous dorsal whitish, above black blotches; soft dorsal pinkish with a series of redder spots along the base; caudal pale pinkish, crossed by about 4 series of bright blood-red blotches; anal pale rosy, whitish at base, with 3 series blood-red blotches; an olive blotch near middle of first and second spines; pectoral and ventral pale rosy.

Color in alcohol, head and body dark brownish, marbled and blotched with lighter; 3 or 4 dark blotches on back along base of dorsal fin, alternating with whitish blotches; a dark blotch on upper edge of caudal peduncle, bounded before and behind by a white blotch; distal portion of caudal peduncle crossed by an irregular whitish bar; tip of lower jaw black, bordered by white on each side, just back of which is an irregular dark crossbar followed by a much broader pale crossbar; branchiostegal membranes barred with black and white; spinous dorsal white at tip, with a subterminal blackish band; middle of spinous dorsal membrane with irregular white areas; soft dorsal splotched with blackish along base, the distal portion bluish or smoky; caudal pale bluish, crossed by 5 or 6 vertical series of brownish blotches; anal similar to soft dorsal; ventrals dusky bluish, unspotted; pectorals bluish beneath, dusky on outside, especially at base.

The above description is based chiefly upon a specimen (No. 04581) 9.75 inches long, from Honolulu.

This is one of the largest and most important species of the family. It seems to be abundant among the Hawaiian Islands, and is represented in our collection by 35 specimens (30 from Honolulu, 3 from Kailua, and 2 from Hilo), 4.4 to 9.75 inches long. It was collected by Jenkins, Wood, Jordan and Snyder, and by us; also by the *Albatross* at Honolulu and Puako Bay.

Suborder LORICATI.—The Mail-Cheeked Fishes.

This group is distinguished by a single peculiar character, the extension of the third suborbital bone across the cheek to or toward the preopercle. From the Craniomi, an offshoot from the same group in which the development of the suborbital stay is carried much farther, the present group is distinguished by the normal character of the shoulder-girdle.

Family LXXXIV. CARACANTHIDÆ.

This family is closely related to the *Scorpænidæ*, from which the species differ in the weak, compressed body and feeble fins. The osteology has not yet been studied. Lower pectoral rays detached.

Genus 207. CARACANTHUS Krøyer.

Head and body very compressed, naked or with small tubercles or prickles; snout very short, truncated; no scales; several bones of the head strongly armed; the preorbital and the interopercle with a strong spine, directed downward; two separate or continuous dorsals, the first with 8 (7) spines, anal with 2; no pectoral filament; ventrals rudimentary; villiform teeth in the jaws only; branchiostegals 5; no aperture behind the fourth gill.

375. Caracanthus maculatus (Gray). Fig. 198.

Head 2.75 in length; depth 1.8; snout 3.75 in head; eye 4.4; interorbital 5.5; width of mouth 2.5; D. viii, 12; A. ii, 12; P. 15; V. 1, 2.

Body deep, elevated, compressed, its greatest depth at ventrals; head deep, compressed; snout blunt, steep, rather long; eye small, high, in first third of head; mouth broad, somewhat low, without

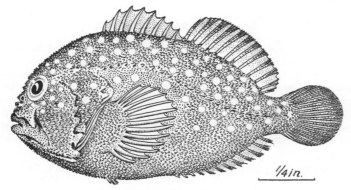

FIG. 198.—*Caracanthus maculatus* (Gray).

deep lateral cleft; lips thick, fleshy, mandible slightly produced; teeth fine, in bands; interorbital space convex; nostrils close together in front of eye, each with raised rim; preorbital with large pointed spine directed down and backward, depressible in a groove; margin of preopercle with 5 broad compressed curved spines; interopercle with strong spine; opercle with 2 compressed spines on upper margin, 1 on lower margin; spinous dorsal with rounded margin, median spines longest, third 3 in head, the 2 dorsals nearly or quite separate; caudal small, rounded, 1.5; base of anal 3.75 in body; pectoral 2 in head, lower rays thick, ventrals very small, spine short, strong; body covered with minute fleshy pointed papillæ directed backward except behind and a little above base of pectoral, those on head and in front of spinous dorsal very small and more or less rigid; lateral line running down till below first 2 dorsal rays.

Color in alcohol brown, lower surface slightly reddish, back dusky; side, back, and top of head marked with round red spots, in most of our examples turning to pale brown; fins all more or less uniform brownish. Described from an example (No. 573) 1.6 inches long, from Honolulu.

This interesting little fish is quite abundant at Honolulu and at Waikiki, being found among the coral rocks on the reefs. It is of wide distribution among the islands of the tropical Pacific. The collection contains 64 specimens 0.6 to 1.75 inches long.

376. Caracanthus unipinna (Gray).

Head 3 in length; depth 1.85; D. vii, 12; A. ii, 11.

General form and appearance of the preceding, but the dorsal fins fully united, a slight depression at their junction; preopercular spines smaller, the limb more rounded. Color, plain dark brown. Found with the preceding, but smaller and more rare, easily distinguished by the united dorsals. We have examined specimens from Makemo (*Albatross* Coll.), but have none from Honolulu, from which place, however, it has been recorded by Günther. The species called *Caracanthus apistus* may be the same as *C. unipinna*, but the soft dorsal is figured as much higher than in *C. unipinna*.

Family LXXXV. SCORPÆNIDÆ.

Body oblong, more or less compressed, the head large, and with 1 or more pairs of ridges above, which usually terminate in spines, sometimes very irregular in form; opercle usually with 2 spinous processes, preopercle with 4 or 5; mouth terminal, usually large, with villiform teeth on jaws and vomer, and usually on the palatines; premaxillaries protractile; maxillary broad, without supplemental bone, not slipping under preorbital; gill-openings wide, extending forward below; gill-membranes separate and free from the isthmus; usually no slit behind the fourth gill; scales ctenoid, or sometimes cycloid, usually well developed, sometimes obsolete; lateral line single, continuous, concurrent with the back; a narrow bony stay extending backward from the suborbital toward the preopercle; ventral fins thoracic, usually of the normal percoid form, i, 2, to i, 5, the rays branched; dorsal fin continuous, sometimes so deeply notched as to divide it into 2 parts, or even 3 parts, with 8 to 16 rather strong spines and about as many soft rays; anal rather short, usually with 3 spines and 5 to 10 soft rays; soft rays in all the fins usually branched, except some or all of rays of the pectorals; pyloric cœca in moderate or small number (fewer than 12). Pseudobranchiæ large; air-bladder present or absent. Actinosts moderate, inserted on the posterior edges of hypercoracoid and hypocoracoid; ribs borne on enlarged pleuraphyses; post-temporal bifurcate, normally connected; myodome more or less developed. Genera and species numerous, inhabiting all seas, but especially abundant in the temperate parts of the Pacific Ocean, where they form a large proportion of the fish fauna. They are nonmigratory fishes, living about rocks, most of them of large size, and all used as food. Many of them have a venom sac at the base of the dorsal spines, and many of them are viviparous, the young being produced when about one-fourth inch in length.

Genus 208. SEBASTAPISTES Gill.

Body oblong, somewhat compressed; head large, not much compressed, naked above, and more or less uneven, with spinous ridges, often with dermal flaps; preorbital with a stout spine hooked downward; mouth large, with bands of villiform teeth on jaws, vomer, and palatines; scales mostly ctenoid, of moderate size, often with skinny flaps; dorsal fin with 12 stout spines; anal with 3 spines, the second commonly the longest; pectoral large, rounded, the base usually procurrent; some or all of the upper rays divided, the lower simple; ventrals inserted behind pectorals; no air-bladder; vertebræ 10+14=24. Species numerous in the tropical seas; dwarf fishes of singular forms and bright colors, very close to *Scorpæna*, but much smaller in size and with a characteristic spine before the eye.

377. Sebastapistes ballieui (Sauvage). "*Poopa'a.*" Plate LXXII.

Head 2.25 in length; depth 2.4; eye 4.25 in head; snout 3.35; interorbital 5.65; maxillary 1.75; mandible 1.75; D. xii, 10; A. iii, 5; P. 16; V. i, 5; scales 7–40–18.

Body moderately elongate, compressed, greatest depth a little before middle of spinous dorsal; back slightly elevated; snout rather short, blunt, rounded; mouth large, oblique; mandible slightly produced; maxillary reaching a trifle behind posterior edge of orbit, its distal expanded extremity 1.4 in eye; lips rather thick, fleshy; teeth fine, in broad bands in jaws; vomer with patch of fine teeth; tongue rather thick, rounded, little free in front; eye anterior, nearly in first third of head; interorbital space deeply concave; nostrils large, anterior with rather broad fleshy flap, posterior a little the larger; nasal, preocular, supraocular, postocular, tympanic, parietal, coronal, and nuchal spines present; a ridge of spines across cheek ending in a spine on edge of opercle below 3 other spines; a ridge of spines behind eye and above opercle; 2 large spines on opercle; 4 preorbital spines present; fourth dorsal spine longest, 2 in head; penultimate 4.5; last 3; third dorsal ray longest, 2 in head; second anal spine longest, 2.2; second anal ray longest, 1.8; caudal rounded, 1.5; pectoral 1.35; ventral 1.5, its spine 2.6; caudal peduncle compressed, its least depth 4; scales rather large, ctenoid; lateral line running obliquely down to base of caudal.

Color in life, head and body light olive-green; back with a large pale-blue area extending from under middle of spinous dorsal to lateral line; a similar but smaller spot under first dorsal rays, interrupted just above lateral line, then continued to base of anal spines, where it connects with the same color of belly; caudal peduncle crossed by 3 irregular lines or blotches of same color; breast pale blue, lower jaw whitish, tipped with red; upper jaw whitish, with many narrow red cross lines; cheek, opercle, and side of body with many very small, round, red spots, most numerous on head and base of pectoral; spinous dorsal dusky bluish, the membranes yellowish or greenish at tips, and a round black spot on distal part of eighth, ninth, and tenth membranes, these spots confluent; soft dorsal pale bluish, with yellowish wash near base, also near border, and with 3 or 4 series of double, short, vertical brick-red lines on the rays; caudal similar to soft dorsal; anal pale bluish and yellowish; 1 or 2 red spots on spines; pectoral pale bluish with 5 or 6 cross series of light-red spots, the lower rays with much red; ventral rosy red at base, then greenish, then rosy red, pale at tip; eye whitish, with radiating brick-red areas.

Color in alcohol, pale brown, marbled above and on side with darker; vertical fins with pale brown, the soft or rayed portions each with 2 broad series of gray-brown spots; base of caudal brownish; pectoral and ventral pale brown, the basal portion of lower rays of former, and middle of latter, deep brown; marginal portion of membrane among eighth, ninth, tenth, and eleventh dorsal spines blackish.

Described from an example (No. 625) taken at Honolulu.

We identify with this species, poorly described by Vaillant and Sauvage, a large series of specimens (85) from Honolulu, Waikiki and Hilo, ranging in length from 1.4 to 4.25 inches.

378. Sebastapistes corallicola Jenkins. Fig. 199.

Head 2.5 in length; depth 2.75; pectoral slightly less than 3 in length; ventral 3.3; caudal equal to ventral; eye 4 in head, a little shorter than snout; D. xii, 9; A. iii, 5; C. 19; P. 16; V. i, 5; scales 40 in the lateral line, 6 in series from fourth dorsal to lateral line, 14 from origin of anal to lateral line; mouth but little oblique, lower jaw projecting very slightly; maxillary 1.6 in head, projecting beyond posterior margin of eye; teeth all small and simple, in bands in upper and lower jaws, bands interrupted at front; teeth on vomer in a V-shaped patch, in bands on the palatines equal in length to width of vomerine patch; suborbital 1.5 in eye; a pit below anterior lower angle of eye, anterior nostril transversely oval, with a tentacle in the inner posterior part of rim; posterior nostril simple, circular; snout with a triangular median elevation, the apex between the anterior nostrils; between each anterior nostril and apex of rostral elevation is a strong short spine; 6 spines on the upper half of ocular rim, first at upper anterior angle, second on upper rim over center of pupil, third over posterior margin of the pupil, fourth on level with upper edge of pupil, fifth back of center of pupil, sixth on level of lower edge of pupil; sixth bifid on each side, fifth bifid on right; occipital depression with 2 spines at each angle, one lateral to the other at the anterior angles, one caudad to the other at the posterior angles; a strong spine at upper end of opercle; posterior to this spine and a little above it 2 smaller spines just before upper end of gill-slit; posterior to these a single spine at upper end of gill-slit; two large diverging spines on opercle; suborbital with a bony ridge without spines except a small one on its posterior end; preorbital with 3 spines, 2 directed downward over upper edge of maxillary, the other forward over edge of premaxillary; at angle of preopercle an upper small and a lower larger spine, below these on arm of preopercle 4 decreasingly smaller spines; supraorbital tentacle well developed, just back of supraorbital spine; a tentacle back of posterior vertical spine, lapping over edge of maxillary; a strong spine at angle of shoulder-girdle above base of pectoral, sharp-pointed, projecting upward and backward; a small, less prominent spine back of this one; gillrakers short, 5+10; interorbital space slightly con-

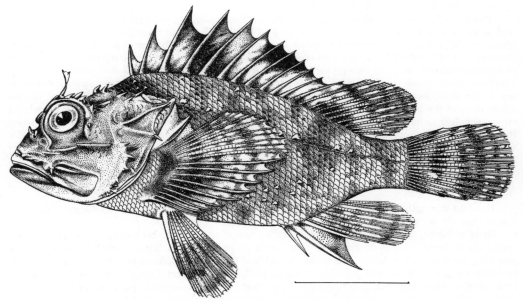

FIG. 199.—*Sebastapistes corallicola* Jenkins; from the type.

cave, with 2 prominent ridges diverging posteriorly and ending in the 2 twin spines of those at anterior angles of the occipital depression; dorsal profile of the body much more convex, greatest depth at fourth dorsal spine; depth of caudal peduncle equal to eye, 3.5 in greatest depth of body; fourth dorsal spine the longest, a little greater than half of head; third and fifth spines equal, but little shorter than fourth; second 1.5 in third, first 1.75 in second; spines back of fourth regularly decreasing in length to next to last, which is 2 in fourth; last longer, equaling second; soft rays abruptly longer than last dorsal spines, second, third, and fourth longest, equaling longest spine; last soft rays equal to next to last spine; second anal spine longest and much thicker than others, 1.75 in head; first slender, 2 in second; third slender, 0.8 of second; first and second soft rays longest, 1.6 in head; caudal slightly rounded; pectoral round, middle rays longest; ventral rounded, second ray longest, its spine equal to sixth dorsal spine; head and fins naked.

Characters very constant. In smaller specimens the posterior spines of orbital rim not so evident as in type and in most the humeral spine smaller. Size of supraorbital tentacle varies much, in some very small or absent, in others very large, fringed, length greater than eye, equal to second dorsal spine.

Color of fresh specimen (field No. 223), whitish, with brownish cloudings and many bright red spots on head, body, and fins; black blotch on dorsal fin on eighth to tenth spines, fin clouded with dark bars; dermal flaps white.

Another fresh example (field No. 206) golden brown on body and fins, with many very bright red spots; a black blotch on spinous dorsal on seventh and ninth spines longer than eye but not so deep.

In alcohol the color varies considerably; in some, fins distinctly branded, in others, fins plain. Some lack the black blotch on posterior part of spinous dorsal, others have it present but small, others have it well developed and reaching from sixth to eleventh spine. A series of dermal flaps along lateral line, also a number of smaller ones on lower half of side; lateral line simple, slightly convex downward posteriorly.

Color of type (field No. 236) in alcohol, head and body mottled with lighter and darker shades of brown, plain pale below; a wide pale transverse band on nape (very indistinct); spinous dorsal with dusky blotch from seventh to tenth spines on distal half of fin; other fins mottled with brown in triangular transverse bands; a dusky rim above margin of eye on eye membrane; dermal flaps white.

Resembles *Scorpæna onaria* Jordan & Snyder from Japan, but differing in absence of knob at symphysis of lower jaw, in having no spine on suborbital except on its end, in having 2 spines instead of only 1 at each anterior angle of occipital depression, and in greater length of maxilliary, which does not reach beyond posterior rim of orbit in *S. onaria*.

Close to *Scorpæna nuchalis* Günther, from Raratonga Island (Fische der Südsee, I, 76, 1873); differing from that species in having maxillary reaching past the posterior rim of eye; but the third, fourth and fifth spines largest, instead of the fourth to the seventh and the black blotch on the posterior part of the spinous dorsal (7–10 spines) instead of on the forepart.

Only 3 specimens of this species known, all collected at Honolulu by Doctor Jenkins.

379. Sebastapistes asperella (Bennett).

D. XII, 10; A. III, 8; P. 17; V. I, 6; C. 12.

The prevailing color is dull fulvous, with paler indistinct patches; anterior half of dorsal fin fuscus, with a rosy spot at its commencement, posterior half hyaline, the projecting tips of the rays edged with black; caudal rounded, transparent, crossed by 2 blackish fasciæ; anal fuscus at base, transparent in the middle, and blackish at tip; pectoral crossed by 2 blackish bands, and by 2 irregular ones composed of numerous minute white points giving to them a frosted appearance; ventral fins similarly colored. The head exhibits the usual asperity of this genus, but only in a moderate degree; on its lower parts are a few short, flattened, white filaments, and similar filaments along the lateral line and on the upper parts of the body, being most numerous in the latter situation; above each eye is a rosy colored cirrus, equaling in length about three-fourths of the diameter of the orbit, and somewhat lobed along its edges; there is a short cirrus on each nostril, and another, which is pinnately branched, on the middle of each side of the upper jaw. (Bennett.)

Hawaiian Islands; not seen by us.

380. Sebastapistes coniorta Jenkins. Fig. 200.

Head 2.4 in length; depth 2.75; eye 3.4 in head; snout 3.25; interorbital 7; maxillary 2; mandible 1.9; D. XII, 10; A. III, 5; P. 16; V. I, 5; scales 7–53–14.

Body elongate, compressed, greatest depth at first dorsal spines; back slightly elevated; snout rather short, blunt, rounded; mandible large, rather strong; mouth large, slightly oblique; maxillary long, reaching below last fourth of eye; breadth of distal expanded extremity 2 in eye; fine teeth in bands on jaws, vomer, and palatines; tongue small, thick, pointed, little free in front; lips rather thin; nostrils close together, anterior with small fleshy flap; interorbital space rather narrow, concave; nasal, preorbital, supraorbital, postorbital, tympanic, parietal, and nuchal spines present; a ridge of spines from behind eye above opercle; a ridge of spines across cheek ending in a large spine on margin of preopercle, below which are 2 others; two large spines on opercle; preorbital with 4 spines; fourth dorsal spine longest, 2.7; soft rays longer, fourth longest, 2.7; second anal spine longest, 2.2; first anal ray longest, 2.35; caudal rounded, 1.9; pectoral rather small, 1.8, rounded; ventral 1.7, spine 2.25; least depth of caudal peduncle 5; scales rather small, ctenoid, except those on belly, which are smooth; lateral line oblique to base of caudal. Described from an example (No. 05769) from Honolulu.

Color in life (No. 278, O. P. J.), light olive, with dark brown mottlings, body, head, and fins covered thickly with small brown spots; posterior margin of caudal red; fins color of body.

Color in life (No. 03524), olive, with irregular brown areas on body and head; numerous small deep brown spots on head; fins olive, with brown markings, except the posterior half of the caudal, which is red, also upper and lower edges of same; edges of anal and ventral red; iris red.

Color in alcohol, brown, marbled with dark brown forming about 3 broad ill-defined vertical bands; upper surface of body covered nearly everywhere with numerous small dark brown dots also extending on all the fins; spinous dorsal with deep brown blotch at middle of base; soft dorsal and

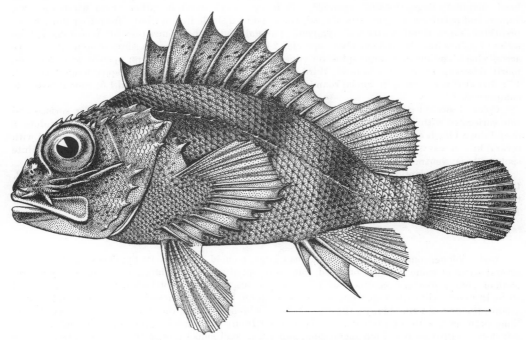

FIG. 200.—*Sebastapistes coniorta* Jenkins; from the type.

anal each with last brown vertical band of trunk extending out on the fins; caudal with brown base and deep brown blotch on outer portion; a brown streak extending back from eye, and a dark spot behind its upper margin; a deep brown blotch at tip of opercular flap.

This is the most abundant species of the family in the Hawaiian Islands, as shown by the very large series of specimens in our collection, 197 from Honolulu and 9 from the reef at Waikiki. The specimens are all small, the length ranging from 1 to 2.8 inches.

381. Sebastapistes galactacma Jenkins. Fig. 201.

Head 2.25 in length; depth 2.7; eye 3.5 in head; snout 3.7; interorbital 6.5; D. xii, 10; A. iii, 5; P. 16; V. i, 5; scales 7–42–12.

Body elongate, compressed, greatest depth under first dorsal spines; back not elevated; snout

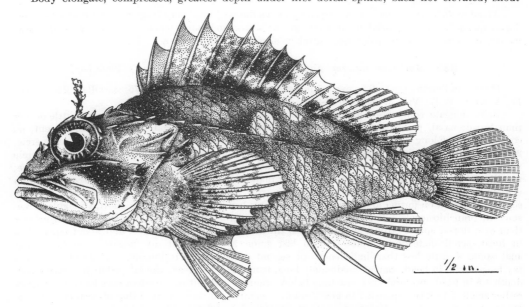

FIG. 201.—*Sebastapistes galactacma* Jenkins; from the type.

short, blunt; mouth rather large, only slightly oblique, jaws about equal; mandible rather large, 2 in head; maxillary large, distally expanded, 1.75 in eye; teeth small, in rather broad bands on jaws, vomer, and palatines; tongue rather broad, thick, pointed, little free in front; lips rather thin; nasal, preorbital, supraorbital, postorbital, tympanic, parietal, and nuchal spines present; no coronal spines; series of spines from behind eye above opercle; 2 large preorbital spines; a series of spines below eye across cheek ending in a large spine on edge of preopercle, below 4 others; opercle with 2 spines; fourth dorsal spine longest, 2 in head; third dorsal ray longest, 2.1; second anal spine longest, curved, 1.7; first anal ray longest, 2; caudal rounded, 1.6; pectoral rounded, 1.3; ventral 1.5; caudal peduncle compressed, 4.

Color in alcohol (type), pale or whitish brown, a little darker on the back; upper surface and side variegated with darker brown; head and trunk marked with very many small whitish dots; a deep brown blotch on outer portion of spinous dorsal between fifth and ninth spines; soft dorsal with several brown wavy lines; caudal with several pale brown cross-bars; pectoral with brown and white spots on base; ventrals pale with white dots.

The above description is based chiefly on the type (No. 2175 of O. P. Jenkins's collection, 50692, U. S. N. M.), 2.6 inches long, from Honolulu, where Doctor Jenkins obtained 80 other examples from the coral rocks of the reef, ranging from 1.3 to 2.6 inches long. The species is known only from Honolulu and Waikiki.

Genus 209. HELICOLENUS Goode & Bean.

Body oblong, somewhat compressed; head large, ctenoid scales on its tip, cheeks and opercles; several series of spinous ridges on head, but no occipital pit; mouth large, with bands of villiform teeth on jaws, vomer, and palatines; dorsal fin continuous, not deeply notched, with 10 stout spines and 10 to 12 rays; anal with 3 spines and 6 rays; pectoral broad, fan-shaped, with rays arranged in 3 groups, the first of 2 simple rays, the second of 8 or 9 branched rays, the third of 8 simple rays, sometimes prolonged, with their tips tendril-like and free from membrane for one-half their length or less; soft dorsal with tips free from membrane; suborbital keel smooth, or with a single anterior spine under eye; preorbital with spines small and hidden beneath skin; vertebræ $10+14=24$; no air-bladder. Very close to *Scorpæna*, differing only in the *Sebastes*-like cranium, the 2 genera probably connected by intermediate forms.

The single Hawaiian species of this genus is fully described in Section II.

Genus 210. PONTINUS Poey.

This genus has the form and general structure of *Helicolenus*, differing in having the pectoral rays all simple and only their tips free; 6 to 9 rays in the anal; the suborbital keel composed of 3 distinct, differentiated, flat, knife-like spines; 2 prominent retrorse spines on each suborbital.

The single Hawaiian species of this genus is fully described in Section II.

Genus 211. MERINTHE Snyder.

Allied to *Helicolenus*, but with a long cirrus above the eye; head very long; pectoral rays all simple; dorsal spines 12, all low; head moderately armed; scales moderate, ctenoid; side of head scaly; jaws naked; teeth on vomer and palatines; gillrakers slender, few in number.

382. Merinthe macrocephala (Sauvage). "*Oopu kai Nohu.*" Plate 55.

Head 2 in length; depth 2.8; eye 5.5 in head; snout 2.7; interorbital 11.75; maxillary 2.2; D. XII, 11; A. III, 6; P. 17; V. I, 5; scales 9–52–22.

Body elongate, compressed, greatest depth about middle of ventral; head very long, a little deeper than broad; nasal, preocular, supraocular, postocular, tympanic, parietal, nuchal spines present; no coronal spines; 5 long spines across cheek, last forming large broad spine on lower margin of preopercle; 2 opercular spines; 2 spines directly behind eye; 2 spines on suprascapula; lower margin of preopercle with 2 broad spines; snout long; eye rather small, high, anterior; mouth large, a little oblique; maxillary long, reaching a little beyond anterior margin of eye, its distal expanded extremity 1.35 in eye; lips narrow, fleshy; teeth fine, in rather narrow bands in jaws; teeth on vomer and palatine similar, V-shaped on former and short straight narrow band on latter; tongue short, triangular, free, smooth; branchiostegals 7, large; a round thin fleshy cirrus over each eye, its length much greater than eye; dorsal spines strong, sharp pointed, third, fourth, and fifth longest and about equal, 3.75 in head; penultimate dorsal spine 0.75 in last spine; second dorsal ray longest, 3 in head; first anal spine a little less than half length of second spine, which is longest, 3 in head; first anal ray longest, 2.8 in head; caudal moderately long, truncate, 2 in head; caudal peduncle compressed, depth 4.8 in head; pectoral long, reaching below origin of first soft ray, median rays longest; ventrals rather small, 2 in head; spine 3.2 in head; origin of ventral a little in front of that of pectoral or below origin of dorsal; scales moderate, ctenoid; snout, jaws, interorbital and preorbital regions, and lower surface of head, naked; scales on top of head behind eyes, very small; gillrakers 2+9, broad, compressed, equal to longest gill-filaments or 2.8 in eye; lateral line armed with long scutes at first and sloping down obliquely to base of caudal.

Color in alcohol, pale brown, darker or mottled with deep or dusky brown on back and upper surface; several short brown lines running from front of lower margin of eye; dorsals, caudal, and pectoral sprinkled with dusky; anal with a few dusky spots. Bright orange red in life and very showy.

Described from a specimen 10.75 inches long (No. 05301) taken at Hilo; another smaller was obtained by the *Albatross* at Honolulu. Examples recently seen in aquarium at Waikiki. Reaches a weight of 4 or 5 pounds.

Genus 212. SETARCHES Johnson.

Head and body compressed; head scaleless above, its bones cavernous, flat between the eyes; only 1 pair of spines at occiput; no transverse groove at occiput, only small spines or none above orbit; opercle and preopercle strongly armed with straight long spines. Eye moderate, near, but not touching, profile. Mouth terminal, broad, somewhat oblique; maxillary extending to posterior edge of eye, much expanded behind. Lower jaw somewhat projecting, the small symphyseal knob received in rostral notch. Villiform teeth on jaws, vomer and palatines. Preorbital with 2 or 3 spines. Opercle scaly. Scales cycloid, moderate. Lateral line a broad, scaleless groove with skinny (about 27 to 30) tubes. No laciniæ. Dorsal deeply notched, with 12 spines, its origin in front of pectoral; soft dorsal shorter, the rays fewer than the spines. Anal inserted under end of dorsal, its spines strong, graduated. Pectoral broad and bony, with 20 or more rays, of which a considerable number of median ones are branched. Branchiostegals 6 or 7. Pyloric appendages few. Deep water.

The single Hawaiian species (*S. remiger*) of this genus is fully described in Section II.

Genus 213. SEBASTOPSIS Gill.

This genus differs from *Sebastodes* in the absence of palatine teeth. D. XIII, 9 or 10; A. III, 5. No dermal flaps; cheeks and opercles scaly; preorbital with obtuse spines or none. The known species are all of very small size and are often preserved in Chinese insect boxes.

383. Sebastopsis kelloggi Jenkins. Fig. 202.

Head 2.5 in length; depth 3.2; eye 3.35 in head; snout 3.65; interorbital 5.5; maxillary 1.65; mandible 1.6; D. XIII, 9; A. III, 5; P. 19; v. I, 5; scales 5–31–9.

Body elongate, compressed, greatest depth about middle of trunk; back not elevated; snout rather short, blunt, rounded; mandible rather large, jaws equal; mouth large, slightly oblique; maxillary large, broadly expanded distally, 1.25 in eye; teeth fine, in narrow bands in jaws and on vomer, none on palatines; tongue thick, small, broad, pointed, free in front; lips rather thin; eye in anterior half of head; nostrils close together, anterior with elevated rim and long, thin, fleshy flap; interorbital

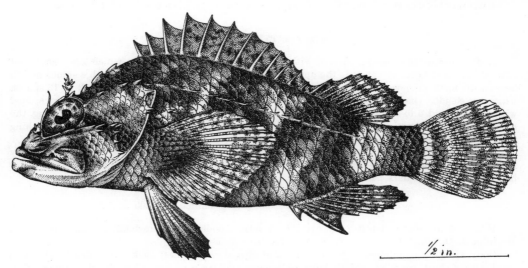

FIG. 202.—*Sebastopsis kelloggi* Jenkins; from the type.

space deeply concave; nasal, preocular, supraocular, postocular, tympanic, coronal, parietal and nuchal spines present; a row of several spines back of eye over opercle; a row of spines across cheek below eye ending in a large spine at edge of opercle, 2 below; 2 spines on opercle; preorbital and supraorbital flaps rather long and thin; dorsal spines all rather low, sixth longest, 3.65 in head; second dorsal ray 2.7; second anal spine largest, 2 in head; third anal ray 1.9; caudal rounded 1.5; pectoral 1.5; ventral 1.5; caudal peduncle compressed, its least depth 3.5; scales rather large, very finely ctenoid; head with small scales on top, cheeks and opercles; tubes of lateral line large, conspicuous, and forming a nearly straight included course to base of caudal. Described from an example (No. 637) taken at Henshaw's Pool, Hilo.

Color in life of a specimen 1.3 inches long (No. 03550), dark parts dark brown, lighter parts gray.

Color in alcohol, rich dark brown, variegated with deeper brown specks; head more or less variegated with brown above, pale or whitish beneath; a deep brown blotch below eye; a pale brown band across first half of caudal peduncle, the remaining portion and base of caudal blackish brown; side in front of caudal peduncle broadly deep brown, extending forward to middle of spinous dorsal, and including basal portion of soft dorsal and anal where it becomes black; remaining portions of soft dorsal and anal, together with caudal, pale gray white with brownish wavy bars; pectoral with outer portion gray white barred with brownish wavy bars, basal portion black; ventral black.

We have 10 examples, 2 (including the type) taken by Jenkins at Honolulu, 5 by us at the same place, 2 by us on the reef at Waikiki, and one from Hilo. Specimens were also obtained by the *Albatross* at Honolulu. Our specimens are from less than an inch to 1.8 inches long.

384. Sebastopsis parvipinnis (Garrett).

Head 3 in total length; depth slightly less than 3; eye nearly 4 in head. D. XIII, 10; A. III, 5; V. I, 5; P. VII, 9; C. 5, 1, 6, 5, 1, 3.

Upper and lower outlines similar, being greatly arched; eye large, circular; 4 spines along upper edge of orbit, the same number on each side of the occipital region and nape, the posterior one the larger; 2 infraorbital spines, 1 on the nasal bone, and a longitudinal row of 4 along the supratympanic region; 2 on opercle, the lower one long and projecting posterior to the margin of that bone; a stout one on humeral region, 1 on infraorbital, 3 on margin of preopercle and a longitudinal row of irregularly disposed ones on cheek; lower jaw slightly longer than upper; maxillary reaching posterior border of eye. Fine scales covering basal portions of all the fins except the ventrals, and all parts of head except the jaws and lower half of maxillary bone; minute filaments on all parts of body, most numerous on upper anterior third.

Dorsal and anal fins small, the former commencing above origin of latter; spinous dorsal very low, gently arched, constituting nearly two-thirds of fin; soft portion of anal very narrow and rounded off.

Color, head and anterior half of body grayish, passing into light carnation beneath, and obscurely clouded with dusky; posterior half of body dusky black, fading into pink beneath, maculated with small darker spots; caudal trunk pink; 2 large dusky black spots on anterior dorsal region; iris greenish-yellow; fins pinky-red; spinous dorsal being mottled with dusky, other fins dotted with pinky-brown, a bar of the same color on the caudal base. (Garrett.)

Known only from Honolulu, from the type, and another specimen obtained by the *Albatross*.

Genus 214. PTEROIS Cuvier.

Body elongate, compressed, covered with moderate or small-sized scales, which are usually not ciliated; bones of head well armed; the upper surface of head with cirri; opercle with a spine; mouth large, with teeth on jaws and vomer, none on palatines; dorsal fin elevated, with 12 or 13 spines, which are slender, sharp, and joined by membrane only at base; soft dorsal with branched rays; anal with 3 spines and 6 to 8 branched rays; caudal rounded or truncate; ventral moderate, or long, the rays I, 5; pectoral greatly elongate, the rays simple and largely free from the base, the tips reaching to or beyond the caudal fin.

Species of rather large size, abounding about the coral reefs in the tropical Pacific, dreaded by fishermen on account of their venomous spines. The coloration is very showy, most of the species being yellowish with dark bands.

385. Pterois sphex Jordan & Evermann. Fig. 203.

Head 2.4 in length; depth 2.65; eye 3.8 in head; snout 3.2; interorbital 5.2; maxillary 2.35; mandible 2; D. XIII, 11; A. III, 7; P. 16; V. I, 5; scales 10–56–13.

Body elongate, compressed, greatest depth at first dorsal spines; back only slightly elevated; snout rather short, rounded; mouth large, oblique; maxillary reaching below anterior rim of orbit, its distal expanded extremity 1.75 in eye; teeth fine, in bands in jaws and on vomer; lips rather thin, fleshy; tongue pointed, compressed and free in front; jaws nearly equal; eighth dorsal spine longest, equal to head; penultimate spine 4; fifth dorsal ray 1.75; third anal spine longest, 2.2; third anal ray longest, 1.5; caudal rounded, elongate, 1.4; pectoral long, the rays more or less free for at least half their length; ventral 1.3 in head, reaching beyond origin of anal; ventral spine 2.1; caudal peduncle compressed, its depth 3.75; nasal spinal very small; preocular, supraocular, and postocular spines present, the upper bony ridge over eye being serrate; tympanic, coronal, parietal, and nuchal spines present, coronal very small and close together and parietal with 4 serrations; a finely serrated ridge

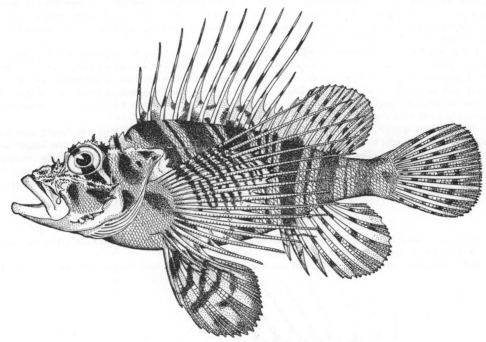

FIG. 203.—*Pterois sphex* Jordan & Evermann; from the type.

from behind eye over opercle to suprascapula; a finely serrated ridge over preorbital and cheek to margin of preopercle, ending in a strong spine, below this 2 other spines; preorbital with a strong spine over maxillary posteriorly, and with fine serrations above; scales ctenoid, present on top of head, cheeks, and opercles, head otherwise naked; tubes of lateral line single, in straight line to base of caudal; several fleshy flaps on head, 1 above eye, 1 from lower preorbital spine, and 2 from along margin of preopercle.

Color in alcohol, very pale brown, whitish beneath; side with 9 broad, deep brown bands, alternating with narrow brown bands on trunk and posterior portion of head, narrow brown bars from below penultimate dorsal spine with a narrower brown line on each side above lateral line; lower surface of head whitish, without crossbands; spinous and soft dorsal and caudal each with 4 dusky brown crossbands; base of anal with 2 broad similar bands, and soft portion of anal with 3 series of irregular crossbands; axil of pectoral above with white blotch; pectoral whitish with 10 blackish crossbands; a brown band in front of base of pectoral extending on lower pectoral rays; ventral with dusky blotch at base, outer portion with about 5 dusky crossbands.

The only example we have seen of this species is the type, No. 50650, U. S. N. M. (field No. 05030), 6 inches long, obtained by us at Honolulu.

Genus 215. DENDROCHIRUS Swainson.

Pectorals short, undivided, the rays branched; otherwise much as in *Pterois*.

386. Dendrochirus barberi (Steindachner).   Plate LXXIII, as *D. hudsoni*.

Head 2.5 in length; depth 2.5; eye 3.4 in head; snout 3.3; interorbital 5; maxillary 2.1; mandible 1.8; D. XIII, 10; A. III, 6; P. 18; V. I, 5; scales 8–52–13.

Body elongate, compressed, rather deep, the greatest depth at fifth dorsal spine; profiles of trunk above and below more or less even; head compressed; snout short, rounded; mouth large, maxillary nearly reaching below middle of eye, its distal expanded extremity equal to half eye; minute teeth in bands in jaws and on vomer; lips thin; tongue pointed, compressed, free in front; jaws nearly equal; anterior nostrils each with a small fleshy flap; interorbital space deeply concave; fifth dorsal spine longest, 1.25 in head; penultimate spine 5.2; second anal spine longest, 2.1; third anal ray longest 1.3; caudal rounded, 1.25; pectoral 2.4 in trunk, reaching below middle of base of soft dorsal, rounded, and only membranes between lower rays slightly incised; ventral rounded, reaching base of first anal ray, caudal peduncle compressed, its least depth 3.5 in head; nasal spines very small, preocular, postocular; tympanic and coronal spines present; parietal and nuchal spines forming a single ridge; a ridge of spines behind eye above opercle; a ridge of spines below eye, ending in a spine on margin of preopercle; 2 spines below this also on margin of preopercle; no opercular spines; margin of preopercle with spine projecting down and back; skinny flap [a] above eye equal to its diameter, and another from preorbital spine; scales small, ctenoid; head naked except some scales on opercle, cheek, and side above; lateral line running obliquely down to base of caudal.

Color in alcohol, pale brown or whitish; side with 3 pairs of deep brown vertical bands, first on posterior part of head preceded by a deep brown streak from below eye, second on middle and posterior part of spinous dorsal, and third extending out on soft anal and basal portion of soft dorsal; soft dorsal, caudal, and anal pale or whitish; membranes of dorsal spines deeply incised in front, each spine with 3 brown crossbands; pectoral grayish with a blackish brown basal blotch and 5 blackish crossbands; ventral blackish with 2 whitish or grayish blotches.

The nominal species, *D. hudsoni*, is especially characterized by the unspotted soft dorsal, anal, and caudal. It was thought to be distinguished from *Dendrochirus barberi* Steindachner by the longer pectoral, which reaches to below the posterior dorsal rays, but this character is found not to be constant.

We have 1 specimen, 1.8 inches long, from Waikiki, and 4 others, 2 collected by us and 2 by Jenkins, all at Honolulu, and ranging from 1.8 to 4 inches long. The *Albatross* also obtained specimens at Honolulu.

387. Dendrochirus chloreus Jenkins. Fig. 204.

Head 2.5 in length; depth 2.75; eye 3.5 in head; snout 3.75; interorbital 6; maxillary 2.1; mandible 1.8; D. XIII, 10; A. III, 6; P. 18; V. I, 5; scales 7–54–14.

Body elongate, compressed, greatest depth at first dorsal spines; back only slightly elevated; snout

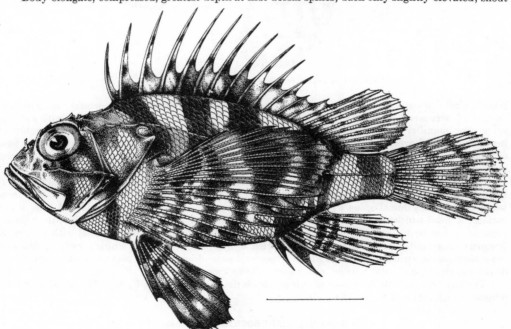

FIG. 204.—*Dendrochirus chloreus* Jenkins; from the type.

rather short, blunt, rounded; mouth large, oblique; mandible large, slightly produced; maxillary large, expanded distally, where its greatest width is 1.8 in eye; teeth in broad villiform bands, in jaws and on vomer, none on palatines; tongue rather broad, sharp pointed, free; lips rather thick and fleshy; seventh dorsal spine longest, 1.5; penultimate spine 4; dorsal spines free for greater part of their length, the membrane extending for nearly half their length posteriorly; fifth dorsal ray longest, 1.6; second anal spine slightly longer than second, 2.3 in head; caudal rounded, 3; pectoral rather short, reaching below base of sixth dorsal ray; fifth and sixth rays longest, the lower rays not as long, and membranes incised so that extremities are free for short distance; ventral 1.25 in head, spine 2.25; caudal peduncle compressed, its depth 3.6; scales rather large, ctenoid; nasal, preocular, supraocular, postocular, tympanic, coronal, parietal, and nuchal spines present; a ridge of spines below eye across

[a] In our Plate LXXIII, accidentally left incomplete by the artist, the ocular flap is omitted.

cheek ending in a spine on edge of preopercle, and below 2 more spines; a ridge of spines from eye above opercle; scales rather large, ctenoid; lateral line sloping obliquely to base of caudal.

Color in life (No. 03446), 6 vertical bands on side dark olive, spaces between dirty white, and red; under surface of head rosy; round dark spots on body under opercular flap; axil and spot on inner surface of base of pectoral dark olive; markings on spinous dorsal dark olive and dull red; soft dorsal with transverse rows of olive spots surrounded by red, membranes transparent; caudal similarly colored; anal dark olive; pectoral dark olive with transverse rows of whitish spots on rays; ventrals alternating olive and dirty white; iris red.

Color in alcohol, more or less brown; side of trunk with about 6 deep brown vertical bars, the last extending down on base of anal; head deep brown above, side pale; a deep brown streak from below eye; angle of preopercle, and region about, dark brown; blotch above base of pectoral blackish brown; a brown band across chest; spinous dorsal pale brownish, each spine with about 3 broad brownish cross-bands; soft dorsal blackish brown; rays of soft vertical fins with 5 or 6 series of blotches or spots; pectoral and ventral blackish, with a number of pale cross-bands; edge of each scale very narrowly pale brown. Described from an example (No. 03446) 6.2 inches long, taken at Honolulu. Known only from Honolulu.

Besides the type and 5 cotypes collected at Honolulu by Jenkins, we have 2 examples obtained by ourselves 2.2 to 6.2 inches long, and a single example obtained recently by Mr. Berndt at Honolulu.

Genus 216. SCORPÆNOPSIS Heckel.

This genus differs from *Scorpæna* in the absence of palatine teeth. The species are of a larger size and more peculiar appearance.

388. Scorpænopsis cacopsis Jenkins. Plate LXXI, and Figs. 205 and 205a.

Head 2.3 in length; depth 3; eye 6.5 in head; snout 3; interorbital 6.7; maxillary 2; mandible 1.6; D. xii, 10; A. iii, 5; P. 17; V. i, 5; scales 9–52–22.

Body elongate, greatest depth at dorsal spines; back not particularly elevated; snout rather long,

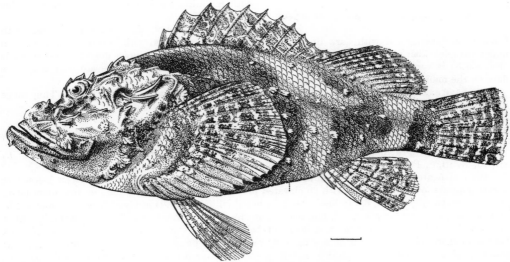

Fig. 205.—*Scorpænopsis cacopsis* Jenkins; from the type.

with an elevated prominence; mouth large, oblique, mandible large, slightly produced; maxillary large, its distal expanded extremity broad, equal to eye; teeth in broad villiform bands in jaws, those on vomer small; no teeth on palatines; tongue small, pointed, free in front; lips rather thick, fleshy; eye small, just in front of middle of head; anterior nostrils with short fleshy flap, posterior close behind, circular, without flap; interorbital space rather narrow, deeply concave; top of head with a square pit, not very deep; nasal, preocular, supraocular, postocular, tympanic, parietal, and nuchal spines well developed; a series of spines across cheek, several along preopercle, supraocular, and upper side of head; two spines on opercle; third and fourth dorsal spines longest, third 2.7 in head, last 3.7; third dorsal ray 2.5; second anal spine enlarged, 2.6; pectoral large, 1.5 in head; ventral 1.6; spine 3; caudal peduncle compressed, its depth 3.5; caudal 1.75; scales rather large, ctenoid; lateral line nearly straight to base of caudal. Described from an example (No. 05297) taken at Honolulu.

Color in life (No. 03349) rusty reddish brown, blotched and mottled with darker and lighter, a few scattered scales white or pale rosy white; top and sides of head similar to sides but darker; under parts of head flesh-color blotched and mottled with orange red, reddish-brown, and a little yellowish; breast and belly yellowish white with a little reddish; posterior part of belly blotched with brownish red; spinous dorsal mottled brown and clay-white, a small dark blotch on base of second membrane, above this a yellowish orange bar across second and third membranes, then a very broad brownish bar from top of second to base of fifth membrane; membrane of rest of fin pale mottled whitish or clay yellow; soft dorsal similar, mottled with clay white, brownish and rosy; caudal with a broad pale bar at base then a broader brown bar mottled with darker, red and yellowish, followed by a narrower pinkish white border, the whole fin freely mottled; anal mottled brown, reddish, whitish, and yellowish; pectoral mottled and barred with brownish on base, followed by alternating bars of brownish, pale yellow, and pinkish, the brownish confined chiefly to upper part of fin; ventrals white, crossed by rosy bars or spots, brownish toward tips; iris yellowish-brown, with small brown specks on outer part.

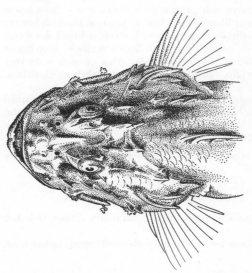

FIG. 205a.—*Scorpænopsis cacopsis*, dorsal view of head.

Another example (No. 03385) was in life brown; belly cadmium with blotches of vermilion and brown; lower jaw pale cadmium with brown spots anteriorly, posteriorly with vermilion spots; dermal flaps of lower and upper jaw, and preopercle edged with vermilion and yellow, the dermal flaps extending over maxillary and from behind pectoral to base of caudal; dorsal marbled with deep brown, slightly olivaceous, the narrower markings of cadmium, vermilion and pale blue; pectoral yellow with narrow irregular bands of brown at top, vermilion toward bottom, outlined with brown; ventral yellow at base, then vermilion marbled with deep brown; anal same as pectoral; caudal yellowish at base, then a broad irregular band of dark brown marbled with vermilion, edge pink with a few small brown spots in the pink; iris yellowish with radiating marking of dark brown from edge of pupil.

Color in alcohol, dark brown, mottled with blackish, and variegated with dark lines; inside of pectoral variegated with brown, outer portion of upper rays blackish, also a large blackish brown spot on middle of spinous dorsal. One example (No. 05655) is very pale or whitish in alcohol, and the darker mottlings above are purplish. The flaps on the mandible are also rather long.

We have examined 14 specimens, all from Honolulu, 13 of which were secured by us. They range in length from 7.5 to 19.5 inches. The species is known only from Honolulu.

389. Scorpænopsis gibbosa (Bloch & Schneider). "*Nóhu;*" "*Omakaha.*" Plate 56ᵃ and Fig. 206.

Head 2.1 in length; depth 2.75; eye 7.25 in head; snout 3.1; interorbital 4.3; maxillary 1.8; D. XII, 10; A. III, 5; P. 18; V. I, 5; scales 9–42–22.

Body elongate, greatest depth at first dorsal spines; back elevated, swollen, or convex below first dorsal spines; snout rather long, with an elevated prominence; mouth large, oblique; maxillary large, expanded extremity broad, 6.5 in head; teeth in broad villiform bands in jaws, those on vomer small; no teeth on palatines; tongue small, pointed, free in front; lips rather thick, fleshy; eye small, a little in front of middle of length of head; a deep pit below eye; top of head with deep square pit just behind interorbital space; anterior nostril with broad fleshy flap; posterior large, without flap; four spines on side of snout above anterior nostril; preocular, supraocular, postocular, tympanic, parietal, and nuchal spines present; a series of spines running across cheek below eye; several large spines on lower part of preopercle; several spines on opercle; side of head above with many small spines; suprascapular with several small spines; dorsal spines rather strong; third longest, 3.75 in head; last dorsal spine 3.8; second dorsal ray 2.7; second anal spine enlarged, a little longer than the third, 3.4 in head; first anal ray longest, 2.4 in head; caudal rounded, 2 in head; pectoral large, lower rays thick, fleshy, curved inward; sixth pectoral ray 1.7 in head, lowest 3.7; base of pectoral broad, 2.25; ventral spine strong, 3.1 in head, second ray longest, 1.9; the innermost ray joined by a broad membrane to belly; caudal peduncle compressed, its depth 4 in head; head and body with many fringed fleshy flaps; scales moderately large, ctenoid.

Color in life (field No. 03382), excessively mottled, streaked, and spotted; body dark purplish brown or claret shaded, the spaces gray tinged with sulphury yellow; head all dull brown, flaps colored like the space about; belly to axillary region whitish with reticulations and irregular marks of yellowish olive; axillary region wine-brown, finely mottled with yellowish white in streaks and spots; a few

---

ᵃ *Scorpænopsis catocala* on plate.

round black spots behind and in axil; inside of pectoral with a large jet-black blotch at upper part of base, bordered with orange; around this a large yellow area, then 6 oblong black spots on the mem-

FIG. 206.—*Scorpænopsis gibbosa* (Bloch & Schneider); after Günther.

branes of upper rays above middle, then a broad rose-red band, fading into violet below, the rim gray; ventrals bright brown and gray, red shaded on inner face; inside of branchiostegals salmon-color, striped with white, the membranes yellow; membranes of upper jaw salmon-color mottled with light yellow; tip of upper jaw orange, with a golden ridge dividing a triangular spot of indigo-blue between vomer and premaxillary; a golden line on each side in front of palatines; tip of tongue light yellow; a triangular indigo-colored spot behind teeth of tip of lower jaw; a golden streak behind it on membrane before tongue; lower lip salmon-color, especially behind, where hidden.

Color in alcohol, dark purplish, beautifully mottled with dusky and darker; head mottled above with dusky; fins with many fine dusky and brown wavy lines; base of pectoral both outside and inside brownish, the latter variegated with white and blackish brown; outer portion of inside of pectoral covering first 5 rays with a series of broad blackish spots; ventrals more or less brownish, variegated with gray and whitish; body whitish, mottled with pale brown; edges of buccal folds, inside of mouth, deep yellow; a deep blue blotch directly behind teeth in front of each jaw.

This species was obtained both at Honolulu and Hilo, and appears to be not uncommon. Our collections contain 8 excellent examples, 2 from Hilo and 6 from Honolulu, 6 to 9.5 inches long.

Genus 217. IRACUNDUS Jordan & Evermann.

Allied to *Helicolenus* and *Pontinus*. Body rather elongate, compressed, covered with small, weakly ctenoid scales; fins not scaly; head not depressed; formed as in *Sebastodes*, the spines moderately developed; head and body with dermal flaps; teeth on jaws and vomer, none on palatines; dorsal fin deeply divided, the spines 11 or 12, the fourth much elongate; pectoral rays undivided; anal rays III, 5 or 6; ventral rays I, 5; caudal rounded; vent at base of first anal spine; air-bladder obsolete.

390. Iracundus signifer Jordan & Evermann. Fig. 207.

Head 2.4 in length; depth 3.2; eye 4 in head; maxillary 2; D. x, I, 9; A. III, 5; P. 17; V. I, 5; scales about 9-55-30, about 45 pores.

Body rather elongate, moderately compressed, the head conic, not depressed; mouth large, oblique, the lower jaw slightly projecting, the maxillary reaching to opposite posterior margin of pupil; teeth in moderate bands in the jaws, the inner teeth in the upper jaw slightly largest; vomer with small teeth; palatines toothless; interorbital area deeply concave, little wider than pupil; spines on top of head low and rather sharp, much as in *Sebastodes;* preocular, supraocular, postocular, tympanic, occipital, and nuchal spines present; a ridge with 2 spines outside the tympanic spine; preorbital moderate, about as wide as eye, with a sharp spine turned forward and a blunt spine turned backward; suborbital stay a narrow, simple ridge, reaching base of preopercular spine, which is straight and very short; 3 lower preopercular spines reduced to blunt points; opercle with 2 slender diverging spines, the upper the larger, their points not reaching edge of membrane; head with numerous broad, fleshy flaps; a fringed flap at the nostril, 2 on edge of preorbital, 2 on lower limb of preopercle, and a high fringed flap above eye, about as long as pupil; small simple flaps on the cheek, the end of the maxillary, and elsewhere on head; large pores on lower jaw, under suborbital stay, and

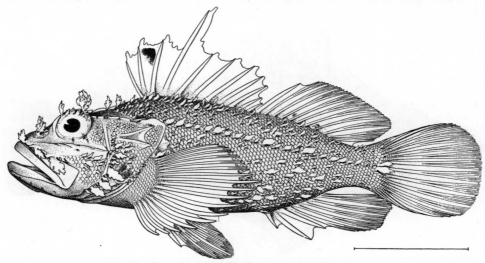

FIG. 207.—*Iracundus signifer* Jordan & Evermann; from the type.

elsewhere; opercle and upper part of cheek with rudimentary embedded scales; jaws naked; top of head scaleless, occiput covered with thin skin and scarcely depressed; gillrakers very short, thickish, and feeble, all but about 6 reduced to mere rudiments; no slit behind last gill; body covered with small, close-set scales, which are slightly ctenoid; scales on nape small, on breast minute; lateral line conspicuous, provided with dermal flaps; numerous scattered flaps on sides of body.

Dorsal fin very deeply notched, the spines rather slender, pungent, the first a little longer than eye, the second and third subequal, about half longer, the fourth greatly elevated, 1.5 in head, almost twice height of third and fifth, which are subequal; sixth, seventh, and eighth slightly longer than fifth, tenth very short, eleventh half length of fourth; soft dorsal high, the longest rays nearly half head; rays of all the fins scaleless; caudal long, rounded, 1.4 in head; anal high, the spines graduated, the third a little longer than second, which is 2.6 in head; longest soft rays 1.8 in head; pectoral with the rays all simple, the longest 1.2 in head, lowest rays shortened and thickened; ventral fins inserted below axis of pectoral, rather long, 1.6 in head, not quite reaching anal, inner rays well free.

Color, pale in alcohol, doubtless vermilion red in life, the flaps on body pinkish; a single jet-black spot about half diameter of pupil near tip of membrane between second and third spines of dorsal.

The only examples known are the type, No. 50886, U. S. N. M. (field No. 635), a specimen 4.2 inches long, taken by us on the coral reef at Honolulu, and a specimen 3.9 inches long recently obtained by Mr. Berndt at Honolulu.

Genus 218. TÆNIANOTUS Lacépède.

Head and body high, strongly compressed, with rudimentary scales, which are concealed upon the skin; the skin roughened; mouth oblique, moderately wide; jaws with a band of velvet-like teeth; vomer and palatine without teeth; several of the bones of the head armed with prominent spines. D. xi or xii, 10 to 12; A. iii, 6; dorsal fin very high; no pectoral fin appendages.

Small fishes, which are rare in the Eastern Archipelago and in the South Sea.

391. Tænianotus garretti Günther.

D. xi, 12; A. iii, 6. Of this species I have only the drawing by Mr. Garrett; it appears to be different from *Tænianotus triacanthus*, not alone in the somewhat different fin formulæ, but on account of the much shorter second dorsal spine, which equals the length of the third; the membrane between the dorsal and anal fin is also much shorter. (Günther probably means the membrane between the dorsal and caudal, a statement which is not borne out by his drawings; the shape of the head was probably not drawn quite true to nature.) Color (in plate) pink, the belly bluish, with white spots; fins pinkish, mottled with darker. (Günther.)

Family LXXXVI. BEMBRIDÆ.

Head not very depressed, armed and scaly on the sides; body covered with rather small scales; 2 dorsals of nearly equal development, the first with 9 to 11 spines; ventrals thoracic, but inserted a little before the pectorals, with 5 soft rays and 1 spine; no pectoral appendages; villiform teeth in jaws, on the vomer and the palatine bones; 7 branchiostegals; air-bladder none.

The single Hawaiian genus and species of this family are fully described in Section II.

Family LXXXVII. PERISTEDIIDÆ.—The Deep-water Gurnards.

Body elongate, fusiform, covered with bony plates, each of which is armed with a strong spine; head bony; each preorbital produced into a long flat process, which projects more or less beyond the mouth; mouth small, inferior, like that of a sturgeon; teeth none; lower jaw provided with barbels; gill-membranes separate, narrowly joined to the isthmus anteriorly; gillrakers slender. Dorsal fin continuous or divided. Pectoral fin short, with the 2 lowermost rays detached. Ventrals i, 5, separated by a broad, flat area. Air-bladder simple. Pyloric cœca about 10. Color generally red. Deepsea fishes; 2 or 3 genera and about 13 species known, bearing some resemblance to young sturgeons.

Genus 219. PERISTEDION Lacépède.

Barbels large, forming large fringed tufts at angles of mouth and on lower jaw; dorsal fins 2; characters otherwise included above.

The 2 Hawaiian species of this genus are fully described in Section II.

Family LXXXVIII. HOPLICHTHYIDÆ.

Head broad, very depressed, with the snout produced and rounded anteriorly, strongly armed, and with the upper surface and sides bony; back and sides of the body covered with bony plates; 2 dorsals, the first much shorter than the second; no pectoral filaments; ventrals inserted a little before the pectorals; minute teeth in the jaws, on the vomer and the palatine bones; air-bladder none; pseudobranchiæ present.

Genus 220. HOPLICHTHYS Cuvier & Valenciennes.

Characters of the genus included above.

The 2 Hawaiian species of this genus are fully described in Section II.

Family LXXXIX. CEPHALACANTHIDÆ.—The Flying Gurnards.

Body elongate, subquadrangular, tapering behind; head very blunt, quadrangular, its surface almost entirely bony; nasals, preorbitals, suborbitals, and bones of top of head united into a shield; nuchal part of shield on each side produced backward in a bony ridge, ending in a strong spine, which reaches past front of dorsal; interocular space deeply concave; preorbitals forming a projecting roof above the jaws; preopercle produced in a very long, rough spine; cheeks and opercles with small scales; opercle smaller than eye; gill-openings narrow, vertical, separated by a very broad, scaly isthmus; pseudobranchiæ large; gillrakers minute; mouth small, lower jaw included; jaws with granular teeth; no teeth on vomer or palatines; scales bony, strongly keeled; 2 serrated knife-like appendages at base of tail; first dorsal of 4 or 5 rather high flexible spines, the first 1 or 2 spines nearly free from the others; an immovable spine between the dorsals; anal and second dorsal short, of slender rays; caudal small, lunate; pectoral fins divided to the base into 2 parts, the anterior portion about as long as the head, of about 6 rays, closely connected, the posterior and larger portion more than twice length of head, reaching nearly to caudal in the adult (*Dactylopterus*); much shorter in the young (*Cephalacanthus*); these rays very slender, simple, far apart at the tip; ventral rays i, 4, the long fins pointed, their bases close together, the inner rays shortest; air-bladder with 2 lateral parts, each with a large muscle; pyloric cœca numerous; vertebræ 9+13=22. Warm seas; the adult able to move in the air like the true flying-fish, but for shorter distances. One genus and 2 to 4 species.

Genus 221. CEPHALACANTHUS Lacépède.

Characters of the genus included with those of the family. Four species known—*C. volitans* on both coasts of the Atlantic, *C. spinarella* in the East Indies, *C. peterseni* from Japan, and one from the Hawaiian Islands, East Indies, and Japan.

392. Cephalacanthus orientalis (Cuvier & Valenciennes). *"Lolo-oau."* Fig. 208.

Head 4.1 in length; depth 5.5; snout 2.5 in head; eye 4; mouth 2.5; maxillary 2.2; mandible 2.3; interorbital 2; D. i—i, v–i—8; A. 7; P. 33; V. 5; scales 47,–21.

Body elongate, depressed, rather broad, lower surface flattened; head broad, depressed, quadrangular; side of head above produced backward in a long bony shield till below fourth dorsal spine; snout short, rounded, obtuse, slightly produced; eye midway between tip of snout and gill-opening, elevated; bones about orbit thick, those above elevated, mouth inferior, maxillary reaching nearly below middle of eye; lips thick, fleshy; teeth blunt, small, in bands in jaws, none on vomer and palatines; tongue broad, thick, rounded, hardly free; anterior nostril with small fleshy rim, posterior nostril higher, without rim; interorbital space broad, deeply convex, flattened in the middle; a spine on lower surface of head pointing backward over preopercle; preopercle ending in a long pointed spine which reaches nearly to the origin of the ventrals; dorsal spines rather slender, first very long, 2.8 in

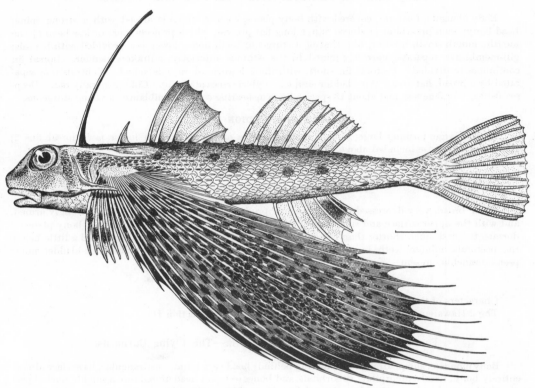

FIG. 208.—*Cephalacanthus orientalis* (Cuvier & Valenciennes).

trunk, its base nearly midway between posterior margin of eye and gill-opening, 2 free spines in front of dorsal; second dorsal spine very short, third much longer, and fourth 1.5 in head; last dorsal spine short, keel-like; origin of soft dorsal a little in advance of middle of space between base of first dorsal spine and base of caudal; anal short, without spines, and its origin nearly midway between base of caudal and gill-opening, or a little behind origin of soft dorsal; caudal truncate, about 1.2 in head; pectoral large, very elongate, reaching tip of caudal, ends of the long median rays ending in rather short filaments; ventral originating just behind base of second dorsal spine, and not reaching anus, 1.2 in head; anus with papilla; caudal peduncle long, depressed, its length nearly equal to head; scales large, each with a keel, so that longitudinal series are formed; lower side of trunk posterior to anus with 4 of the keel-like scales enlarged, the last on base of caudal below, also a keel-like scale on upper base of caudal.   Described from an example (No. 04088) taken at Hilo.

A fresh specimen (No. 03433) from Honolulu was drab above, white below; orange spots less than pupil over top of head and dorsal portion of body; 4 transverse bands of golden on caudal fin; pectoral covered with dusky golden spots smaller than pupil anteriorly, larger and less distinct posteriorly; a bright bracket-shaped yellow band on upper side of dorsal about one-third distance from base to top, concave side toward base; spinous dorsal membrane olivaceous with dusky golden spots; soft dorsal membranes transparent, rays with alternating white and olive areas; ventrals golden; anal transparent with golden color on rays.

Color in alcohol, dull purplish brown, with rather large dark round spots on the back, lower surface whitish; spinous dorsal and pectorals blackish, median and basal portion of the latter first whitish, then running into grayish out on fin; pectoral with blackish and grayish spots.

We have examined 6 examples from Hilo, 3 from Honolulu, and 1 from Molokai, ranging in length from 6.5 to 14 inches.

One specimen was obtained by Doctor Jenkins at Honolulu in 1889, and the *Albatross* collected specimens at Honolulu; Puako, Molokai; Hanalei Bay, Kauai; and Lahaina, Maui.

Suborder TRACHINOIDEI.

Ventrals typically I, 5, jugular, sometimes with the rays reduced; nostrils, jaws, shoulder-girdle and suborbital normal; scales various; gills 3.5 or 4; dorsal spines comparatively few; soft dorsal and anal fins long; tail diphycercal.

Family XC. PTEROPSARIDÆ.

Body oblong, covered with scales; ventrals i, 5, jugular; hypercoracoid pierced by a foramen; no subocular lamina. Species numerous, mostly tropical.

Genus 222. OSURUS Jordan & Evermann.

This genus is allied to *Parapercis*, from which it differs in having the caudal fin deeply forked instead of truncate.

393. Osurus schauinslandii (Steindachner). Figs. 209 and 209a.

Head 3.25 in length; depth 4.8; eye 4 in head; snout 3; interorbital 6; maxillary 2.25; mandible 2.1; D. iv, 21; A. 18; P. 16; V. 7; scales 7–60–13.

Body elongate, compressed; head rather large, its depth 1.5 in length, width 1.4; upper profile of head convex, gently rising from snout to nape; snout rather long, broad, convex; mouth large, slightly inclined, maxillary reaching a little beyond front margin of eye; lips rather broad, fleshy; teeth minute, in rather broad bands in jaws, with an outer series in each slightly enlarged; enlarged canines in front of both jaws, and several on side of each ramus of mandible; vomer with a crescentic patch of minute teeth; nostrils very small, separated a little, anterior with slight elevated rim; interorbital space rather narrow, flattened; opercular margin with a sharp spine above, lower spine with

Fig. 209.—*Osurus schauinslandi* (Steindachner); after Steindachner.

denticulations; gill-opening large, membrane broad, adnate to isthmus; scales small, ctenoid; occiput, cheeks, and opercle covered with small ctenoid scales, head otherwise naked; lateral line superior at first, then gradually sloping down to base of caudal; dorsal spines robust, strong, third longest, with rather broad fleshy flaps; dorsal rays slender, flexible, anterior longest, second 2.75; anterior anal rays longest, third 2.75; caudal elongate, deeply forked, lobes equal, 3.6 in head; pectoral with median rays longest, 1.5; ventral pointed, 1.4; caudal peduncle compressed, short, its depth 3.3 in head.

Color when fresh (No. 03434) with black spots on dorsal fin surrounded by red; scarlet lines from snout through eye bordered on each side with yellow; first dorsal bright opaque scarlet, with dark

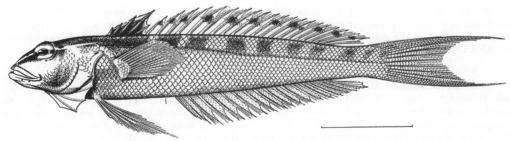

Fig. 209a.—*Osurus schauinslandi* (Steindachner). Type of *Parapercis pterostigma* Jenkins.

blotches near base; membrane of second dorsal transparent, rays yellow and rosy; outer margin of anal rosy, inner portion transparent; blotches on sides rosy, the upper row darker.

No. 03032 in life was rosy on head and body; belly white with pale yellowish-white extensions into the rosy of side; cheek rich rosy; opercle and side of snout with some yellow; lower jaw and throat yellowish-white, the jaw tipped with orange; a few dark rosy spots on top of head; dorsal white with a series of about 10 brownish-black blotches toward outer part of membranes, each surrounded by faint yellow; membranes of first 3 spines black at base, reddish orange above; anal pale orange; caudal reddish orange, distal half of lower lobe black, and 2 rather distinct red spots at base; pectoral pale rosy, yellowish at base, and in axil; ventrals pale yellow; iris rosy.

Another example had a bright scarlet and yellow stripe, from tip of snout through eye and on back, being distinct as a scarlet line in each of the dark quadrate blotches to base of caudal; caudal yellowish, with pearly blue cross streaks of spots; lower lobe red, the distal half black; spinous dorsal black, edged with scarlet; base and axil of pectoral golden.

Color in alcohol, pale brown, a little darker on head; about 8 broad brown saddle-like blotches across back; top of head brownish; a white line running from tip of snout to eye, and continued on postocular region above opercle; spinous dorsal with a large blackish blotch on middle and basal portion; about 10 blackish spots in a single series along upper portion of soft dorsal; caudal with 6 vertical series of whitish dots; anal, pectoral, and ventral pale.

This species, described originally from Honolulu, is quite common at that place, and we have specimens also from Hilo. Twenty-two examples examined are 4 to 5.5 inches long.

Genus 223. NEOPERCIS Steindachner.

Palatines with teeth; dorsal scarcely notched, the middle spines not longer than the posterior ones; dorsal rays v, 23; A. 20; scales about 60; otherwise essentially as in *Parapercis*.

The single Hawaiian species of this genus is fully described in Section II.

Genus 224. BEMBROPS Steindachner.

Head strongly depressed, the snout spatulate; mouth long, subhorizontal; teeth in jaws and on vomer and palatines; maxillary with a fleshy flap or barbel at tip; eyes very large, half lateral; opercle with 2 spines; angle of preopercle with 2 small spines, at least in Japanese species; preorbital entire; gill-opening very long, with 7 branchiostegals; pseudobranchiæ present; ventrals jugular; dorsal fins 2, well separated; belly flattened, back convex; scales rather large, finely ctenoid.

Small fishes inhabiting depths in Asia and America. The single Hawaiian species fully described in Section II.

Genus 225. PTEROPSARON Jordan & Snyder.

Body subcylindrical, depressed anteriorly, covered with large cycloid scales; lateral line continuous; head depressed, flattened anteriorly; snout produced, broadly spatulate; mouth large, the jaws subequal; maxillary without barbel; teeth small, on jaws, vomer and palatines smooth; eyes very large, largely vertical in range, separated by a very narrow ridge; suborbital very narrow; cheeks and opercles scaly; preopercle rounded, entire, but with mucous tubes near its edge; opercle with a partly concealed spine before its membranous tip; gillrakers obsolete; gill-membranes separate, free from the isthmus; dorsal fins separate, the first short, but sometimes greatly elevated; second similar to anal; caudal convex; ventrals I, 5, well separated, a rhombic area before them, inserted before pectorals, the inner rays longest; pectorals normal; lateral line simple, median. This genus is allied to *Bembrops*, from which it differs in the absence of a fleshy flap on the maxillary.

The single Hawaiian species of this genus is fully described in Section II.

Family XCI. CHAMPSODONTIDÆ.

We place provisionally in a separate family a single genus, *Champsodon*, apparently allied on the one hand to *Uranoscopus* and on the other certainly to the *Chiasmodontidæ*, with which Doctor Boulenger places it; but the real affinities of *Chiasmodon* are equally uncertain. The family characters are included below.

Genus 226. CHAMPSODON Günther.

Body rather elongate, fusiform, covered with small, rough, warty, scarcely imbricate scales; belly naked; head flat above, with vertical sides; cheeks and snout scaly; eyes rather small, high, and near together, mostly directed upward; a small cilium over each eye; mouth large, very oblique, the lower jaw projecting; both jaws with slender teeth of unequal size, some of those below longest, many of them long, slender, depressible canines; a few teeth on vomer, none on palatines; upper jaw with a double notch at tip; preopercle with a strong, curved spine at its angle, the spine about as long as eye, the ascending limb with small teeth; opercle rounded, unarmed; preorbital broad, with a flat, three-lobed spine; top of head with a low ridge on each side from snout to nape; gill-openings wide, the gill-membranes separate, free from the isthmus; isthmus long and narrow, not forming a hump; gillrakers slender, of moderate length; gills 4, a slit behind the fourth; suborbitals not dilated; lateral lines 2, the lower curved upward over pectoral, both with lateral vertical branches; the cross-rows of tubes on the back more conspicuous than the lateral lines; dorsal fins 2, the first short, the second long, similar to anal; pectoral small and narrow, placed high; ventrals I, 5, the middle rays longest, inserted before pectorals, but joined to the shoulder girdle by ligament only; caudal forked.

The single Hawaiian species of this family is fully described in Section II.

Family XCII. HARPAGIFERIDÆ.

This family is allied to the *Callionymidæ*, resembling them in external characters though differing very widely in the armature of the head, the preopercle being entire, the opercle and subopercle reduced, each consisting mainly of a nearly straight, sharp, simple spine; the gill-openings are much wider than in *Callionymus*, but the gill-membranes are broadly united to the isthmus; no lateral line; no scales. *Draconetta* has much in common with *Bembrops* and *Pteropsaron*.

Genus 227. DRACONETTA Jordan & Fowler.

The characters of the genus are included above. The single Hawaiian species is fully described in Section II.

Family XCIII. CALLIONYMIDÆ.—Dragonets.

Body elongate, naked; head broad and depressed; the mouth narrow, the upper jaw very protractile; teeth very small, in jaws only; preopercle armed with a strong spine; opercle unarmed; eyes moderate, usually directed upward; lateral line present, often duplicated; dorsal fins 2, sometimes united at base, the anterior with 4 flexible spines; soft dorsal and anal short, the latter without distinct spine; ventrals I, 5, jugular in position, widely separated; pectoral fins large; gill-openings small, the membranes broadly attached to the isthmus; gills 4, a slit behind the fourth; pseudobranchiæ present; no air-bladder; vertebræ usually $8+13=21$. Sexes notably different in color; dorsal fin higher in the male. Small fishes of the shores of warm seas, chiefly of the Old World, allied to the *Trachinidæ*, according to Boulenger, but resembling the *Cottidæ* in form.

Genus 228. CALLIURICHTHYS Jordan & Fowler.

This genus differs from *Callionymus* in the character of the preopercular spine, which is long, simple, straight or curved, and serrulate, but without recurved hooks above. A small antrorse spine at its base below; in the typical species the caudal fin is greatly elongate. The dorsal spines are graduated backward, at least the first 2 being elongate. The single Hawaiian species of this genus is fully described in Section II.

Genus 229. CALLIONYMUS Linnæus.

This genus includes dragonets with the ventral fins entire, without detached ray, the gill-opening reduced to a small foramen, opening upward, and the lateral line single; head triangular, depressed; eyes directed upward; preopercular spine very large, hooked at tip and with one or more recurved spines above, a small antrorse spine at its base below; opercle unarmed; sexual differences strongly marked. Species numerous, living on the bottoms in warm seas. The few species in America live at a considerable depth; in the Mediterranean, in India, and in Japan they are shore fishes, swarming in all bays and living in shallow water. The 3 Hawaiian species of this genus are fully described in Section II.

Group GOBIOIDEI.—The Gobies.

Body elongate, variously scaled or naked, head usually large, armed or not, the suborbital ring without a bony stay for the preopercle; gill-openings reduced, the membranes attached to the isthmus; gills 4, a slit behind the last; pseudobranchiæ present; ventral rays I, 4 or I, 5, inserted below the pectoral, the fins close together or united, widely separated or otherwise peculiar; dorsal fins separate or united, the first of a few weak spines, sometimes wanting; anal rather long, usually with a single weak spine, similar to soft dorsal; caudal rounded; usually no air-bladder nor pyloric cœca. Vertebræ 24 to 35. Carnivorous bottom fishes, mostly of small size in warm regions, some marine, others of the fresh waters. Three families.

Family XCIV. GOBIIDÆ.

Body oblong or elongate, naked or covered with ctenoid or cycloid scales; dentition various, the teeth generally small, but sometimes developed into great canines; premaxillaries protractile; suborbital without bony stay; skin of head continuous with covering of eyes; eyes usually moderate, sometimes concealed; opercle unarmed; preopercle unarmed, or with a short spine; pseudobranchiæ present or absent; gills 4, a slit behind the fourth; gill-membranes more or less united to the isthmus, the gill-openings thus restricted to the sides; no lateral line; dorsal fins separate or connected, the spinous dorsal short, of 2 to 8 flexible spines, or sometimes wanting; anal usually with a single weak spine, the fin similar to soft dorsal; ventral fins close together, separate or united, each composed of a short spine and 3 or 4 soft rays, the inner rays usually longest; the ventral fins, when united, form a sucking disk, a cross-fold of skin at their base completing the cup; caudal fin convex; anal papillæ prominent; no pyloric cœca; usually no air-bladder. Carnivorous fishes, mostly of small size, living on the bottom near the shore in warm regions. Some inhabit fresh waters and others live indiscriminately in either fresh or salt water; many of them bury themselves in the mud of estuaries. Few of them are large enough to be of much food value. The species are for the most part easily recognized, but their arrangement in genera is a matter of extreme difficulty.

Genus 230 ELEOTRIS (Gronow) Schneider.

Body long and low, compressed behind; head long, low, flattened above, without spines or crests, almost everywhere scaly; mouth large, oblique, lower jaw projecting; lower pharyngeals rather broad, the teeth small, bluntish; preopercle with a small concealed spine below, its tip hooked forward; branchiostegals unarmed; eyes small, high, anterior; isthmus broad; tongue broad, rounded; posttemporal bones very strongly divergent, their insertions close together; top of skull somewhat elevated and declivous; interorbital area slightly convex transversely; dorsal fins well apart, the first of 5 or 6 low, flexible spines; ventrals separate; scales moderate, ctenoid, 45 to 80 in a longitudinal series; vertebræ (*pisonis*) 11+15. Tropical seas, entering fresh waters.

394. Eleotris sandwicensis Vaillant & Sauvage. "*Oópu.*" Fig. 210.

Head 2.7 in length; depth 4.25; eye 7 in head; snout 3.8; interorbital 3.25; D. vi, 10; A. ii, 8; P. 17; V. i, 5; scales 70 to 80—20.

Body elongate, depressed in front, compressed behind, greatest depth about middle of belly; head elongate, very broad, depressed, its width 1.4 in its length, and its depth 1.65; snout blunt, broad, depressed, 3.9 in head; mouth large, oblique, 2.8 in head; lips thick, fleshy; mandible large, slightly projecting; teeth fine, sharp-pointed, in rather broad bands in jaws; no teeth on vomer and palatines; tongue rather broad, free, truncate; preopercle with a small curved spine at its angle, forward and more or less concealed in the skin; interorbital space broad, flattened; nostrils well separated, anterior in a short tube; eye high, in first third of head, more or less lateral; gill-opening rather large, oblique; scales very small, ctenoid, and extending on top of head; no lateral line; dorsal fins well separated, fourth dorsal spine longest, 2.5 in head; first dorsal ray 3.65, sixth 2.3; anal inserted a little behind origin of soft dorsal, first ray 3.4, seventh 2.1; caudal elongate, middle rays longest, 1.5, rounded; pectoral rather broad, short, lower median rays the longest, 1.75; ventral 2.2; caudal peduncle long, compressed, 1.7, its depth 3; anal papilla present. Description from an example (No. 04591) taken at Hilo.

Color in life (No. 03024) dirty brownish throughout, belly paler; fins all dark; soft dorsal narrowly white-edged.

Color in alcohol dark dusky brown, lower surface pale brown with dusky on lower surface of head, 2 blackish streaks across cheek, 1 from lower rim of eye backward and the other just below; fins grayish dusky, upper margin of spinous dorsal whitish; edges of soft dorsal, anal, and caudal grayish.

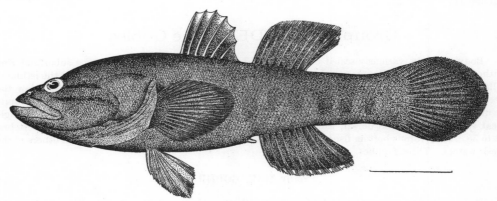

FIG. 210.—*Eleotris sandwicensis* Vaillant & Sauvage.

Medium-sized examples have the body with longitudinal rows of dark brown or dusky spots on the upper surface; dorsals and anal more or less dusky, with small spots on the basal portion of former; caudal and pectoral fins with many narrow dark-gray crossbars. Small examples show indistinct dark brown spots on side of body, and some very small ones have about 9 broad deep-brown cross-bands over the back when viewed from above, and the side specked and spotted with dark brown below its middle; a number of dark brown spots on chest; side of head with dark-brown lines; chin dusky. Some examples with black dots scattered along side of body.

This interesting species is very abundant in fresh, brackish, and shallow water among the Hawaiian Islands. Our collection contains a very complete series of specimens, as follows: From Honolulu 445; Waianae 41, Waialua 21, Moanalua 5, Moana Hotel 4, Waikiki 1, Hilo 119, and Kailua 1. Of those from Honolulu, 384 are in the collection made by Doctor Jenkins and 2 in Doctor Wood's. They vary in length from 1.2 to 9 inches. Numerous specimens were collected also by the *Albatross* at Honolulu, Waimea, and Hanalei; in Huleia and Hanapepe rivers in Kaui, and Anahulu River, Oahu.

Genus 231. ASTERROPTERYX Rüppell.

Body short, deep, compressed, covered with large, nearly smooth scales; eyes moderate; mouth moderate, the teeth medium; chin prominent; no teeth on vomer; 4 or 5 blunt spines on preopercle; dorsals separate, the first of 6 spines, the second like the anal, short and high; ventrals separate, close together, each 1, 5; gill-openings moderate; cheeks and opercles scaly; no papillar ridges; anal papilla moderate. Species rather numerous in the East Indian region, one of them ranging north to Japan and one to Hawaii.

395. Asterropteryx semipunctatus Rüppell. *"Oópu."*

Head 3.25 in length; depth 3; eye 3.5 in head; snout 3.7; interorbital 2.5 in eye; D. vi–12; A. 11; P. 18; V. 6; scales 24?–9.

Body elongate, compressed, greatest depth about origin of anal; head elongate, pointed, upper and lower profiles convex; depth of head 1.1 in length of head, width 1.6; snout rather short, blunt, rounded above; mouth small, oblique, the maxillary reaching front margin of eye; lips fleshy; mandible large, slightly projecting; teeth in jaws uneven, sharp pointed; no teeth on vomer and palatines; tongue broadly rounded, free in front; anterior nostril in a short tube, posterior large, circular; a rather large pore on upper side of snout between nostrils and nearer median line of head; interorbital space narrow; top of snout and interorbital space uneven; eye small, high, posterior margin a little anterior to middle of length of head; lower margin of preopercle with 4 blunt prongs; gill-opening low, its length 2; scales large, finely ctenoid; head covered with large, finely ctenoid scales except on interorbital space, snout, lips, and chin; no lateral line; dorsal fins well separated, the spines flexible, and the second produced in a long filament; first spine 1.6, second 1.25, third 1.75 in trunk; soft dorsal with last rays longest, first 2.25, ninth 1.25, last 1.8; anal similar to soft dorsal, first 2.5, ninth 1.1, last 1.9; caudal broad, round, equal to head; pectoral elongate, pointed, longer than head, 3 in trunk; ventral long, about equal to pectoral; caudal peduncle elongate, compressed, its length 1.5 in head, depth 2.

Color in alcohol, blackish, almost uniform, apparently without any traces of spots; side with about 6 vertical obscure blackish bars; fins dusky. Another example has the body similarly colored, except that it is covered with very many small bluish spots.

Apparently not common, except on the reef at Honolulu, where many specimens were collected by Doctor Jenkins. We have 1 example from Waianae and 5 from Waikiki, 0.8 to 2.2 inches long, common at Samoa.

Genus 232. EVIOTA Jenkins.

Allied to *Asterropteryx*. Body not greatly elongate, head not compressed into a keel; dorsal fins separate, neither dorsal nor anal elongate; sides of head naked; no papillary ridges; preopercle entire. Among the most minute of fishes, inhabiting coral masses.

396. Eviota epiphanes Jenkins. *"Oópu."* Fig. 211.

Head 2.4 in length; depth 4.5; eye 3.1 in head; snout 4.5; interorbital 2 in eye; D. vi–10, A. 9; scales 28, 7.

Body elongate, compressed, greatest depth about gill-opening, head elongate, profiles about evenly rounded in front; opercular region broadest part of head, 1.5 in length, depth 1.4; mouth rather large, oblique, maxillary reaching below middle of eye; lips rather thick, fleshy; mandible large, very slightly projecting; teeth in jaws small, sharp pointed; no teeth on vomer and palatines, interorbital space narrow, level; gill-opening rather large; scales rather large, finely ctenoid; dorsal spines flexible, rather high; soft dorsal and anal similar, anterior rays rather high, but not produced; caudal broad, rounded; pectoral long, pointed, a little longer than head; ventrals separate, close together, long, equal to head; caudal peduncle compressed, its length 1.4 in head, its depth 2. Described from an example taken at Waikiki.

Color when fresh, the specimen (No. 03440) taken in coral rocks, body bluish, more or less covered with brown spots, which also extend on dorsal and anal; spots on body cover groups of points, forming crescent-shaped spots in alcoholic examples.

Color in alcohol, pale brown, with a very faint trace of olivaceous; side marked with a number of dark-brown vertical crescents; nape before spinous dorsal with 3 deep brown crossbars and a dark-brown blotch just behind eye; side of head speckled with brown, side of trunk with about 6 vertical very pale green bars below and running to base of anal, short bars in between; spinous dorsal grayish with 4 black lines sloping down posteriorly; soft dorsal grayish, with about 7 blackish lines sloping posteriorly; other fins grayish.

FIG. 211.—*Eviota epiphanes* Jenkins; from the type.

Young examples have a dusky spot at base of caudal.

This small fish is common about Honolulu and Waikiki, where Doctor Jenkins obtained 50 specimens, and we have 55, 0.4 to 0.75 of an inch in length.

Genus 233. GOBIOPTERUS Bleeker.

Teeth on the jaws large, acute, distant, and equal on the intermaxillary, unequal in the infra-maxillary; 2 canine teeth, especially developed, behind the symphysis; head scaleless, compressed, the gape subvertical; scales 25 to 36 in longitudinal series; B. 4; D. v or vi, 8 or 9; A. 8 to 14. Allied to *Apocryptes*, but with large scales.

397. Gobiopterus farcimen Jordan & Evermann. "*Oópu.*" Plate 59.

Head 3.25 in length; depth 3.5; eye 3.2 in head; snout 3.5; D. vi–11; A. 9; scales 28 (27 to 29)–10.

Body rather robust, compressed, greatest depth at gill-opening; head rather large, depth 1.25 in length, width 1.4; upper profile of head evenly convex from tip of snout to origin of dorsal; jaws large, mandible very large, slightly produced; mouth large, very oblique, maxillary extending beyond front margin of eye; teeth in jaws uniserial, rather large, somewhat canine-like; two small depressible canines on posterior part of bone behind anterior series; lips large, thick, fleshy; tongue not emarginate, large, thick, rounded; nostrils close together, posterior very large, in front of upper margin of orbit with elevated rim; interorbital space very narrow, concave; scales large, ctenoid; a large pore behind and above base of pectoral; gill-opening large, continued forward below; spinous dorsal small, flexible, spines ending in filaments, beginning behind base of pectoral; soft dorsal high, rays of nearly uniform length; anal with posterior rays elongate, much longer than anterior; caudal elongate, rounded; pectoral broad, round, equal to head; ventrals long, equal to head, broad, without any frenum in front; caudal peduncle compressed, its length 1.5 in head, depth 2.25.

Color in alcohol, pale brown, trunk covered all over with very pale minute brown dots; fins very pale brown, dorsals dusky, especially the spinous; 3 vertical pairs of pale brown cross-lines over side of head.

Described from an example 1.1 inches long, taken at Hilo. Type, No. 50654, U. S. N. M.

Known only from Hilo.

Genus 234. GOBIOMORPHUS Gill.

Allied to *Asterropteryx*. Body robust, covered with large, ctenoid scales; snout blunt; mouth large, very oblique, with 2 series of sharp teeth in jaws, the inner depressible; side of head scaly and with several series of short papillary fringes; ventral rays i, 5, the fins joined at base by a narrow frenum; dorsals short, the first with 6 spines, the second with 12 short rays.

The genus is distinguished from other small Eleotrids by the papillary fringes on preorbital, jaws, and opercles.

398. Gobiomorphus eugenius (Jordan & Evermann). Plate 57.*a*

Head 2.8 in length; depth 3.8; eye 3.25 in head; snout 4.25; width of mouth 2.4; interorbital 2 in eye; D. vi–12; A. 10; v. i, 5; scales 25,–12.

Body robust, compressed, greatest depth about middle of belly; head large, elongate, broad, depth 1.4 in its length, width 1.25; snout short, blunt, rounded above; jaws large, lower projecting; mouth large, very oblique, its posterior margin reaching below front of eye; upper jaw with 2 series of teeth, sharp-pointed, outer larger, the inner depressible; mandible with teeth similar to those in upper jaw; no teeth on vomer and·palatines; tongue truncate, front margin not notched; eye large, high, anterior; nostrils separated, anterior in small tube, posterior close to upper front margin of eye; interorbital space narrow, very deeply furrowed; a series of fringe-like papillæ running from preorbital along upper margin of maxillary down behind corner of mouth, where it joins another series running along under surface of mandible, and continued back and upward on margin of preopercle; anterior margin of opercle with a small vertical series of papillæ, each papilla a little shorter than diameter of eye; gill-opening large, continued forward till nearly below posterior margin of eye; spinous dorsal rather small, spines flexible, with tips produced in short filaments; soft dorsal high, median rays rather longer than others; anal more or less similar to soft dorsal, posterior rays very long; caudal rather large, round; pectoral broad, round, equal to head; ventrals small, 1.25 in head, sharp-pointed, and joined at base of inner rays by a narrow frenum; caudal peduncle compressed, its length 1.6 in head, depth 2.4; scales large, ctenoid, those on upper part of head very small; snout, interorbital space, jaws, and lower surface of head naked; no lateral line.

Color in life (field No. 03554), body with transverse bands of dark brown with olivaceous tinge alternating with dirty white; edges of scales in dark brown portions lighter; dorsal, anal, and caudal dark brown, edged in part with white; pectoral light reddish brown.

Color in alcohol, brown; 12 dark brown cross bands on side, the last 6 very broad, much broader than the pale interspaces; vertical fins dark slaty; pectoral pale slaty; ventral pale on outer posterior portion, blackish slaty on inner.

Honolulu and Laysan; not rare. We have 6 examples from Honolulu and 1 from Waikiki, and the *Albatross* obtained the species at Laysan Island. Length 0.8 to 1.4 inches.

Genus 235. MAPO Smitt.

This genus differs from *Gobius* in the emarginate tongue and in the shorter, broader head; pectoral fins with silky rays; cheeks and opercles naked.

The genus *Gobius* is not represented in Hawaiian waters.

399. Mapo fuscus (Rüppell). "*Oópu.*" Fig. 212.

Head 3.4 in length; depth 4.8; eye 5.25 in head; snout 3.5; interorbital 4.35; D. vi–11; A. 9; P. 25, filaments included; scales 38,–12.

Body elongate, depressed in front, compressed behind, greatest depth about middle of belly; head elongate, broad, depressed, its width 1.2 in its length; depth 1.4; snout blunt, broad, its upper profile convex; mouth broad, maxillary reaching posteriorly below middle of eye; lips rather thick, fleshy,

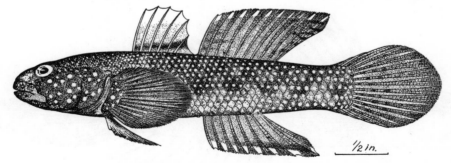

FIG. 212.—*Mapo fuscus* (Rüppell).

with fringe inside; mandible large, slightly produced; teeth sharp pointed, in broad bands in jaws; interorbital space rather broad, slightly concave; nostrils rather close, anterior with a short tube; eye high, in first third of head, directed upward; gill-opening vertical, rather large, slightly oblique, 2.5 in head; scales rather large, becoming very large on side of caudal peduncle, ctenoid, crowded before dorsal, on top of head, and occiput; head, except on top, entirely naked; dorsals well separated; spines flexible, fifth 1.8 in head; first dorsal ray shortest, 2.4, last longest, 1.1, intermediate rays graduated; anal similar to soft dorsal in shape, first ray 3.75, last 1.25; caudal elongate, about 3.1 in body, roundly

---

pointed, middle rays longest, pectoral broad, rounded, middle rays longest, and upper silky; ventrals broad, with rather broad frenum in front, 1.4 in head, and not reaching anal papilla; caudal peduncle broad, compressed, its length 2, and its depth 2 in head. Described from an example (No. 3328) taken at Honolulu.

Color when fresh, very dark, with · black marblings and brown edges to scales; dorsal, anal, pectoral, and caudal all closely and finely barred with brown; ventrals brownish; not much dark below eye. An example from Waialua, when fresh, was marked with pearly blue spots on a ground of mottled light and dark olive, and reddish olive.

Other examples (Nos. 03229 and 201) show a series of 7 or 8 dusky blotches along middle of side, and when viewed from above 4 or 5 broad indistinct cross bands. These are united with a dusky line running from upper base of pectoral to middle of base of caudal, which is also confluent with the upper portions of the lateral blotches described, caudal with dusky blotches.

Very small examples have distinct dark blotches on the side, and both dorsals and caudal with fine cross lines made up of brown spots on the spines and rays. There is also a dark spot just behind the eye.

Color in alcohol, more or less gray-brown, side with about 10 longitudinal series of white spots, head, both dorsals, caudal, and pectoral fins with whitish spots, very small on the latter, and indistinct on the spinous dorsal; lower surface of the head, breast, and abdomen dirty whitish; top of the head finely speckled.

This widely distributed goby is exceedingly abundant in Hawaiian waters and is represented in the collection by 590 specimens from Honolulu, 59 from Hilo, 2 from Moanalua, 1 from Waialua, 20 from Waikiki, 45 from Waianae, and 57 from Kailua. Numerous examples were collected by Doctor Jenkins, and some were found by the *Albatross* at Honolulu, Waialua Bay, Puako Bay, Kealakekua Bay and Hilo. We see no differences between these and American examples (*M. soporator*).

Genus 236. GOBIICHTHYS Klunzinger.

Body elongate, heavy forward, scaly; 2 dorsal fins; anal fin nearly as long as the second dorsal; caudal fin elongated and pointed; pectoral without silky rays; teeth of upper jaw in a single row, in which respect this genus differs from *Gobionellus* Girard.

400. Gobiichthys lonchotus (Jenkins). "*Oópu.*" Fig. 213.

Head 4.1 in length; depth 5.2; eye 4.35 in head; snout 3.1; maxillary 1.9; width of mouth 2.6; interorbital 2 in eye; D. vi 14; A. 15; P. 19; V. 6, 6; scales 105, 22.

Body elongate, compressed, greatest depth about middle of belly; head elongate, compressed, greatest depth about 1.3 in length, width 1.6; anterior profile steep, strongly convex, snout rather long, blunt, rounded; jaws large, powerful, equal; mandible large; mouth very large, oblique, maxillary reaching below eye posteriorly but not to its posterior margin; lips rather broad, fleshy; teeth in jaws in several series, unequal, sharp-pointed, slightly curved and rather small; tongue rounded, rather thick, free in front; eye rather small, high, its posterior margin about middle of length of head; nostrils remote, anterior near front of upper lip, with elevated fleshy rim; posterior nostril much nearer eye than tip of snout; interorbital space narrow, slightly convex; gill-opening rather large, 1.8 in

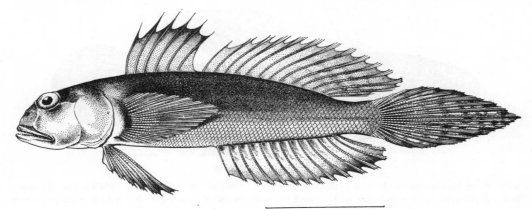

FIG. 213.—*Gobiichthys lonchotus* (Jenkins).   Type of *Gobionellus lonchotus* Jenkins.

head, nearly vertical; scales very small, cycloid; head naked except top, which is densely scaled; dorsal fins separated, spines very flexible, ending in filaments, the first 2 very long; first dorsal spine equal to head, second 1.4, last 1.6; soft dorsal long, low, first ray 2.25, twelfth 1.2, last 2.25; anal similar to soft dorsal, first 2.8, thirteenth 1.4, last 2.9; caudal elongate, the median rays produced into a point, its length 2.7 in trunk; pectoral long, pointed, 3.6 in trunk, ventral large, 4 in trunk; broad frenum in front fringed, caudal peduncle compressed, its length 2 in head, depth 2.2; a narrow thin cutaneous keel between occiput and spinous dorsal.

Color in life grayish-olive, faintly netted and barred with darker, and with a median dark stripe, very faint, scarcely darker at base of caudal; head plain, with 2 dark streaks along cheek and opercle joined by 2 vertical streaks like pen marks; a round black spot just before branchiostegals concealed by the interopercle, and some small dots around it; a dark spot on eyeball above and behind; a faint dark shade below eye, and a dark cross shade on top of head behind eye; first dorsal clear olive clouded with light-reddish brown and blackish brown at base; soft dorsal olive, dotted or barred with darker olive; caudal faintly barred, most distinct on upper and lower rays; prevailing color grayish olive washed in the largest specimens only with bright orange; anal dark olive, distally blackish with dusky dashes at base of each membrane; pectorals and ventrals plain dull olive gray, the base of former with an obscure dusky blue spot, very black in the young. The head also is more distinctly barred in the young.

Color in alcohol, pale brown, side with 5 large brown blotches, and about 11 brown vertical cross-bars running closer together above to form pairs, though becoming indistinct on middle of side; a narrow blackish line across top of head down behind and below eye to corner of maxillary; a blackish, brown blotch at base of pectoral; spinous dorsal dark gray with oblique dusky hues; soft dorsal pale with a number of longitudinal dusky lines sloping backward; anal dark gray, the membrane between the rays blackish; caudal grayish with cross series of dusky spots; pectoral pale gray; ventrals gray black, margin and anterior portion pale brown. Described from an example (No. 846) taken at Hilo. The species is common along the shores and in shallow water about Honolulu, Waikiki, and Hilo. The collection contains 43 examples 2.4 to 5.8 inches long.

Genus 237 VITRARIA Jordan & Evermann.

Body elongate, translucent, covered with very small, thin scales; mouth small, oblique; teeth minute; gill-opening rather narrow; dorsals small, the rays vii–11; pectoral rather long; ventrals small, united in a circular disk. Small gobies of the coral reefs, allied to the Japanese genus *Clariger*, but with the first dorsal of 7 small spines instead of 3.

401. Vitraria clarescens Jordan & Evermann. Plate 60.

Head 4.6 in length; depth 6.7; eye 3.5 in head; snout 4.5; D. vii–11; A. i, 10.

Body elongate, slender, compressed, greatest depth between dorsal fins; head elongate; pointed, conic, depth 1.75 in its length, width 2; snout rather long, rounded; jaws prominent, upper slightly produced; mouth oblique, maxillary reaching a little beyond anterior margin of eye; teeth not evident, tongue broad, truncate; snout above interorbital space and top of head more or less flattened; nostrils well separated, anterior nearly midway in length of snout, posterior close to front of eye; eye rather large, anterior; gill-opening restricted to side, rather small; scales very small; dorsal spines flexible; first dorsal small, the last 3 spines very small (minute stubs, broken in the type), the fin beginning behind tip of ventrals; soft dorsal beginning a little nearer base of caudal than tip of snout, about over insertion of anal, anterior rays of both fins longest, those of anal gradually smaller behind, the last 2 minute and close together; caudal emarginate, lobes rounded; pectoral rather long, lower rays longest; ventrals small, united to form a small round disk whose diameter is 2.25 in head; caudal peduncle compressed, elongate, its length equal to head, its depth 2.25 in head.

Color in alcohol, very pale translucent brown, 7 V-shaped pale brown markings on upper side of body united over back; fins whitish.

We have examined 7 examples obtained at Hilo, each about 1.2 inches in length.

Genus 238. CHLAMYDES Jenkins.

This genus is distinguished from *Gobius* and *Mapo* by the presence of scales on sides of head.

402. Chlamydes laticeps Jenkins. Fig. 214.

Head 3 in length; depth 4; width of head 0.8 of its length, depth 1.5 in its length; D. vi–i, 9; A. i, 8; C. 17; ventral fins united, i, 5; scales 38,–14; head depressed; ventral profile almost straight; dorsal profile rising in very gentle curve from tip of snout to nape; dorsal and ventral outlines of body straight and parallel from base of first dorsal to front of anal, from here slightly converging to base of caudal fin; height of caudal peduncle 2.25 in head, 1.6 in height of body at front of dorsal fin; mouth almost horizontal; snout flat, broad, equal to eye, 3.5 in length of head; interorbital very narrow, less than diameter of pupil; eyes inclined at angle of 45° on sides of head; snout bluntly rounded from above; top and sides of head scaled to posterior border of pupil; branchiostegals 4; teeth villiform, in bands on each jaw; an outer series of enlarged teeth in the upper jaw; fourth dorsal spine longest, 2.5 in head; rays of second dorsal of nearly uniform height, slightly longer than fourth spine, 2.3 in head; caudal rounded; median rays 1.5 in head; middle rays of anal longest, 2 in head; median pectoral rays longest, 1.8 in head, the lower 14 rays normal, above these numerous fine silk-like rays; median rays of ventral 2 in head; basal membrane with a well-developed lobe on each side; scales ctenoid, covering body and top and sides of head, those on posterior part of body and on caudal peduncle but little enlarged, those on head smaller than body scales.

Color in alcohol, plain chestnut brown, pale below; a few darker mottlings on side of body; ventral and pectoral fins dusky brown, ventral pale.

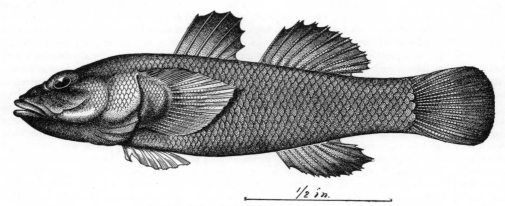

1/2 in.

FIG. 214.—*Chlamydes laticeps* Jenkins; from the type.

This description is based on a single specimen, 1.5 inches long, taken by Doctor Jenkins in the coral rocks on the reef in front of Honolulu.

Genus 239. GNATHOLEPIS Bleeker.

This genus agrees with *Rhinogobius* in all respects, except that the cheeks and opercles are covered with large scales; pectoral with silky rays; dorsal spines 6; tongue rounded.

403. Gnatholepis knighti Jordan & Evermann. "*Oopu.*"   Plate 58.

Head 3.5 in length; depth 4.25; eye 3.8 in head; snout 3.6; width of mouth 2.5; interorbital 2.25 in eye; D. vi–12; A. 12; P. 16; V. 5.5; scales 32–9.

Body elongate, compressed, not depressed in front, greatest depth at the middle of belly; head elongate, its depth 1.25 in its length, its width 1.5; snout oblique, blunt, broad; upper profile of the head obtuse, with a prominence over eye in front; mouth rather broad, the maxillary not reaching posteriorly to below front rim of orbit; lips rather thin; teeth small, sharp, in narrow bands in jaws with an outer enlarged series; no teeth on vomer or palatines; interorbital space very narrow, level; nostrils small, close together in front of eye, anterior with flap of very short, fleshy cirri; eye high, small, a little anterior; gill-opening restricted to side, nearly vertical, its length 2.25 in head; scales large, finely ctenoid, and becoming much larger on posterior side of trunk; scales small on belly in front of ventrals, cycloid; scales moderately large, cycloid on the upper part and side of head, head otherwise naked; dorsal fins well separated, spines flexible and with extremities in most cases free and filamentous; first 1.6 in head, fifth 1.7, last 2.7; soft dorsal long, last rays longest, first 1.7, last 1.25; anal similar to the dorsal, but lower, first ray 2.8, last 1.25; caudal rounded, the median rays very long, a little longer than head; pectoral with upper median rays longest, all rather fine, about equal to length of caudal; ventrals rather large, frenum uniting in front, rather broad, length equal to pectoral; caudal peduncle compressed, length 1.2 in head, depth 2.25.

Color in life, pale flesh-color, upper parts with dark brownish spots and blotches; a series of about 8 brownish blotches along middle of side; a small dark spot on base of pectoral; opercle dusky; fins all pale, spinous dorsal with brown edge; iris bluish white.

An example from Hilo, when fresh, was olive-green, rather pale, and with 7 blackish crossbands; caudal spot small and inconspicuous; black bar below eye, narrow and very distinct; back crossbarred with many spots of dusky olive; side with longitudinal streaks of dark brown spots along rows of scales, these irregular and variable, mixed, especially behind, with spots of pale sky-blue; dorsal, anal, and caudal dotted finely with dark olive; pectoral pale olive; ventrals blackish; anal plain blackish, paler at base. In most examples examined the head was finely dotted with bright pale blue on cheeks and opercles.

Color in alcohol, pale brown, side with numerous small dark brown spots and 7 large dark brown blotches; a dark brown streak below eye, and another across opercle; spinous dorsal very pale brown with about 3 blackish brown cross-lines, very distinct on first spines, running somewhat obliquely, and becoming indistinct posteriorly; soft dorsal with the spines pale or whitish brown and membranes between blackish brown; anal more or less dark gray brown; caudal very pale brown or whitish, spotted in cross-series with brown; pectoral pale brown; ventrals dark brown, paler along edges.

This small but interesting species is generally common in brackish water about Hilo and Honolulu. The collection contains a total of 123 specimens; 101 specimens from Hilo range in length from 1.1 to 2.5 inches, the average length being 1.81 inches. We have 5 specimens from Waianae 1.3 to 1.8 inches in length, the average being 1.62 inches, and 2 examples from the pond at the Moana Hotel at Waikiki, each 0.8 of an inch long. The average length of our 123 specimens is 1.81 inches.

Genus 240. KELLOGGELLA Jordan & Seale, new genus.

This genus is framed for little fishes allied to *Gobiosoma*, but with 6 dorsal spines, and the body and head more elongate. Body naked; fins moderate; teeth small and sharp. We place our single Hawaiian species in this genus, though it differs in the presence of a few rudimentary scales posteriorly.

404. Kelloggella oligolepis (Jenkins). Fig. 215.

Head 4.5 in length; depth 5.75; eye 3.5 in head; mouth 2.75; snout 2 in eye, 4.5 in head; D. vi–11 or 12; A. 7 or 8; P. 15; V. i, 5.

Body elongate, compressed; head elongate, blunt, depth 1.25 in its length, width 1.35; profile of snout very bluntly rounded; profile of back from head to root of spinous dorsal a little concave,

FIG. 215.—*Kelloggella oligolepis* (Jenkins); from the type.

descending from head to base of pectoral, rather gently curving from front of dorsal at base of ventral to base of caudal; snout compressed, short, jaws rather large, equal; mouth low, slightly oblique; teeth in lower jaw rather large, uniserial posteriorly along sides, and in wide band in front; inner ones slender, straight, the outer enlarged, especially several toward front of sides of jaw, which are canine-like and bent backward; teeth of upper jaw similar, with fewer canines; vomer and palatines without teeth; eye anterior, high; top of head flat, interorbital space narrower than pupil; gill-opening low, restricted, and slightly oblique; body apparently scaleless, a few very minute scales on posterior part; first to fifth dorsal spines about equal in length, about 1 to 1.35 in head, last shorter; base of dorsal about equal to head; middle caudal and pectoral rays longest, former pointed, least depth of caudal peduncle 2¼ in head.

Color in alcohol, plain brown, everywhere minutely punctate with black; about 12 dark brown vertical bars on side, those on caudal peduncle very indistinct, and all much wider than the narrow pale interspaces; generally 1 or 2 rather poorly defined similar bands across nape; several short radiating bands from lower border of eye.

One of the smallest of fishes. Described from the type, 17 mm. (0.67 inch) in length, taken at Honolulu by Doctor Jenkins. We have examined 10 examples from Waianae and 13 from Honolulu. The *Albatross* also obtained 2 specimens at Honolulu.

Genus 241. SICYDIUM Cuvier & Valenciennes.

Body subcylindrical, covered with rather small ctenoid scales; head oblong and broad, with cleft of mouth nearly horizontal; upper jaw prominent; snout obtusely rounded; lips very thick, the lower with a series of numerous slender horizontal teeth, of which sometimes only the extremities are visible; upper jaw with a single uniform series of numerous movable small teeth attached by ligament to edge of maxillary; behind this outer visible series numerous other parallel series of young teeth hidden in the gums, and succeeding the former as they become worn out or broken; lower jaw with a series of widely set conical teeth; teeth all simple, slender, the distal half bent inward nearly at a right angle; eyes of a moderate size; 2 dorsal fins, the anterior with 6 (5 to 7) flexible spines; caudal quite free; ventrals united into a short cup-shaped disk; gill-openings of moderate width; 4 branchiostegals.

405. Sicydium stimpsoni Gill. "*Oopu.*" Fig. 216.

Head 4.6 in length; depth 4; eye 7 in head; snout 2.6; interorbital 2.3; D. vi–12; A. 12; C. 16; P. 18; scales 80 to 85–22.

Body long and slender, compressed only posteriorly, head short, snout blunt, ascending abruptly then in a uniform curve to origin of dorsal fin; interorbital broad, concave; mouth horizontal, broad, its width 1.6 in head; lower lip with a fringe of short setæ; teeth of lower jaw unequal slender canines, an anterior larger pair, and usually a rather large tooth on each side; teeth of upper jaw in a single close-set series, more or less concealed in the gums; eye very small, high up; snout prominent, projecting beyond the short lower jaw; gill-opening vertical, its length 2 in head.

Scales finely ctenoid, much reduced and crowded on nape, belly, anterior parts of body, and base of caudal fin; head entirely naked.

Fins well developed; dorsals and anal very high in adult males, the anterior spines and the last rays being produced and filamentous, length of second dorsal spine 1.4 to 2 times length of head; base of spinous dorsal 1.6 in head, and somewhat exceeding distance between dorsals, anterior dorsal rays 1.4 to 2 in head; last dorsal rays produced, their length somewhat less than longest dorsal spine, or about 1.4 times the head; anal similar to soft dorsal, rays shorter, the posterior one longest, 1.2 in head; caudal long, more or less pointed in the males, rounded in the females and young, the middle rays 1.2 to 1.5 times head, pectoral broad, bluntly pointed, the lateral rays short, the middle rays equal to head; ventral disk broad, its width scarcely less than its length, which is about 1.6 in head disk free laterally and behind, the length of the posterior free portion about 2.8 to 3 in head.

Color in life of a specimen 2 inches long from Heeia, dark greenish olive; back and upper parts of sides crossed by about 14 black bars, these sometimes in pairs. head and cheeks vermiculated with blackish and greenish; spinous dorsal smoky with a brownish blotch on base of last 2 spines; soft dorsal smoky; anal pale smoky, with a darker band near the outer edge, other fins pale dusky.

Color in alcohol, brownish black, paler below, side with about 7 more or less distinct darker vertical bars, most distinct in the young, top of head with obscure darker cross bands, fins all bluish black in adult males, paler in females and young; dorsals, anal, and caudal with small roundish pale spots, most numerous near base; pectoral dusky, without spots.

This goby was found in abundance in a small stream at Kaiwiki near Hilo, and a few specimens were obtained in Heneohe Creek at Heeia, Oahu Island.   We have specimens also from Kailua, and

FIG. 216.—*Sicydium stimpsoni* Gill.

the *Albatross* found it in Lahaina and Wailuku rivers, Maui Island.   It is strictly a fresh-water fish, attains a length of 5 to 7 inches, and is used to some extent as food.

The species was originally described by Doctor Gill, and later by Günther, from specimens obtained at Hilo.

406. Sicydium albotæniatum Günther.   Fig. 217.

Head 4 in length; depth 4.5; eye 6 in head; D. vi–15; A. 18; scales about 65.

Body long; head short; snout prominent, projecting beyond the short lower jaw.   Scales large, not reduced but crowded anteriorly; head entirely naked; fins well developed; third and fourth dorsal spines produced, long and flexible, one-third longer than head; base of spinous dorsal 1.3 in head; distance between dorsals 3 in spinous dorsal; soft dorsal and anal long and high, but not produced; caudal long, sharply convex; pectoral broad, bluntly pointed.   Color dark yellowish gray, lighter and more yellowish below; a white lateral band, slightly narrower than eye, extending from base of caudal to tip of snout, on head its upper edge at upper base of pectoral, the line running straight to tip of snout; a row of 8 large black spots on body, below the lateral band, from pectoral to base of caudal; fins all dusky, the dorsal, caudal, and anal edged with light blue, the lower third of anal with many small blue spots; anterior part of ventral disk red.

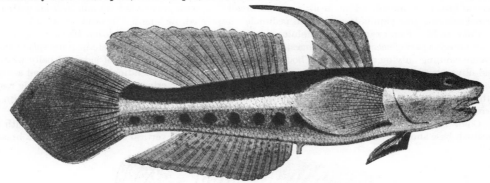

FIG. 217.—*Sicydium albotæniatum* Günther; after Günther.

The above description is taken from Günther's figure, there being practically no description of this species in his text. The fish was not seen by us.

Genus 242. LENTIPES Günther.

This genus differs from *Sicydium* in the scaleless body and in the dentition, which consists of a single row of tricuspid teeth in the upper jaw and of teeth of the same size in the lower jaw.

407. Lentipes concolor (Gill).

D. vi, 10; A. 10; body subcylindrical, naked; head oblong, depressed, with the cleft of the mouth horizontal; eyes of moderate size; lower lip with a series of minute teeth; both jaws with a single series of teeth, the anterior ones in the upper jaw tricuspid, those of the lower widely set; 2 dorsal fins, the anterior with 6 flexible spines; caudal quite free; ventral fins united to a short semicircular disk, adherent to the belly; gill-openings of moderate width. Purplish. Streams near Hilo, Hawaii; not seen by us.

408. Lentipes seminudus Günther.

D. vi, 11; A. 10; a small fish, 2 inches long, and in an indifferent state of preservation, seems to be a second species of this genus, having the same singular dentition as *Lentipes concolor*, but the tail is covered with small scales, the head and trunk only being naked. It is an adult specimen, the ovaries being fully developed. The eyes are small, situated in the anterior half of the length of the head. The length of the head is one-fourth of the total, the caudal not included. The vent is somewhat nearer the root of the caudal than to the head. Length of specimen, 2 inches. Honolulu, in fresh water. (Günther.) Not seen by us.

Genus 243. AWAOUS Steindachner.

Inner edges of shoulder-girdle with 2 or more conspicuous dermal flaps; preorbital region very long; premaxillary and maxillary strong; lips thick; scales rather small, ctenoid, 40 to 80 in a longitudinal series; interorbital groove with a conspicuous median crest; sides of head naked; no silky rays on pectoral; dorsal spines 6; tongue broad, adnate to floor of mouth; otherwise essentially as in *Gobius*.

The species reach a large size and are confined to the fresh waters of the Tropics of America and the Hawaiian Islands. The physiognomy in each is peculiar, the snout being long and convex.

409. Awaous genivittatus (Cuvier & Valenciennes). "*Oôpu.*" Fig. 218.

Head 3.4 in length; depth 4.75; eye 6.75 in head; snout 3; interorbital 7; D. vi–i, 11; A. 13; P. 15; V. i, 6, 6, i; scales 52,— 11.

Body elongate, compressed; head elongate, large, its depth 1.4 in its length, width 1.7; snout blunt, rounded, very convex in profile; mouth large, oblique, 2 in head; maxillary reaching below posterior portion of eye but not to posterior rim; jaws large, terminal. the lower very slightly produced; teeth in jaws small, unequal, sharp-pointed; vomer and palatines edentulous; lips broad, fleshy; tongue broad, more or less truncate, adnate to floor of mouth; anterior nostril very small near upper lip anteriorly, in a short tube; posterior nostril rather large, near front of eye; a large pore behind eye, and many smaller ones on top of head; interorbital space rather broad, flattened, 6 in head; cheek and side of head somewhat swollen, forming broadest part of body; gill-opening rather large, restricted to side, about 2 in head; pectoral rather long; scales small, finely ctenoid, very minute on top of head, enlarged on side of caudal peduncle; dorsal spines flexible, posterior longest; first dorsal spine 2.5 in head, fifth 1.25, sixth 2.2; first ray 2, ninth 1.1, last 1.3; anal similar to soft dorsal, first ray 3.25, ninth 1.2, last 1.7; caudal very long, middle rays longest, pointed 2.6 in head; pectoral broad, expanded, 1.1 in head; ventrals broad, 1.1, with very broad frenum in front without fringed margin; anal papilla large; caudal peduncle compressed, its length 2 in head, depth 2.75.

Color in life of an example at Honolulu, olivaceous, crossed by about a dozen black bars, the 3 below anterior part of second dorsal longest and darkest, the anterior bars obsolete in some specimens, in some running only on upper half of body, the belly being red; lower half of side and belly white; head olivaceous, a broad black band covering interocular space and extending through eye and across cheek to throat, broadening below; belly and branchiostegal region crimson; dorsal and anal pale rosy with cross streaks of brown spots; edge of dorsal fin darker rosy, of anal also darker rosy, and with a narrow white border; caudal and pectoral yellowish olive; ventrals pale rosy; iris brownish black.

Color in alcohol, pale brown, slightly darker above; each scale on the middle of side with a brownish base showing as small vertical streaks; ten narrow brown vertical cross bars on side; a broad

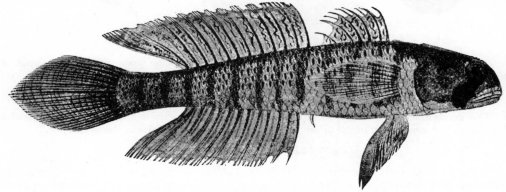

FIG. 218.—*Awaous genivittatus* (Cuvier & Valenciennes); after Günther.

slaty black blotch from below eye across cheek behind maxillary; a dull bluish blotch at base of pectoral fin above; fins grayish dusky, the dorsals with narrow submarginal pale bar, rest of both fins with reticulating dusky lines.   Described from an example (No. 05228) taken at Honolulu.

A common species, widely distributed throughout the tropical Pacific, abundant among the Hawaiian Islands.   We have 74 specimens from Honolulu, 11 from Waikiki, 4 from Moanalua, 2 from Kaneohe Creek, near Heeia, and 38 from Hilo, ranging in length from 0.8 to 5.7 inches.

410. Awaous stamineus (Eydoux & Souleyet).   "*Oópu.*"

Head 3.2 in length; depth 4; eye 8.6 in head; snout 2.2; interorbital 5; D. vi–10; A. 10; scales 63,— 18.

Body short and stout, heavy forward, compressed only posteriorly, head large, broad; snout rather long, anterior profile only slightly convex from tip of snout to origin of first dorsal fin; eyes small, high up, the interorbital space little convex; mouth large, nearly horizontal, very broad, the greatest width 2.2 in head; lower jaw included, lips rather thick; maxillary reaching orbit; teeth in each jaw in a broad villiform band; tongue rounded, adnate to floor of mouth; gill-openings long, separate, the isthmus broad, length of gill-opening equaling snout; shoulder-girdle with 2 short, fleshy papillæ.   Head entirely naked, breast naked, body densely scaled, the scales anteriorly somewhat reduced.   Origin of spinous dorsal midway between tip of snout and base of last dorsal ray; base of spinous dorsal 2.7 in head; length of dorsal spines 1.1 in snout; soft dorsal high, the anterior rays 2.5 in head, the posterior about 3; anal similar to soft dorsal, the rays about equal; caudal long, rounded, the middle rays 1.5 in head; ventral disk short, rounded, its length twice the width of its base or equal to snout; pectoral long, pointed, 1.4 in head.

Color in life (No. 03269), dark olivaceous, with obscure dusky blotches on side; belly pale; a dark blotch at base of caudal fin; dorsals pale yellow, crossed by about 7 narrow blackish bars approximately following the margin; caudal similarly marked, with about 7 vertical blackish bars; anal dusky; pectoral and ventrals dusky olive.   Another example (No. 03270), 5 inches long, differs from the one just described in having the sides more plainly vermiculated with brownish lines and in having the spot on caudal peduncle and bars on fins plainer.

Color in alcohol, pale olivaceous on back and sides, yellowish white below; side with a median series of irregular large blackish blotches, most distinct in the young; a large black blotch at base of caudal fin; spinous dorsal whitish, with blackish retriculations; soft dorsal whitish, crossed by about 7 or 8 zigzag blackish lines; caudal similar to soft dorsal, crossed by about 9 vertical zigzag blackish bars; anal dusky whitish, darkest along the middle; pectoral dusky, palest at base; a small blackish blotch at base of upper rays.

This is the common Oopu of the fresh-water streams and river mouths, and is one of the most abundant gobies occurring among the Hawaiian Islands. Numerous specimens were obtained by us at Honolulu, Waialua, Hilo, Mauna Loa, and Heneohe Creek at Heeia and Kilihi Creek in Pilihi Valley, varving from 0.8 to 12 inches in length.

Suborder DISCOCEPHALI.

Bony fishes "with a suctorial transversely laminated oval disk on the upper surface of the head (homologous with a flat dorsal fin), thoracic ventral fins with external spines, a simple basis cranii, intermaxillary bones flattened, with the ascending processes deflected sideways, and with the supramaxillary bones attenuated backward, flattened, and appressed to the dorsal surface of the intermaxillaries; hypercoracoid (or scapula) perforated nearly in the center, and with 4 short actinosts (carpals)." (Gill.)

This remarkable group consists of a single family, *Echeneididæ.*

Family XCV. ECHENEIDIDÆ.—The Remoras.

Body fusiform, elongate, covered with minute, cycloid scales; mouth wide, with villiform teeth on jaws, vomer, palatines, and usually on tongue; premaxillaries not protractile; lower jaw projecting beyond upper; spinous dorsal modified into a sucking disk which is placed on the top of the head and neck, and composed of a double series of transverse, movable, cartilaginous plates, serrated on their posterior or free edges. By means of this disk these fishes attach themselves to other fishes or to floating objects, and are carried for great distances in the sea. Opercles unarmed. Pectoral fins placed high; ventral fins present, thoracic and close together, 1, 5; dorsal and anal fins long, without spines, opposite each other; caudal fin emarginate or rounded; branchiostegals 7; gills 4, a slit behind the fourth; gillrakers short; gill-membranes not united, free from the isthmus; pseudobranchiæ obsolete; several pyloric appendages; no air-bladder; no finlets; no caudal keel; vertebræ more than 10+14. Genera 4; species about 10, found in all seas, all having a very wide range.

Genus 244. ECHENEIS (Artedi) Linnæus. Remoras.

Body rather robust, the vertebræ 12+15=27; disk shortish, of 13 to 18 laminæ; pectoral rounded, its rays soft and flexible; soft dorsal and anal moderate, of 20 to 30 rays; caudal subtruncate. Species attaching themselves to large fishes, especially to sharks.

411. Echeneis remora Linnæus.

Head 4; disk 2.75; width between pectorals 5.25. D. xviii–23; A. 25; vertebræ 12+15. Body comparatively robust, compressed behind; pectoral fins rounded, short, and broad, their rays short and flexible; ventral fins adnate to the abdomen for more than one-half the length of their inner edge; tip of lower jaw not produced into a flap; head broad, depressed; disk longer than the dorsal or the anal fin; maxillary scarcely reaching front of orbit; caudal lunate; vertical fins rather high; pectoral three-fifths length of head. Color blackish, nearly uniform above and below. Length 15 inches. Warm seas; usually found attached to large sharks. Color in life all more or less violet blackish; the lobes of the caudal paler.

We have but a single example (No. 527), 3.6 inches long, taken at Honolulu; others were taken by the *Albatross* at Hanalei Bay, Kauai, and at various dredging stations.

412. Echeneis albescens Temminck & Schlegel.

Length of disk 3.2 to 3.25 in total length; width between pectorals 5 to 5.3; number of laminæ on disk 13 or 14. D. xiii–22; A. 22; angle of mouth in the vertical from the third lamina of the disk; length of ventral fins equal to the distance between root of pectoral and posterior margin of eye. Color uniform grayish brown. (Günther.) Tropical Pacific, straying to America; a specimen taken at La Paz, Gulf of California (Streets), and 1 in the Gulf of Mexico (Bean). Recorded from the Hawaiian Islands by Fowler; not seen by us.

Group BLENNIOIDEA.

Body more or less elongate, naked or with scales, large or small; ventral fins small, more or less advanced in position, often wanting, the number of soft rays always fewer than 5; hypercoracoid perforate, the shoulder-girdle normally formed; skull not armed with spines; suborbital not developed as a bony stay articulating with the preopercle; pseudobranchiæ present; dorsal fin long, its anterior half and sometimes the whole fin composed of spines; anal long; tail homocercal, the caudal usually rounded, rarely forked; vertebræ numerous, especially in the Arctic species.

A large group, with ill-defined boundaries, the more primitive forms showing affinities with the *Trachinoidea*, *Cirrhitidæ*, and other more typical fishes, the extremes very aberrant and passing directly into the *Ophidoidea*, and other forms lacking spines in the fins.

Family XCVI. BLENNIIDÆ.—Blennies.

Body oblong or elongate, naked or covered with moderate or small scales, which are ctenoid or cycloid; lateral line variously developed, often wanting, often duplicated; mouth large or small, the teeth various; gill-membranes free from isthmus or more or less attached to it; pseudobranchiæ present; ventrals jugular, or subthoracic, of one spine and 1 to 3 soft rays, often wanting; dorsal fin of spines anteriorly, with or without soft rays; anal fin long, similar to soft dorsal; caudal well developed; vertebræ in moderate or large number, 30 to 80; hypercoracoid (or "scapula") perforate, shoulder-girdle normally formed; suborbital without bony stay.

Fishes of moderate or small size, mostly living near the shore in the tropical and temperate or Arctic seas; most of them carnivorous, the *Clininæ*, so far as known, ovoviviparous, the rest viviparous.

Genus 245. ENNEAPTERYGIUS Rüppell.

Body rather robust, covered with moderate ctenoid scales; lateral line incomplete; mouth moderate, the jaws equal; no tentacle on nape; no hook on shoulder-girdle; eye large; dorsal fin divided into 3 fins, the first of 3 or 4 slender spines, the second of 10 to 24, the soft dorsal of 7 to 15 rays; caudal rounded; anal fin long; pectoral long, the lower rays simple and thickened. This genus differs from *Tripterygion* Risso, as typified by the Mediterranean species, *T. tripteronotus*, in the shorter jaws, the presence of a cirrus above the orbit, and in the larger scales. The lateral line is always incomplete. Small fishes of the rock pools of the Tropics, found in most warm seas.

413. Enneapterygius atriceps (Jenkins). Fig. 219.

Head 3.25 in length; depth 4.6; eye 3.5 in head; snout 3.4; mouth 2.5; interorbital 2 in eye; D. iii, xiv 8–10; A. i, 20; scales 4–34–6.

Body elongate, compressed, greatest depth in middle of belly, depth of head 1.5 in its length; width of head 1.4; head pointed, triangular when viewed from above; snout blunt, pointed, oblique; jaws equal, low, and slightly produced; lips fleshy; mouth moderately large, slightly oblique; teeth in jaws fine, in bands; eye high, in first two-fifths of head, with a short filament above; anterior nostril with short fleshy flap; interorbital space narrow; three dorsal fins, first 2 divisions spinous, distinct from rayed portion; fifth dorsal spine 2 in head; second dorsal ray 2; anal fin rather low, lower than dorsal, anterior rays highest; caudal 1.4; pectoral pointed, middle rays longest, equal to head; ventral 1.75; caudal peduncle compressed, its least depth 3; lateral line inferior and straight at first until a little in front of the soft dorsal, where the tubes and pores stop; below this point a median series of deeply scalloped scales to base of caudal; scales ctenoid on side of body, belly naked.

Color in alcohol, very pale brown or whitish, side with about 6 pairs of dark brown irregularly vertical bars more or less confluent; head marked with brown dots above, becoming larger and deeper on the lower surface, where the general color is grayish; fins pale or whitish, with a few dark dots on basal portion of dorsal and anal, otherwise pale; space about gill-opening blackish in front of pectoral

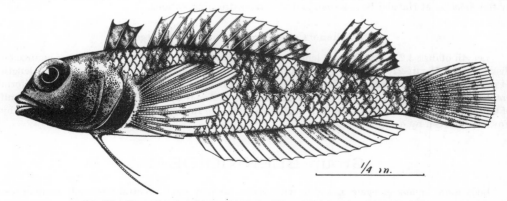

FIG. 219.—*Enneapterygius atriceps* (Jenkins). Type of *Tripterygion atriceps* Jenkins.

and with blackish spots below. Other examples, females, have the head pale, not blackish, with brown dots above and several larger on cheek opercle.

Besides the type, we have examined 9 examples, ranging in length from 0.75 inch to 1.2 inches, obtained by Doctor Jenkins at Honolulu in 1889, and 37 examples 0.6 to 1.2 inches long, collected by us at Waikiki reef, near Honolulu, in 1901.

This dainty little fish is very common in the holes in the coral rocks. It can be most successfully collected by lifting up large pieces of the rock and breaking them to pieces over a bucket or fine-meshed net.

Genus 246. BLENNIUS (Artedi) Linnæus.

Body oblong, compressed, naked; head short, the profile usually bluntly rounded; mouth small, horizontal, with a single series of long, slender, curved, close-set teeth in each jaw, besides which, in the lower jaw at least, is a rather short and stout fang-like canine tooth on each side; premaxillaries not protractile; gill-openings wide, extending forward below, the membranes free from the isthmus or at least forming a broad fold across it; dorsal fin entire, or more or less emarginate, the spines slender; pectoral moderate; ventrals well developed, I, 3; no pyloric cœca; lateral line developed anteriorly. Species numerous, lurking under rocks and algæ in most warm seas; some species in the lakes of northern Italy.

414. Blennius sordidus Bennett.

D. xi, 18; P. 14; V. 2; A. ii, 19; C. 13.

Body transversely wrinkled throughout, except upon the head; extremities of the rays of all the fins projecting beyond the membrane, those of the dorsal having affixed to each a filamentous appendage; anterior ray of dorsal fin strongly curved and more free from membranous attachment than the succeeding ones, which it equals in length; opercle emarginate above; superciliary appendage palmate, about twice as long as diameter of orbit; a very short filament immediately above the lower nostril; on each side of vertex of the head is a swelling, or fleshy cushion, which descends over and covers the whole of the cheeks; teeth nearly uniform in both jaws, diminishing in size backwards; those of the upper jaw rather shorter.

Prevailing color dirty reddish brown, somewhat paler beneath, varied only by 2 or 3 large dark brown blotches on the back, that nearest to the caudal fin the most deeply colored; fins of the same color as the body, the dorsal marked with a darker spot at its anterior part and exhibiting faint traces of a darker longitudinal line near the middle of its hinder portion; the caudal fin crossed by 3 lines or series of spots of a somewhat deeper color. Hawaiian Islands. Known only from Bennett's record.

Genus 247. ALTICUS (Commerson) Lacépède.

This genus differs from *Salarias* in having large posterior canines and the dorsal fin usually divided into 2 parts.

415. Alticus variolosus (Cuvier & Valenciennes).

Head 3.3 in length; depth 3.5; eye 3 in head; snout 3; width of mouth 2; interorbital 2.5 in eye; D. xi, 14; A. 17; P. 15; V. 3.

Body elongate, compressed, its greatest depth at middle of belly; depth of head 1.25 in its length; width of head 1.7; cheeks not swollen; anterior profile very steep; mouth very broad, low, slightly inferior; maxillary reaching a little behind pupil; lips thin, with small papillæ along edges; teeth fine, movable, forming an edge in jaws; two large canines in jaws; eye high, anterior, with a short fringed flap above; nostrils close together, anterior with several fleshy filaments; interorbital space narrow, concave, its width 2.5 in eye; dorsal spines flexible; first dorsal spine 1.7 in head; dorsal fins continuous, of about equal height; caudal elongate, margin rounded, a trifle less than head in length; pectoral broad at base, rays just below middle longest, a little less than head; ventral short, 1.4 in head, reaching a little more than half way to anal; lateral line arched for about first half of its length, then nearly straight but somewhat indistinct along middle of side to base of caudal; a dark fringe of filaments over nape.

Color of a fresh specimen in formalin, leather-brown, dull orange-brown on top of head; some whitish streaks before and behind eye; fringe of tentacles on nape black; little tentacles over eye dusky; no pale spots on body; fins black; a white edge to dorsal; caudal with upper half white; anal and ventrals black; pectoral paler posteriorly.

Color in alcohol, deep brown, more or less uniform; first 3 dorsal spines whitish, upper margin same color except posteriorly, where upper portion is grayish; anal blackish, caudal blackish, upper margin whitish; pectoral and ventral gray.

Apparently not very abundant. Represented in our collections by only 6 examples, all from Honolulu. Length 2 (No. 909), 2.1, 2.3 (No. 277), 2.25, 2.5, and 2.75 inches, respectively, the average being 2.31 inches.

The fish figured and described by Günther in Fische der Südsee as *Salarias variolosus* (p. 203, pl. 116, fig. A), from Tahiti, is a different species.

416. Alticus marmoratus (Bennett). Fig. 220.

Head 4.25 in length; depth 3.8; eye 4.5 in head; snout 3.5; width of mouth 2; interorbital 1.65 in eye; D. xii, 16; A. 17; P. 14; V. 2.

Body elongate, compressed, its greatest depth at middle of belly; depth of head 1.25 in its length; width of head 1.35; cheeks not swollen; anterior profile steep, oblique, mouth very broad, low, and slightly inferior; maxillary reaching below posterior margin of pupil; teeth very fine, villiform,

FIG. 220.—*Alticus marmoratus* (Bennett); after Günther.

movable, forming an edge; lips rather thin, covering the teeth; eye high, in anterior third of head, with small fleshy appendage above about equal to its diameter; no crest on top of head; interorbital space very narrow, concave; spinous dorsal beginning a little before posterior margin of gill-opening, the spines low, short, more or less even, first 2.2 in head; third dorsal ray longest, 1.65; anal beginning a little in advance of soft dorsal, the membranes between rays deeply incised; seventh anal ray 1.9; caudal truncate, equal to head; pectoral very broad at base, pointed, rays just below middle of fin longest; ventrals small, inserted before origin of spinous dorsal, 1.5 in head; caudal peduncle compressed, its depth 2.5; lateral line arched at first, running down abruptly before tip of pectoral to middle of side, and then straight to base of caudal.

Color in alcohol, brown, mottled with darker, lower surface paler, a black blotch behind eye; side with fine dark vertical cross-bands extending on dorsal fins; soft dorsal with oblique dusky streaks; anal with outer portion dusky; caudal with 4 dusky cross-bars; pectoral and ventral gray.

Described from an example (No. 810) taken at Kailua.

The color pattern of this species is variable, as the fish described above is without the dusky cross-bars on the right side of body. Some examples show about 5 ill-defined pairs of brown vertical mottlings. In another example (No. 1010) the colors are well preserved in alcohol; dorsal fins spotted with brown; a dark-brown spot at base of first, fourth, seventh, tenth, and between last spine and first ray; also a dark-brown spot at base of third, sixth, ninth, twelfth, and last dorsal rays; side beautifully variegated with brown, and just below the middle a row of white spots; lower surface of body white; a black streak behind eye and a black blotch above base of pectoral; lower surface of head, lips, and front of snout with white lines and spots; tips of anal rays white, fin with a submarginal grayish band; several whitish streaks about base of pectoral.

From Kailua we have examined 35 examples from 0.8 to 5.5 inches in length, averaging 3.2 inches in length; from Hilo 6 examples from 2.6 to 5.1 inches in length, averaging 3.4 inches; 2 examples from Waianae, 2.75 and 4.25 inches, respectively; and 5 examples from Honolulu, 1.5 to 2.4 inches, average 1.9 inches.

The specimens figured in Günther's Südsee as *Salarias marmoratus* are not this species, but *A. striatus*. *Alticus marmoratus* is thus far known only from the Hawaiian Islands.

417. Alticus gibbifrons (Quoy & Gaimard). Figs. 221 and 221a.

Head 4.5 in length; depth 4.65; eye 4 in head; snout 3.65; width of mouth 2; interorbital about 2 in eye; D, xii, 19, A. i, 20.

Body elongate, compressed, greatest depth about middle of belly; depth of head 1.25 in its length; width of head 1.25; head elongate, upper profile horizontal; interorbital space projecting forward beyond tip of snout; eye high, very far forward in head, the anterior margin before front margin of snout; snout inferior, oblique, convex space between lower margin of eye and corner of mouth a little less than eye diameter; interorbital space narrow, slightly concave; mouth low, inferior, broad; teeth small, in a comb-like band in each jaw; lower jaw with strong canines; lips thin, entire, without fringe; nostrils well separated, anterior with a short flap ending in 4 thin fleshy filaments; a thin filament above the eye 1.35 in its diameter; dorsal spines distinct from soft portion of fin, somewhat flexible, third 2 in head; soft dorsal a little higher than spines, fourth ray 1.5 in head; last ray joined to upper edge of caudal peduncle by membrane; anal rather low, membranes incised along edge of fin, fifth 1.4; caudal elongate, rounded, about 1.1 in head; tenth and eleventh pectoral rays longest, a trifle

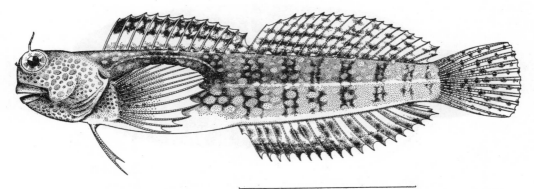

FIG. 221.—*Alticus gibbifrons* (Quoy & Gaimard).   Type of *Salarias rutilus* Jenkins.

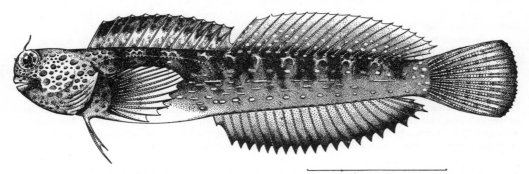

FIG. 221a.—*Alticus gibbifrons* (Quoy & Gaimard).   Type of *Salarias saltans* Jenkins.

over length of head; ventral 1.5; caudal peduncle compressed, its depth 2 in head; lateral line incomplete, running for about first three-fourths lengths of spinous dorsal, straight, only slightly bent down at end.

Color in alcohol, pale brown, side with about 9 pairs of brown crossbars with brown reticulating connecting lines on the back and anterior part of body, very well defined about pectoral fin; body almost everywhere marked with very numerous brown dots; lower surface of head with numerous round brown spots; a black blotch on the upper membrane of dorsal between first and second spines, and another, less distinct, between second and third; rest of upper portion of spinous dorsal with 2 series of blackish brown spots, basal portion of fin brownish; soft dorsal with 3 or 4 irregular series of blackish brown spots; margin of anal whitish, the outer portion with a series of small blackish brown spots, and the middle with a median series of large spots of same color; caudal with dark brown spots arranged in about 5 cross-series; pectoral with many small dusky brown spots on basal portion; ventral pale.

Described from an example (No. 954) taken at Hilo.

We have 3 other specimens from Hilo, 2 from Waikiki, 4 from Kailua, and 8 from Honolulu, including the types of *S. saltans* and *S. rutilus*.   Length 1 to 3 inches.

Genus 248.   ENCHELYURUS Peters.

This genus is closely allied to *Petroscirtes*, differing chiefly in having the vertical fins united, the body shorter, and the gill-openings larger.   Only one Hawaiian species.

418. Enchelyurus ater (Günther).   Fig. 222.

Head 3.75; depth 5.25; eye 3.5; snout 4; width of mouth 3; interorbital 1.65 in eye; D. 31; A. 19.

Body elongate, compressed, greatest depth about root of ventral; depth of head 1.25 in its length; width 1.75; head rather elongate, compressed, swollen a little behind, anterior profile very steep; profile of head above eye rounded, top nearly straight; eye small, high, in anterior part of head; mouth low, inferior, broad; teeth small, fine, in a single series in jaws; lips thin, rather broad; posterior margin of maxillary nearly reaching below middle of pupil; nostrils very small, well separated, in front of eye; gill-opening a short vertical slit; dorsal spines flexible, hardly distinguishable from rays, and of about equal height; posterior dorsal and anal rays broadly joined to caudal by

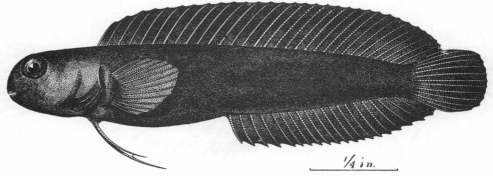

FIG. 222.—*Enchelyurus ater* (Günther).   Type of *Aspidontus brunneolus* Jenkins.

membrane; caudal rounded, 1.5 in head; pectoral rounded, 1.3; ventral long, of 2 rays, and reaching two-thirds the length of space to origin of anal; no lateral line; head and body naked.   Color in life (No. 03551), uniformly black; in alcohol, very dark brown, almost blackish, with very faint or indistinct markings on side; caudal and pectoral grayish.

A diminutive inhabitant of the coral reefs of the Hawaiian Islands; found also in Samoa.   We have 20 specimens from Honolulu (18 of them collected by Jenkins) and 7 collected by us on the reef at Waikiki.   The *Albatross* also found it at Honolulu.

Genus 249. SALARIAS Cuvier.

Teeth uniform, in 1 row only, strong, close-set, compressed laterally, hooked on the end, extremely long and thin and in great number; no canines.   In the young individuals the teeth are arranged like a harpsichord; head compressed on top; upper lip fleshy and swollen; forehead entirely vertical; intestines spiral, more slender and longer than in other Blennies.

419. Salarias zebra Vaillant & Sauvage.   Figs. 223 and 223a.

Head 4.4 in length; depth 4.8; eye 4.5 in head; snout 2.75; width of mouth 2; interorbital 3 in eye; D. XIII, 22; A. 25; P. 14; V. 2.

Body elongate, compressed, its greatest depth at middle of belly; depth of head 1.2 in its length; width of head 1.25; cheeks swollen; anterior profile very steep, vertical, convex; mouth very broad,

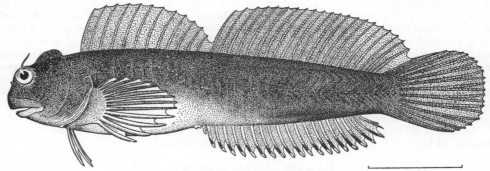

FIG. 223.—*Salarias zebra* Vaillant & Sauvage.

low, slightly inferior; maxillary reaching a little beyond middle of eye; teeth very fine, villiform, movable, and forming an edge; lips rather fleshy, covering the teeth; eye high and anterior in head, with a fleshy appendage above equal to the snout; top of head with a high fleshy median flap, its base equal to width of mouth: nostrils small, close together, anterior with short flap; interorbital space very narrow, concave; spinous dorsal beginning just before posterior margin of gill-opening, and just behind flap on top of head; dorsal spines flexible, base of fin 3.25 in trunk; fifteenth dorsal ray 1.2 in head, and third spine 1.5; eighth anal ray 1.75; caudal long, rounded, 3.9; pectoral with lower rays longest, fin pointed, equal to head; ventral short, of 2 broad rays, 1.8 in head; lateral line strongly arched at first, then running straight along middle of side of tail, pores rather few.   Described from an example (No. 863) 5.1 inches long, taken at Honolulu.

A large example from the coral rocks at Waianae was blackish-brown when fresh, with more or less distinct dark crossbars alternating with golden bars or split patches.   These are most distinct in the young and fade in spirits.   In some about 8 golden spots along base of dorsal, obscure and fading in spirits. A small example shows a bunch of small blue spots on snout, which were not noticed on any others. The fins, which are nearly black in spirits, the dorsal, anal, and caudal were rich blue-black in life; no white edging to any fin, the outer half of the anal distinctly blacker; no black or white speckling on body; pectoral and ventrals blackish.

An example 2 inches long, also from the coral reefs of Waianae, was blackish or dark reddish-brown in life, the belly livid bluish; side with 12 narrow pairs of dark stripes, with a pale olive spot between each pair; dorsal and anal more or less clearly dark edged, especially the latter. This example had much greater powers of leaping than the others.

Other examples from the same locality had the anal very conspicuously white-edged in life, also with more spotting and color. Some had fine dark dots, and oblique dark streaks on soft dorsal. The dark-paired crossbars on side and golden spots at base of soft dorsal are much the same. Ventrals paler than in the other examples.

Color when fresh, of still another example, dark olive with short pale olive bars, rather faint, the dark bars in pairs; dorsal dark olive, with about 8 dark crossbars; anal blue-black, pale flesh-color

FIG. 223a.—*Salarias zebra* Vaillant & Sauvage. Type of *Salarias cypho* Jenkins.

at base, the tips white; caudal dark olive, blue-black below, no spots at base; pectoral somewhat dusky; ventrals rather pale.

Color in alcohol, deep brown, slightly tinged with dusky purple; upper surface darker, and side with about 18 broad, darker brown vertical crossbars arranged in pairs; belly pale or soiled brown; vertical fins and pectoral blackish; basal portion of anal gray; soft dorsal with oblique blackish lines; upper margin of anal rather broadly whitish; ventral gray.

Females differ a little from the males in coloration, being paler in alcohol, and with the belly and lower surface more or less bluish; margin of anal narrowly whitish; the ocular filament short and slender; crest on top of head rather low and shorter than in the male. Many of the females taken in June and July are gravid with ova, and the males show large testes.

One of the most abundant blennies occurring among the Hawaiian Islands; represented in our collections by a series of 171 examples from Waianae, averaging 2.9 inches in length, the largest being 5.3 inches and the smalle t 1 inch, and 81 from Kailua, averaging 2.8 inches, the largest 5.6 and the smallest 0.9 inches in length. We have examined 65 examples from Hilo, the average length being 2.8 inches, the largest 4.75, and the smallest 1.1 inches; 1 from Moanalua 1.5 inches long, and 55 from Honolulu, 1.2 to 4.4 inches in length, averaging 2.7, collected by Doctor Jenkins.

420. Salarias edentulus Schneider.

Dorsal xii, 21; A. 23; depth 6.5 in total length; head 6; a simple and slender tentacle above the orbit and another at the nostril, the former as long as diameter of eye; canine teeth none; dorsal fin deeply notched, not continuous with caudal, anterior portion scarcely lower than posterior, which is higher than anal fin. Grayish, with darker cross-bands; fins yellowish, rays of dorsal dotted with brown; anal with a brownish margin; caudal with 2 or 3 brown transverse bands. (Günther.)

This species was not seen by us, but it has been recorded from the Hawaiian Islands by Steindachner and by Fowler.

Genus 250. EXALLIAS Jordan & Evermann, new genus.

Exallias Jordan & Evermann, new genus of *Blenniidæ* (type, *Salarias brevis* Kner).

This genus is related to *Salarias* from which it differs in the short, deep body, and the small number of soft rays in the dorsal and anal fins.

421. Exallias brevis (Kner). "*Paó'okauila.*" Fig. 224.

Head 3.25 in length; depth 2.65; eye 1.5 in snout; snout 2.65 in head; width of mouth 2.35; interorbital 1.25 in eye; D. xi, 13; A. 15; P. 15; V. 4.

Body short, compressed, greatest depth at middle of belly; depth of head equal to its length; width of head 1.4; cheek flattened, not swollen; anterior profile steep, oblique; mouth broad, low,

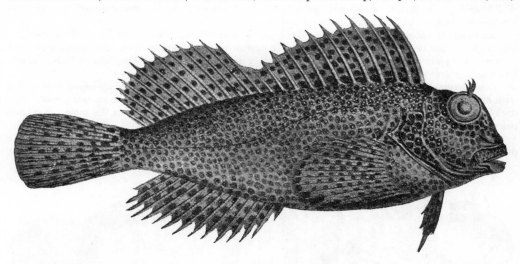

FIG. 224.—*Exallias brevis* (Kner); after Günther.

inferior; snout very blunt, rounded; maxillary reaching below anterior margin of pupil; teeth very fine, forming an edge; upper lip thin, with many small fleshy filaments, lower lip plaited; a pore on each side of the mandible in front, back of which are several fleshy filaments; eye high, in about the first two-fifths of the head; above each eye a rather broad fleshy flap ending in a fringe of cirri; nostrils rather close together on side of snout in front of eye, first with a broad ciliated fleshy flap; a fringe of cirri across top of head; interorbital space rather broad, slightly elevated at first, then slightly concave just over eye; dorsal fin deeply notched; spines rather flexible, second 1.25 in head; third dorsal ray 1.4; membranes between anal rays deeply incised; fifth anal ray 2 in head; caudal 1.1, margin truncate; pectoral pointed, a trifle longer than eye, lower rays enlarged, and those just below middle longest; pectoral short, median ray longest, 1.7 in head; caudal peduncle compressed, 2.5.

Color in life (No. 03552), spots brown with yellowish tinge, interspaces whitish; brown spots on dorsal, caudal and pectoral surrounded by yellow; anal rays with bluish tinge.

Color in alcohol pale gray-brown, head, anterior part of body, and fins with small round dark-brown spots, those on opercle, in front of pectoral, and on belly, large; caudal with spots arranged in 6 cross series; side with 5 broad bands of dark-brown blotches.

Honolulu, not common.   We have 2 examples, and Jenkins obtained 12.   Length 2.2 to 4.6 inches.

Group OPHIDIOIDEA.

This group, as a whole, agrees with the *Blennioidea* in all respects, except that no spines are developed in any of the fins, save sometimes in the posterior part of the dorsal. From the *Anacanthini*, with which the *Ophidioidea* agree in the jugular ventrals and in the absence of spines, they are separated by the form of the hypercoracoid, which is perforate, as in ordinary fishes. The group is a very large and varied one, widely distributed in all seas. The characters here used are all superficial, no comparative study of the skeletons having been made.

Family XCVII. CONGROGADIDÆ.

Body elongate, compressed, naked, or covered with very small scales. Head compressed. Mouth moderate, horizontal, the lower jaw the longer; teeth moderate, no barbels. Gills 4, a slit behind the fourth; pseudobranchiæ present. Gill-membrances more or less broadly connected, free from the isthmus. Dorsal fin long and low, beginning near the tip of the pectoral or the middle of body, of slender, jointed rays; anal similar to dorsal, both connected with the caudal fin; tail tapering; pectoral fins small; ventral fins wanting. Vent remote from the head, without papilla. Vertebræ numerous. As here understood, this family consists of a few species of shore fishes of the Pacific.

Genus 251. CONGROGADUS Günther.

Body elongate, compressed, eel-like, covered with very small scales; vertical fins united, long; ventrals none. Cleft of the mouth of moderate width, with the lower jaw prominent. Jaws with a single series of small teeth, closely set; palate smooth. Branchiostegals 6; gill-openings of moderate width, gill-membranes united below the throat, not attached to the isthmus; gills 4, a slit behind the fourth; pseudobranchiæ well developed. Vent remote from the head. Air-bladder and pyloric appendages none.

422. Congrogadus marginatus Vaillant & Sauvage.

Head 6.5 to 7 in total length; 40 teeth in each jaw, those of the middle of the upper jaw longer than the others and curved backward; insertion of dorsal above base of pectoral; vent considerably nearer snout than end of body.

Body uniform brownish; head of deeper shade; a very narrow black border along the dorsal and upper lobe of caudal.

Known only from the type, said to have been taken at the Hawaiian Islands.

Family XCVIII. FIERASFERIDÆ.—Pearl Fishes.

Body elongate, compressed, tapering into a long and slender tail; no scales; teeth cardiform on jaws, vomer, and palatines; canine teeth often present; no barbels; lower jaw included; vent at the throat; gill-membranes somewhat united, free from the isthmus; no pseudobranchiæ; no pyloric cœca; vertical fins very low, confluent, without spines; no ventral fins; pectoral fins present or absent. Small shore fishes of tropical seas, often living in shells of mollusks, echinoderms, etc., being especially often commensal with the pearl oyster and with the larger *Holothuria*.

Genus 252. FIERASFER Cuvier.

Gill-membranes little connected, leaving the isthmus bare; no distinct caudal fin; pectoral fins developed. A genus with few poorly defined species, only one of which is known from Hawaiian waters.

423. Fierasfer umbratilis Jordan & Evermann.   Plate 61.[a]

Head 10.2 in length; depth 15.2; eye 5 in head; snout 4.8; mouth 2.6; interorbital 4.5.

Body very elongate, compressed; tail very long and tapering gradually in a long point; head elongate, conic, its depth 2 in length, width 2.25; snout rather broad, conic, and produced beyond mandible; mandible broad, flattened below; mouth nearly horizontal, broad, the gape reaching below posterior margin of eye; premaxillary teeth minute, confined to anterior half of jaw, apparently in a single series. The mandibular and palatine teeth seem also in a single series, those on side of mandible directed laterally toward angle of mouth, none of them enlarged; 2 or 3 vomerine teeth, the largest in the mouth, and arranged in a longitudinal series. Eye rather small, anterior, without eyelid, and placed about first quarter of head; nostrils well separated, anterior with elevated rim, posterior a short, crescent-like slit; interorbital space rather broad, convex; gill-opening low, inferior, rather long; gill-membrane free from isthmus, its angle nearly an eye diameter distant from posterior margin of eye; dorsal fin almost rudimentary, very low and thin; anal rather broad, in middle its height about 0.75 in eye, from which point it gradually decreases to tip of tail, where it is rudimentary, like dorsal; tail ending in a fleshy point, caudal fin apparently absent; pectoral small but relatively large, 3.1 in head, rays very minute; lateral line distinct, running down along middle of side on posterior half of tail; no scales.

Color when fresh (field No. 03506), pale olivaceous, with pale greenish spots; a pale bluish streak in each spot over lateral line; pale purplish oblong spots on lower half of body; head greenish-olive, with pale green spots closely set on cheek and jaw; pale purplish dots on upper part of cheek and behind eye; first dorsal same as body, but the spots yellowish; a black spot behind first and second rays, tips pale; rays of second dorsal checked alternately with yellowish-green and white; caudal same as second dorsal, but margin yellowish; anal yellowish olive, tip blackish; pectoral and ventrals pale; iris greenish-yellow; dull red streaks radiating from pupil.

Color in alcohol brown; head and end of tail dark sooty or blackish brown, the color formed of dark points; greater part of anal fin, lower surface of body anteriorly and pectoral and branchiostegal membranes pale straw color; lower surface of trunk more or less blotched with pale brown.

Described from the type (No. 03506) taken at Hilo, where 2 examples were also taken by Jordan and Sindo in 1901. Later 3 examples were sent from the same place by Mr. Henry W. Henshaw, taken from the cavity of a holothurian; another specimen was dredged by the *Albatross*. This species, which also occurs in the South Seas, is readily distinguished from most related species by its dark, nontranslucent coloration. It is very properly made the type of a distinct genus by Doctor Gilbert in Section II.

F. boraborensis from Borabora, briefly described by Kaup, has the pectoral 6 to 7 times in head.

---

a Jordanicus umbratilus on plate.

Family XCIX. ATELEOPIDÆ.

Body terminating in a long, compressed, tapering tail, naked; one short anterior dorsal and no other; anal very long, continuous with the caudal; ventrals reduced to simple filaments, attached to the humeral arch; no pseudobranchiæ.

Genus 253. ATELEOPUS Schlegel.

Head with the snout much protruding and obtusely rounded, the cleft of the mouth being at the lower side of the head; maxillaries protractile in a downward direction; body and tail compressed, elongate, naked; one short dorsal, the rudimentary second dorsal of the *Macruridæ* having entirely disappeared; one long anal, continued on to the caudal; ventral reduced to a filament which is composed internally of 2 rays, intimately connected by a common membrane; this fin inserted at the symphysis of the humeri; teeth in jaws villiform, in bands; vomer and palatine bones smooth. The single Hawaiian species of this genus is fully described by Doctor Gilbert in "Deep-sea Fishes."

Family C. LYCODAPODIDÆ.

Deep-sea fishes allied to the *Fierasferidæ*, differing chiefly in the normal position of the vent, which is remote from the head, and just before the anal fin; gill-openings large, the membranes united anteriorly only, free from the isthmus, as in *Fierasfer*. Pseudobranchiæ wanting; no scales; no lateral line; no ventral fins. One genus with 4 known species, from the North Pacific.

The single Hawaiian genus and species fully described in Section II.

Family CI. BROTULIDÆ.

Body elongate, compressed, regularly tapering behind, the tail generally subtruncate at base of caudal fin, not isocercal; vent submedian; scales cycloid and minute, embedded in the lax skin, which more or less envelopes the fins, sometimes wanting; mouth large, with teeth usually in broad bands on jaws, vomer, and palatines; gill-openings very large, the membranes mostly free from the isthmus; vertical fins united or continuous at base of caudal; dorsal fin beginning not far from nape; caudal narrow or pointed; ventral fins small, few-rayed, attached to the humeral arch and more or less in advance of pectoral. Pyloric cœca few (1 or 2), rarely obsolete or in increased number (12); maxillaries generally enlarged behind and produced toward the upper angle. Pseudobranchiæ small or wanting, hypercoracoid with the usual foramen, as in blennioid fishes. These fishes are closely related to the *Zoarcidæ*. In spite of curious external resemblances to the *Gadidæ*, their affinities are decidedly with the blennioid forms rather than with the latter. Species largely of the depths of the seas; 2 species in Cuba degenerated into blind cave-fishes.

Genus 254. BROTULA Cuvier.

Body elongate, compressed, covered with minute, smooth scales; eyes moderate; mouth medium, with villiform teeth on jaws, vomer, and palatines; lower jaw included; each jaw with 3 barbels on each side. Dorsal fin long and low, the dorsal and anal joined to the caudal. Ventral fins close together, very slender, each of 2 rays separated at the tip. Eight branchiostegals. Air-bladder large, with 2 horns posteriorly. One pyloric cœcum. Vertebræ 16+39=55. Tropical.

424. Brotula marginalis Jenkins. Fig. 225.

Head 4.9 in length; depth 5.75; eye 4.75 in head; snout 4.25; interorbital 6.5; maxillary 2.1; D. 121; A. 100; C. 11; P. 24; V. 2; scales 12–160–32.

Body elongate, compressed, rather deep; head elongate, small, compressed, attenuated, its depth 1.5 in length, width 2; upper profile of head slightly convex from snout to occiput; snout a trifle larger than eye, conic; mouth large, oblique, jaws nearly equal, and maxillary reaching nearly to posterior margin of eye; upper edge of maxillary slipping under broad orbital bones, its distal expanded extremity about equal to eye; lips rather thick and fleshy, upper with 4 long barbels and 2 small ones; mandible with 6 rather long barbels; each posterior nostril with a barbel, and anterior with short flap; teeth in jaws minute, in narrow bands; vomer and palatines with bands of minute teeth; tongue thick, sharply pointed, free in front; two posterior nasal apertures, the anterior with a long barbel, the posterior circular; interorbital space and top of head convex; gill-opening large, isthmus narrow grooved; gillrakers short; compressed, few developed; pseudobranchiæ and gill-filaments fine, numerous; opercle with a sharp spine above; dorsal, anal, and caudal continuous, the latter rounded; origin of dorsal about over first quarter of pectoral, gradually sloping up in height; pectoral short, rounded, 2 in head; ventral bifid, compressed, 2.1 in head, and free portion of outer ray equal to remaining joined portion; height of dorsal and anal in middle about equal to eye; body covered with small cycloid scales, extending out on the fins where they are very minute; head scaled except on lips, maxillary, throat and branchiostegal membrane; lateral line superior, running along upper part of side to base of caudal, tubes far apart, distributed generally 2 or 3 scales distant from one another.

Color in life, raw umber, paler toward belly, head slightly darker; pectoral at base same as general color, outer half lighter; anal at base same color as rest of body, nearly black along outer portion, and with a narrow white edge; caudal slightly darker than general color; dorsal same as caudal; eye blue.

Color in alcohol, rich dark brown, the pigment easily slipping from scales, which when thus exposed are white; vertical fins dark gray brown, becoming blackish toward margin, which is nar-

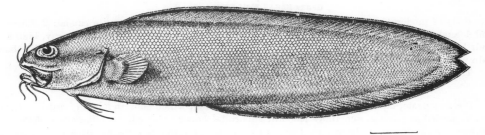

FIG. 225.—*Brotula marginalis* Jenkins; from the type.

rowly whitish; pectoral brownish on middle basal portion, outer part pale brown; lips brownish with blackish tinge on side; lower surface of head more or less whitish, especially along branchiostegals.

Described from the type (field No. 03388) taken at Honolulu. Other specimens were obtained by the *Albatross*.

425. Brotula multicirrata Vaillant & Sauvage.

Head 5 in total length; depth 5; interorbital equaling eye; snout a little longer than eye; maxillary reaching line of posterior edge of orbit; teeth villiform, uniform in size; palatine band short, oval; opercle terminated by a rather strong spine; 6 barbels on mandible, 8 on the upper jaw; dorsal inserted above middle of pectoral; distance of anus from head greater than length of head; pectoral rounded, 2 in head; ventral filaments bifid at the end, 2 in head; scales rather large; lateral line little marked.

Close to *B. multibarbata*, distinguished by the position of the dorsal and the number of barbels.

Known from the original description, and from specimens collected by J. K. Townsend and now in the Museum of the Philadelphia Academy. Another specimen was recently received by the Bureau of Fisheries from Mr. Berndt at Honolulu.

Suborder ANACANTHINI.—The Jugular Fishes.

Vertical fins very long, destitute of true spines; tail isocercal, the posterior vertebræ progressively smaller; ventrals jugular, without spines; hypercoracoid typically without perforation or foramen; no pseudobranchiæ. The osteological characters of this group, called by him *Gadoideæ*, are thus given by Doctor Gill:

"Jugulares with the orbito-rostral portion of the cranium longer than the posterior portion, the cranial cavity widely open in front; the supraoccipital well developed, horizontal and cariniform behind, with the exoccipitals contracted forward and overhung by the supraoccipital, the exoccipital condyles distant and feebly developed, with the hypercoracoid entire, the hypocoracoid with its inferior process convergent toward the proscapula, and the fenestra between the hypercoracoid and hypocoracoid." (Gill, Proc. Ac. Nat. Sci. Phila. 1884, 170.)

A large and important group, chiefly confined to the cold depths of the ocean and the northern seas. From all other typical fishes they are separated by the entire hypercoracoid.

Family CII. GADIDÆ.—The Codfishes.

Body more or less elongate, the caudal region moderate, coniform behind, and with the caudal rays procurrent above and below; vent submedian; suborbital bones moderate; scales small, cycloid; mouth large, terminal; chin with a barbel, more or less developed; gill-openings very wide; gill-membranes separated or somewhat united, commonly free from the isthmus; no spines, the fin rays all articulated; dorsal fin extending almost the length of the back, forming 1, 2, or 3 fins; anal fin long, singled or divided; caudal fin distinct, or confluent with the dorsal and anal; ventral fins jugular, but attached to the pubic bone, each of 1 to 8 branched rays; gills 4, a slit behind the fourth; no pseudobranchiæ; edge of preopercle usually covered by skin of head; pyloric cœca usually numerous, but sometimes few or none; air-bladder generally well developed. Genera about 25, species about 140; an important family, many of its members being highly valued as food; inhabiting chiefly the northern seas, sometimes venturing into the oceanic abysses. One genus (*Lota*) is confined to the fresh waters.

Genus 255. ANTIMORA Günther.

This group differs from *Lepidion* in the form of the snout, the backward position of the vent, the imperfect division of the anal, in which latter respect it approaches *Mora*. In *Lepidion* the snout is subconical, obtusely rounded; in *Antimora* it forms a flat, triangular lamina, sharply keeled at the sides, resembling the snout of *Macrourus*. Body elongate, compressed, tapering into a slender tail; scales very small; head entirely scaly, even to the gill-membranes; snout depressed, thin and flat, projecting beyond the mouth; mouth rather large; chin with a barbel; jaws with bands of villiform teeth; a small roundish patch of teeth on vomer, none on palatines; dorsal fins 2, the first short, its anterior ray produced into a long filament; anal fin deeply notched, almost separated into 2 fins; ventral fins with 6 rays, 1 of them filamentous; caudal truncate; branchiostegals 7. Deep-water fishes.

The single Hawaiian species is fully described in Section II.

Body of moderate length, covered with small scales; fins naked; a separate caudal; 2 dorsal fins and 1 anal, the anterior dorsal composed of 5 rays; ventrals reduced to a single long ray, bifid at its end; bands of villiform teeth in jaws; a small group of vomerine teeth, none on the palatine bones: chin with a barbel; branchiostegals 7. Deep sea.

The single Hawaiian species is fully described in Section II.

Family CIII. MACROURIDÆ.—The Grenadiers.

Body elongate, tapering into a very long compressed tail, which ends in a point; scales moderate, usually keeled or spinous, sometimes smooth; suborbital bones enlarged, sometimes cavernous; teeth villiform or cardiform, in bands, on the jaws only; tip of lower jaw with a barbel; premaxillary protractile; dorsal fins 2, the first short and high, of stiff, spine-like branched rays; the second dorsal very long, usually of very low feeble rays, continued to the end of the tail; anal fin similar to the second dorsal, but usually much higher; no caudal fin; ventrals small, subjugular, each of about 8 rays; branchiostegals 6 or 7; lateral line present; gills 3½ or 4, a slit behind the fourth; gillrakers small; gill-membranes free or narrowly united to the isthmus, usually more or less connected; pseudobranchiæ wanting or rudimentary; pyloric cœca numerous; air-bladder present. Genera 18; species about 50, chiefly of the northern seas, all in deep water; differing from the cod-fishes chiefly in the elongate and degenerate condition of the posterior part of the body. Doctor Gill succinctly defines the group as "Gadoidea with an elongated tail tapering backward and destitute of a caudal fin, postpectoral anus, enlarged suborbital bones, inferior mouth, subbrachial ventrals, a distinct anterior dorsal, and a long second dorsal and anal converging on end of tail."

A family of deep-water fishes, descriptions of the several Hawaiian species of which will be found in Section II.

Suborder HETEROSOMATA.—The Flat-fishes.

"Cranium posteriorly normal; anteriorly with twisted vertex, to allow 2 orbits on the same side, or 1 vertical and 1 lateral; basis cranii not quite simple. Dorsal fin long, of jointed rays; superior pharyngeals 4, the third longest, much extended forward, the inferior separate." (Cope.) This suborder includes the two families *Pleuronectidæ* and *Soleidæ*. Its nearest relationship is probably with the *Gadidæ*, although the developed pseudobranchiæ and the thoracic ventral fins indicate an early differentation from the anacanthine fishes. In the very young fishes the 2 sides of the body are alike and the eyes are 1 on each side, with normal cranium.

Family CIV. PLEURONECTIDÆ.—The Flounders.

Body strongly compressed, oval or elliptical in outline; head unsymmetrical, the cranium twisted, both eyes being on the one side of the body, which is horizontal in life, the eyed side being uppermost and colored, the blind side lowermost and usually plain. In the very young fish the bones of the head are symmetrical, 1 eye on each side, and the body is vertical in the water. In most species the cranium becomes twisted, bringing the upper eye over with it. Eyes large, well separated. Mouth small or large, the dentition various, the teeth always present; premaxillaries protractile; no supplemental maxillary bone; pseudobranchiæ present. Gills 4, a slit behind the fourth; lower pharyngeals separate; no air-bladder; preopercle with its margin usually distinct, not wholly adnate or hidden by the skin of the head; vent not far behind head, the viscera confined to the anterior part of the body. Scales various, rarely absent, usually small. Lateral line usually present, extending on the caudal fin, sometimes duplicated or wanting. Dorsal fin long, continuous, of soft rays only, beginning on the head; anal similar, shorter; caudal various, sometimes coalescent with dorsal and anal; pectorals inserted rather high, rarely wanting; ventrals under the pectorals, usually of several soft rays, one of them sometimes wanting. Fishes mostly carniverous, inhabiting sandy bottoms in all seas, some species ascending rivers. Many of them are important food fishes. Genera about 55; species nearly 500.

Genus 257. PELECANICHTHYS Gilbert & Cramer.

Eyes and color on the left side; mouth symmetrical, of enormous extent, gape about as long as head; mandible extending anteriorly far beyond tip of snout, the projecting portion decurved and falciform, the rami very slender and flexible, each rotating inward, so that the teeth of the 2 rami meet and interlock in the closed mouth, instead of being opposed to those of the upper jaw; mandibular membranes voluminous, forming a veritable gular pouch and permitting wide divarication of the mandibular rami, which can be also closely apposed for their entire length. The posterior angle forms a slender process, projecting beyond the mandibular articulation and extending behind the posterior margin of the opercle; premaxillary, maxillary, and palatopterygoid formed of 3 very slender bony rods, parallel and closely juxtaposed for the greater part of their length; branchiostegals 7; gillrakers absent; preopercular margin free; dorsal and anal fins very long, the former commencing on the snout; caudal peduncle extremely short, a low fin-fold joining dorsal and anal with rudimentary caudal rays; caudal lanceolate; ventrals unsymmetrical, the left slightly more anteriorly placed, inserted on the ridge of the abdomen, its membrane leading to base of first anal ray; vent displaced well to the right side of the ridge slightly in advance of front of anal, a small papilla (genital papilla?)

occupying a corresponding position to the left of the ridge; scales excessively fine; lateral line single, conspicuous, continued on to the caudal fin; with a short, low anterior arch.

426. Pelecanichthys crumenalis Gilbert & Cramer.   Fig. 226.

Head (horizontal length) 4.3 to 4.5 (5.25 in smallest specimen); depth 3.5 to 3.6 (4 in smallest); D. 121; A. 88; P. 13 or 14; V. of both sides with 6 rays; about 230 to 240 pores in the course of the lateral line.

Body slender, excessively compressed, tapering slowly and uniformly toward tail, the 2 outlines very weakly arched for the greater part of their extent.   Anterior outline of head strongly decurved, the physiognomy resembling that of *Glyptocephalus*.   Bases of dorsal and anal fins wide, translucent, sharply marked off from rest of body, constituting together half the greatest depth of body.   Abdomen very short.

Head very obliquely placed, the eyes closly approximated near the upper anterior profile, the cheeks narrow, oblique, upper limb of preopercle nearly horizontal, lower limb nearly vertical; mandible extending beyond premaxillaries for over one-fourth its length; rami so articulated as to permit a slight inward and outward rotation on their long axes, in addition to other movements; gular membrane large and loose, falling into folds when the jaws are closed; the entire mechanism of the lower jaw seems adapted to seizing food between the rami, and forcing it down between and below them.   Teeth in both jaws in a somewhat uneven single series, those in mandible largest, smaller teeth irregularly alternating with the larger ones in both jaws.   Posterior third of each jaw toothless; palate smooth.   Anterior nostril with an overarching flap or short tube; posterior nostril without tube.

Eyes elliptical, nearly even, long axis of lower eye very oblique.   Oblique diameter of upper orbit 3.75 in head; snout short, five-sevenths diameter of upper eye.   Interorbital space narrow, grooved, the width one-fifth diameter of upper eye.

Dorsal fin beginning above anterior nostril, the first few rays slightly displaced toward the blind side; pectoral narrow, pointed, about 1.75 in length of head, that of blind side apparently shorter; caudal lanceolate in a young individual (mutilated in adult), the middle rays 1.25 in head.

Jaws, snout, and interorbital space naked; head and body elsewhere covered with minute cycloid scales; lateral line nearly axial, its anterior arch low, above the head, the posterior downward curve abrupt, above base of pectoral; length of arch nearly equal to half depth of body.

Color in alcohol, head and body light brown, the outlines of the scales dusky, the wide bases of dorsal and anal fins semitranslucent; abdomen in the adult with narrow vertical stripes of blue-black, alternating with wider muscular bands which are of the ground-color; head and anterior median portion of trunk with faint darker brown spots about one-third size of pupil.   In addition to these, the median part of body is marked with about 45 larger round spots, darker than the others, but still faint and ill-defined. These are nearly as large as eye, and are arranged on anterior part of trunk in 7 lengthwise series, all but 3 of which gradually disappear on tail.   The larger spots are much more distinct in the young than in adults.   Mouth and gill-cavity white; peritoneum black; fins dusky.   Taken in deep water about the Hawaiian Islands at depths of 238 to 344 fathoms.

Found only in the Pailolo Channel and its approaches, and in the southerly continuation of the Kaiwi Channel, where it was originally obtained. Three specimens 7 to 10 inches long, from stations 3472 and 3476, were obtained by the *Albatross* in December, 1891, while engaged in surveying a cable route between California and Honolulu.   Other examples were collected by the *Albatross* in 1902.

Genus 258. CHASCANOPSETTA Alcock.

Mouth very wide, the maxillary being more than half the length of the head; jaws and teeth equally developed on both sides, each jaw being armed with a

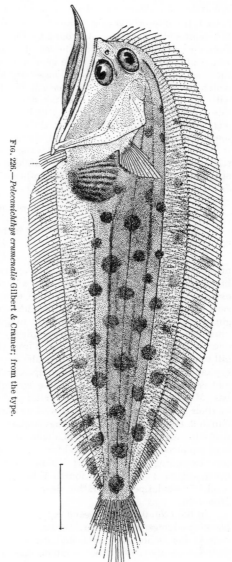

Fig. 226.—*Pelecanichthys crumenalis* Gilbert & Cramer; from the type.

single row of long, slender, depressible teeth; eyes on left side; dorsal fin commencing near tip of snout, its rays, and those of the anal, being simple, slender, and scaleless; scales minute, membranous, hardly imbricate; lateral line with a strong curve above the pectoral; gill-openings wide, the gill-membranes united to the isthmus in front; gill-rakers none. One Hawaiian species, described in Section II.

Genus 259. PŒCILOPSETTA Günther.

Mouth rather narrow, the length of the maxillary being one-third of that of the head, each jaw with a narrow band of villiform teeth; vomerine and palatine teeth none; the dorsal fin commences above middle of eye; scales very small; gill-membranes united below the throat. The single Hawaiian species of this genus is fully described by Doctor Gilbert, in Section II.

Genus 260. PLATOPHRYS Swainson.

Eyes and color on left side; body ovate, strongly compressed; mouth of the large type, but comparatively small; the maxillary .33 or less of length of head; teeth small, subequal, in 1 or 2 series; no teeth on vomer or palatines; interorbital space broad and concave, broadest in adult males; gill-rakers moderate; dorsal fin beginning in front of eye, all its rays simple; ventral of colored side on ridge of abdomen; caudal convex behind; pectoral of left side usually with 1 or more filamentous rays, longest in the male; scales very small, ctenoid, adherent; lateral line with a strong arch in front. Coloration usually variegated.

The sexual differences are greater than usual among flounders, and the different sexes have often been taken for different species. As a rule, in the males the pectoral fin on the left side is much prolonged, the interorbital area is much widened and very concave, and there are some tubercles about the snout and lower eye. The young fishes, as is usually the case, resemble the adult females. Lately Doctor Emery has shown that the larval flounder, known as *Peloria heckeli*, is in all probability the young of *Pleuronectes podas*. The generic name *Coccolus*, based on forms slightly more mature than those called *Peloria*, probably belongs here also. We have seen no larval forms so young as those which have been described as *Peloria heckeli*, but we have examined small transparent flounders, one with the eyes quite symmetrical, taken in the Gulf Stream, and another with the eyes on the left side, taken at Key West, which may be larvæ of *Platophrys ocellatus*. The figures published by Emery seem to make it almost certain that the corresponding European forms belong to *P. podas*, although some doubt as to this is expressed by Facciola. The species of *Platophrys* are widely distributed through the warm seas, no tropical waters being wholly without them. All are extremely closely related and can be distinguished with difficulty. On the other hand, the variations due to differences of age and sex are greater than in any other of the Hawaiian genera.

427. Platophrys pantherinus (Rüppell). *"Pakii;" "Uiui."*

Head 3.6 in length; depth 2; eye 3.9 in head; snout 4; interorbital 5.4; maxillary 3.2; D. 92; A. 69; P. ɪ, 9; V. 6; scales 31–88–36.

Body elongate, very deep and compressed, ellipsoid; head a little deeper than long, orbicular, the upper profile evenly convex; snout obtuse; jaws slightly produced; mouth curved, oblique; lips rather broad, fleshy; maxillary reaching below anterior portion of eye, but not to pupil, its distal expanded extremity 2 in eye; teeth in jaws minute, forming rather broad bands; eyes well separated, lower anterior, its posterior margin midway in length of head, upper nearly half an eye diameter posterior; margin of preopercle obtuse, and, like that of gill-opening, undulate; nostrils close together in front of upper rim of orbit, each with a short fleshy tube; several bony elevations in front and above lower eye; interorbital space deep, concave; from the posterior portion of each eye are 2 fleshy filaments; gill-opening large, gillrakers small; scales covering head except on lips, about eyes and part of interorpital space; small scales extending upon greater portion of dorsal and anal and caudal rays; pectoral and ventral without scales, lateral line strongly arched for a short distance in front, then straight to base of caudal; extremities of most all dorsal rays free, those anteriorly on head free for greater part of their length; dorsal beginning well forward on snout, first ray 3.2 in head, second 1.9, third 1.6, fourth 2, sixtieth 2.5; anal somewhat simllar to dorsal, only anterior rays with their extremities short, first 4 in head, fortieth 2.6; caudal elongate, middle rays pointed, 1.3; pectoral very long, the upper rays produced beyond the caudal for a distance equal to depth of caudal peduncle; membranes of pectoral extending only for a short distance; ventrals close together, left larger, its base 1.8 in head, first ray 3, second 2.6, third 2.1, fourth 1.25; right ventral with base 5, first ray 3.7, fifth 2.8; right pectoral 1.7; caudal peduncle rather deep, compressed, 2.8. Described from an example (No. 05303) from Honolulu.

In life (No. 03257) was sand color, the ocelli light grayish brown, bluish gray, and some with blackish edgings; fins similar. Color, when fresh, of examples from Hilo, centers of large ocelli clear deep yellow; some other spots and marks of yellow, besides grayish, bluish, brown and blackish; 4 yellow spots above and 4 below lateral line in series; then centers of ocelli above noted.

Color in alcohol, grayish brown on the left side, with numerous pale blue rings of spots bordered with dusky; a large dusky blotch at beginning of straight portion of lateral line and another about midway in the latter; everywhere small indistinctly defined whitish spots; dorsal pale gray with 12 large brownish spots formed on bases of rays, rest of fin speckled with brownish and whitish; anal similar to dorsal with 8 large brownish spots formed on bases of rays; caudal speckled with whitish and brown, base with pale blue spots; pectoral rays pale gray with brownish cross-lines, membrane black with white reticulating lines; ventral grayish with brown and whitish spots; right side yellowish white, scales on side of head with brown dots.

Young examples have short pectorals and are deeper. The variation in scales is as low as 67 in a lateral series in one small example; others are found with 75 or 80. This species is common among the Hawaiian Islands. The collection contains 39 examples from Honolulu and 20 from Hilo, ranging in length from 1.5 to 7.75 inches. Specimens were obtained by Doctor Jenkins in 1889 and by the *Albatross* in 1902.

428. Platophrys mancus (Broussonet).

Head 3.28 (4.25) in length; depth 2 (2.25); D. 98; A. 78; scales about 95; Br. 6.

Body elliptical, the profile continuous with the dorsal curve, the snout projecting, and the nasal bones forming a prominent knob; ventral outline a regular and gentle curve from gill-opening to caudal peduncle; lower jaws produced beyond upper, a pointed knob below and behind symphysis. Head not much higher than long; mouth moderately oblique, small for a large-mouthed species, the maxillary reaching little beyond anterior rim of eye, 2.66 in head; pointed teeth in 2 series in each jaw, those of the inner and larger series becoming somewhat smaller posteriorly, the teeth on maxillary not extending as far back on the blind side; the outer series of few small teeth; eyes small, the lower orbit 7 in head, the upper one slightly smaller; lower orbit wholly in advance of upper, the concave interorbital space 2.83 in head; orbital rim a sharp ridge without distinct knobs. Nostrils apparently wanting; cheeks and opercles more or less scaly; gillrakers rather long, the length of longest 2 in upper orbit; 10 on lower part of arch, none above. Scales cycloid, not deciduous, similar on both sides, but without accessory scales on the blind side. Dorsal fin beginning on the snout, the first ray on the blind side, about as long as superior orbit, the rays gradually increasing in height to the posterior third of the fin, where they are 2.66 in head, thence rapidly decreasing to end of fin; anal similar, its highest rays not opposite the highest part of dorsal, but a little farther back; pectoral of eyed side falcate, the second ray one-fourth longer than head, produced into a filament; pectoral of blind side 1.83 in head; ventrals moderate, when depressed reaching past front of anal; caudal bluntly pointed, 1.6 in head.

Coloration in spirits, everywhere mottled with gray and brown; the fins (except pectoral on blind side) marked with same colors, but the spots more nearly round and less complicated; on the colored side there is a large, irregular blackish blotch behind pectoral, a round black spot on the lateral line halfway between head and caudal fin; about 12 blackish spots at regular intervals on dorsal fin, 6 or 7 similar ones on anal; the ventral on the eyed side marked like the anal; the colors and spots extending over on the blind side on the nasal bones, premaxillary, chin, and interopercle. The skinny flap in the mouth between the teeth and vomer is also spotted. Length 16 inches.

This species is common in the South Seas and has been recorded from Johnston Island. It resembles *P. pantherinus*, but is more variegated, has a larger number of anal rays (about 80) and the arch of the lateral line is different. The figures of *P. pavo* and *P. pantherinus* in Bleeker's Atlas show the 2 species well.

Genus 261. ANTICITHARUS Günther.

Mouth wide, or rather wide; maxillary more than one-third length of head; teeth conical, unequal, in a single series in both jaws; no vomerine and palatine teeth; origin of dorsal on snout; scales of moderate size, smooth, deciduous; lateral line strongly curved above pectoral; eyes on left side; gill-membranes broadly united below throat; gillrakers short and lancolate. The single Hawaiian species of this genus is fully described in Section II.

Genus 262. ENGYPROSOPON Günther.

This genus is allied to *Platophrys*, differing in the large adherent scales and the narrow interorbital space. Gillrakers few and short.

429. Engyprosopon hawaiiensis Jordan & Evermann. Fig. 227.

Head 3.8 in length; depth 1.75; eye 3.25 in head; snout 4.25; interorbital 6.3; maxillary 2.8; D. 79; A. 56; P. i, 10; V. i, 5; scales 14–46–15.

Body elongate, deep, rather ovoid, greatest depth about end of pectoral; head very deep, its length 0.7 in depth; upper profile very convex in front, steep; snout short, obtuse; jaws small, produced a little, the mandible slightly projecting; lips rather thin; mouth curved a little, very oblique, the small maxillary reaching a little beyond front margin of eye; teeth in jaws very small, sharp-pointed; eyes well separated, lower anterior placed in first third of head, the upper about two-fifths an eye diameter posterior; nostrils close together, with elevated rims; interorbital space a little more than half an eye diameter in width, deeply concave; gill-opening small; gillrakers rather short; scales large, finely ctenoid, very small on rays of vertical fins; lateral line strongly arched at first for first two-ninths its length, then straight to base of caudal; dorsal beginning on snout, the anterior rays free for only a short portion of their extremities, first 5 in head, fiftieth 2.1, this the highest region of the fin; anal more or less similar, first 3.25, thirtieth 2; caudal rounded, middle rays longest, 1.1; pectoral short, pointed, 1:4; ventrals rather broad, base of left 3, first and last rays about equal; right ventral smaller; caudal peduncle compressed, its depth 1.9.

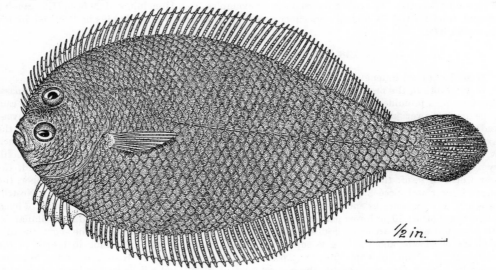

FIG. 227.—*Engyprosopon hawaiiensis* Jordan & Evermann; from the type.

Color in alcohol, dark olivaceous brown, fins dark gray-brown, each ray finely specked with olivaceous brown; left pectoral specked with dark brown, right pectoral dull creamy or brownish white, like the right side of body

Type, No. 50657, U. S. N. M., taken at Hilo, the only example we have seen, 3 inches long.

430. Engyprosopon arenicola Jordan & Evermann.   Plate 62.

Head 3.6 in length; depth 1.9; eye 4.3 in head; maxillary 3; D. 78; A. 57; P. i, 11; V. 5; scales 14–36–17.

Body elongate, very deep, rather ovoid, the greatest depth at tip of pectoral; head much deeper than long, the upper profile steep, strongly convex; snout obtuse; jaws very oblique, mandible slightly projecting; maxillary very oblique, reaching below anterior margin of eye; lips rather thin, fleshy, fringed along margins; teeth in jaws minute, sharp-pointed; eyes close together, lower anterior placed about first third of length of head; upper eye about one-third an eye diameter posterior; nostrils well separated, with raised fleshy rims forming a flap; interorbital space very narrow, concave; gill-opening rather small, restricted to side; gillrakers small, short, few; scales large, finely ctenoid; lateral line strongly arched for anterior fourth of its length, then straight to base of caudal; anterior dorsal rays free distally for one-half their length, first ray 3 in head, forty-fifth 1.8, which is the highest region of the fin; anal similar to dorsal, but anterior rays not free for half their length; first ray 3.5, thirtieth 1.8; caudal elongate, median rays longest, equal to head; pectoral short, pointed, 1.5; ventrals rather large, the left with its base 5 in head, first ray 3.6, last 2.6, almost entirely in front of the right, which is much smaller; caudal peduncle broad, compressed, its depth 2.2 in head.

Color in alcohol, very pale brown; side marked with many large incomplete rings of blackish or dusky, and with a number of dusky spots in between; fins whitish; the vertical or unpaired with large blackish spots on membranes between rays and similar small ones scattered about, those of caudal forming about 4 cross-bands; several dusky spots at base of pectoral; right side whitish.

We have seen but 2 examples, both taken at Hilo: Type, No. 50658, U. S. N. M., 2.5 inches long. Cotype, No. 7471, L. S. Jr. Univ. Mus., 1.9 inches long.

Family CV. SOLEIDÆ.—The Soles.

Body oblong or elongate, usually scaly; mouth very small, much twisted toward the eyed side; the teeth in villiform bands, very small or obsolete; eyes small, close together, with or without a bony ridge between them; edge of preopercle adnate, concealed by the skin and scales; gill openings narrow, the gill membranes adnate to the shoulder girdle above; pectoral fins small or wanting; ventral fins small, one or both sometimes wanting. Small fishes living on sandy bottoms, similar to the Pleuronectidæ in structure, but much degraded, the fins and teeth having lost many of their distinctive qualities; the vertebræ usually in increased numbers. Species numerous in the warm seas, and those of sufficient size valued as food.

Genus 263. SYMPHURUS Rafinesque. Tongue-Fishes.

Body elongate, more or less lanceolate in outline, with the eyes and color on the left side; eyes small, very close together, with no distinct interorbital ridge between them; mouth small, twisted toward the blind side; teeth little developed, in villiform bands; edge of preopercle covered by the scales; gill-openings narrow, the gill-membranes adnate to the shoulder-girdle above, joined together and free from the isthmus below; pectoral fins wanting (in the adult); vertical fins more or less confluent; scales ctenoid; lateral line wanting; ventral fin of eyed side only present, free from the anal; head without fringes.

The 2 Hawaiian species are fully described in Section II.

Order M. PEDICULATI.

Carpal bones notably elongate, forming a kind of arm (pseudobrachium) which supports the broad pectoral. Gill-opening reduced to a large or small foramen situated in or near the axil, more or less posterior to the pectorals. Ventral fins jugular if present; anterior dorsal reduced to a few tentacle-like, isolated spines; soft dorsal and anal short; no scales. First vertebra united to cranium by a suture; epiotics united behind supraoccipital; elongate basal pectoral radii (actinosts), reduced in number; no interclavicles; post-temporal broad, flat, simple; upper pharyngeals 2, similar, spatulate, with anterior stem and transverse blade; basis of cranium simple, no air-duct to the swim-bladder. Marine fishes, chiefly of the Tropics and the oceanic abysses. The group is an offshoot from the Acanthopteri, its chief modification being in the elongation of the actinosts and in the position of the gill-opening. The *Batrachoididæ* are perhaps its nearest relatives.

Family CVI. LOPHIIDÆ.—The Anglers.

Head wide, depressed, very large; body contracted, conical, tapering rapidly backward from the shoulders; mouth exceedingly large, terminal, opening into an enormous stomach; upper jaw protractile; maxillary without supplementary bone; lower jaw projecting; both jaws with very strong, unequal, cardiform teeth, some of the teeth canine-like, most of them depressible; vomer and palatines usually with strong teeth; gill-openings comparatively large, in the lower axil of the pectorals; pseudobranchiæ present; gillrakers none; gills 3; skin mostly smooth, naked, with many dermal flaps about the head; spinous dorsal of 3 isolated, tentacle-like spines on the head, and 3 smaller ones behind, forming a continuous fin; second dorsal moderate, similar to the anal; pectoral members scarcely geniculated, each with 2 actinosts and with elongate pseudobrachia; ventrals jugular, ı, 5, widely separated, large, much enlarged in the young. Young with the head spinous; pyloric cœca present. Two genera, with 4 or 5 species, living on sea bottoms, at moderate or great depths; remarkable for their great voracity

Genus 264. LOPHIOMUS Gill.

This genus is closely allied to *Lophius* in external characters, but it is strikingly distinguished by the reduced number of its vertebræ, which are only 18 or 19, a fact associated with its tropical habitat. The single Hawaiian species is fully described by Doctor Gilbert in Section II.

Family CVII. ANTENNARIIDÆ.—Frog Fishes.

Head and body more or less compressed; mouth vertical or very oblique, opening upward; lower jaw projecting; jaws with cardiform teeth; premaxillaries protractile; gill-openings small, pore-like, in or behind the lower axils of the pectorals; no pseudobranchiæ; gills 2½ or 3; skin naked, smooth, or prickly; pectoral members forming an elbow-like angle; pseudobrachia long, with 3 actinosts; ventral fins present, jugular, near together; spinous dorsal of 1 to 3 serrated, tentacle-like spines; soft dorsal long, larger than anal; pyloric cœca none. Inhabitants of tropical seas, often living on or among floating seaweed, and enabled, by filling the capacious stomach with air, to sustain themselves on the surface of the water; therefore widely dispersed by currents in the sea.

Genus 265. ANTENNARIUS Commerson.

Body oblong, compressed, very deep through the occipital region, tapering behind; breast tumid; mouth rather large, more or less oblique, or even vertical; cardiform teeth on jaws, vomer, and palatines; eye small; skin with small granules or spinules, these usually forked, and often with numerous fleshy slips; first dorsal spine developed as a small rostral tentacle; second and third dorsal spines strong, covered with skin, often with numerous fleshy filaments; soft dorsal high and long; anal short and deep; caudal fin rounded, the peduncle free; pectoral fin wide, with a rather wide wrist, at the lower posterior angle of which are the very small gill-openings; ventral fins short. Fantastic-looking fishes, often gayly colored. Very numerous in warm seas.

431. Antennarius sandvicensis (Bennett).

Entire length 4.5 inches; depth of body 2 inches. Color, dull-orange or yellow-red, with circular black spots on the body and fins. Eyes small and placed high in the head; when touched or threatened instantly retiring for protection beneath the upper eyelid. Iris red. Jaws and palate armed with many rows of teeth. Lower jaw protruding beyond upper. Forehead furnished with a long and rigid filament or barbel, which, from its use as a bait for prey, has obtained for this family of fish the name of "anglers." The fins on the upper surface of the body are peculiarly arranged. The first (which I dare call a dorsal) is composed of one stout spinous ray, with a membrane attached and is placed in front of the summit of the head; the second is similarly formed, and situated immediately behind the head; the third occupies the posterior two-thirds of the back, and is composed of 12 branched rays. Rays of the anal fin 7; caudal 9.

The pectoral fins bear a very close resemblance to the anterior extremities of a frog or lizard, and the 10 distinct rays, at the termination of each, complete the comparison by their resemblance to toes. A long membranous air-tube, communicating with the gills, passes beneath the integuments of this fin, and opens as a circular orifice at its joint or elbow.

The solitary example of this species, which we obtained from the shores of Oahu, Sandwich Islands, continued alive for many hours after it had been removed from the water. During this time its abdomen and throat remained distended to a great size, but previous to death both air and water were evacuated from the mouth, and the body collapsed. Dissection proved that the cavity of the stomach was the part thus distended. The fish has no ribs, though it has a very distinct sternum. The swim-bladder is small and of ovoid form. (Bennett.)

We have one specimen from Honolulu which agrees closely with fig. C, plate 100, in Günther's "Fische der Südsee" regarded by him as a variety of *A. commersonii*. Our specimen is probably identical with Bleeker's *horridus* and appears to be Bennett's *Lophius sandvicensis*. It shows the following characters:

Eye very small, its diameter contained 3 times in length of maxillary; "bait" hair-like, its length equal to that of maxillary, reaching beyond base of second spine when depressed, the tip with a cluster of short filaments; first spine reaching base of second when depressed, surrounded by thickened tissue, the membrane extending from near tip of spine to base of second, very thin; second spine easily elevated, connected with occiput by a thick membrane, the spine surrounded by a large amount of tissue, its width equal to diameter of eye; spine when depressed not reaching soft dorsal; dorsal of the same height throughout, just reaching base of caudal when depressed; rays 12; anal reaching beyond base of caudal, its edge rounded; length of space between base of anal and caudal one-half that between base of dorsal and caudal; caudal rounded, its length 2.5 in length of body; anal opening at base of pectoral. Skin with very fine prickles, a few small cutaneous flaps on head, chin, and back.

Color in spirits, light gray, thickly mottled and spotted with dark gray; a few white-edged blackish spots on body and fins, located as follows: At base of second dorsal spine, origin of dorsal, between eighth and ninth dorsal rays, on side between origin of dorsal and base of pectoral, on side posterior to pectoral, on anal fin, on upper and on lower edge of caudal.

Known to us only from one specimen, which is 3.07 inches long.

432. Antennarius commersonii (Lacépède).

Head 3 in length; depth 1.7; eye 3.5 in snout; snout 2.5 in head; maxillary 1.25; width of mouth 1.5; D. I-I-12; A. 7; P. 10; V. 5.

Body deep, compressed, rather thick at pectoral region; head deep, profile above oblique, below convex; snout short, very broad, convex above; mouth very large, slightly oblique forward; mandible large, vertical, with small knob at symphysis, and lower portion slightly produced; teeth in jaws in bands, slender, sharp-pointed, depressible; teeth on palatines similar; tongue large, thick, fleshy; eye very small, high, anterior; nostrils close together, anterior with raised fleshy rim; interorbital space very broad, elevated, uneven; bait long, reaching middle of second spine; extremity of bait bifid, one portion a broad cutaneous flap, the other forming a bunch of fleshy tentacles; no pit on top of head; first dorsal spine united to top of head by a membrane, and depressible; second spine large, adnate to top of head; dorsal rather high, thick, margin between rays incised, length of base 2.25 in body, and last ray not adnate to caudal peduncle by membrane; anal rounded, its base half that of dorsal, and last ray adnate on lower portion with caudal peduncle; caudal rounded; pectoral very broad; ventral small, inserted below anterior part of second dorsal spine; caudal peduncle compressed, its depth half length of head; head with many mucous pores, those above marked more or less by excrescences;

lateral line superior and distinct at first till under second dorsal, then obsolete and running down toward anus; no cutaneous flaps.

Color in alcohol, deep blackish brown, the side marbled with a deeper color; a large blackish brown spot on basal portion of posterior dorsal rays, and a similar one on same portion of anal; several blackish spots on side; tips of caudal, anal, and outer portions of pectoral and ventral rays pale or whitish brown; a whitish spot above base of pectoral.

Described from an example (No. 2153) taken at Honolulu by Dr. Jenkins, which, with another obtained there by the *Albatross*, is the only example we have seen. The species is known by its very dark coloration, and is widely distributed in the tropical Pacific.

433. Antennarius leprosus (Eydoux & Souleyet). Fig. 228.

Head (to end of opercle) 2.8 in length; depth 1.7; eye 2.5 in snout; snout 3.5 in head; maxillary 1.8; width of mouth 1.8; interorbital 1.4; D. I–I–12; A. 6; P. 10; V. 6.

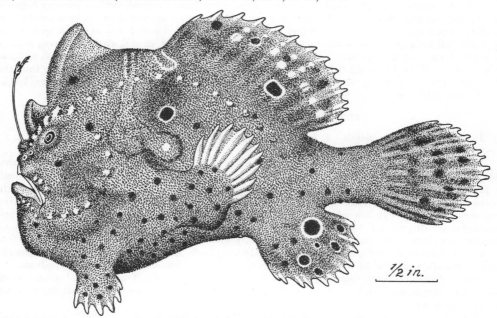

FIG. 228.—*Antennarius leprosus* (Eydoux & Souleyet).

Body very deep, compressed, back well elevated; head very deep, with bluntly conic profile in front and above; snout broad, surface uneven; mouth broad, maxillary very oblique, reaching well below posterior margin of eye; mandible large, with symphyseal knob, and projecting slightly; lips rather thin; teeth in broad bands in jaws, sharp pointed, more or less unequal in size, and depressible backwards; vomer and palatines with patches of sharp pointed small teeth; tongue large, broad, thick nostrils with elevated fleshy rims, rather close together near end of snout; interorbital space broad, elevated; bait reaching to middle of second spine, bifid and rather broad at extremity; first spine large, very rough, adnate by membrane, 2.6 in head; second spine larger, similar, 1.75; eighth dorsal ray 1.5; anal rounded, third ray 1.7; caudal rounded, median rays longest, about 1.2; pectoral broad, upper median rays longest, fourth 2; ventrals small, rounded; caudal peduncle compressed, its depth 2.35; pores on head and upper side of back with rough excrescences, those which form lateral line running back below posterior part of soft dorsal, then obliterated; skin rather rough velvety, fins also rough.

Color in alcohol (No. 554) grayish brown, more or less marbled with dusky; a ragged brown blotch from between second dorsal spine and soft dorsal and a pale ocellus above pectoral; margin of vertical fins whitish, submarginal portions mottled with white, black, and gray; a large black ocellus on basal portion of posterior dorsal and anal rays; a black ocellus above base of pectoral; belly and lower side spotted all over with black.

Described from an example (No. 554) taken at Honolulu. We have examined also 1 specimen 5.1 inches long collected by Doctor Jenkins at Honolulu, where the *Albatross* obtained yet another example.

434. Antennarius laysanius Jordan & Snyder. Plate 63.

Mouth large, the width equal to length of maxillary, 4.5 times diameter of eye; "bait" long and slender, reaching middle of second spine when depressed, the tip with a small knob bearing filaments, one of which is lanceolate, seven-eighths the length of rod, the others short and thread-like. First spine inserted above anterior edge of orbit, reaching base of second spine when depressed, connected posteriorly with head by a thin membrane, the free edge of which is convex, the tip of spine with a movable joint; second spine equal in length to maxillary, immovably and closely attached throughout its length to the occiput and back, the tip with a small, movable joint; soft dorsal not connected with second spine by a membrane or crest, separated from the caudal by a space equal in length to 2.5 times diameter of eye, the last rays when depressed not reaching base of caudal; rays 12, the longest (posterior) equal in length to distance between base of bait and tip of first spine when depressed; posterior margin of fin rounded; anal when depressed reaching base of caudal, rays 7, about equal in length to those of dorsal; caudal rounded; gill-opening at base of pectoral.

Skin hispid with minute, simple, and bilobed prickles; upper half of eye covered with thick prickly skin; minute, filamentous, dermal appendages scattered about over the sides and back, especially prominent below dorsal spines and fin, none on ventral surface.

Color in spirits, yellowish white, densely clouded with dusky; a small ocellus midway between base of pectoral and origin of soft dorsal, many small black spots scattered about on breast and belly, an oblong black spot half as large as eye on posterior half of soft dorsal, a row of black spots along edge of dorsal fin, a large one on base of anal and 2 near border of fin, caudal with a few spots as large as pupil; dorsal, caudal, and anal narrowly edged with white; pectorals white below, dusky above; chin dusky, with an indistinct light ocellus; tongue with small black spots. Known only from the type (No. 8439, Stanford University Museum), a specimen 3.8 inches long collected at Laysan Island by Mr. Max Schlemmer.

435. Antennarius bigibbus (Lacépède)

Head 2.25 in length; depth 1.5; eye 4 in head; snout 5; maxillary 2.2; width of mouth 2.2; D. I-I-12; A. 7; P. 11; V. 5.

Body deep, compressed, back elevated; head deep, with blunt conic profile in front, somewhat oblique above; snout broad, obtuse, conic, smooth; mouth broad, very oblique, nearly vertical; teeth in jaws small, sharp pointed; lips rather thin; mandible large, slightly projecting; eye small, high, anterior; nostrils circular, close together, with rounded fleshy rims; side of snout with a convex groove running from eye toward tip; top of head with groove, the anterior dorsal spine free and depressible within; second dorsal spine not depressible, very robust, and forming a large hump on back in front; bait longer than first spine, apparently with undivided filament at extremity and not reaching to base of second spine; dorsal rays moderately high, base of fin 1.7 in trunk, and last ray adnate to caudal peduncle by membrane; anal rounded, lower portion adnate to caudal peduncle by membrane; caudal elongate, rounded; pectoral broad; ventral small, about under end of second dorsal spine; body rough, pores on head and in lateral line with rough excrescences; no dermal flaps; lateral line curving down to front of anal fin.

Color in alcohol, pale creamy, or creamy white, the sides marbled with brown; fins more or less pale; caudal with a dark brown submarginal cross-line and two similar lines close together across middle of fin; anal with a submarginal brown longitudinal line, a similar median dark brown longitudinal band; pectoral and ventral with brown margins and base narrowly of same color.

Described from an example taken by Doctor Jenkins, at Honolulu. Four others were taken by him, 1 by us, and 3 by the *Albatross*. These are 1 to 1.25 inches long.

436. Antennarius drombus Jordan & Evermann. Plate 64.

Head (to end of opercle) 2.5 in length; depth 1.75; eye 5 in head; snout 4; width of mouth 2; D. I-I-12; A. 7; P. 12; V. 5.

Body very deep, compressed, back elevated; head deep, with blunt conic profile in front, somewhat oblique above; snout broad, obtuse, surface uneven; mouth broad, large, nearly vertical; maxillary concealed under skin, reaching below anterior part of eye; lips fleshy; teeth in jaws minute, in narrow bands; teeth on palatines rather large, sharp-pointed, none on vomer; tongue broad, thick; mandible large, with fleshy knob at symphysis, projecting; nostrils circular, well separated, with rounded fleshy rims; interorbital space convex, roughened; top of head with rather large concave pit; eye high, anterior; bait rather short, only reaching a little beyond first spine, with fleshy caruncle at extremity; dorsal spines short, first free, rough, depressible in pit on top of head; second dorsal spine twice length of first, equal to width of mouth, depressible, and united with skin of back to its tip; posterior dorsal rays longest, and the last, like that of anal, united to caudal peduncle by a membrane; anal similar, rounded, elongate, 1.5 in head; pectoral broad; ventral small, rounded; caudal peduncle small, compressed, its depth equal to interorbital space; body rather rough, mucous pores on head and in lateral line with excrescences; side of body with many pointed cutaneous flaps; second dorsal spine and first dorsal ray very rough, also with cutaneous flaps; lateral line very convex, running down toward middle of base of anal.

Color in alcohol, pale plumbeous gray, more or less spotted or mottled with darker; belly and lower surface rather pale, the spots distinct; fins all more or less pale with dark spots, some at basal portions of dorsal and anal darker; iris blackish with radiating lines of golden.

The above description is from the type, No. 50659, U. S. N. M. (field No. 541), taken at Waikiki, near Honolulu.

Another example (field No. 539) shows some differences: Head (to end of opercle) 2.5 in length; depth 1.7; eye 3 in head; maxillary 1.8; width of mouth 1.7; interorbital 3.7; D. i–i–12; A. 7; P. 12; V. 5.

Body very deep, compressed, back elevated; head deep, gibbous, with blunt conic profile in front, somewhat oblique above; snout broad, obtuse, short, surface uneven; mouth large, obliquely vertical; maxillary large, reaching a little beyond front portion of eye; lips fleshy; teeth in jaws minute, sharp, in bands; teeth on roof of mouth large, sharp-pointed; tongue large, broad, thick; mandible large, with knob at symphysis, projecting; nostrils well separated, close to end of snout, each with elevated fleshy rims, the anterior higher; interorbital space broad, elevated, uneven; top of head with rather large pit; eye high, anterior; bait short, reaching tip of first dorsal spine, with caruncle at extremity; dorsal spines short, depressible; first dorsal spine half length of second, free, depressible in pit on top of head; second dorsal spine large, joined by skin to its tip; dorsal rays of about equal height, seventh 1.3 in head, and the last, like lower portion of last anal ray, adnate to caudal peduncle by a membrane; anal rounded; caudal elongate, rounded; pectoral broad; ventral small; body rather rough, mucous pores on head and lateral line with excrescences; many cutaneous flaps along the lateral line and anterior region of dorsal; lateral line convex, running down to above middle of anal.

Color in alcohol, dark gray-brown; edges of vertical fins whitish, the pale border rather broad and very distinct along posterior, dorsal, anal, and caudal rays; side with about 6 large round blackish spots; caudal with some pale or indistinct mottlings; pectoral and ventral with rather broad margins, median portion dusky; iris more or less silvery.

A. drombus seems most nearly related to *A. nummifer* Cuvier & Valenciennes, originally described from Malabar. Probably the specimens from the South Seas referred to the latter belong rather to *A. drombus*. *A. nummifer* is said to be red in color with dark spots, and, as figured by Doctor Day, differs in several respects from *A. drombus*. Both these species differ from *A. commersonii* and its numerous allies or variants (*A. niger*, *A. leprosus*, *A. rubrofuscus*, and *A. sandvicensis* from Hawaii) in the shortness of the first dorsal spine or fishing rod. This is scarcely longer than the second spine in *A. drombus*, but in *A. commersonii* it is twice as long.

Our collections contain but 2 examples of this species, the type, No. 50659, U. S. N. M. (field No. 541), and cotype, No. 7472, Stanford Univ. Mus. (field No. 539), both taken on the reef at Waikiki, near Honolulu. This species is also known from Samoa, where it was obtained by Jordan and Kellogg.

437. Antennarius duescus Snyder.   Plate 65, fig. 2.

Head, body, and fins, except the edges of the latter, covered with bifid and trifid prickles; small dermal filaments scattered here and there, a conspicuous one, somewhat longer than diameter of eye, above and a little behind base of pectoral; gill-opening small, circular, located far back, half way between axil of pectoral and anal opening; "bait" slender and hair-like, the length equal to depth of caudal peduncle, the fleshy tip a flat, folded membrane with minute tentacles; first dorsal spine seated close to "bait," slender, without a membrane, its shaft covered with minute granules, the tip with a small, fleshy knob, slightly shorter than the "bait," not quite reaching base of second when depressed; second spine strong, curved backward, its length equal to distance between gill-opening and anus, capable of free movement up to a vertical position, the posterior membrane fleshy; dorsal rays 12, the highest contained 3 times in base of fin; fin extending far posteriorly, the length of the free caudal peduncle equal to diameter of pupil; anal rays 7, equal in length to those of the dorsal; caudal rounded posteriorly, its length contained 3.5 times in head and body.

Color in spirits, pale brick red, the dorsal, anal, and caudal darker on the edges; rayed portion of pectorals and ventrals gray below, dusky above; head and body sparsely clouded and spotted with dusky and gray; a large, irregular crossband on chin, extending upward a little beyond mouth; a dusky cloud above pectoral; a large, gray spot, bordered with dusky, on the head between snout and pectoral; a small, ocellated gray spot below the latter, and a similar one on body midway between gill-opening and dorsal fin; caudal peduncle with a narrow, vertical, gray band bordered with dusky; mouth immaculate within; prickles white.

In life, purplish lilac throughout (the color of the algæ brought up in the trawl), save for a few pinkish spots and the tips of pectorals and ventrals, which were whitish.

Described from type, No. 50884, U. S. Nat. Mus., 1.8 inches long. A smaller specimen, 0.75 of an inch long, cotype, No. 7736, Stanford Univ. Mus., differs from type only in size; in life it was light bronze colored on upper parts, yellowish bronze below, a wide pinkish crescent on upper part of opercles. Station 3872, between Maui and Lanai, depth 32 to 43 fathoms. Another specimen, 0.75 of an inch long, is from station 4128, vicinity of Kauai, depth 75 fathoms; the body is brownish black except on the nape, where there is a small cloud of reddish color; fins narrowly edged with red.

The species is distinguished by the following set of characters: First and second dorsal spines with thickened fleshy tips; dorsal and anal extending far posteriorly, length of free caudal peduncle equal to diameter of pupil; gill-opening located midway between axil of pectoral and the anal opening.

438. Antennarius nexilis Snyder. Plate 65, fig. 1.

"Bait" short, equal in length to longitudinal diameter of eye, the fleshy tentacle half as long as the rod, with 7 filaments. First spine curved backward, its length equal to 1.5 times the longitudinal diameter of eye; when depressed, the tip not reaching over half way between its base and the base of second spine, no membrane connecting posterior part of spine with the head; second dorsal spine equal in length to distance between its base and tip of snout, very closely bound down throughout its length to the back, the tip with a movable joint; soft dorsal with 12 rays, the middle ones equal in height to distance between tip of snout and base of third spine; fin extending posteriorly to bases of caudal rays; anal rays 7, equal in length to the dorsal rays; edge of fin rounded, extending posteriorly as far as the dorsal; caudal rounded posteriorly, 3.5 in the length; pectoral rays 12.

Body and fins covered with granules and prickles, the latter usually bifid or trifid, many of them having fleshy tentacles; a lateral line of pores begins on snout, passes over eye, curves downward to a level with lower margin of eye, extends backward to a point below base of second or third dorsal ray, then bends downward and backward to a point above the origin of anal, from which it runs backward to lower edge of base of caudal; another line of conspicuous pores extends from the chin downward, curving far below the mouth, then upward, joining the lateral line behind the eye; other large pores are present on the chin and head.

Color gray, with duksy spots and clouds, large and close together on the dorsal parts of body; eye with radiating dark and light elongate spots; a large, irregular, reddish orange spot on the nape; a few small spots of same color on snout and face; fins closely covered with black spots a little larger than the pupil, the membranes of the fins near their edges white; pectorals and ventrals white and almost without spots on ventral sides; inside of mouth without dark color.

The description is from the type, No. 50883, U. S. Nat. Mus., taken at Honolulu. In another example, cotype, 7735, Stanford Univ. Mus., the upper parts of the head and body are almost covered with reddish clouds, the tint more intense anteriorly   First spine 1.33 times as long as diameter of eye.

Genus 266. CHAUNAX Lowe.

Head very large, depressed cuboid; mouth large, subvertical, jaws and palate with bands of small teeth; skin with small, sharp spines; spinous dorsal reduced to a small tentacle above the snout, retractile into a groove; soft dorsal moderate, low; anal short; ventrals small; gills 2½; no pseudobranchiæ; muciferous channels very conspicuous; lateral line prominent, undulate; another series of mucuous tubes extending from lower jaws to axil, and still another backward from snout and maxillary to a point behind eye, where it ceases, uniting with a vertical line which extends from the lateral line to the lower line; these lines thus inclose a quadrate area on the cheek; gill-openings small, well behind pectoral under front of soft dorsal.

The single Hawaiian species of this genus is fully described in Section II.

Family CVIII. CERATIIDÆ.—The Sea-Devils.

Head and body compressed; mouth terminal, more or less oblique; gill-openings small, in the lower part of the axils; no pseudobranchiæ; spinous dorsal represented by one or more tentacles; pectoral members not geniculated, with short pseudobrachia and 3 actinosts; no ventral fins; fishes of the open seas, usually inhabiting considerable depths; uniform blackish in color.

The single Hawaiian genus and species of this family are fully described in Section II.

Family CIX. OGCOCEPHALIDÆ.—The Bat-Fishes.

Head very broad and depressed, the snout more or less elevated, the trunk short and slender. Mouth not large, subterminal or inferior, the lower jaw included; teeth villiform or cardiform. Gill-openings very small, above and behind the axils of the pectoral fins. Body and head covered with bony tubercles or spines. Spinous dorsal reduced to a small rostral tentacle, which is retractile into a cavity under a prominent process on the forehead; in one genus the rostral tentacle is obsolete; soft dorsal and anal fins small and short; ventrals well developed; pectoral fins well developed, the base strongly angled, with long pseudobrachia and 3 actinosts. Branchiostegals 5, no pseudobranchiæ.

Genus 267. MALTHOPSIS Alcock.

Resembling *Ogcocephalus*, but having only 2 gills on each side instead of 2.5.   (Goode & Bean.)

439. Malthopsis mitriger Gilbert & Cramer.   Fig. 229.

Branchiostegals 4; D. 1, 4 or 5; A. 4; P. 14; V. 1, 5; pores of lateral line behind disk 9.
Disk strongly depressed, triangular, its greatest width (exclusive of the posterior lateral projec-

tions) 1.66 in length of body exclusive of caudal, its depth about 4; body behind disk tapering nearly uniformly; body nearly everywhere covered with radially striated tubercular plates; gular region and

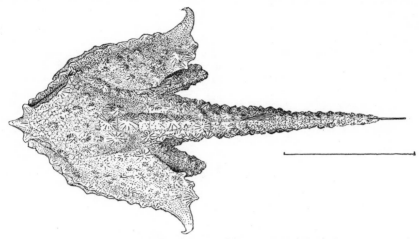

FIG. 229.—*Malthopsis mitriger* Gilbert & Cramer; from the type.

branchiostegal membranes naked; vent in center of a naked, somewhat elliptical basin surrounded by a ridge of tubercles; a shallow pit behind base of ventrals; head vertical in front; the tentacular pit triangular, higher than wide, its upper angle on level with upper edge of pupil, the pit surmounted by a large conical median tubercle projecting upward and slightly forward, the length about 2 in orbit; at each side of this tubercle a smaller one projecting upward and outward; the club-shaped tentacle when extended not quite reaching front of upper jaw; eyes large, the orbits strongly convergent, distance between their anterior edges 2.5 in distance between their posterior edges; mouth somewhat oblique; bands of very minute teeth on jaws, vomer, and palatines; width of mouth and diameter of orbit about equal; gills 2 on each side, only a narrow membrane on first arch; gillrakers minute; subopercular spine flat, long, extending laterally and armed at tip with 2 to 5 small spinelets; pectoral about 4.5 in length of body, the rays very close-set; ventrals about 7 and caudal 6 in length of body; vertical fins weak. Color in alcohol, body and all the fins pale yellowish; peritoneum dusky. In water of moderate depths about the Hawaiian Islands.

Genus 268. HALIEUTÆA Cuvier & Valenciennes.

Head very large, broad, depressed, its outline nearly circular; cleft of mouth wide, horizontal; jaws with small cardiform teeth; no teeth on vomer or palatines; skin everywhere covered with small stellate spines; forehead with a transverse bony ridge, beneath which is a tentacle, retractile into a cavity, the only rudiment of the spinous dorsal fin; soft dorsal and anal very short, far back; gills 2½, the anterior gill-arch without laminæ. Branchiostegals 5; vertebræ 17. Pacific Ocean.

The single Hawaiian species of this genus is fully described in Section II.

Genus 269. DIBRANCHUS Peters.

Head merged in body, very large, much depressed, forming a broadly ovate disk, with margin laterally prolonged; cranial portion not elevated; the interorbital area low, narrow, with orbits partly superior; supraoral cavity large, protected above by a transverse bony ridge; mouth terminal, horizontal, wide; lower jaw convex; teeth in cardiform bands, none on vomer or palatines; gills 2, no gillrakers, gill-openings small, anterior to pectorals; rostral tentacle retractile, trilobate at tip; skin with numerous strong stellate spines above and below, those at margins of disk especially strong, 3-pointed. Distinguished from related genera by the reduction of the gills to 2 pairs.

The 2 Hawaiian species of this genus are fully described in Section II.

INDEX TO NATIVE NAMES OF HAWAIIAN FISHES.

The popular or common names by which the fishes of Hawaii are known to the fishermen are naturally the native Kanaka or Hawaiian names. Very few English or other common names have as yet come into use. The total number of names in actual use is far fewer than the number of species, due to the fact that many of the names are generic in their application, the same name being applied to several different species.

In the following index are given all those native names which we have been able to identify certainly with definite species. Following each native name is the scientific name of the species to which it is applied. The list serves, therefore, not only as an index to the common names used in the body of this report, but also as a table for the determination of the equivalent scientific name.

For the verification of the spelling of these native names we are greatly indebted to Lieut. William E. Safford, of the Bureau of Plant Industry, U. S. Department of Agriculture. Mr. Safford's cruises in the Pacific and residence in Guam gave him a familiarity with Polynesian languages which has enabled him to give us very valuable assistance in connection with this list.

COLOR PLATES

NOTE: Page numbers refer to descriptions in the text.

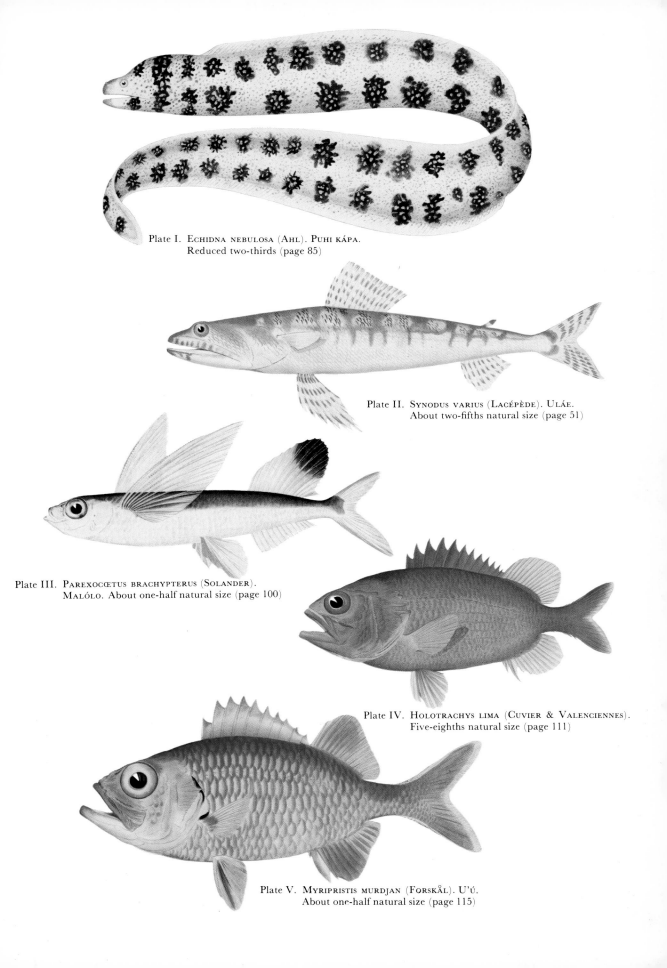

Plate I. Echidna nebulosa (Ahl). Puhi kápa.
Reduced two-thirds (page 85)

Plate II. Synodus varius (Lacépède). Uláe.
About two-fifths natural size (page 51)

Plate III. Parexocœtus brachypterus (Solander).
Malólo. About one-half natural size (page 100)

Plate IV. Holotrachys lima (Cuvier & Valenciennes).
Five-eighths natural size (page 111)

Plate V. Myripristis murdjan (Forskål). U'ú.
About one-half natural size (page 115)

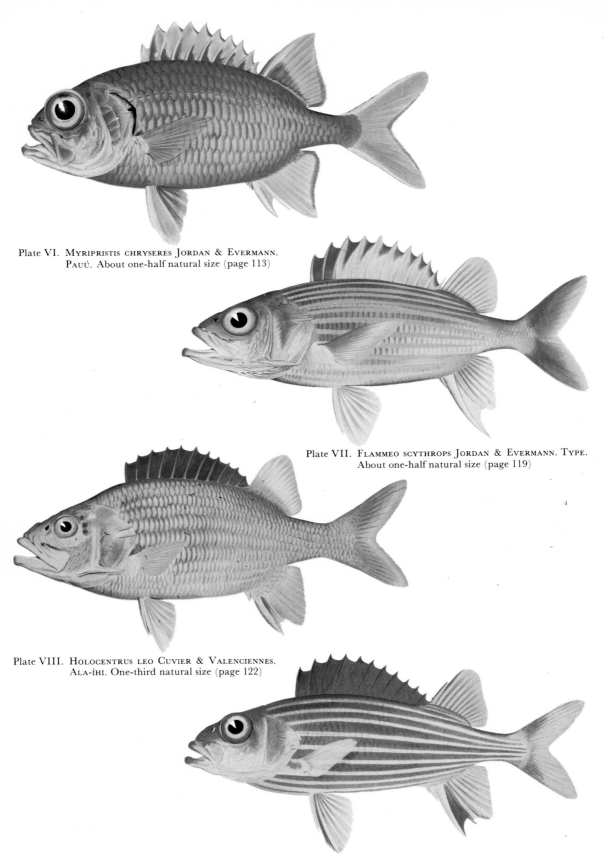

Plate VI. MYRIPRISTIS CHRYSERES JORDAN & EVERMANN.
PAUÚ. About one-half natural size (page 113)

Plate VII. FLAMMEO SCYTHROPS JORDAN & EVERMANN. TYPE.
About one-half natural size (page 119)

Plate VIII. HOLOCENTRUS LEO CUVIER & VALENCIENNES.
ALA-ÍHI. One-third natural size (page 122)

Plate IX. HOLOCENTRUS XANTHERYTHRUS JORDAN & EVERMANN. TYPE. ALA-ÍHI.
About five-eighths natural size (page 124)

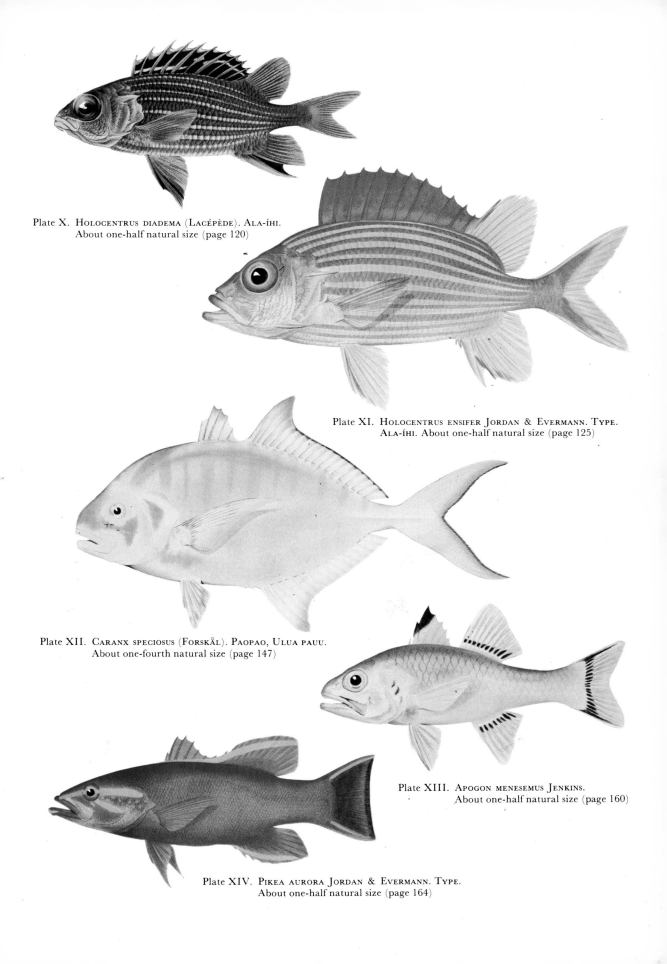

Plate X. Holocentrus diadema (Lacépède). Ala-íhi.
About one-half natural size (page 120)

Plate XI. Holocentrus ensifer Jordan & Evermann. Type.
Ala-íhi. About one-half natural size (page 125)

Plate XII. Caranx speciosus (Forskål). Paopao, Ulua pauu.
About one-fourth natural size (page 147)

Plate XIII. Apogon menesemus Jenkins.
About one-half natural size (page 160)

Plate XIV. Pikea aurora Jordan & Evermann. Type.
About one-half natural size (page 164)

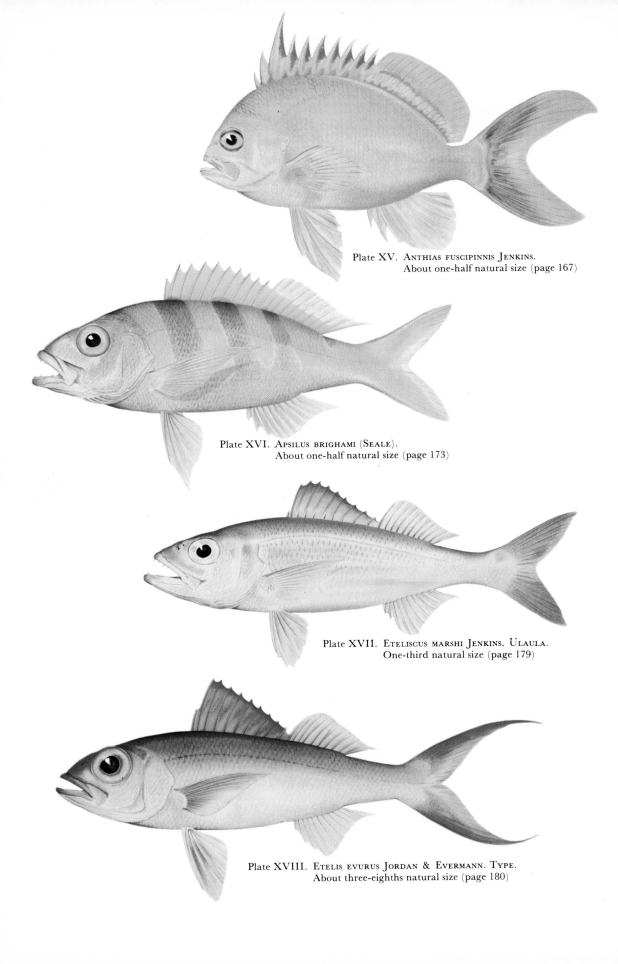

Plate XV. Anthias fuscipinnis Jenkins.
About one-half natural size (page 167)

Plate XVI. Apsilus brighami (Seale).
About one-half natural size (page 173)

Plate XVII. Eteliscus marshi Jenkins. Ulaula.
One-third natural size (page 179)

Plate XVIII. Etelis evurus Jordan & Evermann. Type.
About three-eighths natural size (page 180)

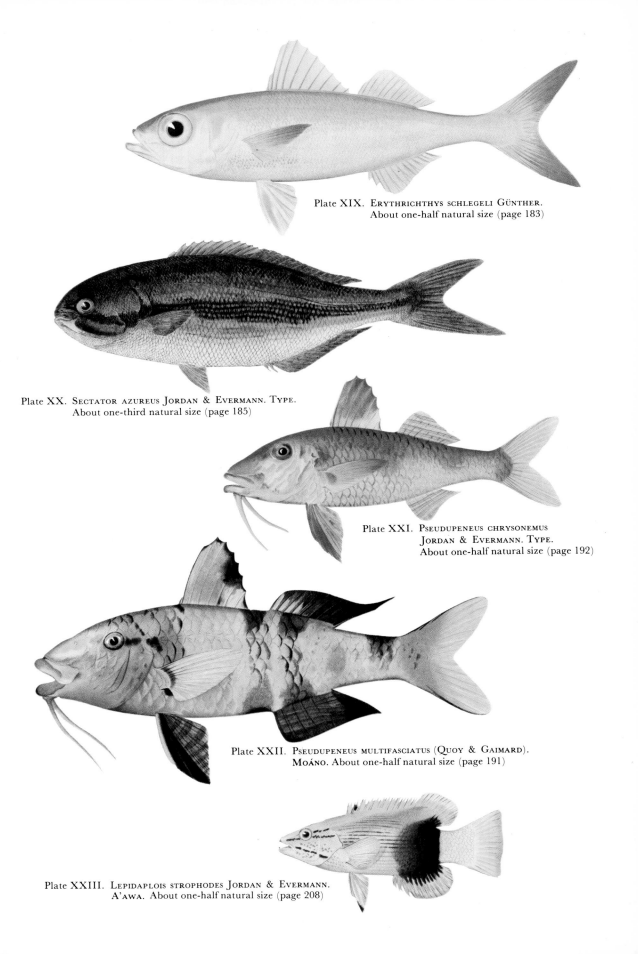

Plate XIX. Erythrichthys schlegeli Günther.
About one-half natural size (page 183)

Plate XX. Sectator azureus Jordan & Evermann. Type.
About one-third natural size (page 185)

Plate XXI. Pseudupeneus chrysonemus
Jordan & Evermann. Type.
About one-half natural size (page 192)

Plate XXII. Pseudupeneus multifasciatus (Quoy & Gaimard).
Moáno. About one-half natural size (page 191)

Plate XXIII. Lepidaplois strophodes Jordan & Evermann.
A'awa. About one-half natural size (page 208)

Plate XXIV. Lepidaplois bilunulatus (Lacépède). A'awa.
About one-half natural size (page 206)

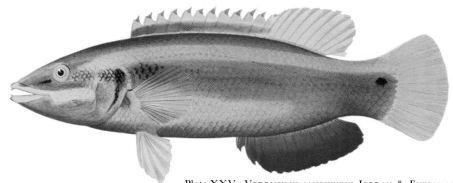

Plate XXV. Verriculus sanguineus Jordan & Evermann.
Type. About three-fifths natural size (page 209)

Plate XXVI. Stethojulis albovittata (Kölreuter).
Natural size (page 211)

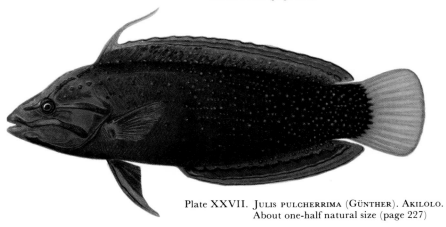

Plate XXVII. Julis pulcherrima (Günther). Akilolo.
About one-half natural size (page 227)

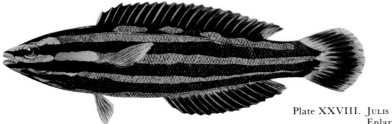

Plate XXVIII. Julis flavovittata Bennett.
Enlarged about five-sixths (page 229)

Plate XXIX. Julis eydouxi Cuvier & Valenciennes.
About two-fifths natural size (page 230)

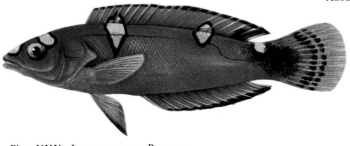

Plate XXX. Julis greenovii Bennett.
Natural size (page 229)

Plate XXXI. Hemicoris venusta Vaillant & Sauvage.
About one-half natural size (page 232)

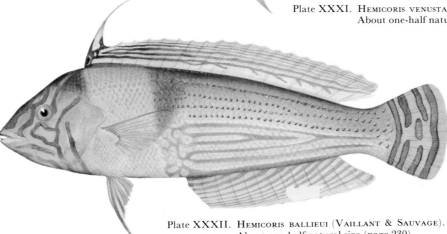

Plate XXXII. Hemicoris ballieui (Vaillant & Sauvage).
About one-half natural size (page 230)

Plate XXXIII. Cheilio inermis (Forskål). Ku-pou-pou.
About one-half natural size (page 234)

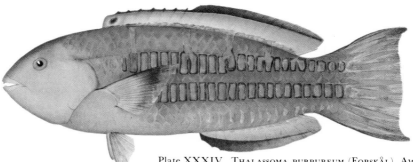

Plate XXXIV. Thalassoma purpureum (Forskål). Awela.
About one-half natural size (page 222)

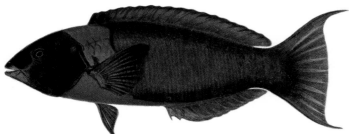

Plate XXXV. Thalassoma duperrey (Quoy & Gaimard).
Hinalea lauli. About one-half natural size.
(page 224)

Plate XXXVI. Gomphosus tricolor Quoy & Gaimard.
Three-eighths natural size (page 216)

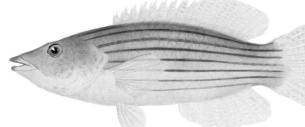

Plate XXXVII. Pseudocheilinus octotænia Jenkins.
About three-fourths natural size (page 236)

Plate XXXVIII. Cheilinus bimaculatus .
Cuvier & Valenciennes. (page 238)

Plate XXXIX. Hemipteronotus baldwini Jordan & Evermann.
Type. Lae-níhi. About one-half natural size
(page 248)

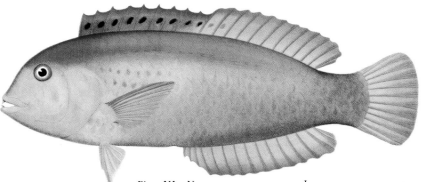

Plate XL. Novaculichthys woodi Jenkins.
About seven-tenths natural size (page 239)

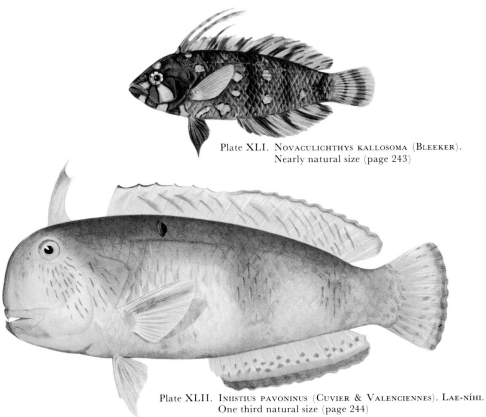

Plate XLI. Novaculichthys kallosoma (Bleeker).
Nearly natural size (page 243)

Plate XLII. Iniistius pavoninus (Cuvier & Valenciennes). Lae-níhi.
One third natural size (page 244)

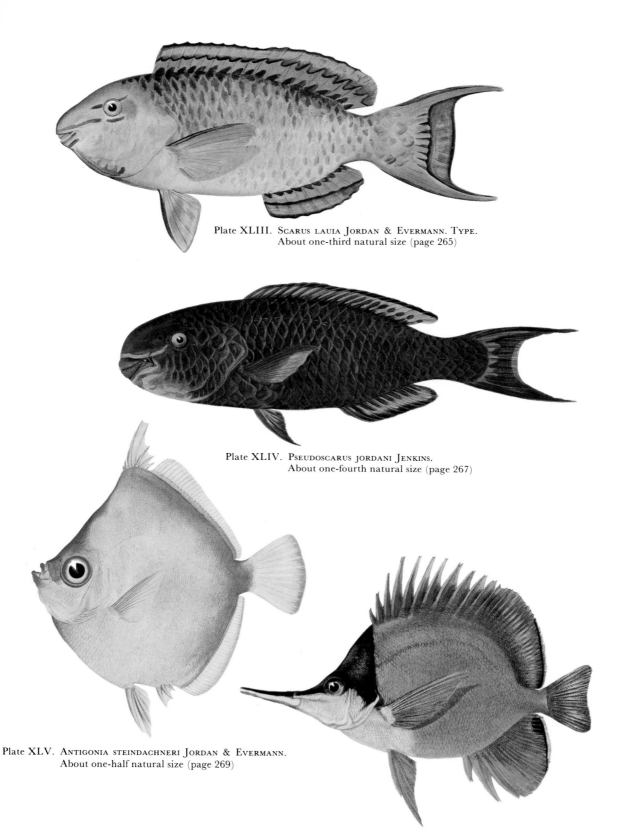

Plate XLIII. Scarus lauia Jordan & Evermann. Type.
About one-third natural size (page 265)

Plate XLIV. Pseudoscarus jordani Jenkins.
About one-fourth natural size (page 267)

Plate XLV. Antigonia steindachneri Jordan & Evermann.
About one-half natural size (page 269)

Plate XLVI. Forcipiger longirostris (Broussonet).
About two-thirds natural size (page 270)

Plate XLVII. Chætodon setifer Bloch.
About one-half natural size (page 271)

Plate XLVIII. Chætodon miliaris Quoy & Gaimard.
About one-half natural size (page 276)

Plate XLIX. Chætodon quadrimaculatus Gray.
About one-half natural size (page 278)

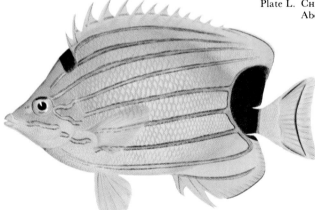

Plate L. Chætodon unimaculatus Bloch.
About one-half natural size (page 274)

Plate LI. Chætodon fremblii Bennett.
About one-half natural size (page 279)

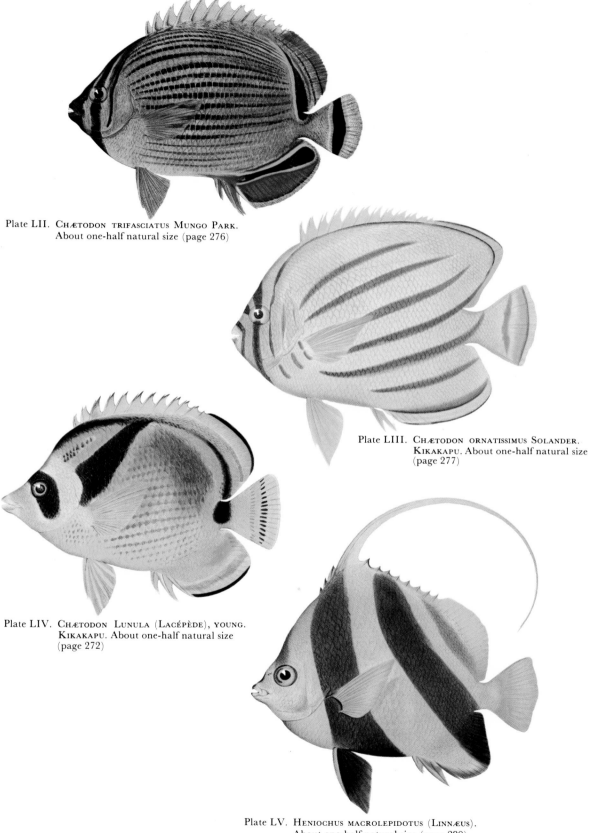

Plate LII. Chætodon trifasciatus Mungo Park.
About one-half natural size (page 276)

Plate LIII. Chætodon ornatissimus Solander.
Kikakapu. About one-half natural size
(page 277)

Plate LIV. Chætodon Lunula (Lacépède), young.
Kikakapu. About one-half natural size
(page 272)

Plate LV. Heniochus macrolepidotus (Linnæus).
About one-half natural size (page 280)

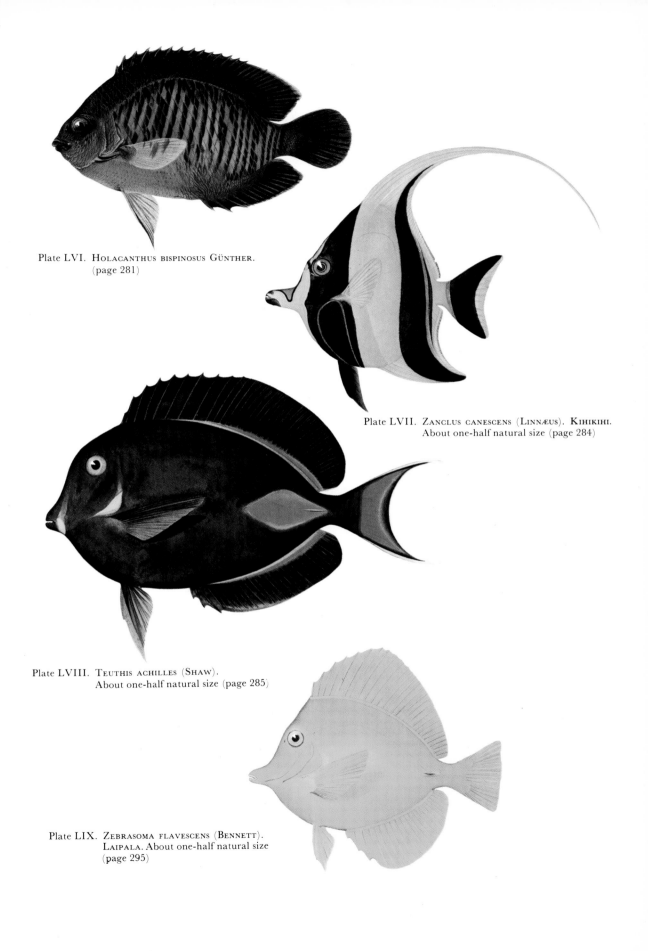

Plate LVI. Holacanthus bispinosus Günther.
(page 281)

Plate LVII. Zanclus canescens (Linnæus). Kihikihi.
About one-half natural size (page 284)

Plate LVIII. Teuthis achilles (Shaw).
About one-half natural size (page 285)

Plate LIX. Zebrasoma flavescens (Bennett).
Laipala. About one-half natural size
(page 295)

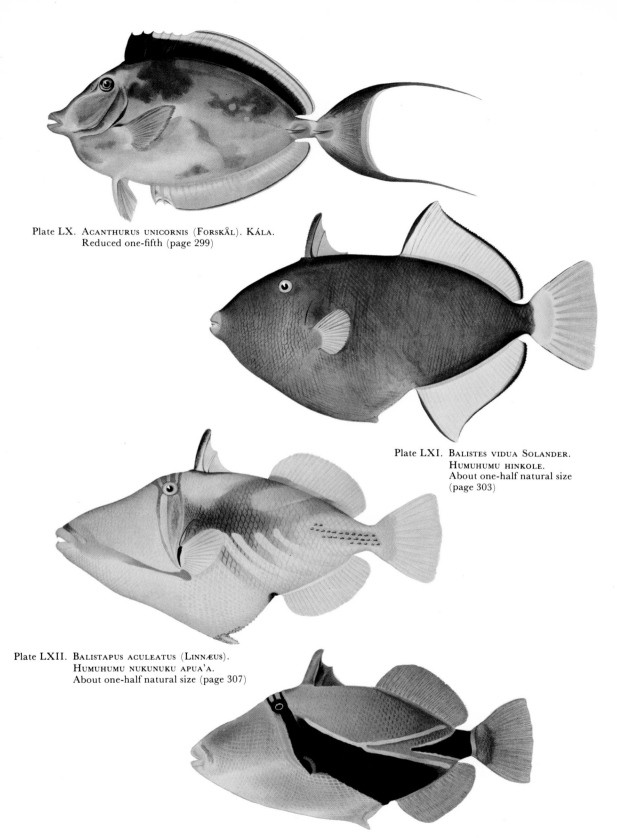

Plate LX. Acanthurus unicornis (Forskål). Kála.
Reduced one-fifth (page 299)

Plate LXI. Balistes vidua Solander.
Humuhumu hinkole.
About one-half natural size
(page 303)

Plate LXII. Balistapus aculeatus (Linnæus).
Humuhumu nukunuku apua'a.
About one-half natural size (page 307)

Plate LXIII. Balistapus rectangulus (Bloch & Schneider).
Humuhumu nukunuku apua'a.
About one-half natural size (page 306)

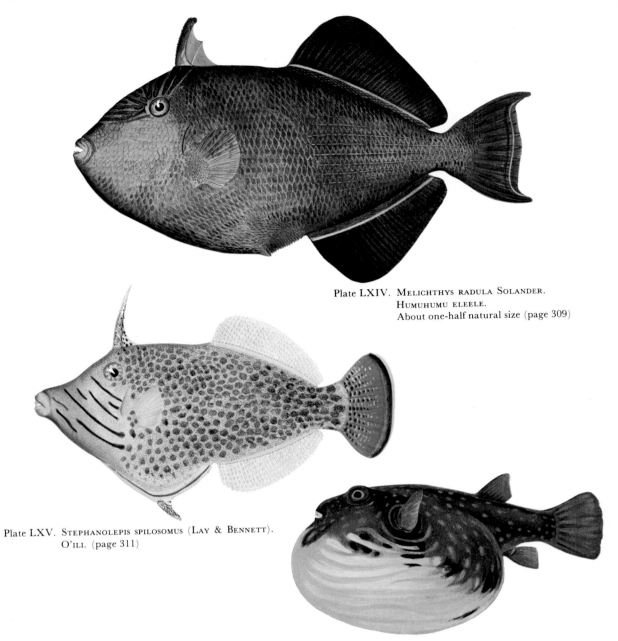

Plate LXIV. MELICHTHYS RADULA SOLANDER.
HUMUHUMU ELEELE.
About one-half natural size (page 309)

Plate LXV. STEPHANOLEPIS SPILOSOMUS (LAY & BENNETT).
O'ILI. (page 311)

Plate LXVI. TETRAODON HISPIDUS LINNÆUS. MAKI-MAKI; OOPUHUE.
About one-half natural size (page 315)

Plate LXVII. PARACIRRHITES FORSTERI (BLOCH & SCHNEIDER).
HILUPILIKOA. (page 332)

Plate LXVIII. Paracirrhites cinctus (Günther).
Pilikoa; Oopuka-hai-hai.
About one-half natural size (page 331)

Plate LXIX. Paracirrhites arcatus
(Cuvier & Valenciennes).
About one-half natural size
(page 333)

Plate LXX. Cirrhitus marmoratus (Lacépède).
Oopupoopaa; Oapukai. (page 334)

Plate LXXI. Scorpænopsis cacopsis Jenkins.
About two-fifths natural size (page 345)

Plate LXXII. Sebastapistes ballieui
(Vaillant & Sauvage).
(page 336)

Plate LXXIII. Dendrochirus hudsoni
Jordan & Evermann. Type.
About natural size (page 343)

BLACK AND WHITE PLATES

NOTE: Page numbers refer to descriptions in the text.

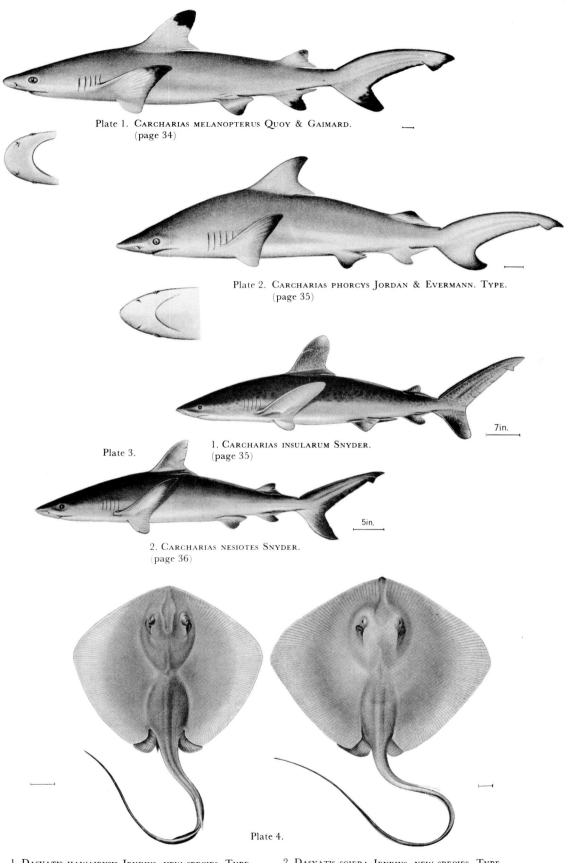

Plate 1. CARCHARIAS MELANOPTERUS QUOY & GAIMARD.
(page 34)

Plate 2. CARCHARIAS PHORCYS JORDAN & EVERMANN. TYPE.
(page 35)

Plate 3.

1. CARCHARIAS INSULARUM SNYDER.
(page 35)

7in.

2. CARCHARIAS NESIOTES SNYDER.
(page 36)

5in.

Plate 4.

1. DASYATIS HAWAIENSIS JENKINS, NEW SPECIES. TYPE.
(page 41)

2. DASYATIS SCIERA JENKINS, NEW SPECIES. TYPE.
(page 40)

Plate 5.

1. Veternio verrens Snyder.
(page 62)

2. Sphagebranchus flavicaudus Snyder.
(page 63)

Plate 6. Microdonophis fowleri Jordan & Evermann. Type.
(page 64)

Plate 7. Brachysomophis henshawi Jordan & Snyder. Type.
(page 65)

Plate 8.

1. Callechelys luteus Snyder.
(page 67)

2. Moringua hawaiiensis Snyder.
(page 68)

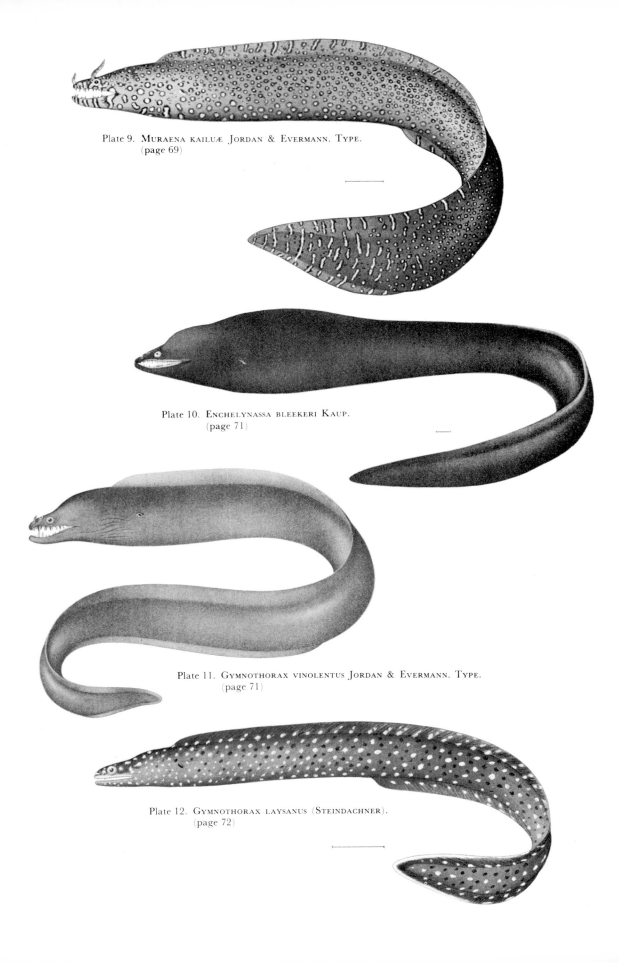

Plate 9. MURAENA KAILUÆ JORDAN & EVERMANN. TYPE.
   (page 69)

Plate 10. ENCHELYNASSA BLEEKERI KAUP.
   (page 71)

Plate 11. GYMNOTHORAX VINOLENTUS JORDAN & EVERMANN. TYPE.
   (page 71)

Plate 12. GYMNOTHORAX LAYSANUS (STEINDACHNER).
   (page 72)

1. Gymnothorax waialuae Snyder.
(page 75)

Plate 13.

2. Uropterygius leucurus Snyder.
(page 86)

1. Gymnothorax mucifer Snyder.
(page 76)

Plate 14.

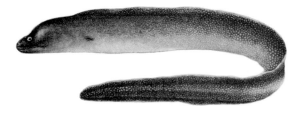

2. Gymnothorax xanthostomus Snyder.
(page 81)

1. Gymnothorax nuttingi Snyder.
(page 80)

Plate 15.

2. Gymnothorax berndti Snyder.
(page 76)

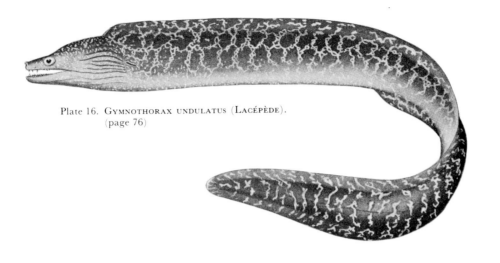

Plate 16. GYMNOTHORAX UNDULATUS (LACÉPÈDE).
(page 76)

Plate 17. GYMNOTHORAX FLAVIMARGINATUS (RÜPPELL). TYPE OF G.
THALASSOPTERUS JENKINS. (page 77)

Plate 18. GYMNOTHORAX HILONIS JORDAN & EVERMANN. TYPE.
(page 79)

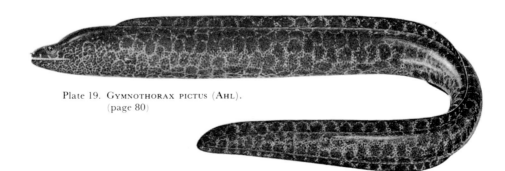

Plate 19. GYMNOTHORAX PICTUS (AHL).
(page 80)

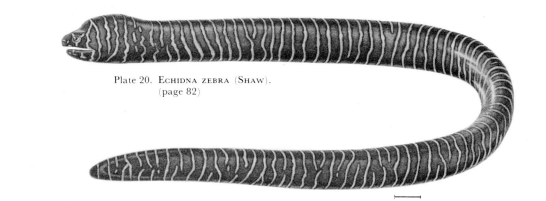

Plate 20. Echidna zebra (Shaw).
(page 82)

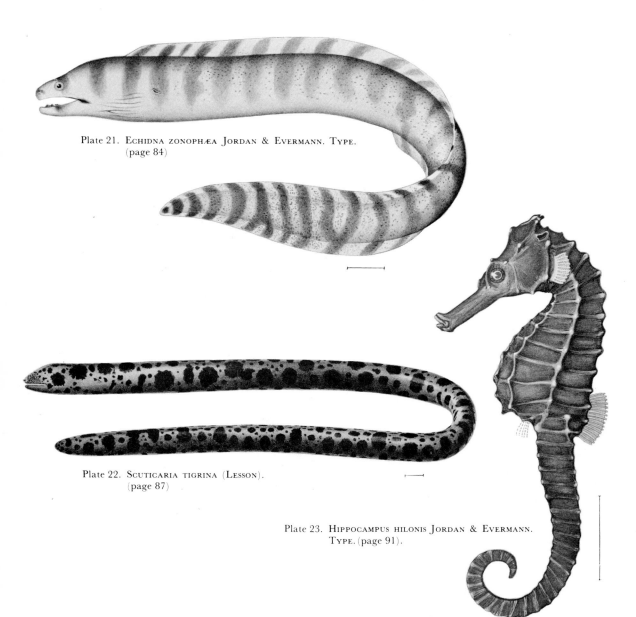

Plate 21. Echidna zonophæa Jordan & Evermann. Type.
(page 84)

Plate 22. Scuticaria tigrina (Lesson).
(page 87)

Plate 23. Hippocampus hilonis Jordan & Evermann.
Type. (page 91).

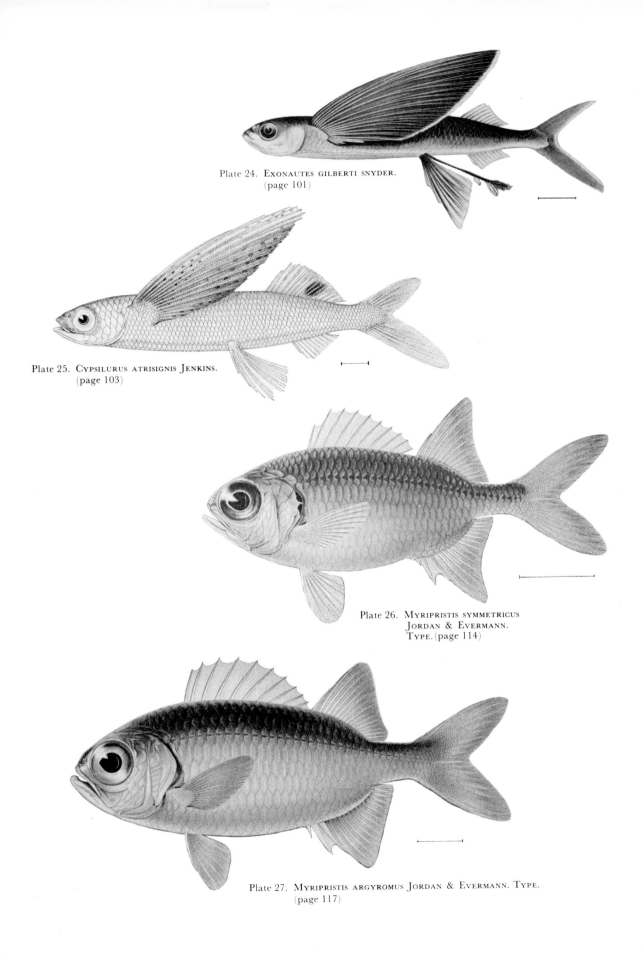

Plate 24. EXONAUTES GILBERTI SNYDER.
(page 101)

Plate 25. CYPSILURUS ATRISIGNIS JENKINS.
(page 103)

Plate 26. MYRIPRISTIS SYMMETRICUS
JORDAN & EVERMANN.
TYPE. (page 114)

Plate 27. MYRIPRISTIS ARGYROMUS JORDAN & EVERMANN. TYPE.
(page 117)

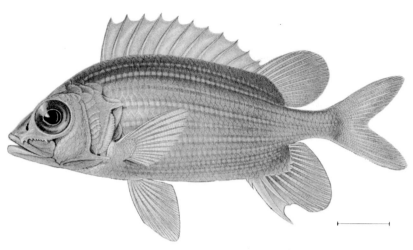

Plate 28. Holocentrus ensifer Jordan & Evermann. Type.
(page 125)

Plate 29. Promethichthys prometheus (Cuvier & Valenciennes).
(page 134)

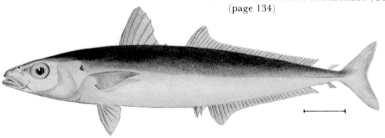

Plate 30. Decapterus sanctæ-helenæ (Cuvier & Valenciennes).
Type of D. canonoides Jenkins. (page 139)

Plate 31. Carangus elacate Jordan & Evermann. Type.
(page 142)

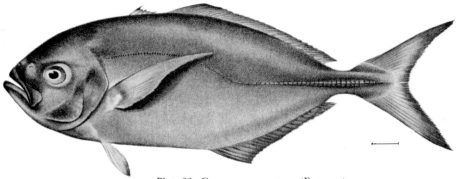

Plate 32. CARANGUS HELVOLUS (FORSTER).
(page 146)

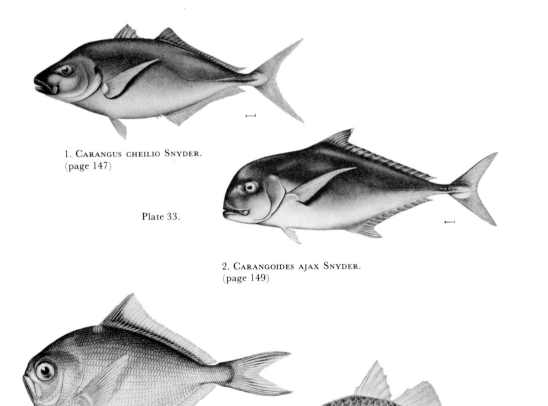

1. CARANGUS CHEILIO SNYDER.
(page 147)

Plate 33.

2. CARANGOIDES AJAX SNYDER.
(page 149)

1. COLLYBUS DRACHME SNYDER.
(page 151)

Plate 34.

½in.

½in.

2. APOGON ERYTHRINUS SNYDER.
(page 161)

Plate 35. APOGONICHTHYS WAIKIKI JORDAN & EVERMANN. TYPE.
(page 156)

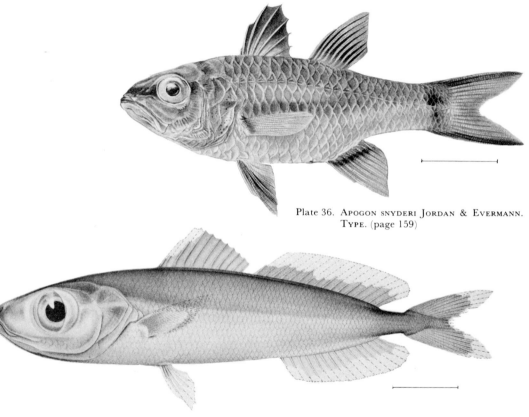

Plate 36. APOGON SNYDERI JORDAN & EVERMANN.
TYPE. (page 159)

Plate 37. ARIOMMA LURIDA JORDAN & EVERMANN. TYPE.
(page 161)

Plate 38. ETELIS EVURUS JORDAN & EVERMANN. TYPE.
(page 180)

Plate 39. UPENEUS ARGE JORDAN & EVERMANN. TYPE.
(page 197)

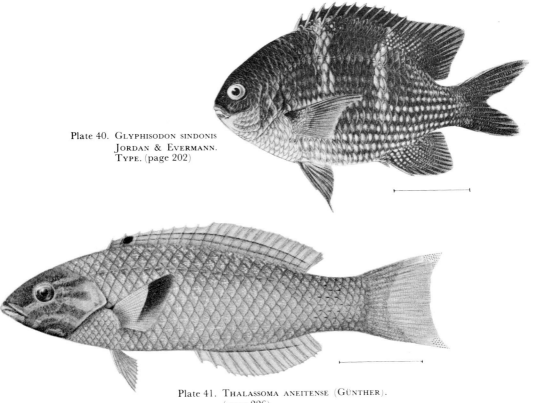

Plate 40. GLYPHISODON SINDONIS
JORDAN & EVERMANN.
TYPE. (page 202)

Plate 41. THALASSOMA ANEITENSE (GÜNTHER).
(page 226)

½in.

1. CIRRHILABRUS JORDANI SNYDER.
(page 234)

Plate 42.

2. HEMIPTERONOTUS JENKINSI SNYDER.
(page 250)

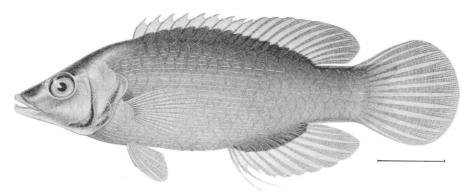

Plate 43. PSEUDOCHEILINUS EVANIDUS JORDAN & EVERMANN. TYPE.
(page 235)

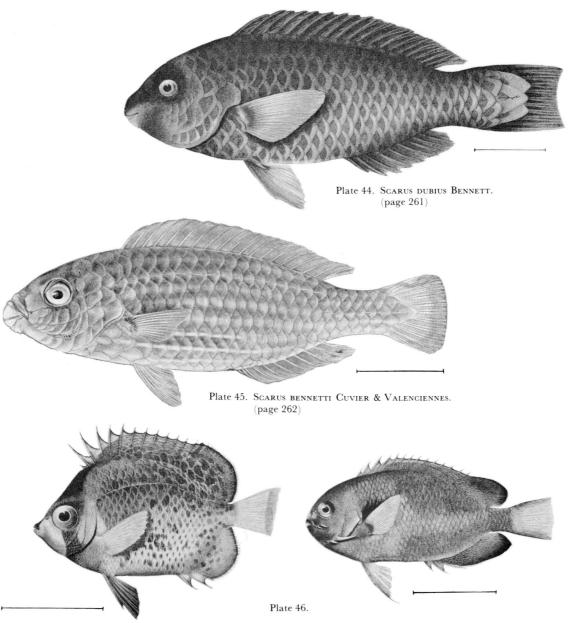

Plate 44. SCARUS DUBIUS BENNETT.
(page 261)

Plate 45. SCARUS BENNETTI CUVIER & VALENCIENNES.
(page 262)

Plate 46.

1. CHÆTODON CORALLICOLA SNYDER.
(page 278)

2. HOLACANTHUS FISHERI SNYDER.
(page 282)

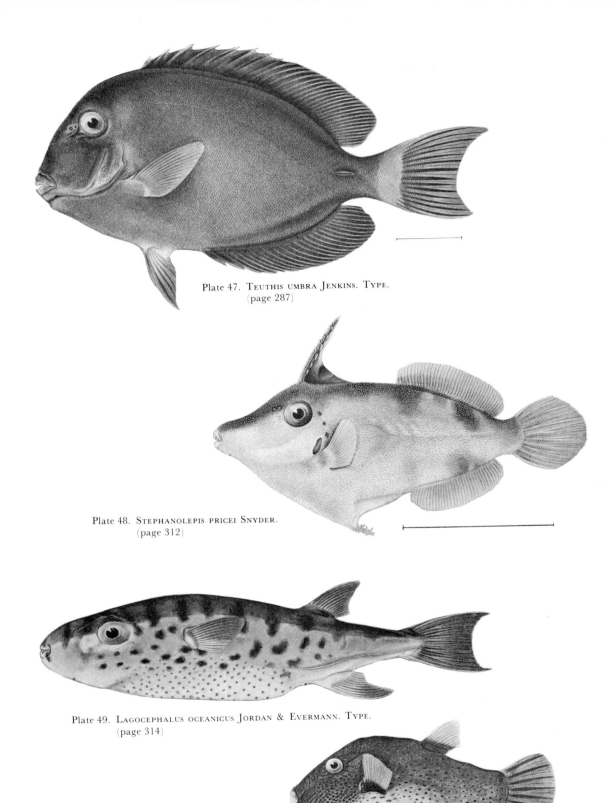

Plate 47. TEUTHIS UMBRA JENKINS. TYPE.
(page 287)

Plate 48. STEPHANOLEPIS PRICEI SNYDER.
(page 312)

Plate 49. LAGOCEPHALUS OCEANICUS JORDAN & EVERMANN. TYPE.
(page 314)

Plate 50. TROPIDICHTHYS PSEGMA JORDAN & EVERMANN. TYPE.
(page 320)

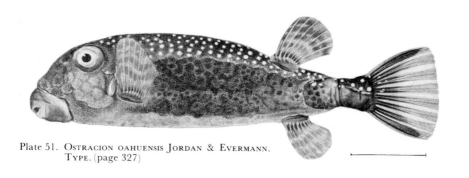

Plate 51. OSTRACION OAHUENSIS JORDAN & EVERMANN.
TYPE. (page 327)

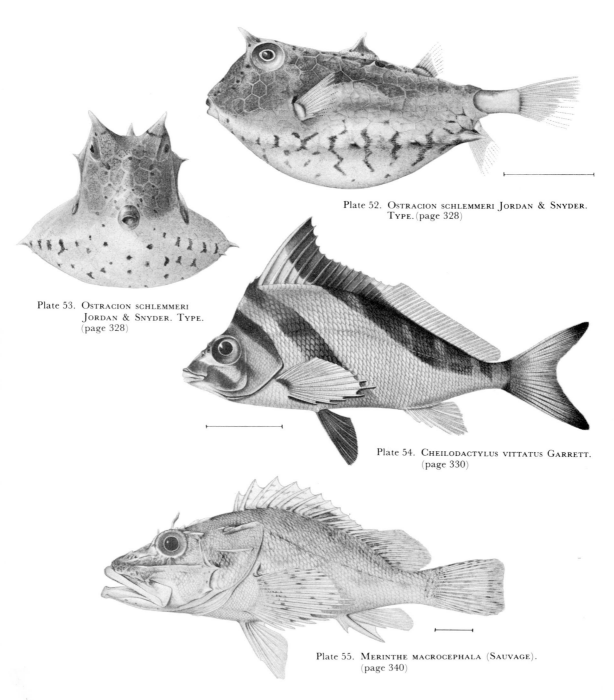

Plate 52. OSTRACION SCHLEMMERI JORDAN & SNYDER.
TYPE. (page 328)

Plate 53. OSTRACION SCHLEMMERI
JORDAN & SNYDER. TYPE.
(page 328)

Plate 54. CHEILODACTYLUS VITTATUS GARRETT.
(page 330)

Plate 55. MERINTHE MACROCEPHALA (SAUVAGE).
(page 340)

Plate 56. SCORPÆNOPSIS CATOCALA JORDAN & EVERMANN. TYPE.
(page 346)

Plate 57. QUISQUILIUS EUGENIUS JORDAN & EVERMANN. TYPE.
(page 357)

Plate 58. GNATHOLEPIS KNIGHTI JORDAN & EVERMANN. TYPE.
(page 360)

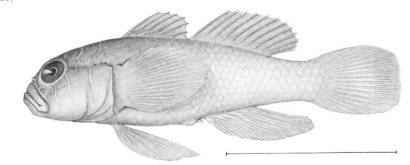

Plate 59. GOBIOPTERUS FARCIMEN JORDAN & EVERMANN. TYPE.
(page 356)

Plate 60. VITRARIA CLARESCENS JORDAN & EVERMANN. TYPE.
(page 359)

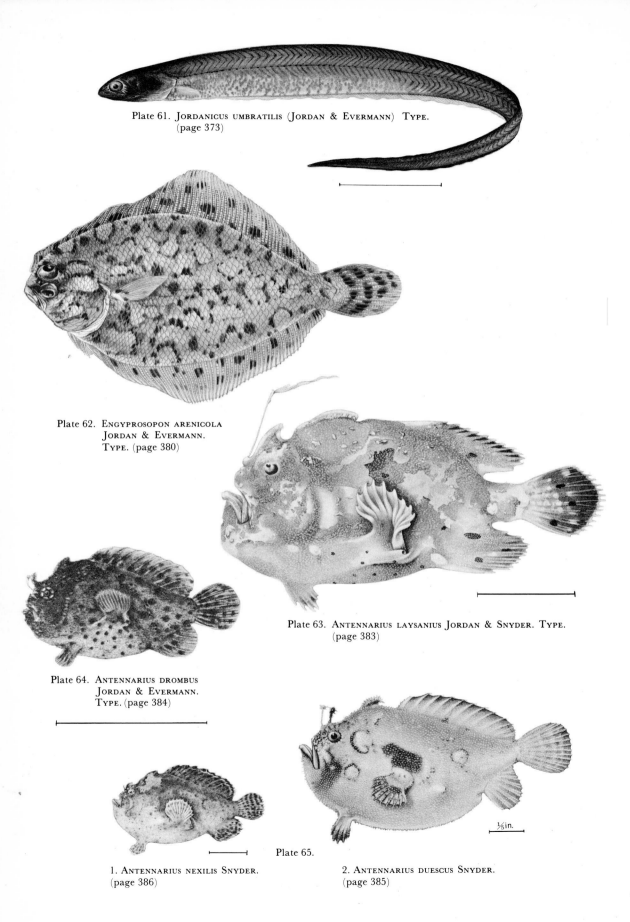

Plate 61. JORDANICUS UMBRATILIS (JORDAN & EVERMANN) TYPE.
(page 373)

Plate 62. ENGYPROSOPON ARENICOLA
JORDAN & EVERMANN.
TYPE. (page 380)

Plate 63. ANTENNARIUS LAYSANIUS JORDAN & SNYDER. TYPE.
(page 383)

Plate 64. ANTENNARIUS DROMBUS
JORDAN & EVERMANN.
TYPE. (page 384)

Plate 65.

⅓ in.

1. ANTENNARIUS NEXILIS SNYDER.
(page 386)

2. ANTENNARIUS DUESCUS SNYDER.
(page 385)